COLLEGES
OF
DISTINCTION

COLLEGES OF DISTINCTION

2018

Go beyond the rankings of commercially-driven lists.

Discover the college that's right for you.

WWW.COLLEGESOFDISTINCTION.COM

CONTENTS

SCHOOL PROFILES

WHAT ARE THE COLLEGES OF DISTINCTION?

Colleges of Distinction was founded by parents who once assisted their own students through the college search process. These parents were surprised to discover the challenges they encountered while trying to look beyond the popular, "brand name" institutions, struggling to find colleges that would truly offer the best undergraduate educations. After a lot of hunting, they successfully looked past the flashy names and found the best options for their kids. Thanks to all their hard work, these proud parents were then able to enjoy the following four years and beyond, embracing the growth their students experienced at the "hidden gem colleges" they discovered. In colaboration with academic professionals, these parents have created Colleges of Distinction in order to help other students and parents find colleges that they might not have originally considered, but which might be exactly the right fit for them.

Every featured college is unique, but they all share key characteristics:

- Their students are bright, motivated, and engaged.
- Their classrooms are interesting, exciting places to explore and learn.
- They offer their students vibrant campuses and communities.
- They turn good students into well-rounded, successful citizens with the capacity to contribute to their communities, their nation, and their world.

If this sounds like what you are looking for in a college, then you are the student (or parent of a prospective student) for whom we wrote this book.

With *Colleges of Distinction*, our goal is to help you get beyond the advertisements and the rankings to find the colleges and universities that consistently provide a remarkable undergraduate college experience and produce successful graduates.

These are schools that get praise from high school guidance counselors across the country, as well as from college admissions officers, professors, students, and satisfied alumni. So why haven't you heard of them?

The truth is, many schools are famous for reasons that have nothing to do with the quality of their education programs. They may have big-time football or basketball programs. They may be known for the path-breaking research conducted by scientists who never actually teach. Or, they may be recognized for the quality of their PhD programs and medical schools.

The colleges in this book may not receive that kind of publicity, but employers and graduate schools know that *Colleges of Distinction* produce real winners.

How Do They Do This?

Colleges of Distinction welcomes students who demonstrate both academic promise and community involvement. They keep classes small, so professors get to know their students as individuals, not numbers. They encourage athletics and a wide range of cultural, intellectual, and social activities, but they help students keep it all in balance with their studies. They encourage their students to get involved with their own communities, as well as exposing them to the global community.

Year after year they do a great job, and looking back, their graduates say, "that might not be the right college for everyone, but it was exactly right for me."

You'll find many small, private, liberal arts colleges in this book. Schools of this kind have long been recognized for their focus on personal attention and student engagement. There are public universities in this guide as well, proving that these institutions can be just as personalized as their private counterparts. There are also single-gender schools, engineering schools, Christian colleges, and more.

As different as these colleges may be from each other, among people "in the know," they each have an outstanding reputation. We hope you benefit from finding out more about the best-kept secrets in college education today.

Finding the right college is one of the biggest decisions you'll ever make. It ranks right up there with choosing a spouse and deciding on a career. Finding the right college can change your life; getting stuck at the wrong one can leave you frustrated, unhappy, and ill-prepared for the future.

How Do Students Choose? How Can Parents Help?

So, how do high school students select the right college? And, if you are a parent, how do you help your son or daughter make the right choice?

Let's be realistic. It's your junior or senior year of high school. You're busy with your school work, concentrating on the SAT or ACT, fitting in school activities, and trying to have a social life, too. Are you likely to devote a huge number of your hours carefully reading every college's marketing materials, pouring over piles of guidebooks, studying the characteristics of hundreds of colleges and universities, and eventually making a deliberate, well-considered decision? Of course not.

According to research by the College Board, the most important source of information for deciding which colleges to apply to is *word-of-mouth information*. Students listen to advice from teachers and guidance counselors, parents and other family members, and—often most compellingly—from their friends.

College guidebooks are another source of information, and many students and parents make good use of them.

Often, of course, this process will guide you to the right college. Yet there may be excellent schools—maybe the perfect school *for you*—that no one tells you about, that you haven't heard of, and that you won't discover by scanning the top 10 colleges in an annual numerical ranking.

That's where Colleges of Distinctions comes in.

College Guidebooks

It's the "best" college—or the second or third or twentieth best. It ranks at "the top of the list" and it has an "excellent reputation."

Ever wonder what these phrases really mean? Can diverse institutions really be rank-ordered using statistics? How relevant are these measurements to what is going to be the ideal college experience *for you*?

The truth is, it's extremely difficult to quantify and qualify all colleges and universities. For one thing, the very act of measuring colleges is based on the assumption that all students are alike, that they want and need the same things, and that it might be possible to create a single ideal college that would be perfect for everyone. Of course that isn't true.

Unlike high school, college students spend their time studying vastly different subjects. They enter college with a huge variety of expectations, hopes, and dreams. There are no SATs or ACTs to measure achievement, no national "standards of learning" to compare the quality of one college with that of another. There are no published statistical measures on how happy and satisfied students are at over 3,000 colleges in the country.

SO HOW DO WE JUDGE QUALITY?

The Rankings and Ratings Approach

A number of widely-read guidebooks make an attempt at comparing schools. *US News and World Report*'s annual "Best Colleges" uses a statistical approach that considers many different factors, all of which they claim contribute to the overall quality of a college. Among the factors *U.S. News* plugs into their statistical formula are:

- The college's overall faculty to student ratio
- The number of faculty members with PhDs
- The size of the college's financial endowment
- Faculty salaries
- SAT/ACT scores of incoming students
- Percentage of entering students in the top 10% of their high school class
- Level of alumni giving
- Percentage of applicants rejected
- Student retention and graduation rates

But can you really find the "best" school—especially, the best for you—from statistics alone?

For example, selectivity is fairly easy to measure: divide the number of applicants by the number of applicants rejected. But if a school is hard to get into, does that necessarily mean it is a better place to learn, live, and grow? Would it be the best place for you?

And exactly what does "high selectivity" mean, anyway?

Some schools—in the Northeast, especially—receive so many applications just because of the location. Schools in other parts of the country may have equally as tough entrance requirements, but because fewer students choose to apply to them, they appear—statistically—less selective.

When guidebook editors decide which characteristics to measure, they are making value judgments that greatly affect the results—and they don't necessarily value the same things you do.

For example, if ethnic diversity is important to you, does the guidebook use it as one of its statistical criteria? What about safety on campus? Federal law requires that this information be available in the Campus Safety Office, but it is often not included in the college's marketing materials or in a college guidebook.

When guidebook editors decide what to measure, they shy away from the hard-to-quantify intangibles—quality of life, actual classroom experience, friendliness of the campus—that are vitally important to each student's college experience.

Rankings-based guidebooks provide important information. But, as a smart consumer, you should be aware of their limitations. As you thumb through the rankings, we suggest you ask:

- Is "the best college" really the best college for you? What facts and figures make it "the best"? Are these criteria you value highly?
- Do you value something that can't be measured by statistics? Are spiritual identity, classroom excitement, and active residence life programs important to you?
- As a student at this particular college, will you be able to participate in all the activities in which you have an interest? For example, do you need to be a theatre major in order to audition for a role in a play, or are auditions open to all students? Are all interested athletes welcome to try out for the college's teams?
- How much learning actually goes on at the college you're considering? Who actually does the teaching? Are students excited about what goes on in the classroom and lab?

In addition to college guidebooks based on statistics, there are many kinds of guides, websites, and studies, which may or may not be useful in your college search.

YOU WILL FIND:

The Inside Scoop

Some guidebooks, like *The Princeton Insider's Guide*, emphasize surveys of students and faculty members. They usually deliver on what they promise: an "inside look," an informal and unauthorized view of the campus–things you definitely won't find in the college's marketing materials. On the down side, their editors may choose quotes for dramatic effect.

One dissatisfied student's response has been known to give a false impression of an otherwise very fine school.

Expert Advice

Other guides give you "expert opinions" based on a lifetime of working in education or in education-related journalism. Loren Pope's *Colleges That Change Lives* and Jay Mathews' *Harvard Schmarvard* are excellent examples of these books. Both of these gentlemen spent a lifetime as education journalists, and are intimately acquainted with the college admissions process. Interestingly, both writers avoid strict rankings, although both offer lists and comments on colleges they recommend.

Measuring Engagement

On the scholarly end of the scale, a few ongoing research projects attempt to do what *U.S. News* doesn't: measure the actual learning that takes place at various colleges. The National Survey of Student Engagement (NSSE), based at Indiana University, collects detailed survey information from students at many colleges and universities. Another is the Cooperative Institutional Research Program (CIRP), an ongoing national study of 11 million students, 250,000 faculty and staff, and 1,600 higher education institutions. NSSE and CIRP provide interesting and valuable data about the experience of students at American colleges and universities. Unfortunately, these are overall reports that are not organized for individual schools.

THERE MUST BE A BETTER WAY!

With *Colleges of Distinction*, we are trying to do something a little different–give you a reliable, journalistic look at schools that may not have the biggest names in higher education, but that consistently do a great job educating undergraduate students.

Every one of these colleges excels in the four areas we have defined as most important in the college experience: attracting and supporting engaged students, promoting and understanding teaching, encouraging a vibrant campus life, and producing successful graduates. But every one of them does so in different ways.

That's why we don't rank the schools in this book. We explain how each of them commits itself to achieving the four elements of successful colleges, and we leave it up to you to determine the one that matches your talents and interests, that promises to be the place where you want to live and learn–the one that's best *for you*.

"Rather than wondering, 'What will I do with my college education?' the more important question to ask as you consider college is, 'Who will I be? What kind of person do I want to become? What kind of qualities do I want to nurture? What kind of contribution do I want to make to the world?'"

- Ronald R. Thomas, Former President, University of Puget Sound

Why Do We Call Them Colleges of Distinction?

They may be modest about it, but these schools have just as much history and heritage as the better-known, brand-name colleges. What's more, they have a proven record in four key areas:

Engaged Students

GPAs and standardized test scores are important, but *Colleges of Distinction* look for students who will be engaged outside the classroom, as well as inside it. These students compete in sports, do volunteer work, conduct independent research, and study abroad. They are not just thinkers, they are doers.

Great Teaching

Professors who teach in *Colleges of Distinction* know students by name and are committed to seeing them succeed. They're experts in their fields and they are dedicated to teaching. Their students learn in environments that encourage lots of reading, writing, research, and personal interaction. Their students learn to analyze problems, think creatively, work in teams, and communicate effectively.

Vibrant Communities

Colleges of Distinction provide a rich, exciting living-and-learning environment, both on and off campus. They offer a variety of residential options, clubs, and organizations to satisfy every interest, plenty of cultural and social opportunities, and avenues for leadership, character, and spiritual development. Whether they are in rural or urban settings, they provide ways for students to be involved in the life of the surrounding community.

Successful Outcomes

Colleges of Distinction have a long record of graduating satisfied, productive alumni who go on to make their mark in business, medicine, law, education, public service, and other fields. In terms of the return they offer on investment, these schools are outstanding educational values.

How did we identify the schools in this book?

First, we asked people "in the know" about colleges. We polled high school guidance counselors from across the country, asking them to tell us which schools belonged on our list and which ones did not. We solicited recommendations from heads of admissions at different colleges.

Informally, we talked to parents, students, and professors at a variety of institutions around the country, seeking even more feedback on our list.

From this diverse community, common opinions began to emerge. Some schools came up again and again.

Having thoroughly polled the available opinions, we then began our own investigation of the institutions that remained on our list. We visited campuses, interviewed a cross-section of the campus community, and sat in on classes. We dug into school records and spoke frankly with admissions directors.

We then sifted through this rather large list looking for certain characteristics:

1. Evidence of schools looking for—and keeping—engaged students. For the most part, we avoided schools that rejected a majority of their applicants, giving preference to those that consider factors beyond SATs and ACTs in admissions. We looked for schools that excelled in scores tabulated by NSSE. We considered retention and four-year graduation rates. We also considered each school's rate of study abroad, internship participation, and other "hands-on" learning opportunities.

2. Evidence of schools that value great teaching. We looked for schools with lots of chances for students to interact with professors and where faculty members are rewarded primarily for teaching, rather than research or publishing. Specifically, we looked for large proportions of full-time faculty, good student:teacher ratios (16:1 and below), small average class-sizes, and programs that encourage student/faculty interaction.

3. Evidence of vibrant campus communities. Although we decided to accept universities with as many as 13,000 or 14,000 undergraduates, we held such institutions up to close scrutiny, looking for evidence that they still managed to build a strong sense of community through their residence halls, campus activities, and opportunities for student involvement.

4. Evidence of successful alumni. We looked for schools with graduates who show consistently strong records of graduate school and professional school success and good results in employment after graduation. Where possible, we also considered alumni satisfaction, as measured by satisfaction surveys and rates of alumni giving.

The result is a book with colleges that we're convinced are terrific places to learn. Measured by both quantitative and qualitative data, these schools come out ahead. While we can't guarantee that you'll have heard of every one of the *Colleges of Distinction*, chances are you'll find a number that interest and intrigue you.

ENGAGED STUDENTS

Who Are You? (And How Do You Learn?)

Different is good. We like to think of ourselves as unique individuals.

When it comes to education, however, we often talk as if one size fits all. Students figure that colleges are pretty much all the same. If it's a "good school," it must be good enough for me. But educators know that different people learn in different ways.

If you're the kind of person who learns best from talking things through, you're not going to thrive in an environment where you are in a crowd of 500 and listening to talking heads. If you learn by solving problems, then tests or papers emphasizing rote memorization are going to turn you off. One of the best ways to start figuring out how you like to learn is to think about situations where you have learned new information or skills more easily.

When someone gives you directions, do you need to see a map or can you listen to directions by ear? Does it help you to be told what landmarks to look for while driving or do you prefer to think in terms of distance and direction?

How do you prefer to study for tests? Do you like to read material alone, or does it help you to talk it over with a friend? Does it help you to actively write or type material by hand, or is it better to listen to someone repeat it to you?

What activities or hobbies give you pleasure? Are you a physical person who prefers sports or dance? Do you like other performance-based activities, such as singing or acting? Do you enjoy "hands-on" hobbies like carpentry or sculpture? Do you enjoy the process of collecting and classifying items like stamps or dolls? Do you read or write for pleasure?

It's quite likely that you are unaware of your best learning style. It may be that you've never had the chance to combine your hobbies and passions with your academic interests. Maybe some of your grades have even suffered as a result.

The good news is that college can give you a chance to be a hands-on learner. You can travel abroad to learn a language or take an internship to try out a job. Your campus activities can teach you leadership skills or even academic knowledge while you have fun. The *Colleges of Distinction* offer you a wide range of ways to get engaged in learning.

Measuring Engagement:

What is it? How can I find it?

The term "engagement" is more than a buzzword. It is a serious part of how good colleges reach their students. Hands-on learning gives you practical skills for the future, as well as making learning easier. Important forms of engaged learning include:

1. Classroom experiences that emphasize reading, writing, and speaking. Whether it is history, biology, Spanish, or engineering, you should be actively engaged in the skills of analysis and expression. Some lecture-based courses are inevitable at most (though not all!) colleges, but classes that emphasize active learning—learning in which you are actively involved in the learning process—help you develop the skills you'll need for success in the workplace and other aspects of your life.

2. Collaborative learning in and outside the classroom. Whether it's working on a group project in class or undertaking joint research with a professor, collaborative learning reflects the reality

that most people do not work alone. Learn to work with others in college and you'll be ahead in almost any field.

3. Field Experience. Learning outside the classroom is especially important in research-based disciplines, but almost any course that involves field experience will give you a leg up on your résumé. Internships, which let you try out a career, and service learning which allows students to serve their community as part of a class, are good forms of field experience.

4. Interacting with other cultures. Whether through studying abroad or through multicultural experience in the U.S., college students have more opportunities than ever to learn about different peoples, which is great preparation for a job market that is increasingly international and multicultural.

WORD TO THE WISE: ARE YOU ENGAGEABLE?

"College and university admission officers at selective institutions typically have a broad definition of merit, as well as a deep commitment to fairness and equity. They know that the ability to contribute and succeed in college goes beyond grades and testing. Typically, selective colleges consider:

- The quality of courses a student has chosen.
- The student's involvement in the school or community.
- The ability of the student to write effectively.
- The student's character and ability to function in a common community (as reflected by recommendations from teachers, employers, and others)."

- *Dean of Admissions, Centre College of Kentucky*

"Standardized exams cannot measure heart (and neither can I, by the way), but we do have ways of getting a read on how much initiative or drive, or whatever you want to call it, plays in the process. Is the student involved outside of class? Is she a leader? Does he write well? How are her interpersonal skills? What do his peers and teachers think of him? All these elements contribute to the equation of whether or not a student is admitted to TCU. Our decisions are holistic in nature as we try to take into account everything we are able to discover about the student."

- *Ray Brown, Dean of Admissions, Texas Christian University*

Before You Visit

Look over any materials you have received from the college. Are there any interesting opportunities that you would like to learn more about?

When making the appointment for your visit, ask if you can meet with someone who knows more about the programs that interest you. For example, is it possible to visit the Study Abroad Office or to meet with a professor who conducts research with students?

Ask School Representatives

Ask an admissions counselor what the school values in an applicant. Does the description sound like a good match for you?

How many students participate in study abroad, internships, student research, service learning, and other hands-on opportunities?

- Is there a time when students generally engage in these opportunities (the beginning of junior year, for example)?
- Do you need to qualify for any special programs (like an Honors College) in order to have these opportunities? If so, how well do your qualifications stack up?

Talk with the admissions counselor about your current high school interests and activities. Are there groups on campus in these categories?

Ask Students

What kind of engaging experiences have they had? Study Abroad? Internships? Service? Do they have any planned?

What are their favorite classes? What makes these classes interesting? Do they sound interesting to you?

Have students had any hands-on experiences that they especially enjoyed?

Have they been involved in any research projects, fieldwork, or special trips related to a class? Do these experiences sound interesting to you?

How well does the school work with local resources (businesses, philanthropies, government, museums, and artistic groups) to enrich student education?

A Checklist for Finding...Engaged Students

Doing Your Research

- ☐ If they do not use NSSE (National Survey of Student Engagement), does the college offer any other measures of how well students are learning?

- ☐ To what degree does the faculty subscribe to "active learning"? Ask for examples of professors who teach this way.

- ☐ What percentage of students participate in study abroad, internships and undergraduate research experiences? (More than one-third usually represents a significant part of the campus.)

- ☐ Does the school have short one-month terms? (Usually offered in January or May, these can make off-campus experiences easier to integrate into you regular course schedule.)

- ☐ What summer opportunities are available at the school?

- ☐ Do scholarships and other financial assistance cover off-campus study?

- ☐ What opportunities are there for students to build résumés?

- ☐ Does the school offer research opportunities? (This is especially important for science-oriented students or those considering graduate school in any field.)

- ☐ Does the school have programs for service learning?

- ☐ How well does the school work with local resources (businesses, philanthropies, government, museums, and artistic groups) to enrich student education?

GREAT TEACHING

I t's common sense. Better teaching means more learning. But how do you define good teaching? Most prospective college students would like to find a school where they will enjoy the best teaching available. Unfortunately, teaching quality isn't as easy to measure as endowment dollars or the size of dorm rooms.

There are some widely accepted standards defining what "good teaching" is. Once you're familiar with them, it's easier to know which questions to ask.

Most colleges will promise that they have "great faculty," but not every school delivers. Learning about good teaching can help you get beyond the promises to find the quality you're looking for at the colleges you're considering.

According to the American Association of Higher Education, there are seven basic practices in good undergraduate education. Good teaching should:

1. Encourage contact between students and faculty. It's easier for faculty to help students when they know each other by name. Likewise, when students feel comfortable approaching professors, they can ask more questions, get involved and get better help.

2. Develop reciprocity and cooperation among students. Good teachers help students learn from each other, not just from the teacher. Not only does this help students learn the subject matter, but it also helps them learn valuable career skills like leadership, creativity, and working in teams.

3. Use active learning techniques. Students tend to learn more when they take an active role in their education, rather than just sitting back and waiting for the information to flow in. Active learning techniques include discussion seminars, independent research projects, field work, lab work, internships, and other hands-on opportunities.

4. Give prompt feedback. Students need to know what they're doing right, what they're doing wrong, and how to improve. The more opportunities they have for feedback on assignments, the better students can improve and grow.

5. Emphasize time on task. Good learning requires time and effort; good teachers help students learn to manage their time by offering concrete guidelines for learning outside the classroom. Unlike high school learning (which emphasizes in-class activities), college learning requires a great deal of commitment outside of the classroom.

6. Communicate high expectations. Expect more from students, and they usually deliver. When professors let students know how much they can strive for, students have more incentive to work harder and learn more.

7. Respect diverse talents and ways of learning. Different students learn in different ways. Good teaching is more than standing behind a podium; it engages students who learn from visuals, hand-on experience, reading, listening, speaking, and other ways of learning.

As you can imagine, there are different ways to ensure good teaching practices; each of the *Colleges of Distinction* has its own approach.

Research and Teaching: A Better Relationship

What is a professor's job? Unlike a high school teacher, college professors are not trained teachers in most cases. They are hired as scholars—as experts in their fields. In most schools, that means they are expected to spend time researching and publishing as part of their duties. "Publish or perish" is true whether the field is biochemistry or political science. In addition, most professors are expected to take a hand in running their department or participating on a college committee. Whether that's helping to get books ordered for the library, deciding promotions for fellow faculty, or raising money for the school's annual appeal, service is an important part of the professor's job.

On some campuses, teaching comes far behind research and service in faculty priorities. To put it bluntly, not every school rewards good teaching. Many schools promise personal attention and a great classroom experience; not all of them deliver. At some, most instruction is done by graduate students working as teaching assistants.

Fortunately, many colleges are learning that there's a better way to encourage both research (which helps to keep academics up to date in their fields) and good teaching (which is what brings most undergraduates to the college). At the *Colleges of Distinction*, you will find classes that are deliberately kept smaller so faculty can give meaningful assignments and get to know their students. Furthermore, they are encouraged to involve students in their research.

Schools that are serious about teaching usually run teaching seminars, institutes, and other serious programs to help professors continue to develop as teachers and academics.

Finally, most teaching-centered schools recruit faculty who genuinely enjoy students. If the faculty at the schools you visit seem happy to speak with their students and are genuinely interested in them—and if professors are happy to speak with you during your visit—chances are you've found a school that really values great teaching.

Profile: The Teaching Scholar at a *College of Distinction*

Teaching at a *College of Distinction* is more than lecturing and overseeing work in the laboratory. Among the activities that might fill a professor's typical day are:

- Giving a lecture to first-year students
- Participating in a student-faculty panel about current events
- Attending a departmental meeting on updating class offerings
- Calling prospective students to describe the program
- Moderating a discussion panel in an upper-division class
- Writing graduate school references for former students
- Eating lunch with a student service group in order to plan a weekend project
- Moderating a chat room discussion for an honors class
- Writing feedback for student essay projects
- Working with a student on a paper they are publishing together

Before You Visit

Ask if it is possible to meet with a faculty member in your area of interest. Prepare some questions about the program's requirements, what jobs recent graduates are doing, and what activities and research projects are possible.

If it is not possible to meet with a faculty member, ask if you can e-mail your questions.

Arrange to visit a class, preferably one for freshmen. Don't worry too much about finding one in your proposed major; just ask for an interesting class that is popular with students. Is this a class you would like to take?

Ask School Representatives

Ask your admissions counselor to clarify any questions you have about class sizes, student to faculty ratio, etc. If the schools uses Teaching Assistants (TAs), ask about their role and how often you will encounter them.

Ask your admissions counselor some specifics about student-faculty interaction. Will you have a faculty member as an advisor (helping you pick classes and chart an academic path)? What other opportunities will you have to work closely with faculty?

Ask Students

Ask students about their favorite professors, and why they are favorites.

If you eat in the cafeteria or take a campus tour, look at how professors and students interact outside the classroom. Do professors seem accessible?

Do students want to talk to their professors? Does the school use TAs? If so, how? Is it mostly the professors who grade and teach, or mostly the teaching assistants?

A CHECKLIST FOR FINDING...GREAT TEACHING

Doing Your Research

☐ Take a close look at student to faculty ratios. 16:1 is about average for any of our *Colleges of Distinction*, and usually indicates plenty of time for faculty to student interaction. The closer this gets to 20:1, the more difficult interaction becomes.

☐ Take a close look at full-time versus part-time faculty. Also look to see how many faculty members are tenured or tenure-track. These faculty members will most likely be at the school from year to year, providing you continuity between your courses.

☐ Does the school use TAs? If so, how? Is it mostly the professors who grade and teach, or mostly the teaching assistants?

☐ Look at average class sizes. What percentage of classes are under 25 students? Under 35?

☐ If some classes are large, what does the school do to promote personal attention? Common ways to promote face-to-face interaction include freshman study groups and small labs in science classes.

☐ Is there a special freshmen-year experience that attempts to integrate the major areas of human knowledge and that stresses writing and speaking, instead of just requiring freshmen to take unrelated introductory courses in large (over 50 students) classes?

☐ What resources are available to help freshmen adjust academically?

☐ Is there a special office for students with learning disabilities?

☐ Does the school offer majors or programs that will help you achieve your career goals? (Even when a school does not offer the precise major you are looking for, it may offer individualized study options that will make career preparation possible.) Does the college make an effort to relate courses in the humanities, sciences, and social sciences to careers and vocations, perhaps through credit-bearing internships?

☐ If you are undecided about your career goals, how well will the school's curriculum help you find your way? Is there a Career Planning Office that works closely with the faculty?

VIBRANT COMMUNITY

"Just Right:" Where Do You Want to Be?

As with other aspects of choosing a college, finding the right community can be tricky. You'd be surprised how many students transfer, not because of academic difficulty but because they are unhappy with their campus life. The big city that one student finds exciting may be too anonymous and distracting for another student. From athletic opportunities to religious atmosphere, from campus political opinion to cultural opportunities, from community service to residence life, there are a lot of variables to consider when looking at a college campus.

Some Self-Assessments on Campus Life

When you're thinking about campus communities, it's important to be honest with yourself about who you are and what you want. By using these three self-assessments, you can get an idea of what size college you might like, what kind of campus life interests you, and what setting you'd like to study in.

SELF-ASSESSMENT #1: COLLEGE SIZE

(Pick A or B)

I like….

(a) my teacher to know my name and understand my problems.

(b) to be somewhat anonymous in class.

When I go to a sporting event as a fan, I like to…

(a) know people in the crowd and on the team as I cheer them on.

(b) be part of a huge crowd in a huge stadium.

If I go to a party where I don't know anybody, I really like it when…

(a) someone introduces themselves and goes out of their way to make me feel welcome.

(b) people leave me alone and let me observe.

When I go to college, I think I would like to…

(a) know everything that's going on, and be able to try many different options.

(b) stick with one or two favorite activities.

ASSESSMENT #2: MY ACTIVITY AND LIVING PRIORITIES

(Check all that apply)

My dream campus would offer...

- ☐ A particular varsity sport
- ☐ A particular intramural or club sport
- ☐ A variety of intramural or club sports
- ☐ Cheerleading or other sports-booster activities
- ☐ Political or issue-oriented organizations
- ☐ Multicultural/ethnic organizations
- ☐ Camping or outdoor sports
- ☐ Greek-letter fraternities/sororities
- ☐ ROTC or other military opportunities
- ☐ A particular religious affiliation with college-sponsored spiritual life
- ☐ No particular religious identity, but many spiritual/religious life groups
- ☐ Women-interest organizations
- ☐ LGBT organizations
- ☐ Newspaper, radio, TV, or other media activities
- ☐ Film or literary clubs
- ☐ Specific hobby or interest clubs (gun club, anime club. etc.)
- ☐ A wide array of service-oriented groups
- ☐ Theatre opportunities for non-majors, both as performers and technicians
- ☐ Music opportunities for non-majors
- ☐ Other performance arts, such as dance or mime
- ☐ Clubs for a particular academic subject or career interest
- ☐ The chance to live in a "theme" house or residence (all French-speaking, for example, or a service-themed house)
- ☐ The chance to live in an apartment-style situation
- ☐ The chance to live in a fraternity or sorority house
- ☐ Women's-only or men's-only housing
- ☐ Another residence preference
- ☐ A wide range of weekend trips and off-campus fun for students
- ☐ A wide range of touring bands and other visiting performers

ASSESSMENT #3: CAMPUS IDENTITIES

(Check all that apply)

I would be open to exploring campuses that are...

- ☐ Public (state-supported)
- ☐ Private
- ☐ Private, where religion plays a strong role
- ☐ Single-sex (all women or all men)
- ☐ Military-style
- ☐ Historically black
- ☐ Primarily undergraduate
- ☐ Largely graduate/professional
- ☐ Engineering-focused
- ☐ Art-focused
- ☐ In a very large city or its suburbs
- ☐ In a smaller or medium-sized city (such as St. Louis, Cincinnati or Portland) or its suburbs
- ☐ In a large "college town"
- ☐ In a small "college town"
- ☐ In a rural or wilderness setting

Assessment Outcomes

Assessment #1: College Size

"A" answers are more typical of students at smaller schools; "B" are more typical of students at large universities. If you find you're somewhere in between, then "medium" may be just right for you.

Assessment #2: My Activity and Living Priorities

This exercise should help you sort out what you would like in a campus. You may find it helpful to update this list as you continue your college search and get a better idea about what you like.

Assessment #3: Campus Identities

Don't worry if some of these things are contradictory—the more options you have at first, the better. You can re-visit this list as you learn more about various options.

Involvement and Community

Colleges of Distinction offer opportunities inside as well as outside the classroom. Today, campus-life is considered to be one of the most important elements in a college education. The Association of College Unions International (ACUI) states that campus life provides a "complement [to] the academic experience through an extensive variety of cultural, educational, social, and recreational programs. These programs provide the opportunity to balance course work and free time as cooperative factors in education."

This also makes you a stronger student. Studies have shown that students who are involved in extracurricular activities graduate at higher rates and do better academically.

In other words, a good campus life not only means doing better academically, but getting more out of your education through more exposure to activities, more chances to apply the ideas you learn in class, more personal growth and discovery, more fun and friends. That "more" also means more opportunities after college, when being well-rounded really helps you stand out from the crowd of job applicants.

Some students persuade themselves that campus life really isn't all that important. They figure that college will be a lot like high school: go to class, go to a practice or a meeting, go home. But college is a 24/7 environment: It's your classroom, your social life, and your home all wrapped into one package.

Other students assume that they have to attend a huge campus to have a lot of opportunities. In fact, many discover that small or medium sized schools make it easier to get involved, whereas big schools may be so anonymous that it's difficult to meet people.

You may also want to think about schools with unique identities—church-affiliated colleges, historically black colleges, single-gender colleges and other special places. What activities are you interested in? Are you a big city or small town person, or somewhere in between? Do you want to be recruited to a professional team, or just compete in the sport you love? The lists in this chapter can give you some places to get started, but don't be afraid to add your own personalized requirements for a college. The choices depend on you and your personality. Finding the right environment is important as you look ahead to a great college experience and a great future.

Ask School Representatives

Drive or walk through the surrounding community/neighborhood. Is it an area that you like? Ask whether the college has a relationship with the community or whether there are tensions.

If you have a particular activity interest, arrange to visit these programs and their facilities. If possible, ask to speak with faculty or staff who work with the program.

If you are interested in a sport, try to arrange to visit with a member of the coaching staff. If it's not possible to meet, try to get a name and an e-mail address for an inquiry.

Ask Students

Ask students what they do on weekends and for fun. What campus events do they most enjoy?

Visit residence options for freshmen. If possible, ask a resident assistant or hall assistant about the programs available to those living in the residence. Are they programs in which you would like to participate?

Look at signs, posters, and announcements around campus. Are there many activities and events that interest you? Does the political and social atmosphere of the campus seem to fit your personality and values? Reading the student newspaper should give you a sense of what is going on from a student perspective.

Ask a student about his or her favorite campus activities and traditions. Do these sound fun and interesting to you?

WORDS TO THE WISE: ABOUT GETTING INVOLVED

"It was apparent to me early on that though I was new to the university, I was in a place where I could contribute to my school, and affect my community in a way I thought was reserved for older, more seasoned veterans in the college arena."

- *Byron Sanders, Alumnus, Southern Methodist University*

"Some of the greatest lessons come from campus involvement. Currently, I am the president of the campus chapter of a national economics honor society, chair of elections/secretary for the Student Government Association, and a representative of the Office of Admissions in the Tower Council. Through these associations, I have gotten to really know the women I work closely with day in and day out. This does not just include members of

the student body, but various deans, school administrators, and professors. They teach us by listening to us—students have a say in almost all decisions made on campus."

- *Mary Frances Callis, Alumna, Agnes Scott College*

"We hold our student athletes in high regard as students and as athletes. We respect their contributions on the playing field because we insist that these contributions remain part of a larger undergraduate experience where the classroom comes first and out-of-class activities second… Athletic competition can also be extremely fulfilling at our level. When everyone plays by the same rules, not only is competition spirited and intense, but great athletic traditions can develop."

- *Baird Tipson, President of Washington College*

A CHECKLIST FOR FINDING…VIBRANT COMMUNITY

Doing Your Research

☐ What activities available on campus match your interests? Are most of the activities you enjoy open to non-majors? For example, if you are interested in theatre but majoring in biology, will you still be able to participate in theatrical productions?

☐ What percentage of students are involved in campus activities?

☐ Are there campus activities that you have never tried but which sound interesting to you?

☐ If you are interested in athletics, does the college offer the sport you play? If you are interested in varsity competition, what are its policies regarding walk-ons? Is there an active intramural program for non-varsity athletes?

☐ What cultural and entertainment opportunities does the campus provide? How does it make use of facilities in the surrounding community?

☐ What special events or speakers were on campus in the last year?

☐ Is the college a suitcase campus? That is, what percentage of the students leave campus on weekends? If there is a vibrant city nearby with a wide range of cultural and social opportunities, students going off campus during the weekend might be a good thing; but it is not a good thing when everyone is going home every weekend!

☐ What kind of residence options does the college offer? What programs are available to help you make friends, meet people, and settle in? How will your roommate be selected?

☐ Are there health facilities or programs on campus? What kind of counseling and crisis support does the campus offer? Does the college provide resources for students with physical or learning disabilities?

SUCCESSFUL OUTCOMES

One of the problems with *U.S. News and World Report*'s annual survey of colleges is that it measures a college's quality largely by SAT scores and high school grades. But if you think about it, these are indicators the college had nothing to do with.

Perhaps a better way of measuring a college's quality would be by studying "outcomes," or what happens after students graduate. Indicators of successful outcomes include the acceptance rate into graduate or professional schools, and the percentage of seniors getting employment in their chosen fields soon after they graduate.

Ultimately, successful outcomes are linked to the alumni who, in a real sense, are the "product" of a college education. What kinds of professions did they enter? Have they distinguished themselves in these professions?

This is how *Colleges of Distinction* measures successful outcomes.

While entering students are not expected to know right away what their major will be or what they want to become in life—freshman and sophomore years should be largely reserved for experimentation and discovery—it is too often the case that by senior year students still don't know what they want to do.

Colleges of Distinction are especially good at orienting students, right from the beginning, to what they might become in life. They often begin this process by introducing freshmen to the Career Services Office during orientation so that they know what resources are available to them.

Sophomores are then encouraged to consider employment-related internships and externships. Tied closely to these programs are career counseling seminars that help students orient themselves to career possibilities, workshops for resume writing and mock interviews, and career fairs where firms can meet future employees.

By senior year, students enrolled at *Colleges of Distinction* not only have a fairly good idea of what they will do in their first job, but are well on their way to submitting résumés and having interviews.

For those who plan to go on to a graduate or professional school, the same Career Services Office, working with pre-professional advisors (especially pre-med and pre-law) will give advice about available scholarships and the various exams necessary to get into graduate, medical or law school. College professors, of course, have all gone to graduate school and are an excellent source of advice on master's and doctoral programs.

At most *Colleges of Distinction*, more than 85% of those seeking employment after graduation will find well-paying jobs with advancement potential within six months of graduating. Similarly, 20% or more of the graduating class will go directly to graduate or professional school. Sixty percent will have gone on for further education within six years of graduation.

Finally, the "product" of *Colleges of Distinction*—the ultimate outcome—are alumni. Perhaps the major goal of these colleges is to prepare the future leaders of our society—the business leaders who keep our economy strong, the political leaders who govern us, the professional leaders who impact our lives in many ways and on a daily basis. *Colleges of Distinction* are especially strong in the number of these leaders who attended these institutions. These people not only contribute to society in general, but also support their institutions in various ways, including helping new graduates get their first job.

In the first place, education should not–indeed cannot–be seen as preparation for only one career. Because of the massive changes we are seeing in society, created in large part by advances in technology, current college graduates will have as many as six or seven entirely different jobs or careers before they retire! Therefore the best preparation for a rapidly changing and utterly unpredictable future is a liberal arts and sciences education. Why? Because liberal arts and sciences provide students with three basic and universal skills that are at the core of any successful career: intellectual flexibility, the ability to communicate effectively, and the skills to engage in life-long learning.

How is this done? *Colleges of Distinction* require students to take a wide variety of courses in the social sciences, humanities, and natural and mathematical sciences, in addition to majoring in a liberal arts or vocational discipline. The result is a graduate who has the intellectual tools to adapt to the shifts and changes we can expect in the 21st century.

Colleges of Distinction prepare their students not only for the first job, but also for the last job!

Before You Visit

Arrange a visit to the Career Services Office. Make a list of questions to ask about internships and other career exploration opportunities.

Ask if there are recent alumni available in your area with whom you can speak about the school.

Ask School Representatives

Ask your admissions counselor about graduation rates, employment rates, and similar issues.

Ask staff in the Career Services Office or the Alumni Office how alumni help current students.

Ask Students

Ask students about their plans for the future. What is the school doing to help them achieve their goals?

A CHECKLIST FOR FINDING...SUCCESSFUL OUTCOMES

Doing your Research

☐ What information does the school provide about employment-related internships and externships? How many internships can a typical student take?

☐ What professional development does the school offer students? Does the school offer résumé support, mock interviews, career fairs, and other employment support?

☐ What are the employment rates for graduates within 6 months of graduation? Within one year?

☐ If you are considering graduate or law school, does the school provide information about rates of acceptance and give examples of schools to which graduates were accepted?

☐ What is the school's rate of alumni giving? Rates of 30% or more are generally considered fairly strong.

☐ If the school publishes an alumni magazine, ask for a copy with your admissions packet. How important and well-organized does the alumni association seem to be? Are alumni involved in student life? Do they provide a network for students seeking employment?

NAVIGATING ADMISSIONS AND THE COST OF COLLEGE

If you feel that college admissions is a competitive game, you're not alone. College rankings have given the general public the idea that it's no longer enough to be admitted to college. Instead, they imply that to be successful, a student must get accepted to a top-ranked school. Different regions of the country experience this pressure in different ways, but the symptoms are universal.

These days, students and parents spend an enormous amount of time and money on guidebooks, SAT tutors, private admissions counselors, and other tools. In some cases, students may actually be missing out on valuable high school experiences and learning because they focus so much energy on getting into the "right" college.

Many college admissions personnel agree that the climate has become overly competitive, but there is no quick fix. What can you do?

First and foremost, decide which schools are really the best for you—not just a magazine's "best." Where can you be happiest? What schools offer the programs that are right for you? We urge you to worry less about what school is "the best" and instead ask, "Which school is the best for *me*?"

You are going to spend a lot of valuable time on the college admissions process. Having been through the process ourselves, we at *Colleges of Distinction* suggest you look past Big Name University. Find the Hidden Gem College that is perfect for you and tailor your strategy to what that school really wants, rather than wasting your resources on a "one-size-fits-all" approach to test prep and applications strategies.

Use the following checklist to prioritize what's important for you as you're looking at schools. You may also want to use our self-assessment in the previous chapters as one of your tools. Good luck!

Narrowing the Field

Once you have finished this section, you should have a fairly complete picture of what you are looking for in a college. Think about the colleges you have visited. Look at the materials colleges have sent you. How many fit the bill? Knock off the ones that just do not match what you're looking for. You'll be left with a list of colleges that approach the ideal college for you.

How well do your SATs, ACTs and GPA stack up against their average admissions? You can find some of this information in our book; for more up-to-date figures, consult the school's website or other online resources that list this data. Do you score significantly above or below the average? This can give you a very rough estimate of how well you will stack up against other applicants. Don't be discouraged if your scores are lower than the college's average; remember, half of all students admitted to any given college end up having scores and grades below the mid-point, and many of those students have great careers in college and beyond.

Keep in mind that the schools that qualify as *Colleges of Distinction* consider many other factors when they evaluate student applications.

Do you have any special skills or interests that might appeal to one or more of these schools? Schools with extensive service programs or special service scholarships may take special note of your service activities. Every

A CHECKLIST FOR...CHOOSING A COLLEGE

Location

I am looking for a school that is:

- ☐ In my hometown
- ☐ Within an easy drive of my hometown
- ☐ Within a one-day drive of my hometown
- ☐ Within a short flight of my hometown
- ☐ Anywhere

Specifically, I am interested in schools in the following states:

Hint: Are you looking for new experiences? Is climate a concern? Do you want to be close to your parents, siblings or other relative?

(List the states you are interested in.)

I am interested in a location that is:

Hint: What do you consider a "big" city or a "small" town? People from Los Angeles or New York City may consider cities like St. Louis or Albuquerque very small. If you are from a town of under 10,000, these same cities may seem very large.

- ☐ A really big city
- ☐ A regionally important city
- ☐ A college town
- ☐ A very small town or a rural campus

Academic

Hint: Most students change their majors at least once, so don't feel too concerned if you don't quite know what you want right now. Also, be aware that colleges offer majors that will help you achieve your goals under many different names. And be sure to look for opportunities to design your own curriculum.

Learning experiences that I think I might enjoy include:

- ☐ A unified curriculum, all students take the same classes
- ☐ A core curriculum, where all students take some of the same classes
- ☐ Special freshmen seminars or other freshmen-only classes
- ☐ Classes under 10 people before my junior and senior year
- ☐ Classes under 25 people
- ☐ Classes over 100 people
- ☐ Living-and-learning communities where my roommates and neighbors are studying the same major, taking some of the same classes, or have other academic options in common
- ☐ Service-learning programs where my classroom experiences are connected to community service.
- ☐ Studying abroad at a foreign university (specify institution if you know)
- ☐ Studying abroad at a program run by my college (specify country if you know)
- ☐ Studying off-campus in the United States

Career and Life

I am looking for a college:

- ☐ Where I can explore my career through an internship
- ☐ Where I can explore more than one internship
- ☐ Where there are special resources for undecided majors
- ☐ With a multi-year professional/career development program (begins before senior year)
- ☐ That has specific programs to support my career goals: (specify)

I am looking for a college that will:

- ☐ Help me get involved in service opportunities (specify your interests)
- ☐ Give me the chance to play a certain sport (specify)
- ☐ Help me deepen my spirituality (specify your interests)
- ☐ Let me pursue my hobbies and interests through co-curricular activities or groups (specify your interests)

Co-curricular programs that interest me are:

(List them)

Other programs that might be interesting to explore include:

(List them)

Help me pursue the following interests: (List them)

college needs a flute player in the band, an actor for the drama program, and a reporter for the school newspaper. Schools with competitive swim teams might be especially interested in recruiting a talented swimmer. Be sure to mention these interests and talents.

Are you a member of a group that is under-represented at one of the colleges you are considering? Many schools have far fewer men than women in their student body and, though they won't admit it, are interested in recruiting men to help correct the imbalance. Some campuses have special programs to encourage first-generation students or members of certain ethnic and racial groups to apply. Still other campuses would like to recruit more "legacies," children or grandchildren of alumni.

Do you have life-experiences that make you stand out from the crowd? Have you lived abroad or participated in educational travel opportunities? Have you won any special awards or been recognized for your activities? Have you started clubs or programs in your community, at your school, or through your faith group?

Refine your list based on these questions and narrow your choices down to eight or ten colleges: four or five that closely match your interests and to which acceptance is likely; two where the profile might be above yours ("stretches"); and two that have the profiles below yours where admission is almost guaranteed ("safeties"). If you think you'll be unhappy with an acceptance from any of the colleges on your list, cross that school off immediately.

The Facts About Financial Aid: Can You Afford Not to Go to College?

One final issue needs to be discussed: the cost of a college education.

The cost of college is a big public policy issue in America. Parents are usually in shock when they see how expensive college can be, especially private colleges and universities where tuitions have been skyrocketing at rates far beyond inflation.

The truth is, if done the right way, college can be very affordable. If you have financial need, there are federal, state and institutional grants to help pay for a college education. But even students who do not qualify for need-based financial aid can receive merit-based aid if their high school grades and extracurricular activities are noteworthy. So don't look at the so-called sticker price.

After scholarships, campus jobs, and loans are taken into consideration, most colleges are quite affordable.

What About Private Colleges vs. Public Universities?

We all know that tuition at public universities is lower than tuition at private colleges. That's because taxpayers subsidize, or pay to offset the costs of, public tuitions. The fact that the total four-year tuition plus room and board costs at many public universities is $50,000 or less compared to $100,000 or more at private colleges and universities, is discouraging many parents from considering these institutions.

But Things Are Not Always as They Seem!

In many states, large public universities are overcrowded. As a result, students often cannot get their first choice of a major. And since classes are frequently full, it often takes five or six years to graduate! Looking at the situation this way, the student attending a public university will not only pay a total of $65,000 in tuition, room and board for five years, but also forgo a year earning a salary (often another $40,000+) for a total "real" cost of over $100,000. Now the $100,000+ paid to attend a private college that graduates its students in four years or less doesn't look so bad. This fact, together with the scholarship support private colleges can offer, considerably levels the playing field. So you really do have a choice.

Finally, one might ask, "Why take on all these loans? Wouldn't I be better off just getting a job after high school?"

The fact is that college graduates, over a lifetime, earn $2 million more in income than high school graduates. Of course this should not be the major reason you go to college. College-educated people are usually happier in their jobs, healthier, and enjoy all the intangible benefits that a college education provides. Taking on $25,000 or more in college loans (scholarships are free gifts and don't have to be repaid) is insignificant in the long run compared to the earning power of a college degree.

Good luck with your college search. We hope you find the campus that is truly the best for you!

COLLEGE INSIGHTS: WHAT YOU SHOULD KNOW

BIG PICTURE - PICKING A COLLEGE

WANT YOUR KIDS TO HAVE A SECURE FUTURE? INVEST IN A LIBERAL ARTS EDUCATION

by Christine Henseler, Professor of Spanish and Hispanic Studies, Union College

It's no secret that the dynamics surrounding higher education and postgraduate employment are changing fast these days, and it's no question that our interconnected world is also evolving rapidly. These changes, fueled by technology, politics, and economics, affects the way we learn, work, play, and connect to one another. It's exactly for these reasons that there is no better time to invest in a liberal arts education.

In the world that awaits future graduates, the competitive edge belongs to those with bright, curious, and agile minds. Objective, technological, or scientific knowledge will no longer be enough; the world you or your child will enter after college is already demanding more human-centric solutions to our collective challenges. With this in mind, here are just a few reasons why a liberal arts education is so valuable.

Global Trends

All facets of today's world are bound across borders through digital networks. News can spread in an instant, change is constant, and the future is sure only to become increasingly complex. New technologies, like self-driving cars and 3D printing, are already disrupting the way we work and do business.

The leaders of the future, therefore, will have to apply novel theories and think across disciplines in order to tackle the challenges of the 21st century. They will be individuals who can think differently and challenge the status quo. They will have keen observations, explore new possibilities, and make new and surprising connections.

The goal of liberal arts colleges and universities is to cultivate the kind of innovative thought needed for such new and challenging demands. Though each school's mission is slightly different, most aim to produce leaders who make thoughtful life choices, succeed professionally, and commit themselves to lifelong learning and cultural understanding. With a student-centered focus, these schools engage their students with a wide variety of learning experiences, better preparing them for the challenges of our time.

Employer Trends

"I personally think there's going to be a greater demand in 10 years for liberal arts majors than there were for programming majors and maybe even engineering…"

-Billionaire Investor, Mark Cuban

The needs and demands of employers definitely reflect the global trends of workforce demands. According to the 2016 Job Outlook survey conducted by the National Association of Colleges and Employers, hiring personnel increasingly value and prioritize the skills that are inherently developed in liberal arts institutions. Of those polled:

- 80.1% seek candidates with good leadership skills
- 78.9% want graduates with the ability to work in a team
- 70.2% need employees with good written communication skills
- 70.2% look for workers with good problem-solving skills
- 68.9% prioritize employees' excellent verbal communication skills

Liberal arts graduates have the clear advantage here. Many of their schools implement programs that promote active collaboration between students of different disciplines, and others are challenged with capstone courses and projects to demonstrate their mastery of a subject. They've also been steeped in writing-intensive courses to develop their communication skills, and they have improved their ability to discern context and solve problems through humanities courses like history or philosophy. To students and employers alike, the benefits of learning and thinking across disciplines is invaluable.

Leading businesses are taking notice of these facts. Last year, Forbes published an article explaining why companies like Slack and Ubisoft value their employees' humanities degrees as well as why some American entrepreneurs have chosen to major in philosophy. It is truly apparent that companies need more than technology to gain the competitive edge they seek.

To connect, engage, and to sell to clients, today's employers must build bridges between technology and humanity. Their products must relate their target audiences' histories, cultures, languages, and values. In essence, such an ability to make connections like these is what a liberal arts education is all about.

Academic Trends

Hong Kong, Japan, and other Asian countries are in the process of adopting the United States' liberal arts model. In a recent article in The Atlantic, businessman Po Chung and other education reformers have acknowledge that "it's past time for (Asian) colleges to introduce a broader range of subjects, to promote greater intellectual curiosity, and to foster creative thinking." Chung and other backers appear to echo the insights of their Silicon Valley counterparts. They, too, are "convinced that these changes will, in turn, build a workforce of rigorous, creative thinkers—just what

they think is needed to meet the fast-changing needs of a transforming global economy."

Forward-thinking leaders are recognizing that the future of work and social well-being depend on human-centric solutions. Because of this fact, students who narrowly focus on technical skills are automatically limiting their future options. Unless they make connections, think outside the box, and market themselves more broadly, their professional skills will not withstand the ever-shifting demands of the professional world.

STEM and the Humanities

Tensions are growing around the humanities in western academia. Citing a shortage of scientists and engineers, some have been framing the humanities as an 'unnecessary indulgence' and pressuring students to hone in on STEM (Science, Mathematics, Engineering, and Technology) fields.

Countering this notion is computer science educator Valerie Barr, who adamantly defends the virtues of the arts and humanities and deems them essential to her field. She writes:

"…those who excel in STEM understand that there are non-technical considerations that should guide their work, and those who study humanities understand that there are powerful problem-solving mechanisms and tools that can open up new avenues of application for their knowledge. We need those with strength in the humanities to feel comfortable talking with those who have strength in STEM, and vice versa. This isn't either-or, we have to expose students to both."

While Barr's view is insightful, it hardly begins to settle the debate. More emerging studies have suggested that there is far more to the humanities than its detractors claim. While its benefits may not be immediately obvious, the arts and humanities are far more than a simple "indulgence;" rather, they are a necessity.

Leadership

Leadership, though hard to define, is understandably at the top of employers' wishlists. The kinds of leaders who are sought by hiring managers are to be empathetic visionaries. They are expected know how to collaborate with a group and guide them through to the end of projects. In contrast, however, the available applicants often end up being the kind of people who look to their superiors to give them the "right answers" without making a real effort to find their own appropriate solutions. These average job-seekers tend to be better trained in rote memorization, not the more subtle, interpersonal, and agile thinking skills that define leaders.

This is where the value of a liberal arts degree becomes clearer. New data suggests that the smaller class sizes and unique programs of liberal arts colleges and universities cultivate the leadership qualities sought by employers. In a recent study, graduates were shown to be 25-45% more likely to become leaders in their localities or professions if they had talked with faculty members about academic and nonacademic subjects outside of the classroom. When their discussions had included peace, justice, and human rights, those numbers jump to 27-52%. In this light, liberal arts degrees become true assets to a job market that favors leaders.

Field of Study	Leadership Skill Gained
English	Writing and Communication
History	Perspective
Philosophy	Logical Thinking
Literature	Critical Thinking
Culture	Understanding Audiences
Arts	Creativity

Earning Potential

There is a common belief that liberal arts graduates earn less than others; however, research finds that this is only true for the first few years after graduation. In fact, a recent study finds a high correlation between a broad undergraduate education and financial success. Those who take the arts and humanities in addition to their main field of study are 31-72% more likely than others to have higher-level positions and earn more than $100,000. This should come as no surprise to us at this point, as the arts and humanities cultivate the kinds of skills that make it easier to rise through positions in business.

Putting the Myth of "Worthless Degrees" to Rest

Tomorrow's challenges call for creative, collaborative workers to reinvigorate and reshape our social and educational structures as well as our business models. To do so, students need rich, diverse educational opportunities to open and expand their minds.

The striking value of a liberal arts education comes from the way it enable students to think through various challenges, contradictions, and tensions. It helps them recognize that the only change worth working for is one that always keeps sight of humanity.

That's why a liberal arts education is a necessity in today's world: our shared humanity requires thoughtful leadership that considers the well-being and progress of all. That's why it's time to put the myth of "worthless degrees" to rest.

HOW TO MAKE THE MOST OF YOUR GUIDANCE COUNSELOR MEETINGS

by Tyson Schritter

You've got a deep bench of support to help you apply to colleges and take the next big step in your education, but did you that know your school guidance counselor can be your MVP? Your counselor can be one of your best resources when preparing for college, so why not make the most of all they have to offer? We've gathered to-do items, questions to ask, and topics to discuss so that you can use your meetings to the max.

Academic Prep for College

It's best to start your academic prep for college as early as possible, so make it a priority in your junior year (or in the early fall semester of your senior year) to meet with your counselor and review your transcript. Find out what classes, if any, qualify for college credit, and ask how you can strengthen your GPA for your college applications.

For your scheduled appointment, bring your résumé and have your counselor look it over to review and revise. What is your résumé lacking? How can you get it to help you stand out? Your counselor can give guidance as to what extracurriculars or classes you can engage in to boost your résumé appeal.

Lastly, check with your counselor about SAT/ACT dates and locations. Your counselor can remind you of important dates, deadlines, and test-taking locations. And, not only can they help tell you where to go for the texts, but they can also tell you how to prepare for them. With years of experience, counselors are full of pro tips to help you nail these pivotal exams.

Career Guidance

You may know that you're a big fan of world history and exploding science projects, but how does that actually translate into finding out what kind of career you'd like? Your counselor can help you review and discuss your interests, academic strengths, and goals to identify the career paths that may be right for you.

Once you start to clarify what careers you may enjoy, you'll have an easier time deciding your major and finding potential colleges that fit you perfectly. You can even ask your counselor to get you in touch with any high school grads whom they know are studying the majors you're interested in. By reaching out to current college students, you can get your information straight from the source!

College Selection & Application Guidance

You know yourself best, so come to your counselor with a list of colleges you're already interested in! With this prepared, your counselor can provide insight on the schools' specific requirements, quality majors, or even

challenges you might face while applying to them.

Ask your counselor to weigh your interests and academics to compile a list of college he or she thinks is right for you. This will give you a chance to compare your wishes with the more objective consideration of your performance and lifestyle. Additionally, make sure to ask whether your high school will be hosting any college fairs so that you can hear from representatives of the schools themselves!

It's your counselor's job to know a thing or two about college applications! Bring them some rough drafts of your college applications and ask them all your questions: What are good topics for college essays? What can I do to make my application stand out? What GPA do I need to get into my dream school?

Lastly, your counselor can be most directly involved in your application by writing one of your recommendation letters. Ask them whether they'd be willing to write you a recommendation letter, find out their availability, and see what guidance you can provide so they can really personalize your letter.

Scholarships & Financial Aid

When applying to colleges, you should also apply for as many funding opportunities as possible. Your counselor can give you the inside scoop on any local scholarships, alumni scholarships, or any additional alternative funding. Is FASFA a complete mystery? Don't know heads from tails about student loans? Ask your counselor to explain the difference between scholarships, financial aid, and student loans so that you can wisely cover your college expenses. With your counselor's help, you can look forward to a truly rewarding college experience.

5 STRATEGIES FOR FINDING THE RIGHT COLLEGE FOR YOU

There are around 5,000 colleges in the United States and hundreds of new schools open every year. How can you swim through such a vast sea of choices and land on the right college for you? Here are five simple strategies to navigate those waters:

Think Big

College will be more than just classes, dorms, and parties. A world of opportunities will open up the minute you

set foot on campus. You could study abroad, try out professions through on-the-job courses, on-campus jobs, and internships, join teams and clubs for everything from soccer to pickle-making, and, most importantly, invent new groups, new activities, and even new courses of study if you have a mind to. Look for schools that offer innovative learning programs such as these alongside traditional classes to ensure that you get the most from your college experience.

Lists, Lists, Lists

The best way to know if you've found what you're looking for is to define what you want. Make two lists: "Must Haves" and "Do Not Wants." Never be afraid that you're being too picky. There are so many options out there; you need a way to narrow them down. Picky is good!

Here are some questions to consider: Big school or small? Near home or far away? Big city or small town? Structured program or independent study?

In addition to the lists you make for yourself, you'll see a lot of other lists out there. Some track academics, cost, and even which is the best party school. The best advice, however, will come from lists that look at the whole college experience and not just one isolated aspect. Colleges of Distinction is one such site that looks at the entire experience a school offers.

Don't forget, though, the most important opinion about which college to choose is yours.

Make a Plan

Maybe you aced the SAT, rocked your GPA, and have a huge college trust fund. Lucky you! Even when luck is on your side, however, getting into and finishing college requires persistence and patience.

So stay determined! If necessary, you can start at one school and transfer later on. If you are low on funds, look for a lower-cost school that will allow you to go part-time while working and saving up. If your scores aren't ideal, look for a school that's easier to get into. Over 30 percent of college students transfer at some point, so you're in good company.

The important thing is to have a plan in mind that will get you where you want to go in the end. In other words, finishing strong is a lot more important than starting out on top.

Ask Questions

The college system is big and confusing for everyone. Don't let the complexity get you down, though. The solution is to ask a million questions until you understand. And don't worry—they're used to answering them.

Go to the college's website, find the department you're looking for, and zap them an email. If even figuring out the website is a pain, do it the old-fashioned way: pick up the phone, dial the college's main number, and bumble

through your half-formed question to whoever picks up. The college operator has probably heard every question a million times before and will be able to route you to the right person in seconds.

Most importantly, though, do not be afraid to ask questions until you understand. Don't worry. Even the professors and administrators have trouble understanding the system at times. Really.

You've Got This

Graduating from high school and the years afterward are a busy time. You might be juggling grades, a job, saving for college, and saying goodbye to your hometown. It's a fun time, too, of course, with new freedom to stay out late, travel, and make your own choices. However, all that adds up to having a lot of other things to do besides deciding on a college, writing essays, and taking all the necessary steps on the road to becoming a college student.

So, just don't forget: you don't have to decide everything at once. Start early by gathering information from sites like Colleges of Distinction, building your lists of Must Haves and Do Not Wants, and making plans for how you will get in, pay for, and finish college. If you give yourself time to plan, you'll have the luxury of blowing off college planning when you're busy and then picking it up again later. After all, this is your plan, your life, and your adventure!

The most important quality you will need to make it through applying to college is persistence. The right college plan will eventually take shape the more you find out about colleges. By the time you know what you want, you'll be ready to go for it and give it everything you've got.

IS COLLEGE PREPARING YOU FOR REAL LIFE?

by Tyson Schritter

Many of today's students report that their undergraduate experience had not prepared them adequately for life after college. Rightly expecting to use their degrees to find jobs in their chosen career path, they are too often dissatisfied with their employment outcomes upon graduation.

According to a survey by McGraw-Hill Education, only 40% of college seniors feel prepared to pursue a career after they receive their degree.

In contrast to the lacking resources and experiences that are most often offered at schools around the nation, McGraw-Hill's research shows that the majority of students across majors recognize the need for internships and other experiential learning, the opportunity to take advantage of career services and training for the job market, and professional networking opportunities while in college. In fact, 71% of students in their survey view the kind of career planning that is commonly overlooked as an "extremely important" aspect of their college education. They reported a need for greater assistance in identifying transferable skills from their majors and promoting themselves to potential employers.

How High-Impact Practices Prepare Students for Life After Graduation

While I'm frustrated by the results of the McGraw-Hill survey, I'm here to tell you that it doesn't have to be this way. In such an increasingly competitive job market, there are things we can do to prepare the next generation to enter the workforce and have successful careers.

The first—and, possibly, the most significant—way we can better help our students is by implementing number of "high-impact practices" into the college curriculum. These practices are a variety of educational opportunities that involve in-depth academic inquiry, collaborative learning, and experiential education.

Many administrators and faculty have already recognized the limitations of lecture-based learning and continually work to create enhanced academic experiences for the undergraduates on their campuses. These programs may include first-year experiences, service-learning, capstone projects, hands-on research, study abroad, and internships. It is with high-impact practices like these that allow students to learn the value of teamwork, develop leadership skills, and apply classroom learning to real-life problems.

The goal is ultimately to create more well-rounded graduates who are better trained to face the challenges of a 21st-century world.

Importance of Internships

When we consider the needs of students who are preparing for new careers, internships have the most noticeable benefit.

Internships (as well as cooperative education, or co-ops) may have been around for decades, but they weren't ever high priorities for many academic institutions that otherwise focused their resources on classroom learning.

Internship programs take students off campus, giving them real-life experience in their chosen career field to contrast their more stagnant lectures within the classroom. To gain temporary, highly useful job experience, students apply for internships at private companies or nonprofit organizations to do part-time work as they continue to take classes. Or, by working in co-ops, students can take a full semester off to work on a full-time basis. Regardless of program, students who participate get practical training and guidance from professional, hands-on mentors.

Interns not only receive practical work experience, but they also gain opportunities to learn more about their intended profession while networking with others who may even be their future employers. As a result of their experiences and new connections, many students can leverage their internships and co-ops into full-time careers.

As the job market tightens up, employers don't want to take chances with untested college graduates. Having at least one internship or co-op experience while in college can dramatically improve a student's chances of getting hired. In fact, as reported by the National Association of Colleges and Employers (NACE) in 2015, 56% of students who had an internship or co-op received job offers upon graduation in contrast to 36% of students without internships.

The Type of Education Matters

There's little question that internships are critical to improve students' chances in the job market. However, graduates' ongoing success also depends on their ability to adapt to changing professions as well as to function within an increasingly global and technological society.

In 2015, the Roosevelt Institute in New York published "Creative Schools for a Thriving Economy," a document in which it is argued that schools should teach creativity instead of "routine cognitive skills."

This research reinforces my own belief that we need to change the fundamental nature of higher education itself. By pursuing an education that incorporates such high-impact practices as writing-intensive classes, research, and capstone projects that incorporate the entirety of a student's academic career, college students can learn how to synthesize a variety of different information. They interact with people from different cultures through service-learning and study abroad, teaching them to consider and appreciate diverse perspectives. And through collaborative courses, first-year experiences, and learning communities, they learn how to work with others in a creative effort to solve problems with an interdisciplinary approach.

How Can College Students Become Better Prepared?

It's no longer enough to attend classes and get good grades. Instead, college students should consider what kinds of extracurricular, interactive, and hands-on experiences their universities offer, taking advantage of programs that promote truly interactive learning. Education beyond the classroom is key, and prospective college students should choose schools with a consideration not just of the campus culture, but also of the out-of-the-box opportunities they provide.

For all college students, it's imperative to communicate effectively and work collaboratively. All should take advantage of communities and initiatives that challenge them to be intellectually and socially successful.

By encouraging students to be active participants in their degrees, as by reimagining college education itself, we can better prepare our students for the demanding world that awaits them beyond their undergraduate careers.

THE TREND TOWARD HOLISTIC EDUCATION IN AMERICAN UNIVERSITIES

by Jamie Odom, Admissions Counselor, John Brown University

When American universities first began, they were structured with an emphasis on holistic education. Recent decades, however, then saw a major shift to a knowledge-based economy, prompting the "college experience" to focus on building more specialized skills for well-paying jobs. However, the pendulum is beginning to swing back to general "horizontal" education rather than specific "vertical" education.

Holistic Education

Students now are not only searching for a university to grow them intellectually, but they are also searching for a university that will develop them holistically: emotionally, spiritually, and intellectually.

Additionally, more and more companies are looking to hire individuals with just as strong EQs (Emotional Quotients, or their ability to recognize and relate to other people's emotions) as they are individuals with high IQs (Intelligence Quotient, the test that supposedly quantifies a person's intelligence based on a series of questions).

The reason for this is simple: graduates who exhibit skills in a diverse grouping of areas are more adaptable in the workplace, making them a strong asset to prospective employers.

For instance, an engineer with a strength in writing and communication who can not only number-crunch, but also deliver an engaging presentation to a board of potential clientele, would make any company proud.

Communication is Key

An area of strong emphasis in the liberal arts education is communication. Whether that be verbal communication or communication using the written word, universities and companies alike are beginning to recognize the importance of such a skill.

Consider the concept of "ethos" when attempting to establish rapport with a future client. Now, imagine these two brief email scenarios:

Client's question: "I'm working on a home electrical issue. Can you give me an estimate on your company's costs?"

Company 1 Reply: "Where's the problem at in the house and I'll tell you how much for the cost."

Company 2 Reply: "We'd love to be of service. What seems to be the problem? That will give us a clearer idea of your cost breakdown."

Both responses technically communicate the same thing, and both companies may be completely competent at their work. In fact, Company 1 may even be better at their work.

However, when presented with both responses, which company do you think the client will choose?

That's right: the company with which they feel is more competent, due to their brief but clear communication style. They instill confidence.

That is one of the goals of the core curriculum: to help students achieve clarity of communication regardless of major.

Everything in Perspective

A growing desire of students in particular is to better understand the world around them from a perspective broader than the one they grew up with. A liberal arts education can help provide that.

For instance, in the honors college at John Brown University, students have the opportunity to take what are known as colloquia courses. In these one-hour courses (designed so that, no matter how heavy the student course load is, they are still able to participate), students can take such classes as International Cinema, Service and Community, the Monastic Life, and Slavery Narratives, to name a few.

In these courses, students from English to Engineering can delve into worlds of study with which they may not otherwise interact.

Students who take these courses not only begin to see layers in which their spheres of study influence others, but it also sparks in them a curiosity to see things from another point of view.

In future careers of teaching or even city design and management, a propensity to see things from multiple points of view can be extremely important.

A common university core, while it may seem frivolous or unimportant to some, are growing a new generation of students into stronger "whole" people, who not only have a strength in their personal field of study (vertical education), but also have the power of a multifaceted education outside their chosen field (horizontal education).

WHOSE OPINION CAN YOU TRUST? AVOIDING BIAS WHEN CHOOSING A COLLEGE

by Tyson Schritter

There are so many outlets from which to gather information about going to college—websites, magazines, books, high school counselors, and even paid advisors—but how can you know who's giving you the best information?

Some magazines may rank colleges while also running advertisements from those same schools. Does that mean the ranking is slanted? Not necessarily; it is common for publications to write about a business while also accepting advertising from it. In fact, there are common rules of practice meant to keep the two sides of the journalism business separate.

That isn't to say that bias never happens, so it's important to approach college rankings with caution. The key to cracking the code of any publication's ranking system is to read all the information provided, not just a number on a list. Each publication will probably reveal some its methods in compiling the rankings, but in reality, it can be easy to pick out decision factors that are not so objective. If you look carefully, you might be able to see some patterns in their choices; they might favor big schools over small ones, small towns over cities, or Ivy League schools over newer ones.

Of course, a little slant doesn't mean that rankings aren't valuable. Any viewpoint or perspective you find about a college can help you piece together your own opinion. Just remember: though these rankings are often based on statistics, the formulas are written by human beings, which means they're neither perfect nor absolute.

Websites are different from print publications in that they often include crowdsourcing, which can provide up-to-the-minute information about a school directly from current students. Look for online reviews, starred rankings, and even comment threads to give you that valuable insider perspective. Of course, any time a site allows reviews and comments, you can naturally expect there to be spam, trolls, and all the hijinks that come with an open door to the general public. You might even find yourself reading paid reviews that are written to be overly positive or super negative prank reviews written by students at rival schools. Even so, it's a good idea to weed through the spam and look around for those "average Joe or Jane" points of view.

High school guidance counselors and paid college advisors–if you can afford them–provide invaluable assistance to help you navigate the maze of college applications, and it can be so helpful to have a professional voice of authority cut through the noise of so many other opinions. One of the best things about working with someone face-to-face is that you get to have a productive dialogue. They can give personally catered recommendations and guidance, and you can ask follow-up questions. Just keep in mind that relying on any one person's opinion on which college to choose is probably not sufficient.

The key to avoiding bias in your college research is to gather as much information as possible from as many sources as you can find. Never let any one source of information make your decision for you; instead, consider multiple perspectives to help construct your conclusion. And finally, choose schools based on the factors that matter most to you. Choosing a college is very personal and highly individual. No matter how many sources you read, the opinion that ultimately matters most is your own.

GET THE MOST OUT OF A COLLEGE VISIT

by Colleges of Distinction Staff

No amount of research can replace the experience of visiting a campus firsthand. By going to a school itself, you can talk directly to current students, take a close look at the residence halls, and make meaningful contact with the admissions office.

Despite the tremendous value that can come from a college visit, some students and parents do not come aptly prepared. In many cases, people don't take the time to plan properly, simply showing up or driving by. Without some foresight, you might risk getting a hasty–and often incorrect–impression of the school.

Get the most out of your college visit! Here are a few tips that will help you:

Pre-Planning

Call to schedule your college visit at least two weeks ahead of time

Many people do not pre-plan their college visit, which can end up leading to an unproductive, spoiled experience. If you call ahead of time, the admissions office will be able to accommodate you and ensure that you get what you need out of your visit.

Make sure to get proper directions to the admissions office

In order to make a good first impression, make sure you know where you're going so that you can arrive on time. Don't only trust your GPS! If you have any questions, ask for help from someone on campus or call the admissions office to help clarify your directions.

If there is anything specific you wish to see, ask ahead of time

Depending upon the time of year, the staff involved in your college visit may not be able to accommodate you with everything you wish to see. For example, it may not be possible to audit a class or stay overnight during a visit in the summer months. Regardless, it can never to ask if there is ever something of specific interest to you.

Be flexible

It may not be possible for the school you're visiting to schedule everything you would like to see, especially during the summer. Be willing to try something else, and always remember that you want to present yourself positively; you still might want to apply to this school later.

If you need to cancel or reschedule, call ASAP

It goes without saying that you can't ever predict emergencies or unforeseen circumstances, but it's nevertheless a common courtesy to contact the admissions office to let them know you can't come. It's important to respect the admissions staff's time, so try not to inconvenience them by failing to show up without any warning.

During the Visit

Ask questions

Take an active role. The college visit is a golden opportunity for you to ask questions about what really matters to you.

Try to do some extra things on your own

Eat in the cafeteria, talk to students, see where people hang out, and tour the neighborhood around the school. If you take a close look on your own, you can get a more complete picture of the school, not just what the admissions office wants to highlight.

Don't discount the school because of bad weather or other uncontrollable circumstances

Some students are quick to cross a school off their list simply because it rained or because they visited during a school break when there weren't many activities going on.

Don't fall into this trap! There are going to be good days and bad days no matter where you go, so try to look past the the inconstant factors and instead focus on the school for what it is and what it can be for you.

Post-Visit

Always write a thank-you note

In order to make a great and lasting impression, write a thank-you note to those you met on campus. This makes it more likely to be remembered when it comes time to review your application.

Make sure you have contact information for any future questions or concerns

Keep business cards and pamphlets in some organized folder so that you can refer to them if necessary.

Make sure to remain in contact with the school

Some schools keep a record of contact information and sometimes use a prospective student's correspondence as a measurement of how interested they are in being admitted.

Talk with your high school counselor about the visit

It's a great idea to bounce your ideas off of parents, relatives, and friends when you weigh the options and experiences from your college visits. You should also make sure, however, to discuss your visit with your counselor, as they can provide a neutral and informative perspective on your experiences.

USING SOCIAL MEDIA IN YOUR COLLEGE SEARCH

Almost every college is building virtual communities through social media. As you conduct your search, there are plenty of opportunities to connect with the school, admissions counselors, prospective and current students, even alumni. You can follow colleges on social media to learn about campus life, take virtual tours and ultimately, help you decide if the college is a good fit for you. Let's consider some of the most popular social network platforms and how to use each of them:

Facebook

Start by "liking" the college's page, and you'll get a sense of the personality of the school, what conversations are important, and the hot topics on campus. More importantly, use the information you learn about the college during your interview or in your essay—admissions counselors appreciate that you've taken the time to find out all you can about the school. Beyond the school's official Facebook page, look to see if there are groups that correspond to your special interests or if you can ask questions of admissions counselors.

Twitter

Follow your prospective college on Twitter to discover everything from what lectures and events are happening to what's being served in the dining hall that week. You'll also learn news about what current alumni are doing and what issues are important, whether it's sports, the environment, social change or new classes.

YouTube

You can watch convocation speeches, take virtual tours, hear guest lectures and listen to the school's singing group perform. It's a great way to see how active the campus life is, and if this seems like a place where you would happily fit in.

Instagram, Flickr, Tumblr and Pinterest

A picture really is worth a thousand words. Take a look at these image sites, and you'll find everything from ideas for decorating dorm rooms to student life to campus buildings.

Student Bloggers

This can be a great way to learn about and connect with current students. Hear what they are going through, their likes and dislikes, and opportunities they are getting there. Feel free to stop by the comment section and ask a question or two.

Social Media Tips for Students

Just as employers often check a job applicant's online presence, college admissions officers often take a closer look at their candidates. Use common sense, and don't post anything that might give a negative impression in your language, photos or images. Set up your privacy settings to restrict access; that includes protecting your tweets and if there are YouTube videos you wouldn't want to be seen, set those to private as well. Make sure your email address is professional (not sexxygurrl96@example.com). Use either firstnamelastname@example.com or create a user name to highlight a special skill (smithkicks@example.com for a high school football kicker looking to stand out, or smith88keys@example.com for a pianist).

Use your social media presence to highlight your achievements, share your volunteer work, and create your "brand" that will showcase you in your very best light. Create a video of your soccer goals, start a blog of your creative writing, or set up a Pinterest account to "pin" your artwork. The Common Application and the Universal College Application both have places to link to a site. Make the most of social media, both in your search and the application process, to find the college that's your best fit.

APPLYING/GETTING ACCEPTED

9 TIPS TO HELP WITH YOUR COLLEGE APPLICATIONS

College applications take time, and they should! After diligent research to find the colleges and universities where you can study, learn, and grow for the next four years, it's now time to explain to the admissions counselors at those schools why you belong there.

1. Organize!

Collect all application due dates and supplemental pieces. Most college applications require letters of recommendation. Email calendars, smartphone calendars, and even the classic wall calendar work well. Remember to check it often! Many colleges and universities have different due dates.

2. Ask Early

Many college applications require letters of recommendation. Remember that teachers and mentors are much more likely to write a letter for you if you give them ample time. Keep in mind that your first choice of teacher may be asked by many students applying to write letters of recommendation.

3. Remember your Audience

Spend a few minutes thinking about what makes you uniquely who you are. Extra-curriculars? Athletics? Honor societies? Community involvement? Most people applying to your schools are strangers to the admissions counselors who will be reviewing your application. Learn as much as you can about each school you apply to, and highlight your characteristics that align with your prospective schools' values. Make an outline of what you want to make sure to mention—what makes you unique and what makes you a good fit. Go over this outline with someone who knows you and your academic history well—a parent or a counselor.

4. Create a First Draft

Nowadays, most college applications are done online. Never fill in an application without creating a first draft! Keep this first draft out of the actual application website so you do not accidentally submit an application before you are ready. Never leave an answer blank.

5. Ask for Review

After answering ALL questions via your first draft, ask someone—or better yet, a few people—to review your first draft application. Your reviewers may be able to offer edits that will convey information about you in a better way. College essays are tough work! Don't do yourself a disservice by skipping the editing process.

6. Include All Supplemental Information

Before you apply, make sure your applications have the necessary supplemental information which may include relevant test scores, an activities résumé, and letters of recommendation.

7. Before Applying, Make a Copy

Even if you apply via the internet, there can be times where your applications can be lost in the ether. Computers and mail are not foolproof. Always have a copy.

8. Proofread Again

Make sure to proofread one last time before you send in your college applications. Careless mistakes and incomplete information may cost you a spot.

9. Apply!

Send in your applications and supplemental information! Make sure you confirm receipt with each school to which you apply. Good luck!

RIGHTS AND RESPONSIBILITIES IN THE ADMISSIONS PROCESS

Those who may be beginning their college search sometimes assume that colleges and universities have complete control over the admissions process. In fact, there are established regulations that almost every college, university, and high school must abide by to be fair and ethical.

The Statement of Principles of Good Practice (SPGP), set forth by the National Association of College Admission Counseling (NACAC), specifies some important rights and responsibilities for every member of the process: students, parents, and counselors.

The Right to Know

One of the most important rights for students and parents is the right to information. College and university professionals (as well as high school college counselors) must provide all of the open, honest information that students need in order to make the best decision about college.

Colleges must be open and consistent about deadlines. The SPGP states that a "College and University member agree that they will include a current and accurate admissions calendar. They will state clearly all deadlines for application, notification, housing, and candidates' reply requirements for both admissions and financial aid." In fully understanding this statement, students have the right to know specific deadlines for submitting their applications without penalty.

Parents and students also have the right to information from their high school guidance counselor. The SPGP says that counselors must "provide a program of counseling which introduces a broad range of postsecondary opportunities to students." That means that parents and students can reasonably expect their high school counselor to make presentations, hold information sessions, and find other ways of making good information about the process available to them.

The Responsibility to Work

Parents and students also have clear obligations in the process. Students would often prefer someone else to do research for them—after all, it's a big, confusing project. But every college-bound student should take the main responsibility of researching all of his or her college possibilities.

By doing this, the student will learn not only a college's requirements for admission, but also about the institution as a whole—an important part of the decision-making process. The more students know about the schools they're considering, the better their chances of being happy with their choices.

Students also have the responsibility to complete their own essays, questions, activity résumé, and all other parts of the application. Parents sometimes feel they should help with the application in order to enhance their son or daughter's chances for admission. In fact, by helping in this way, they will be doing a great deal of harm. Colleges and universities frown on such parental "help"; if it is suspected that Mom or Dad wrote the admissions essay, then the student is much less likely to be admitted.

So what can parents do to help? It is perfectly acceptable for parents to take charge of paying application fees, making sure test scores are sent, and making sure that everything is organized. It is also a great idea for parents to go over admissions materials with students, brainstorm questions to ask during a visit, and even ask questions themselves. Although they should not re-do a student's work, it is acceptable for parents to proofread student essays for spelling and grammar. There are many ways that parents can help their son or daughter with this difficult process.

For More Information

If you are interested in a particular college or university, ask for clear information on what their admissions policies are and what kind of academic programs they offer. The admissions office should be able to provide this information to you.

WHY YOU SHOULD TAKE THE ACT MORE THAN ONCE

The Second Time (or Even the Third!) is the Charm

Yes, we know that taking the ACT can be a nail-biting, stressful experience. After all, there's a lot riding on the results. But often, the first time you take the test, you're not at your best. It's early, it's Saturday, and most likely you're taking the ACT in a school you have never visited. It's all so foreign and new, that it's no wonder your first test scores might not be what you had hoped. The good news is that you can take the ACT again—plenty of juniors (and seniors!) do it. There's no shame in taking the test multiple times. And the odds are good that you will score better the next time you take the ACT. Here are a few reasons why you may want to take the ACT more than once:

More Time to Practice and Prepare for the ACT

Maybe you took an ACT prep course before your first test, or maybe you decided to wing it. Once you have your scores, you can pinpoint those areas in which you need a little extra practice and prep. Some high schools have ACT prep classes either built into their curriculum or after school. Take advantage of the convenience of test prep offered at your high school, if it's available. Or, buy an ACT prep guide with practice exams, and take the ACT under the same time constraints as the actual exam.

You'll Be Less Nervous

The first time you take the ACT, there's the fear of the unknown. You're jittery, and there's a lot of hype about the importance of your score for college admission. Once you've taken the test, you know what to expect— how long it really takes to finish, the type of questions, and which sections will require a little more of your time. So the second time you take the ACT, you'll have more confidence. And you'll know that your parents really weren't kidding when they said you should get a good night's sleep and not skip breakfast!

You'll Be a Better Test-Taker

After you take the ACT once, you'll have a better understanding of the time constraints and how to pace yourself. If you don't know the answer to a question, move on and come back later if you have time. On difficult questions, the process of elimination is the most effective tool. Remember, the ACT does not count wrong answers against you. Only correct answers are used to determine one's composite score.

Raise Your ACT Score and Your Scholarship Opportunities

According to the College Board, 57% of high school students take the ACT, and nearly 60% of those who retake the exam will see an increase in their composite scores. A higher test score can mean more scholarship opportunities and better financial aid packages offered to you. Check with the admissions offices of the colleges to which you're applying, and ask which test scores qualify to be considered for additional aid.

More Choices

When you take the ACT more than once, you get to choose which scores to send along with your college applications. If you're on the wait list at your top choice, sending higher test scores may help the admissions office move you onto the accepted list. And higher scores might open up new possibilities—schools that may have been previously out of reach may be worth an application.

So sign up for the ACT in your junior year, and plan to take it at least once more. You'll be glad you did!

FIGHTING SENIORITIS: DON'T LET POST-ACCEPTANCE GRADES SLIP

One of the biggest struggles high school seniors face is a lack of motivation. Often times, students enter into their winter term with less inspiration than the fall. This is because colleges and universities begin sending out decision letters, and students take those decisions as a ticket into the future. Acceptance into college should be celebrated because it is a great achievement. However, an acceptance is never set in stone. It can be taken away just as easily as it was given. This is a reminder to all senior students that grades do matter, up until the very last day.

Senioritis

Senioritis is a change in behavior by high school students. The change generally takes place in the second semester of one's senior year, and it involves a lack of motivation. Senioritis has been known to affect academic performance. Students tend to feel burned out from their first three years and give up toward the end. The result of senioritis, however, can be disastrous. Students that let their grades slip too far risk having their acceptances taken away.

Consequences

When grades take a nosedive during second semester, there can be unfortunate consequences. Aside from rescinding an acceptance, colleges can adjust financial aid packages to reflect the lack of motivation. Admissions officers have also been known to approach students and ask for an explanation regarding poor grades. What's most troubling is the time frame in which students will receive news of their revoked acceptance. Final grades are not reviewed by colleges until the summer, which means a student might not receive the unfortunate news until July or August. By that time, it would be too late to get into another school, as slots will have filled up.

Avoid Falling Behind

There are ways to avoid the dangerous effects of senioritis. The best way to stay on top of the game is to get involved. Second semester seniors should develop a set of academic and personal goals. Establishing objectives keeps students actively engaged and develops a mentality of working toward something. This attitude will be incredibly helpful when it comes time for students to graduate and start their college career.

Preparation Today, Success Tomorrow

One of the most important things to remember is that a lack of motivation during senior year can hurt students in college. Students that lose motivation can easily develop lazy academic habits. This can be disastrous when the student starts their first year of college. Academic standards at the collegiate level are usually much higher than what they were in high school. Therefore, students that have been slacking are more likely to struggle with their new academic demands.

WHAT DOES IT MEAN TO BE WAITLISTED OR DEFERRED?

After all the frantic work of putting together an application, waiting for an answer can seem to take forever. Most applicants assume that eventually they will receive a letter with one of two simple outcomes: acceptance or rejection. Yet there are actually other possible outcomes—as if there weren't enough confusion already in the college search process!

You may be informed that your application has been "waitlisted" or "deferred." What does this mean? Should you be concerned? The answer depends on a number of factors.

Waitlists and deferrals are two different things, but they share some similarities. While neither is an outright rejection, they both mean you will have to wait longer to see if you will be admitted.

Being **deferred** can mean a wide variety of things. In most cases, the college has not completed its review of your file and is "deferring" their decision to a later date. Deferrals typically fall into two categories:

- You applied under the Early Action or Early Decision plan and have been pushed back into the regular pool. This may be frustrating, but also has an advantage. If you are accepted into the college/

university under regular decision, you are not obligated to attend as you would have been if you were accepted under an Early Decision plan (Early Action is non-binding to begin with). You may feel free to consider offers from other schools.

- You have applied under a regular decision or rolling admission and the college/university would like to have more information in order to make a decision about your application. In almost every case, a college or university would like to see more grades from the senior year or new test scores. If a school receives the information they want, they could admit you earlier.

Being **waitlisted** is unlike being deferred; the college has finished reviewing your file and made a decision to put you on a waiting list for admission.

- Being on a waitlist typically means that you are placed within a "holding pattern" of sorts. The admissions committee may or may not admit students from the waitlist. And unlike a deferral situation, new information does not usually change a waitlist decision.

- If you are placed on a waitlist, you can usually find out if the school has gone to their waitlist in the past and if so, how many students they admitted from the waitlist. In some cases, your chances of eventually getting in are very good; at other colleges, waitlisted applicants are almost never admitted.

It is always wise to apply to another institution and ensure that you have a place somewhere. Do not pin your hopes on a waitlisted college; this is the time to make plans with one of your backup schools.

Whether you are deferred or waitlisted, avoid the temptation to begin a flood of recommendation letters and phone calls to the admissions department. In almost every case, this can have an adverse effect on your chances for admission. Some institutions even state in the letters that they do not take any additional letters of recommendation or phone calls on the student's behalf. If the admissions office does need more materials, they are generally interested in concrete information (test scores, grades, etc.) rather than personal testimony or recommendations.

Remember that if you have been waitlisted or deferred, you have not been denied admission. It's as if you have been asked to stay in the waiting room a little longer, pending an ultimate decision. As with any waiting period, use the time wisely. Improve your grades or test scores, or simply continue your good academic performance. Make sure you have alternate plans with another school, and don't despair. Being waitlisted or deferred is frustrating, but it's not the end of the world, or of your college search.

PAYING FOR COLLEGE

ATTENDING A PRIVATE SCHOOL CAN BE AFFORDABLE

by Tyson Schritter

For most high school students, the cost of college can be daunting. Students have to choose between in-state schools, public universities, religious colleges, and private colleges, all while weighing their options against their budget.

Most students start with the misunderstanding that all private colleges are unaffordable. This is unfortunate, because some of the best higher education in this country is administered in private colleges. If you're looking for a private college that's affordable, look no further—we've created a collection of colleges and tips to help you seek out affordable options for private college.

Why Private Schools Are Affordable

The initial sticker shock that many applicants to private colleges feel is normal. The tuition listed on private college websites can range from $20,000 to $60,000 a year before financial aid, leading many applicants to believe that such schools are not affordable for them.

The truth, however, is that many private colleges offer more financial aid packages, often of a higher value, than public universities. Once you factor in these aid packages, the cost of tuition can many times be equal to or less than that of public schools.

What's the Actual Price of Tuition?

Let's take a moment to define a couple terms to better understand the actual cost of attending a private college.

Posted price: This the price that colleges post on their website, typically considered the maximum price of a full-time student. It's unlikely you'll have to pay that much money.

Net price: This is the price a student will pay after scholarships and grants are deducted from the posted price. This is the price that you should use when comparing the cost of colleges. If one school has offered you a great scholarship, it's net price is likely to be better than that of a comparable school that has not offered any aid.

Knowing the difference between the posted price and the net price can make a big difference in which schools you choose to apply to and attend. Your ultimate decision in which school you choose is deeply impacted by your understanding, calculation, and comparison of your options' net prices.

The Private School Cost Calculation Process

If you're certain that you want to attend a private school, it's time to start looking into which schools will offer you financial aid and how much that aid affects your cost of attendance.

Below are some foolproof steps for you to take in order to calculate the cost of each private school you're interest in. Keep in mind that some factors of the final cost of college won't be included here; special, merit-based scholarships cannot be included in this calculation until you've applied and received the award. If you know how much merit-based scholarship you've been offered, you can get an even more accurate picture of the school's final cost.

Steps to calculate college costs:

- Gather tax documents (ask your parents if you'd like some help).
- Go to a tuition calculator website.
- Plug in your numbers to the tuition calculator.
- Save the results, including the starting cost of tuition, for later comparison.
- Go to the next private college website on your list.
- Continue these steps until you've calculated the cost of each private college you're interested in attending.

Then it's time to make comparisons. Once you've collected all of your data, you can compare the cost of attending each school. This may not be a complete picture if you can't include merit-based scholarships, outside scholarships, or government grants, but it's a good first step in assessing the cost of different private colleges.

The Value of Private Schools

When you consider the actual price you end up paying, private colleges may actually be a better value. Consider that many private schools offer:

- Smaller class sizes
- More interaction between professors and students
- Classes that are more often taught by professors than graduate students
- A smaller, more tightly knit student body
- More opportunities to gain leadership experience

Depending on the experiences and outcomes you want in your college experience, a private school may be an even better value than a public one.

5 Tricks to Make College More Affordable

Public or private, college is a big investment. There's no way to get around this fact in the modern world. Here are five more tips and tricks to help lower your out-of-pocket cost for college.

- **Earn credits elsewhere.** Most colleges allow you to transfer credits from other colleges. There are often limitations to what can transfer and a maximum number of credits that can be completed at other schools, but any transferred credits can help to lower your tuition cost. Look into the credit transfer

rules of any school you're interested in attending. Credits can be earned through community college courses either prior to attending college or throughout the summer and winter breaks.

- **Explore all aid options.** You can receive scholarships and grants from many different sources. Your school may offer some, the government has ways of helping out, and there are numerous scholarships out there for special interests, personality traits, and even body characteristics. Don't think that there isn't scholarship money out there for you; aid is available for everyone.
- **FAFSA.** Be sure to fill out your FAFSA application properly and on time. Even if you don't think you're eligible for aid from the government, fill it out and see if you are. Be sure to research other federal aid programs or even aid from your local government.
- **Be creative.** Not only can you earn credits elsewhere, but you can even fulfill requirements in high school by taking AP course, college-level courses online, and through dual-enrollment classes that afford you both high school and college credit at the same time.
- **Reduce materials.** College materials, like textbooks and various supplies, can make up a significant portion of your college costs. Be sure to start your research early and look at many different options before making any purchases. There are many options out there for you to get textbooks for a significantly lower price than at the college bookstore.

Affordable Private Colleges of Distinction

Colleges of Distinction has vetted many of the finest private schools in the country. We hope that this breakdown has helped you realize that an education at a private college is within your financial reach.

FINANCIAL AID TERMS DEFINED

Paying for college can be confusing if you don't understand the terminology. Below are some helpful definitions to common financial aid terms.

Bursar

A college office that handles both the distribution of financial aid and payment of fees and tuition. May also be called financial office, or something similar.

CSS Profile

A secondary financial aid form that the colleges use to help them determine if the student is eligible for their own money. These should be filed early, along with the FAFSA, to receive early information regarding your status for financial aid.

EFC (EXPECTED FAMILY CONTRIBUTION)

This term refers to the results from the FAFSA that shows what your family can contribute financially for educational expenses. In many instances, the EFC is calculated without taking into consideration any unexpected changes in income (not shown by the results from taxes) or other emergencies.

FAFSA

A standard form from the Department of Education that determines eligibility for all state and federal grants. Generally, you must fill this out before a college can begin processing your request for financial aid. They are usually available in November, but most require current tax information to fill out fully.

Federal Stafford Loan Program

Government-subsidized loans that are adjusted by need. No repayment is required while the student is in school.

Financial Aid Package

An offer of money for a student from a college. It usually consists of several kinds of aid, including loans, grants, campus jobs, and may or may not include scholarships. This package fills the gap between parents' contribution and the total cost of college.

Merit Scholarships

Money given to students on the basis of demonstrated ability—academic, performance, service, athletics, etc. It is not based on need, and does not need to be repaid. Most scholarships come from colleges themselves and vary widely from institution to institution. There are also some scholarships available from businesses, alumni organizations, and programs like the National Merit Scholarship.

PLUS Loans

Government-subsidized loans that are limited to the cost of education. Parents do not need to demonstrate need. Interest rates can vary.

Pell Grants

These government grants are awarded to students who need a great deal of financial aid. They do not need to be repaid.

Unsubsidized Stafford Loans

Loans that do not require demonstration of need, and for which interest must be paid while the student is in college. Repayment of the principal begins after graduation.

Work Study

A campus job that may be offered as part of a financial aid package. These usually require 15-20 hours a week on campus and usually allow the student to do some studying while working. Examples might include proctoring a test, or working at a library desk.

MONEY MATTERS: THINKING ABOUT FINANCIAL AID

Many families find that applying for financial aid is just as confusing as applying to colleges. Along with the huge number of required forms, they must contend with a new language of terms and abbreviations.

But there is light at the end of the tunnel! Here are some tips to get you going.

Explore All of Your Options Early and Discuss Them with Each Other

The old adage "the early bird catches the worm" is very true when it comes to financial aid. By taking an early look and discovering all possibilities, it can offset a lot of extra work later on and also give the family a head start on reducing the cost.

Check with Your Schools to See What Forms Are Required

All colleges and universities require the FAFSA. Some require the CSS Profile. Others may have their own institutional forms.

Talk to Each Other About Realistic Expectations

Discussing financial matters can be uncomfortable. But the more that your child understands about the family's financial possibilities, the more realistic attitude he or she will take to the college process.

Investigate Every Scholarship Opportunity

Leave no stone unturned! Look everywhere! From guidebooks and websites, the more you search for scholarships, the more possibilities that you uncover. You can begin by asking family members if they belong to any organizations (or their place of employment) that sponsor scholarships for which your child might be eligible. Talk to your counselor—and of course, check with the school to see if there are any special applications necessary for scholarships. (Music scholarships, for example, may require an audition, while others may require interviews, essays, and so forth.)

Establish a Good Working Relationship with the Financial Aid Office

As with the admissions office, you should consider the financial aid office a valuable source of information. By instituting a rapport with your financial aid counselor, your family will have another outlet in which to discuss any special circumstances or ask basic questions.

If You Have Any Special Circumstances, Be Sure to Communicate Them Effectively

Remember: your initial financial aid package is not always the last word. The FAFSA and other forms do not always take into account special circumstances, such as a change in income or a medical emergency that is not reflected in any tax information. Talk to the schools' financial aid office and see if your specific situation can be taken into consideration.

Above all, remember that if you take the time to understand the financial aid process, it will become an easier task than you might have initially imagined. Explore every option, talk to everyone, and make sure to breathe!

PREPARING FOR COLLEGE AND MAKING THE MOST OF YOUR OPPORTUNITIES

HIGH-IMPACT PRACTICES – THE KEYS TO YOUR FUTURE

by Dr. Ross Peterson-Veatch, Interim Vice President of Academic Affairs and Academic Dean, Goshen College

When I was in college, I studied abroad, spending 12 months in South America. The experience completely changed my attitude about why I was in college, what college was for, who I was, and what I wanted to do with my life.

To paraphrase philosopher and educator John Dewey, you don't prepare for the future by drawing a straight line between what you're doing now and what you want, because you don't know what's coming in the future. The real preparation comes in learning to wring the most meaning and knowledge out of the present moment so that you're ready for whatever comes after graduation.

Interestingly, study abroad is a "High-Impact Practice" (HIP), a term coined by the Association of American Colleges and Universities to describe the research-proven top 10 educational practices that are the most beneficial to college students of all backgrounds.

HIPs are the best resource for you to ensure that you're getting the most out of your college education. They provide a platform for synthesizing what you've learned into a coherent narrative, often involving invaluable collaboration and hands-on education.

Research has shown that HIPs are linked with higher grade point averages, and even more importantly, higher student satisfaction with their education.

As you're evaluating college options, look for opportunities like first-year seminars that encourage critical reflection, study abroad programs, internships, and capstone projects. Search the colleges' course catalogs, talk HIPs with your admissions counselor, or set up a meeting with a professor or academic advisor to ask about High-Impact Practices.

One example of an effective High-Impact Practice is Goshen College's Study-Service Term. According to the National Survey of Student Engagement, Goshen students were more likely than their national peers to interact with students of a race or ethnicity other than their own, more likely to complete an internship or field experience, more likely to participate in co-curricular activities, and more likely to acquire a broad general education.

Keep in mind that, just because a school has HIPs available, that doesn't necessarily mean that they're easily accessible to all students. You should also find out what percentage of students at the school have participated in at least one High-Impact Practice.

Remember—your goal for college is to get a great education, and that's exactly what HIPs help ensure. To fully prepare for life after graduation, make sure that High-Impact Practices are a part of your college search process!

COLLABORATIVE AND COMMON LEARNING: LEARN AND GROW WITH YOUR PEERS

by Carol Burton, Associate Provost for Undergraduate Studies, Western Carolina University

Whether you live with a roommate or not, college is all about getting involved and getting to know others.

One of the key elements of any collegiate experience is honing your skills to become a successful member of society upon graduation. Our increasingly diverse world demands that we be interconnected in dynamic and relevant ways, and institutions that prize this aspect of the collegiate experience are setting their graduates up for success. While there are a number of ways to promote and support your personal and professional development, two proven practices that many colleges employ are *collaborative* and *common learning*. Regardless of your chosen career, you will need to work with others to achieve your goals and advance the desired outcomes of your employer. Opportunities for being involved in collaborative and common learning include jointly working on projects and research; sharing learning experiences around broad, integrated themes; enrolling in courses that are team taught by faculty from different disciplines; engaging with campus interdisciplinary themes that link curricular and co-curricular experiences; completing common readings across college levels (e.g. freshman reading); and attending guest speaker series' that are combined with individual reflection and group discussions.

Collaborative Assignments and Projects

Increasingly popular at colleges and universities today, collaborative assignments and projects often mirror the real world of work and life beyond college. Whether you work in healthcare, business, education, the sciences, or some other field, you are sure to find you and your fellow employees frequently organized in teams and expected to work successfully within those teams. Collaborative problem-solving, diverse viewpoints, and different modes of thinking contribute to students' development of:

- richer solutions to problems,
- multi-dimensional and hypothetical thinking,
- consensus-building skills, and
- effective teamwork.

Some universities require students to work on a community-based project that requires multiple angles to solve. For example, at Western Carolina University in North Carolina, this approach to learning has led to a partnership with the local community to respond to the major economic downturn by 1) having students who major in marketing work with the merchants in the town to create and implement a vibrant marketing plan; 2) employing communication student majors to develop public relations jingles for local radio and television broadcast; 3) allowing students majoring in computer information systems to develop an online application for the town that includes business locations, historic data, and calendar of events; 4) engaging students majoring in business to develop a business sustainability plan for various merchants in the town; and 5) hosting special events for the university community to participate in themed events at a discounted price. Faculty, staff, and administrators provided oversight and support for students in their work with the community.

Common Learning Experiences

Common learning experiences go hand-in-hand with collaborative assignments and projects; however, these experiences often take place university-wide or at the program level rather than in individual courses. An example of common intellectual learning experiences includes campus-wide themes where curricular and co-curricular opportunities are linked by a common topic. For example, at Western Carolina University each year, a committee of students, faculty, and staff propose and vote on a common these around which to entire the entire campus. Topics such as "the decade of the 1960's," "citizenship and civility," "water," "global poverty," "economic inequality," "North Carolina—our state, our time," and "Africa: more than a continent" have been considered and/or adopted at WCU. Students learn by completing common readings across their general studies, attending speaker sessions, engaging in community service, viewing historic and art exhibits, and enrolling in specific courses that focus on the theme.

As a more specific example of a campus theme, WCU most recently selected the theme "Africa—more than a continent" and had a two-year (2015-17) focus on the cultures, diversity, political structures, foods, religions, arts, geography and geology, business, histories, music, hospitality, education, and demographics of the continent. Faculty and students could travel to Africa to study (through courses in anthropology, sociology, and criminal justice), conduct exchanges for professional development (like the partnership between Botswana and WCU's department of Communication Sciences and Disorders), perform musically (in ensembles like the brass quintet), and conduct service-learning projects. The university's dining division even participated in the campus theme by hosting several days' worth of menus to highlight the cuisines of various African countries and cultures. The campus community experimented with Moroccan spiced whitefish, African peanut soup, East African eggplant stew, and West African Jollof rice. Students, staff, and faculty were afforded opportunities to discuss global issues in an African context while learning about the continent and its diverse countries and cultures. See Africa.wcu.edu for additional information on WCU's campus theme.

Common intellectual learning experiences promote learning by A) helping students to see the world as a connected entity; B) providing common language to foster communication and understanding of various topics; C) fostering student camaraderie and campus engagement; and D) offering faculty and staff new and innovative ways to enhance teaching and learning.

However you define success in college, let a part of that definition be to involve yourself in the unique and innovative ways that universities are helping to shape you for a world beyond your campus.

GLOBAL LEARNING THROUGH GLOBAL SERVICE

by Stefanie Leiter, Director of Content Strategy and Public Relations, Anderson University

Some lessons can't be taught or tested in classrooms, but can rather only come from real-life experiences. Global learning programs, like Anderson University's Tri-S (Study, Serve, Share) program help students explore and discover the world in highly impactful ways. As 2016 Tri-S trip leader, Maggie Platt, puts it: "Our world needs leaders who have experienced different cultures, learned about those cultures, and in turn, learned about themselves through those cultures. Exploring the world is about so much more than the awesome adventures. It's about expanding the mind and learning to think critically about current issues."

The trips do more than just educate; they enhance the lives of participants in ways that remain with them for a lifetime. Senior Eric Stone, a psychology and youth leadership development double major, has traveled to India, Australia, London, Peru, Washington, D.C., and New York. He plans to travel to Uganda with Tri-S this spring.

"Some of my best friendships have started or been significantly enhanced from going on a trip together," said Stone. "Tri-S has dramatically enhanced and refocused my educational experience at AU. I was able to tangibly see how many different ways there are to look at a problem and the world. [Seeing] issues and topics from outside my own lens is a skill that Tri-S developed for me."

While such results are typical in most Study Abroad Programs, Anderson University's Tri-S program goes a bit further. According to Anderson's Tri-S and Study Abroad director, Aurora Doster, "Each trip is carefully planned to help students engage with the people and environment around them."

Some of the trips include:

- Wounded Knee on the Pine Ridge reservation (South Dakota) to serve the Oglala Lakota people
- The Caminul Felix orphanage in Romania and Hungary
- Mother Teresa's Missionaries of Charity in India
- Leading Vacation Bible Schools in Grand Cayman and London

Jennifer Myhre, leader of several Tri-S trips, calls the trips "a time of intentional community, where we share our stories, learn from each other, and live out our calling to love and to serve." On the trips, she witnessed students develop an "appreciation for what they have" while being challenged to live a life of faith and service when they return.

Most important of all may be the lasting impact the program has had over the past five decades, forging lifelong bonds between students and trip leaders.

After graduation, many find ways to serve their own communities. Others find their calling as a result of the trip and even return to the places they visited as ministers. "Relationships are most important," says Doster, "and the impact of Tri-S can be seen most vividly in those relationships. God calls us to love Him, love others, and serve the world."

HOW TO PARTICIPATE IN CLASS AND WHY IT'S IMPORTANT

We can all remember a time in class when we hoped the teacher or professor wouldn't call on us. Our fear of saying the wrong thing and sounding silly in front of our classmates is a strong deterrent from raising our hands and volunteering to speak in front of others. In fact, when given the choice most students choose to fly under the radar and avoid the embarrassment of speaking in front of their peers. This is unfortunate because class participation, while sometimes scary, is necessary for getting the most out of an education. Participation actively engages students with the subject matter, pushes them to create concepts, and forces them to show evidence for their claims. Put simply, it makes students work harder. A college education is expensive. Why not get the most out of it?

Students that regularly participate in class are constantly involved with the material and are more likely to remember a greater portion of the information. Active class participation also improves critical and higher level thinking skills. Students who participate in class have studied the material well enough to introduce new concepts to their peers. This level of thinking goes beyond simple comprehension of text, and can also improve memory. Participation can also help students learn from each other, increasing comprehension through cooperation. This can in turn improve relationships between students and between the student and professor.

Avoiding Class Participation

Despite the many benefits of class participation, the vast majority of students do not regularly contribute to their classes. There are several reasons why students choose not to participate in class including class size, time, and course policies. Larger classes, for example, have been shown to increase public speaking fears, as students struggle with the idea of sharing their ideas in front of a large group of people. With that in mind, colleges that encourage their faculty to focus on teaching, rather than research, are more likely to experience higher participation rates, as professors are more engaged with their students.

Encouraging Class Participation

A professor's attitude toward his or her students can dramatically affect class participation in one direction or another. Students are more likely to participate in class if they have a comfortable relationship with their professor. This means that the professor does not write off the student's response or contribution. This also means that the professor is patient with all his or her students, listens to every response with attention, and provides feedback that is both positive and constructive. Professors can increase participation by creating a safe and respectful class environment. They can also improve the situation by learning the names of their students, so that each individual feels that their opinion is valued.

Course policies drastically affect participation. Studies show a greater level of participation when students' contributions were factored into their final grade. In some courses, professors require participation and include it in every student's final grade. Participation can mean anything from asking questions to leading discussions. In other classes, professors simply take mental notes of their students' involvement and contribution to the subject matter.

How to Participate in Class

There are ways to overcome the fear of participation. First, establish a relationship with your professor. It's ok to be honest and explain that you have a fear of public speaking. Second, construct a plan to move forward. Find a participation method that works for you, whether that's asking thought-provoking questions or commenting on the reading. Prepare yourself for success by summarizing the material you would like to share with the class. Next, work your opinion into the discussion so you can demonstrate a higher level of thinking that goes beyond simply reading the assigned material. Finally, provide some evidence as to how you came to your opinion or conclusion. This will show your peers and your professors that you have made an effort to understand the subject. Preparation is key, so practice on your own before class. Saying it once aloud will ease the pain of saying it in front of your peers.

COMMUNITY-BASED LEARNING: YOUR CHANCE TO GROW PERSONALLY AND PROFESSIONALLY

by Abagail Van Vlerah, P.h.D., Dean of Students, LIU Post

For many students, service work and community involvement are motivating factors in their college education. These students seek the knowledge and skills that will empower them to change their world for the better. For others, community-based learning is essential preparation for life after college. These service opportunities are key to crafting and projecting the image of a well-rounded applicant who will eventually benefit the organization he or she works for.

Service is an increasingly valuable element of a college education. A university that provides plentiful and meaningful opportunities for service—in its local community and beyond—is an institution that truly creates a rewarding college experience, touching both students and graduates.

Of course, serving those in need has its own intrinsic value, which is why so many young people are focused on tackling the challenges that face their communities and the world. But as an added bonus, the power of service is also clearly visible in the job market, as candidates who can articulate meaningful service experiences are more likely to be hired for sought-after jobs. Several factors that drive this correlation are:

- **Building self-confidence:** Young people who commit themselves to a cause gain self-esteem and experience personal growth. Meaningful public service provides a sense of accomplishment that empowers young people to handle the pressures and challenges of the workplace. Employers know that a job candidate with a track record of successful public service has the potential to be a valuable addition to any team.

- **Learning by doing:** Colleges of Distinction are defined in part by their commitment to providing a wide variety of learning experiences that bring education outside of the classroom. When schools incorporate challenging volunteer projects into coursework, they add a new level of engagement to their students' education; these service-learning projects allow students to hone leadership and decision-making skills in an endeavor with real, impactful results.

- **Working across cultures:** As a result of technological advances and shifts in population, our world is constantly becoming more interconnected. This changing world demands professionals who can work across cultures. Students who engage with problems that take them out of their comfort zones—whether into an underserved community in their region or to an underprivileged community on the other side of the world—become more sophisticated and better suited for cross-cultural work at the professional level.

- **A Spirit Of Community:** Successful service and philanthropy programs are often rallying points for campus communities, bringing together large groups of students, faculty, and staff in support of worthy causes. These programs, which often take the form of extended fundraising events (such as the American Cancer Society's "Relay for Life" or the American Foundation for Suicide Prevention's "Out of the Darkness" walks), do far more than raise money; they provide the setting for many students' fondest memories of their college years, as do programs like "Alternative Spring Break," which engage students in service projects in communities around the country and the world.

A college with a robust tradition of service and philanthropy does more than give you experiences to add to your résumé. It gives you opportunities to join and engage with a community that you will always be able to call your own.

What to Look For

When looking for the college that's right for you, take some time to find out about the service opportunities offered on campus. As you do, keep an eye out for the following hallmarks through which service can make a real difference in your experience:

- **Long-running service programs:** Look for opportunities to be part of an ongoing campus tradition or a large-scale community service event. The power of service is even greater and more rewarding when it helps you create a lifelong commitment.

- **International opportunities:** Programs that give you the opportunity to travel abroad to perform service are often powerful experiences. They can also add another dimension to your personal development and career preparation, enabling you to learn to work in a new cultural environment.

- **Integration into coursework:** Look for schools in which you'll have the chance to put the lessons you learn in the classroom into action through service of a charitable cause. You'll gain valuable real-world experience while serving a worthy cause, resulting in some of the most memorable days of your college career.

WHAT IS A LIVING LEARNING COMMUNITY?

Living Learning Communities (LLCs) are residential programs that allow you to connect with diverse groups of students who share a common focus. Students live together and participate in shared courses, special events, and service projects as a group. LLCs are sponsored by various academic departments, and are designed to foster academic and personal growth. As more colleges and universities introduce LLCs, the possibilities are expanding for these unique housing initiatives, where collaboration and learning extend beyond the classroom.

Why Should I Participate?

Research suggests that participation in a Living Learning Community leads to increased academic engagement and satisfaction with college experiences. This is even true for students at larger institutions, where Living Learning Communities can make a campus feel smaller and more accessible. Many LLCs are open to first year students, which can help make the transition from high school to college more comfortable. Students involved in an LLC enjoy a built-in network of friends with shared passions and interests.

What Kinds of Living Learning Communities Are Available?

Living Learning Communities vary from campus to campus, but you'll find almost every topic imaginable, including sustainable living, science and engineering, social justice, global studies, and leadership. Languages and shared cultures are also common themes among LLCs. Some communities are devoted to a specific language like Spanish, French, Mandarin, or Japanese. In other cases, an LLC will focus on culture, offering residence opportunities for students who are Native American, African-American and Latino. There are also communities for first-year students, transfers, and honors students. Some colleges and universities even allow students to design their own LLCs, which can include everything from electronic music to plant-based eating!

How Is Living in a Living Learning Community Different from Traditional Student Housing?

The goal of a Living Learning Community is to help you engage intellectually outside the classroom. Typically, each community gathers weekly for discussions or workshops related to their topic. Dinners, lectures, presentations about off-campus experiences, and social service projects are all part of the living learning experience. You'll live on the same floor or in the same house as other students in the LLC, so they'll be your neighbors and your classmates.

These communities are a great way to connect with students and faculty who share your passions. You'll also have the opportunity to broaden your horizons, while acting as a member of a vibrant and collaborative living learning experience.

THE IMPORTANCE OF INTERNSHIPS IN COLLEGE

by Evan Kilgore, Special Projects Coordinator, Grace College

During college, immersive internships in your field of study are essential to successful outcomes after graduation. Classroom environments may involve you with discussion, debate, peer interaction, and shared learning experiences, but it's important to seek opportunities for you to apply and develop the academic concepts you're learning in a professional setting as well.

Learning, growing, and most importantly, preparing for life and a career, is what college is all about. Here are a few reasons why college internships are so vital to aid in your career readiness, such as an internship at The Box Tiger Music!

Career Development

Generally, an internship is a task-specific exchange of service for experience between a student and a business. Within internships, classroom concepts suddenly become real tools of the trade as you interact and learn in a professional setting. Internship experiences are formal, formative, and foundational to your career.

Developing your knowledge of workplace collaboration, business etiquette, and strong communication tactics are among the vital "soft skills" that can only be learned on the job. In this way, internships in your area of study will build your résumé and teach you instrumental, career-developing qualities.

Character Growth

Not only do internships help develop your professionalism, but they also encourage character growth. Many employers even value personal qualities over professional knowledge when it comes to employment.

Characteristics like integrity, commitment, and self-motivation are several traits that are learned through an internship. In an article by Chris Myers, a contributing writer for Forbes, he recounts his own experience as an intern as well as the ways it shaped his character. Over the course of his experience, he found a mentor who helped him learn to be humble and indispensable to his employers. These lessons remained with him even as he grew and became a business owner with his own interns. When you leave school, employers will want college graduates with more than just knowledge; they'll want those who possess the individual qualities needed to get the job done well.

Sharpening one's competence is a major benefit of an internship, but building character in the workplace is an equally great advantage. Internships are the perfect place to learn, test your skills, and grow personally, so you can step out and apply what you know to the real world.

A Door to Opportunity

Internships are foundational in preparing students for the workforce and providing opportunities after graduation. Most employers seek career-ready college graduates who have been equipped with prior experiences and skills in a given field.

According to a recent survey by the National Association of Colleges and Employers, the starting annual salary for college graduates who completed a paid internship and were employed in a private, for-profit company was $53,521, while those who did not complete an internship started with an average of $38,572.

The analysis also found that 72.2% percent of college graduates with internship experience received a job offer in contrast to only 36.5% for those who did not complete one.

Real-Life Application

At Grace College in Winona Lake, IN, students complete 12 "field" credits as part of their "Applied Learning" requirement. These credits are earned through internships, job-shadowing, research fellowships, student teaching programs, and many more career-developing positions—all of which benefit students as they expand their professional portfolios.

Here are what several Grace students have said about the internship experiences they've been a part of and how those work opportunities validated what they've learned in the classroom.

"I've always heard that internships are incredible learning opportunities, but didn't realize how true that is until mine. The number-one thing I learned is that soft skills and integrity are the most important factors in business."

- Joel Wesco (B.S. Accounting 2017), Audit and Tax Intern at Crowe Horwath LLP, in Indiana

"I benefited greatly completing my bachelor's and master's while interning and learned so much about the medical device industry as well as hip and knee replacements. I'm excited to continue in my new role (with the company I interned for) and am thankful for my internship. It helped me get my foot in the door and land my full-time position after graduation, I believe."

- Cody Sprague (B.S. Biology 2017, M.S. Orthopaedic Regulatory and Clinical Affairs 2017), Paid Intern in Clinical Affairs at Zimmer Biomet in Warsaw, IN

"I grew not only in my business skills, but also as a young professional, and I am so thankful for the opportunity to learn from such a talented team in the marketing and networking field,"

- Gabrielle Lawrence (B.S. Marketing 2017), Marketing Intern at Hello Events in Nashville, TN

Deliberative preparation for a rewarding career is a must. Internships are beneficial because they help develop your professional aptitude, strengthen personal character, and provide a greater door to opportunity. By investing in internships, you'll give yourself the broadest spectrum of opportunity when seeking and applying for a job after college.

TRADING SPACES: A PACKING LIST OF ESSENTIAL STUFF FOR YOUR DORM ROOM

Many families know some of the usual items that a college student should bring, but it's hard to think of everything. Of course, personal items from home will aid in the transition, but you'll need more than photos and a teddy bear to get through the year.

Before you buy or pack anything, be sure to check with your school about what items are and are not allowed. Most schools have to be very careful about health and safety regulations, and rules differ from place to place. One school might not allow microwaves; another might have specific regulations about what size of refrigerator is allowed. (See more examples below).

Also, consider talking to a current student about what to pack. They can tell you about the "don't bothers" and "must-haves" for the residences at your new college. They may even know specifics about your building that will be a real help.

In addition, be sure to carefully complete and review your housing contract. By omitting certain information or sending it back incomplete, this could alter your living situation very dramatically. Once you arrive on campus, you could be locked into a living situation you do not care for simply because of a few errors.

In the meantime, here's a list to help you start planning your move. Good luck!

BED AND BEDDING

☐ Sheets. Make sure that you know whether your bed will be regular or extra-long. Many college dorms have twin extra-long beds so you will have to buy special sheet sets.

☐ Comforter and/or quilts, blankets, etc. Consider bringing sturdy, easy-to-wash items.

☐ Towels: bath, washcloths and hand towels. Consider marking your name on a tag in permanent marker, especially if you have plain white or other "anonymous" towels.

☐ Alarm clock.

☐ Extra pillow(s) if you will lounge/study on the bed.

HEALTH AND GROOMING

☐ Shower shoes, especially if you will be sharing a shower.

☐ All necessary toiletries (toothbrush, toothpaste, soap, shampoo and all grooming/cosmetic) items. Since space will be cramped, consider buying smaller sizes, at least at first.

☐ Shower bucket/basket/caddy to carry items.

☐ Women who wear makeup might want a portable makeup kit/box, since it may not be feasible to store cosmetics near where the mirror is.

☐ Bathrobe (Especially important if the shower is down the hall!).

- ☐ Prescription medicines and copies of each prescription.
- ☐ First Aid kit, including basic adhesive bandages, disinfectant, aspirin, etc. (This will cut down on trips to the health center!).

CLOTHES AND LAUNDRY

- ☐ Clothes. Your space will be limited, so only bring what you think you will wear. You can always bring more back to school after your first trip home.
- ☐ Weather-appropriate outer clothes. You will probably be walking to class; be sure your coat or jacket is right for the climate.
- ☐ Laundry basket and/or bag.
- ☐ Laundry detergent, dryer sheets, stain remover stick.

DECOR

- ☐ Posters. You will probably also be able to buy some of these on campus.
- ☐ Sticky wall mounts and removable adhesive hooks. Most schools do not allow you to put nails in the walls, so you will need other ways to hang your décor.
- ☐ Personal pictures, photos, and other favorite items. Avoid heavy frames, since you may not be able to hang them.
- ☐ Curtains and spring rod, if you like them and your school allows them. Some people like this touch in their room.
- ☐ Rugs or a piece of carpet if you have vinyl floors, which can be cold and uncomfortable. Check to see if the school allows this.

STUDY STUFF

- ☐ A sturdy backpack or book bag for everyday use.
- ☐ Computer and any necessary supplies/accessories. Some schools also offer great discounts on or provide computers, printers and other electronic necessities.
- ☐ School supplies, including a calendar or planner as well as basic pens, paper, pencils, notebooks.
- ☐ Dry-erase board and marker. You'll want this so people can leave you messages.

FURNISHINGS

- ☐ Storage for under the bed.

- ☐ Other storage or organization units. A few stacking plastic crates will come in handy.
- ☐ Folding chairs for cheap extra seating.
- ☐ Trashcan and trash bags.
- ☐ Lamps. Many schools have special fire-safety rules about the size and power of lamps that are allowed, so make sure your lamps are within regulations.
- ☐ Cleaning supplies. Find out what areas you will be responsible for cleaning. If you have a private or semi-private bathroom, for example, you may be responsible for cleaning the shower and/or toilet.
- ☐ If you have hard floors, bring a broom. If you have carpet, consider bringing a small, light vacuum. Your floor will get pretty disgusting without it!
- ☐ Fan (box or floor). Depending on the climate control in the building, you may want this to adjust to your individual needs.

ELECTRONICS AND EQUIPMENT

- ☐ Multiple outlet surge protectors and extension cords. Check out school safety regulations about allowed cords.
- ☐ TV, stereo/speakers, DVD player, game systems, tablets, etc.

FOOD AND SNACKS

- ☐ Small refrigerator. During the first week of school, schools may have refrigerators and microwaves to rent or buy.
- ☐ Microwave, hot plate, coffeemaker, etc. Check first— many schools have especially strict safety regulations about these items. Also, find out what communal kitchen space may be available.
- ☐ A few unbreakable dishes: plastic cups, microwave-safe bowl, and small plastic food storage tubs.
- ☐ A small bottle of dish soap, scrubber, small dishtowel
- ☐ Snacks: popcorn, chips, sodas, etc. Check about food regulations.

MISC.

- ☐ A small and inexpensive tool kit.
- ☐ A large backpack or shoulder bag for possible weekend trips you might take.

AURORA UNIVERSITY

AURORA, ILLINOIS

Aurora University is one of the premier universities in Illinois. Its mission statement, "an inclusive community dedicated to the transformative power of learning," is experienced each day in the lives of AU students. Aurora University believes in taking students from where they are to where they want to be by following core values of integrity, citizenship, continuous learning, and excellence.

HANDS-ON LEARNING: In class, AU students from various majors take advantage of special hands-on learning opportunities. For example, the psychology majors conduct research studies and present their findings to the campus community, and students in the Dunham School of Business gain practical knowledge as well as engage with the local community through the VITA (Volunteer Income Tax Assistance) program. Through this program, accounting students prepare tax returns free-of-charge for taxpayers, including the elderly, low-income citizens, individuals with disabilities, and people who do not speak English.

STUDENTS WHO SERVE: Aurora University students are active members in shaping the community around them. They complete numerous off-campus internships and take part in service and educational events around campus. Recently, students participated in "A Day Without Shoes," during which members of the community spent a day barefoot while bringing awareness to global poverty. AU students also hosted "Sleep out on the Quad" while bringing an understanding to homelessness. Programs like these go beyond classroom learning to engage students with issues that affect communities all throughout the world. Students can also take advantage of international and domestic travel opportunities during Travel in May, learning about the cultures, struggles, and histories of such places as Berlín, Costa Rica, Guatemala, and Puerto Rico.

UNDERGRADUATE RESEARCH CONFERENCE: A highlight even of each spring semester is the Undergraduate Research Conference. Students who participate have the opportunity to explore topics in-depth and gain valuable experience presenting to their peers, professors, and surrounding community. Their research projects are perfect representations of the University-wide sense of curiosity that keeps Aurora's academics fresh.

MY TIME AFTER-SCHOOL PROGRAM: An interesting and popular opportunity available to Aurora students is the "MyTime After-School Program," which is a joint venture between AU, the City of Aurora, and area grade schools. MyTime serves more than 1,000 students from the Aurora elementary and middle schools every afternoon, engaging kids in positive activities in academics, the fine arts, recreation, and community service. Employed as activity leaders, AU undergrads get the chance to build their résumés as they prepare for careers in the fields of education and social work.

SERVICE-LEARNING: The core objectives of an Aurora University education are excellence, integrity, citizenship, and continuous learning. These objectives are proliferated through service-learning, which is emphasized throughout each major. Students learn to see the world holistically and are prepared to leave not only with a degree, but also with the ability to make a leading impact in the world around them. Hands-on learning is emphasized in all programs by the University's effort to provide students with practical experience in their chosen fields.

REAL-WORLD EXPERIENCE: AU works to give its students real-world exposure in their fields. For example, education students are immersed in on-site classrooms as early as their sophomore year and continue student teaching through to their last semester of school. Students in the Schools of Nursing and Social Work complete clinical and practicum hours at local hospitals, mental health clinics, and schools throughout their undergraduate careers, and athletic training students apply their burgeoning skills by working with student-athletes. Through these initiatives and many others across all the programs at AU, students gain real-world experience to complement and deepen what they learn in the classroom.

http://www.aurora.edu/
P: (800) 742-5281

PRIVATE

STUDENT PROFILE

3,204 undergraduate students

88% of undergrad students are full time

33% male — 67% female

20% of students are from out of state

71% freshman retention rate

58% graduated in 6 years

FACULTY PROFILE

135 full-time faculty

359 part-time faculty

16 to 1 student/faculty ratio

ADMISSIONS

SAT Ranges: CR 450-540, M 460-560

ACT Ranges: C 19-24, M 18-24, E 19-23

TUITION & COSTS

Tuition: $21,120

Fees: $200

Total: $21,320

R&B: $10,350

Room: $5,750

Board: $4,600

Total: $31,670

FINANCIAL

$14,543 avg grant/scholarship amount (total)

$6,113 avg loan amount (total)

CONCORDIA UNIVERSITY CHICAGO

RIVER FOREST, ILLINOIS

Founded in 1864 as a college for teachers, Concordia University Chicago is a comprehensive liberal arts-based Christian university affiliated with The Lutheran Church–Missouri Synod. Through its College of Arts and Sciences, College of Business, College of Education, College of Graduate Studies, and College of Innovation and Professional Programs, CUC offers more than 100 areas of undergraduate and graduate study in small classes that are taught by passionate professors. Students who choose Concordia University Chicago open up their world and are continually inspired throughout their collegiate career and beyond.

PROFESSORS WHO MENTOR AND GUIDE: Concordia-Chicago students are sure to find their path to career success. Professors provide personalized guidance and support as they help their students identify their career interests and master the knowledge and skills they need to excel in their chosen field. Through the First-Year Experience, incoming freshmen benefit from a close-knit community and immediately find out what it's like to develop personal connections with their professors.

VARIED EXPERIENTIAL LEARNING ENVIRONMENTS: Students expand their opportunities through a range of diverse experiences. The University's variety of dynamic academic disciplines are grounded in Christian faith, and students learn by doing as they engage in service activities, internships, applied research, leadership, and off-campus opportunities throughout the world. Their community is made up of students who hail from various backgrounds and cultures, contributing to the inherent way that Concordia-Chicago widens students' perspectives, versatility, and future prospects.

OPPORTUNITIES TO SERVE AND GROW: Concordia-Chicago students get an education that is meant to contribute to the whole person. Rich in the Lutheran tradition of education, CUC provides an impactful experience that includes faith enrichment and guidance toward ethical lives of integrity. The spirit of community inspires students to meet the needs of the world in which they live, serve, and work.

SMALL CLASS SIZES: With an average undergraduate class size of 15, CUC faculty and staff are devoted to giving students individualized attention and thus create a genuine and caring atmosphere in which strong student-faculty relationships facilitate each student's learning and leadership development. As true experts of their fields, CUC professors mentor their students with an outstanding level of clarity and compassion.

A LOCATION THAT'S THE BEST OF BOTH WORLDS: Concordia-Chicago's 40-acre suburban campus in upscale River Forest is like its own small town with a big backyard; the diverse resources of downtown Chicago are only 10 miles away (just a 20-minute ride on the 'L')! CUC is big enough to afford exceptionally diverse opportunities yet small enough to provide genuine, easy access to all that is offered. Students also consider downtown Oak Park-River Forest an extension of campus, taking advantage of the nearby variety of options to shop, see movies, sample food from around the world, or take part in artistic, musical, and theatrical performances.

FAITH THAT ENGAGES: Concordia University Chicago's faith community reflects the Lutheran tradition and provides a welcome environment for other Christian denominations as well. Within a Christian framework, students seek greater meaning in their spiritual and work lives, discovering ways to serve the greater good and mature in their faith. Growing as godly servants, student actively participate in a variety of philanthropic activities as well as daily chapel services, spiritual life campus ministries, and mission trips.

CONCORDIA
UNIVERSITY
CHICAGO

http://www.cuchicago.edu/
P: (708) 771-8300

PRIVATE - CHRISTIAN

STUDENT PROFILE

1,603 undergraduate students

94% of undergrad students are full time

42% male – 58% female

36.05% of students are from out of state

62% freshman retention rate

49.44% graduated in 6 years

FACULTY PROFILE

265 full-time faculty

164 part-time faculty

15 to 1 student/faculty ratio

ADMISSIONS

4,448 Total Applicants

2,238 Total Admissions

297 Total Freshman Enrollment

50.31% of applicants admitted

SAT Ranges: CR 450-550, M 470-590

ACT Ranges: C 20-25, M 18-25, E 20-25

TUITION & COSTS

Tuition: $30,640

R&B: $9,172

Total: $39,812

FINANCIAL

$15,829 avg grant/scholarship amount (need)

$4,268 avg loan amount (need)

GREENVILLE UNIVERSITY

GREENVILLE, ILLINOIS

GREENVILLE
UNIVERSITY

Serving Christ, creation, and community: that's what Greenville University has been doing for the past 125 years. The institution aims to educate students to be ahead of the curve in their careers while also inspiring them in their walk with God. Due to this, Greenville University has a unique dynamic in which cutting-edge course structure meets compassionate and experienced individuals. This school contains that perfect mix of new experiences and familiarity that truly grows a valuable and lasting student experience.

THE BEST EXPERIENCES FOR THE BEST EDUCATION: Greenville University offers students the opportunity to continue their education from wherever they are. It provides unique programs that allow its students to tailor their educational plans to their individual needs and wants. Many degrees can be completed through a 3-year program and, each year, the university continues to broaden its portfolio of online classes. Furthermore, Greenville's focus on the student experience offers opportunities to learn both inside and outside of the classroom. Undergraduate research and field experience are core pieces of its curriculum. Study abroad programs also continue to expand, sending students all around the globe to destinations such as England, Spain, Nicaragua, and Israel.

LIBERAL ARTS CURRICULUM: Greenville University is dedicated to offering an exceptional liberal arts education across over 40 disciplines. Committed to "experience first" learning, Greenville has created unique programs that get students out of the classroom and into the workplace. Starting from their first day of classes, students are engaged in freshman seminars and discussion groups to help them navigate their transition to both college and adulthood. As these individuals become upperclassmen, they begin to complete real-life projects to solve problems for local schools, businesses, and community organizations. In the classroom, they learn the latest theories, methods, and practices. Their courses hone their skills not only within their disciplines, but also in the broader areas of writing, critical thinking, and interpersonal relationships.

HOLISTIC DEVELOPMENT: The Greenville University experience is not limited to what happens in the classroom. Each of the departments and offices is involved in nurturing the holistic development students by including them in the campus community. This means celebrating solidarity and unity through the traditional Ivy Planting Ceremony during New Student Orientation. It also means challenging students' minds by hosting high-profile guest speakers and thought-provoking colloquia. The University's vision states that each student is created with a unique capability to shape the world. For this reason, students are encouraged to nurture all types of interests, whether they be classical music, hip-hop, athletics, fine arts, cultural studies, or video game design. Whatever a student's passion, Greenville University is full of resources to help them develop it for the Lord's glory.

PREPARED FOR GREATNESS: Greenville University is dedicated to producing graduates who are well rounded and prepared for lives of character and service to the community around them. Students gain practical experiences in their fields through internships and practicums that count toward their degrees. Service-based learning is also a part of the curriculum; for example, Psychology students have served at nursing homes and schools, and accounting majors have provided tax services to low-income communities. As seniors prepare to graduate, they also complete capstone projects that showcase their expertise in their fields as well as their abilities to apply them to real-world problems. Notably, Briner School of Business students complete three entrepreneurial projects through the "Experience First" program by the time they receive their degrees. In the end, there's nothing like a quality liberal arts education, and Greenville University consistently goes a step further to ensure that its graduates stay on top.

http://www.greenville.edu/

P: (618) 664-7100

PRIVATE - CHRISTIAN

STUDENT PROFILE

1,077 undergraduate students

96% of undergrad students are full time

50% male – 50% female

40% of students are from out of state

82% freshman retention rate

57% graduated in 6 years

FACULTY PROFILE

63 full-time faculty

2 part-time faculty

13 to 1 student/faculty ratio

ADMISSIONS

1,901 Total Applicants

1,070 Total Admissions

260 Total Freshman Enrollment

56.29% of applicants admitted

SAT Ranges: CR 440-530, M 430-540, W 410-520

ACT Ranges: C 19-25, M 17-25, E 18-25, W 6-8

TUITION & COSTS

Tuition: $24,864

Fees: $224

Total: $25,088

R&B: $8,288

Room: $4,012

Board: $4,276

Total: $33,376

FINANCIAL

$15,858 avg grant/scholarship amount (total)

$7,113 avg loan amount (total)

ILLINOIS WESLEYAN UNIVERSITY

BLOOMINGTON, ILLINOIS

ILLINOIS WESLEYAN
UNIVERSITY

IWU is a true renaissance university at which students are encouraged to explore all of their interests. Double majors are not uncommon, and students are encouraged to explore all of their interests even across such diverse subjects as physics and music. Plenty of compelling opportunities enrich the classroom education by sending students on off-campus adventures, including a year of study at Pembroke College/Oxford University and a semester at American University in Washington, D.C.

A PLACE TO DO IT ALL: IWU offers a balanced liberal arts education that nurtures the diverse talents of its students and provides them with the resources to understand and prepare for a global, complex society.

UNDERGRADUATE RESEARCH: Because IWU does not enroll graduate students, it is able to dedicate all of its funds, resources, and unique opportunities to its undergraduate community. Many students take advantage of such a rare privilege by conducting high-quality research in a variety of disciplines. The projects are supported by the University and honored at the annual John Wesley Powell Research Conference. This popular, on-campus showcase provides the platform to students to present findings in the natural and social sciences, original music compositions, reflections on international studies, and so much more.

STUDY ABROAD: IWU students often complement their education with a study abroad experience. Students can take advantage of nearly 300 semester- and year-long programs that span across 75 countries or participate in month-long study abroad courses that are offered during the distinctive May Term portion of the 4-4-1 academic calendar. IWU is also one of 12 schools nationwide to have a partnered exchange program with Oxford University. Such a broad collection of programs makes it easy for students to travel when is most convenient for their schedules as well as where is most beneficial for their studies and interests.

OFF-CAMPUS STUDY: The community that surrounds Illinois Wesleyan offers distinctive opportunities for students to supplement their classroom experiences with off-campus, hands-on learning experiences. One shining example of this is the Action Research Center, which coordinates research projects to be undertaken by Illinois Wesleyan University students, faculty, and staff in partnership with groups in the larger central Illinois community. Current projects include McLean County's ten-year plan to end homelessness, a tutoring and mentoring program, and an initiative through the Ecology Action Center to reduce pesticide use.

GATEWAY COLLOQUIUM COURSE: Professors develop meaningful relationships with their students very early on with the help of the distinctive Gateway colloquium course, a small, discussion-oriented seminar that is designed to develop first-year students' proficiency in written and spoken discourse. The sections for this course are capped at 15 students to ensure that each professor is accessible and that each student is involved.

SMALL COMMUNITIES: Faculty members at IWU make an active effort to include their students in independent studies and research projects. While the University's traditional semesters afford opportunities for these kinds of scholarly pursuits, the one-month May Term is often utilized for highly intensive and engaging experiences. Most classes at IWU are small, personal, and discussion-based. In fact, courses can often be as small as six students, making class participation and active, open communication an inherent part of the IWU experience.

STUDENT LIFE: IWU's 10 Greek fraternities and sororities account for 30 percent of the campus population, and so there is a fairly even balance between Greek life and independent life. But regardless of their affiliation, students are sure to find the community that is perfect for them. The University's diverse student body, professional schools of music and theatre, 18 successful NCAA Division III sports teams, and lively student-run clubs and government, campus life is always filled with extracurricular excitement.

http://www.iwu.edu/
P: (800) 332-2498

PRIVATE

STUDENT PROFILE

1,842 undergraduate students

99% of undergrad students are full time

44% male – 56% female

14% of students are from out of state

93% freshman retention rate

83% graduated in 6 years

FACULTY PROFILE

159 full-time faculty

63 part-time faculty

11 to 1 student/faculty ratio

ADMISSIONS

3,744 Total Applicants

2,318 Total Admissions

450 Total Freshman Enrollment

61.91% of applicants admitted

SAT Ranges: CR 540-640, M 640-730, W 540-670

ACT Ranges: C 25-30, M 25-29, E 25-32

TUITION & COSTS

Tuition: $42,290

Fees: $200

Total: $42,490

R&B: $9,796

Room: $6,134

Board: $3,662

Total: $52,286

FINANCIAL

$21,149 avg grant/scholarship amount (total)

$7,805 avg loan amount (total)

JUDSON UNIVERSITY

ELGIN, ILLINOIS

At Judson University, students thrive within an active campus community, creating friendships and memories that go on to last a lifetime. Incredible facilities provide abundant resources for research, internships, and exploration among the many avenues of each student's desired path.

STUDY ABROAD: Judson sees an amazing value in study abroad and encourages all students to taste, touch, and feel the experiences that lie in other cultures. Students who study abroad often develop a greater sense of independence, learning to navigate and excel in cross-cultural communication. Judson students have studied abroad in several different countries, including Austria, Japan, Russia, and more. The opportunities are endless, as interested students can find the perfect trip for them through the Council of Christian Colleges and various other external programs.

THE CHICAGO SEMESTER: Judson offers its students the opportunity to engage in prolonged off-campus study in the city of Chicago. Participants of the Chicago Semester program take part in an intensive internship experience, learning the ins and outs of an industry by delving into the processes within the major city center. Aside from professional development, students have the chance to test their independence and grow through an exploration of all the cultural attractions that Chicago has to offer. In addition to the internship, students are expected to take and pass two seminars over the course of the semester. This means that the Chicago Semester is academically demanding, but also immensely rewarding.

ON A MISSION: Every year, Judson offers students the chance to go on a variety of mission trips during spring break, Christmas break, and the summer intersession. Students who attend Judson are always in touch with many opportunities to serve, whether that take place locally in the U.S. or abroad in Central and South America, Africa, Asia, Europe, or the Caribbean.

THE RISE PROGRAM: Judson's Road to Independent living, Spiritual formation, and Employment (RISE) Program is a unique opportunity to provide a post-secondary education for individuals who have intellectual disabilities. The RISE Program gives students with intellectual disabilities the college-life experience along with the chance for them to build upon their strengths and grow toward independent living and customized employment within a caring Christian community.

CITY LIFE - ELGIN AND CHICAGO: Judson's location offers incredible opportunities to students looking to explore the community outside of campus. Judson may be located in Elgin, but its proximity to Chicago allows students to enjoy the cultural attractions and amenities of both cities. Elgin is a lively suburb that offers a wide array of restaurants, shopping, and entertainment. Chicago's urban environment is filled with huge opportunities for work, networking, food, and leisure. Some of its major attractions include Navy Pier, Millennium Park, and the Shedd Aquarium.

WORLD LEADERS FORUM: A true highlight of the year at Judson University is the remarkable World Leaders Forum. This event brings international thought leaders to the Judson campus, inviting them to speak and interact with students and area professionals. The funds that are raised from the Forum even go toward scholarships for Judson students as well as an endowment toward an upcoming Entrepreneurial Studies program. Previous keynote speakers have included George W. Bush, Mikhail Gorbachev, Tony Blair, Condoleezza Rice, and Felipe Calderón.

THE IMAGO FILM FESTIVAL: Every spring, Judson University hosts a five-day film festival that explores the intersection between film and faith. The festival screens original, independent films submitted from all over the world and features nationally known speakers. It also acts as a platform through which to host discussions, workshops, and an awards ceremony.

STUDENT SUCCESS CENTER: The Student Success Center is an on-campus resource that assists students with academic, personal, and professional goals. Through curricular and co-curricular activities, the center aims to help each student set and reach realistic goals throughout their college career.

http://www.judsonu.edu/

P: (847) 628-2500

PRIVATE - CHRISTIAN

STUDENT PROFILE

1,110 undergraduate students

68% of undergrad students are full time

41% male – 59% female

73% freshman retention rate

52% graduated in 6 years

FACULTY PROFILE

61 full-time faculty

129 part-time faculty

10 to 1 student/faculty ratio

ADMISSIONS

653 Total Applicants

461 Total Admissions

156 Total Freshman Enrollment

70.60% of applicants admitted

SAT Ranges: CR 520-570, M 450-590

ACT Ranges: C 21-26, M 19-26, E 20-27

TUITION & COSTS

Tuition: $27,290

Fees: $880

Total: $28,170

R&B: $9,450

Total: $37,620

FINANCIAL

$19,207 avg grant/scholarship amount (total)

$8,176 avg loan amount (total)

LEWIS UNIVERSITY

ROMEOVILLE, ILLINOIS

Lewis University, guided by its Catholic and Lasallian heritage, provides students a liberal and professional education that is grounded in the interaction of knowledge and fidelity in the search for truth. Lewis promotes the development of the complete person through the pursuit of wisdom and justice. Fundamental to its Mission is a spirit of association, which fosters community in all teaching, learning, and service.

LASALLIAN TEACHING: Following the teachings of St. John Baptist de La Salle, the patron saint of educators and founder of the De La Salle Christian Brothers, Lewis faculty are devoted to great teaching and Catholic leadership. In recognition of their excellence, the Distinguished Lasallian Educator Award is granted annually to celebrate a particular faculty member who has shown their devotion to student learning and the University Mission. The University Mission is a guiding principle that promotes the development of the complete person through the pursuit of wisdom and justice, fostering a spirit of association and community throughout all teaching, learning, and service. With this campus-wide commitment, Lewis students, faculty, and staff all come together to challenge and support each other toward academic, personal, professional, and spiritual growth.

COMMON READER SERIES: The Common Reader Series at Lewis University engages first-year students in their Introduction to the College Experience (ICE) courses. Selected by faculty and staff, the assigned book is meant to teach a life lesson that is useful for all students to take to heart. First-year students are introduced to the book over the summer during their Student Orientation, Advising, and Registration (SOAR) sessions and continue to address the material throughout the year.

APPLIED RESEARCH: Student researchers are able to share their findings through the Lewis' Summer Undergraduate Research Experience (SURE). The eight-week SURE program was created to encourage and enhance research opportunities for Lewis faculty and students. It functions to engage students directly with faculty mentors so that they may pursue incredible research experiences that provide depth to their respective disciplines. Lab and research work within SURE includes team meetings among disciplines as well as educational field trips to access resources and sample materials.

CELEBRATION OF SCHOLARSHIP: The annual Celebration of Scholarship symposium provides a rich opportunity for students to present their scholarly work to an audience of the Lewis community, showcasing the kind of academic excellence that is central to the Mission of the University. Undergraduate and graduate students in any major are encouraged to submit posters, present a paper, or display creative work.

SERVICE LEARNING: Lewis students are active global citizens, travelling on mission trips throughout the world to such countries as Bolivia and the Philippines as well as supporting their own community through frequent volunteer work. The opportunity to give back as part of the Lewis community begins before classes even start—the Welcome Days "SOAR into Community" event takes nearly 500 new students out into the community to work on various projects, bonding with one another as they make a true impact on the surrounding area.

BUSINESS PLAN COMPETITION: To encourage and support student entrepreneurship, the University hosts the Business Plan Competition for all undergraduate and graduate students. Those who participate get useful business practice as they formulate an idea, develop a business plan, and pitch their idea to a panel of judges. The winner(s) of the competition earn $5,000 to be used toward their business venture.

CAREER SERVICES: Lewis students have the useful support of the Office of Career Services, which regularly runs internship and job fairs for Lewis students and alumni. The office also assists with internship placement, having helped students get into internships with such employers as American Airlines, Argonne National Laboratory, the U.S. Department of Energy, and LaSalle Bank.

---

http://www.lewisu.edu/

P: (815) 836-5250

PRIVATE - CATHOLIC

STUDENT PROFILE

4,652 undergraduate students

82% of undergrad students are full time

44% male – 56% female

9% of students are from out of state

84% freshman retention rate

66% graduated in 6 years

FACULTY PROFILE

232 full-time faculty

443 part-time faculty

13 to 1 student/faculty ratio

ADMISSIONS

5,728 Total Applicants

3,542 Total Admissions

702 Total Freshman Enrollment

61.84% of applicants admitted

SAT Ranges: CR 500-560, M 500-600

ACT Ranges: C 20-25, M 19-25, E 20-25

TUITION & COSTS

Tuition: $29,950

Fees: $100

Total: $30,050

R&B: $10,320

Total: $40,370

FINANCIAL

$14,425 avg grant/scholarship amount (need)

$4,448 avg loan amount (need)

LOYOLA UNIVERSITY CHICAGO

CHICAGO, ILLINOIS

Preparing people to lead extraordinary lives

An outstanding, nationally lauded institution, Loyola University Chicago continues to advance the 450-year-old Jesuit tradition of rigorous academic study that is grounded in the liberal arts. Loyola helps students prepare for meaningful careers with top programs in business, the sciences, and other disciplines, along with opportunities for internships in Chicago and beyond. Loyola's well-rounded, transformative education is designed to develop the whole person—intellectually, physically, socially, and spiritually.

STUDY AND SERVICE ABROAD: Loyola provides excellent opportunities for international education through its John Felice Rome Center in Italy, the Beijing Center for Chinese Studies, and the Vietnam Office. Students may also select from any of Loyola's 100 study abroad programs in 55 countries, all of which offer students a chance to expand their global perspective. Each fall, spring, and summer break, University Ministry's Alternative Break Immersion sends more than one hundred students to domestic and international community organizations for immersive experiences related to social justice.

OFF-CAMPUS GROWTH: Loyola gives students multiple opportunities to engage in their education by learning outside the classroom. The Loyola Undergraduate Research Opportunities Program (LUROP) allows undergraduates to participate in collaborative research, and many outlets give students the chance to participate in internships and service-learning. Such immersive programs enhance students' understanding of theories that they learn in the classroom, all while simultaneously providing invaluable opportunities for hands-on experience.

HONORS PROGRAM: Loyola's interdisciplinary honors program serves to challenge and excite the most highly motivated students at the University. In an atmosphere charged with rigorous teaching and enthusiastic student participation, professors and students work together to explore critical issues that span across disciplines. Involved students capitalize on this through active involvement in their professors' research projects and by attending colloquia with resident and visiting scholars.

RIGHT OUTSIDE THE CITY: Loyola combines the best of campus life and city life through its diverse living and learning opportunities in Chicago. Loyola's picturesque Lake Shore Campus is situated on the shores of Lake Michigan and provides a campus oasis just eight miles north of downtown Chicago. Students have immediate access to concerts, museums, plays, a vibrant nightlife, and other cultural and recreational activities. And getting around town is easy; both campuses have stops on the local CTA transit line, and the student U-Pass provides unlimited rides throughout Chicago's public transportation system.

THE WATER TOWER CAMPUS: Located on Chicago's Magnificent Mile in the heart of the city, Loyola's Water Tower Campus connects students to myriad internship, job, and service opportunities. The Water Tower Campus is also home to Baumhart Hall, a twenty-five-story residence hall that features a student center, fitness center, study lounge, food court, and more.

CAREER SERVICES: Loyola's Career Development Center (CDC) provides all of the resources students need to start their careers after graduation. It annually lists thousands of jobs and internships and helps both students and alumni connect with prospective employers The CDC also provides mock interviews, job fairs, résumé referral services, and regular internship newsletters.

INTERNSHIPS AND SERVICE: Opportunities for internships and clinical experiences abound throughout Chicago and beyond, ranging from such well-known companies and organizations as Abbott Laboratories, the Chicago Bears, Chicago Public Schools, Children's Memorial Hospital, the Ford Motor Company, Kraft Foods, Motorola, NBC, Smith Barney, the Target Corporation, the Tribune Company, the United States Armed Forces, Verizon Wireless, Walgreens, and many more. The city's vast cultural, business, and civic resources also enrich Loyola's curriculum with numerous outlets for service-learning, immersion, and volunteerism.

http://www.luc.edu/
P: (800) 262-2373

PRIVATE - CATHOLIC

STUDENT PROFILE

11,079 undergraduate students

88% of undergrad students are full time

35% male – 65% female

35% of students are from out of state

86% freshman retention rate

74% graduated in 6 years

FACULTY PROFILE

962 full-time faculty

888 part-time faculty

14 to 1 student/faculty ratio

ADMISSIONS

21,555 Total Applicants

15,360 Total Admissions

2,194 Total Freshman Enrollment

71.26% of applicants admitted

SAT Ranges: CR 520-630, M 518-630, W 520-630

ACT Ranges: C 24-29, M 23-28, E 24-31, W 8-9

TUITION & COSTS

Tuition: $37,883

Fees: $1,296

Total: $39,179

R&B: $13,310

Room: $8,380

Board: $4,930

Total: $52,489

FINANCIAL

$19,095 avg grant/scholarship amount (total)

$8,595 avg loan amount (total)

MACMURRAY COLLEGE

JACKSONVILLE, ILLINOIS

MacMurray College is a private, four-year, coeducational college with a focus on career-directed, comprehensive education. It prides itself on providing an accessible and affordable education to students of all ages in the form of both online and blended courses. MacMurray College provides a quality education with engaged faculty who care about student learning and success. MacMurray's learning community is filled with outstanding people—faculty, staff, students, and alumni alike—many of whom become lifelong friends. The College also offers financial aid through grants and scholarships to 98% of students. With 33 majors and pre-professional programs, three online programs, 10 athletic teams, and an active and involved student body of more than 550 co-eds, MacMurray is sure to have something for anyone!

STUDY ABROAD: MacMurray students have many opportunities to study beyond the MacMurray campus in Jacksonville. Opportunities exist in the United States and all over the world. Those who study abroad don't need to worry about taking time away from their major; approved off-campus programs can grant academic credit toward graduation!

GUEST SPEAKERS: Every year, MacMurray College seeks to bring speakers from across the across the world to visit campus and give voice to a range of different topics. Each year, the College chooses a different theme around with to connect its speakers, providing attendees an array of perspectives that ultimately deepen their understanding and spike their curiosities.

DESIGNED TO PREPARE: MacMurray College believes that experience is the best teacher. MacMurray's curriculum is designed to offer experiential education opportunities and internships in order to better prepare students for their chosen career field. It is because of this that the MacMurray degree opens a world of opportunity, enabling graduates to be successful throughout their professional and personal lives. Mac alumni know that their school has equipped them with a love for "lifelong learning," and they know that attaining a job requires more than a quick-fix résumé. Their promising futures are enabled by the way they had been nurtured to think creatively and communicate effectively.

INTERNSHIPS: Whether through curriculum-based practica or the Career Experience Program, the internship opportunities offered at MacMurray College are "custom designed" for the individual student. Interns are able to gain professional experience in a particular career field and earn academic credit while taking part in the bustling world of their industry. These internships provide students the direction and tools needed to succeed in today's fast-paced work environment.

STUDENT ORGANIZATIONS: MacMurray College offers students the opportunity to learn and grow outside of the classroom by participating in one or more of 25 student organizations. By participating in clubs, students meet people with common interests and develop leadership skills. With so many kinds of organizations on campus, it's easy to deepen one's involvement in something they love as well as to dive into new activities that they may never have explored before.

JACKSONVILLE: The MacMurray campus is located in west-central Illinois in the city of Jacksonville, about 30 miles west of the state capital of Springfield. Jacksonville is a community rich in historical treasures, thriving with arts, education, and culture, and wrapped in Midwest hospitality. From its historical connections to the Civil War and Abraham Lincoln to its platform of modern businesses today, the area is loaded with culture. There is a small-town friendliness mixed with vibrancy from a richness of natural sites, intellectual institutions, and businesses.

https://www.mac.edu/
P: (800) 252-7485

PRIVATE

STUDENT PROFILE

570 undergraduate students

95% of undergrad students are full time

49% male – 51% female

25% of students are from out of state

71% freshman retention rate

33% graduated in 6 years

FACULTY PROFILE

35 full-time faculty

22 part-time faculty

14 to 1 student/faculty ratio

ADMISSIONS

959 Total Applicants

601 Total Admissions

130 Total Freshman Enrollment

62.67% of applicants admitted

SAT Ranges: CR 390-428, M 413-460

ACT Ranges: C 17-22, M 16-23, E 15-22

TUITION & COSTS

Tuition: $23,472

Fees: $700

Total: $24,172

R&B: $8,112

Total: $32,284

FINANCIAL

$13,797 avg grant/scholarship amount (total)

$9,027 avg loan amount (total)

MCKENDREE UNIVERSITY

LEBANON, ILLINOIS

The McKendree experience enlightens, empowers, excites, and educates inquisitive minds. Its balanced educational equation allows for success in the classroom as well as intellectual development outside the classroom. And with small class sizes that facilitate close relationships between professors and students, the University's model offers a personal approach to education.

INDIVIDUALIZED EDUCATIONAL EQUATION: McKendree guarantees a number of opportunities for students to learn outside the classroom. Many students can earn credit through independent study, while others can take part in projects organized by their professors, a large majority of whom are published scholars of well-respected journals and research. Faculty often receive assistance from their students in exchange for college credit, which is highly valuable for both parties.

STUDY ABROAD: McKendree's study abroad program is coordinated through the Institute for Study Abroad at Butler University. This program gives McKendree students the option to study across thirteen countries and five continents. Additionally, any institutional aid awarded to students continue to assist with their tuition at the international universities of their choice.

COMPETENT AND CARING: The most unique thing about the McKendree experience is the deep connection between faculty and students, which is best described as a mentor-mentee relationship. Students frequently address professors by their first name, and many faculty members include their personal phone numbers on their class syllabi and host class dinners at their homes. Together, the McKendree community fosters a true, family-oriented campus atmosphere. The University even boasts a unique faculty-in-residence program through which professors are selected to live on campus and be that much more accessible to their students.

FACULTY ADVISORS: Each student works with a faculty advisor to develop a course plan that both meets their degree requirements and nurtures their personal interests. Advisors are often associated with a student's respective major, ensuring that students are guided by people who know the best plan of action to navigate their academic journey.

THE RURAL AND THE URBAN, BLENDED FOR BALANCED LIVES: McKendree's unique location is a blend of a small-town environment with a pleasant suburban feel. The 236-acre main campus is within twenty-five minutes of downtown Saint Louis and equally close to the popular Carlyle Lake. It is in this prime location that McKendree students truly get the best of both worlds, experiencing the serenity and security of a small town while having access to all the advantages of a large metropolitan area. Its proximity to the city makes career opportunities, cultural events, shopping, professional sports, and entertainment easily within reach.

GREEK LIFE: McKendree has a long and rich tradition of Greek life that extends back to 1837. Throughout their history, The University's Greek organizations have encouraged their members to cultivate skills in leadership, scholarship, character development, and service to the community. A variety of Greek organizations are available for students to join, including fraternities, sororities, and coed organizations.

INTERNSHIP OPPORTUNITIES: As a campus of 2,292 undergraduate students, McKendree is well known for prioritizing its students. Since the University is located only twenty-five minutes from downtown St. Louis, it is proud to connect its students to endless career opportunities, including a range of internships. Through the office of career services, students can find internship programs to provide them with valuable work experience as well as class credit. Student interns work with close supervision from faculty members, on-site supervisors, and the director of career services.

---

http://www.mckendree.edu/
P: (618) 537-4481

PRIVATE

STUDENT PROFILE

2,292 undergraduate students

79% of undergrad students are full time

48% male – 52% female

28% of students are from out of state

71% freshman retention rate

56% graduated in 6 years

FACULTY PROFILE

105 full-time faculty

158 part-time faculty

14 to 1 student/faculty ratio

ADMISSIONS

1,904 Total Applicants

1,209 Total Admissions

362 Total Freshman Enrollment

63.50% of applicants admitted

SAT Ranges: CR 450-550, M 420-530

ACT Ranges: C 20-25, M 19-24, E 18-25

TUITION & COSTS

Tuition: $27,740

Fees: $1,000

Total: $28,740

R&B: $9,200

Total: $37,940

FINANCIAL

$16,621 avg grant/scholarship amount (need)

$4,199 avg loan amount (need)

MONMOUTH COLLEGE

MONMOUTH, ILLINOIS

Since its founding in 1853 as an academy for high school and college students on the Illinois prairie, Monmouth College has grown into a nationally recognized liberal arts college. It is fully dedicated to educating young men and women to become critical thinkers, engaged citizens, and creative leaders who are capable of addressing the complex challenges of contemporary society.

ESTEEMED PROFESSORS: Monmouth College is distinctive for its commitment to undergraduate research, small and interactive classrooms (the average class size is 13), and personalized academic advising. The strength and vitality of the academic programs is a direct result of the commitment of the College's outstanding faculty. Monmouth professors are great teachers because they are active scholars: they present papers, publish books and articles, perform in nationally recognized ensembles, and exhibit work in leading galleries. Some faculty—particularly in the areas of business and communication—come from successful careers in industry, bringing their business experiences and perspectives to their teaching. Other faculty members share their nationally recognized talents and wisdom through innovative teaching, shared research findings, and collaborative projects.

STUDENT AND FACULTY RESEARCH: Many Monmouth students participate in collaborative research projects with faculty mentors. Its signature summer research/new-student bridge program brings together advanced students, incoming first-year students, and a faculty research sponsor for collaborative projects in the three weeks preceding the fall semester. Some research teams are science focused; others pursue humanities, social sciences, and even musical and artistic projects. These opportunities help students—new and old—learn and grow together with an impressive diversity of knowledge and perspectives. They pull from each other's wisdom and collectively pursue and discover new findings.

STUDY ABROAD: Study abroad at Monmouth takes many forms. Summer research trips are particularly notable, as they lead students and faculty members in travel to such destinations as Yellowstone National Park, Hawaii, the Galapagos Islands, Malaysia, Indonesia, and Singapore to conduct innovative analyses of the environments firsthand. Short-term travel/study courses have recently occurred in countries such as Turkey, Greece, Spain, and Bulgaria. Semester programs are also available through Monmouth's partnerships with the University of Highlands and Islands in Scotland, the International Student Exchange Program (ISEP), and other exchange affiliations. Semester courses have been taught in India, Italy, the U.K., Costa Rica, Tanzania, and more.

FROM THE CLASSROOM TO THE COMMUNITY - LIVING WHAT ONE LEARNS: Connections with the larger community are supported through the Wackerle Career and Leadership Center. Its professional staff members assist students in identifying internship possibilities, making career decisions, and preparing for graduate and professional study. The center offers workshops in résumé writing, interviewing, professional dress, and etiquette. Staff members support volunteerism and community engagement through leadership workshops, promoting a very active network of alumni who are eager to assist new graduates with career advice.

CAMPUS FACILITIES: Monmouth College operates within one of the most beautiful residential campuses in the United States. It is full of outstanding academic buildings and residence halls, first-class athletic facilities (including a natatorium and sauna, weight room, climbing wall, soccer field, and baseball fields, newly renovated all-weather track and football field, and new football stadium), and an acoustically superb performance auditorium and theater. The Monmouth Educational Garden and Le Suer Nature Preserve serve as beautiful (and highly functional) outdoor laboratories and classrooms.

SENIOR CAPSTONE: Monmouth College has always been dedicated to the connection between the liberal arts, citizenship, professional fulfillment, and meaningful lives. A capstone requirement for all students is an interdisciplinary, thematically focused course entitled "Citizenship." This senior-year course engages students in community partnerships to tackle real-world issues as they pertain to society and policy.

Monmouth
COLLEGE®

http://www.monmouthcollege.edu/

P: (800) 747-2687

PRIVATE

STUDENT PROFILE

1,300 undergraduate students

98% of undergrad students are full time

46% male – 54% female

11% of students are from out of state

74% freshman retention rate

56% graduated in 6 years

FACULTY PROFILE

88 full-time faculty

41 part-time faculty

12 to 1 student/faculty ratio

ADMISSIONS

2,851 Total Applicants

1,969 Total Admissions

396 Total Freshman Enrollment

69.06% of applicants admitted

SAT Ranges: CR 480-570, M 510-630, W 420-550

ACT Ranges: C 19-25 , M19-25, E 19-25

TUITION & COSTS

Tuition: $33,200

R&B: $8,010

Room: $4,400

Board: $3,610

Total: $41,210

FINANCIAL

$24,332 avg grant/scholarship amount (total)

$7,625 avg loan amount (total)

NORTH CENTRAL COLLEGE

NAPERVILLE, ILLINOIS

As a top-tier, comprehensive liberal arts college, North Central blends the highly personalized qualities of a small college with the diversity and resources of a large university. At North Central, students collaborate with faculty who are passionate about teaching and skilled in their disciplines, benefitting greatly from a curriculum that prepares them to think, speak, and write clearly. North Central offers the best of both worlds—a beautiful 65-acre campus in the middle of the Naperville Historic District as well as easy train Chicago, one of the most cosmopolitan cities in the world.

PURSUE AND CONQUER: North Central offers over fifty undergraduate majors. The most popular are elementary education, biology, and psychology. Education majors take advantage of the college's proximity to suburban, rural, and urban areas, exploring a variety of choices and environments in which to student teach. Additionally, biology and psychology students have many opportunities to engage in research projects and internships.

ALTERNATIVE SPRING BREAK: Alternative Spring Break is an exciting opportunity for North Central students to learn outside of the classroom. ASB programs take advantage of the week-long intersession by traveling in groups to perform acts of service. In recent years, athletic teams have built houses for Habitat for Humanity, while other groups have helped with hurricane relief and rebuilding efforts. The ENACTUS group, which competes nationally in business, entrepreneurial, and leadership activities, has traveled to Guatemala to meet with coffee producers as part of an effort to promote free-trade goods.

STUDY ABROAD: North Central students take advantage of off-campus and study abroad opportunities, too. There are almost 40 programs on five continents for students to choose from. The college's December term, a significant break between Thanksgiving and the beginning of the new calendar year, allows North Central students to participate in unique trips both domestically and abroad. Some involve faculty-led trips to cultural events as well as explorations of diverse neighborhoods in the Chicago area. Others are networking-building study abroad programs that enrich students' perspectives through academics and hands-on internships.

CHICAGO TERM PROGRAM: Students interact with faculty outside of the classroom in such dynamic contexts as the Chicago Term program. Chicago Term courses are taught right in the middle of the city, which allows students to take advantage of North Central's convenient location and access the incredible resources and experiences intrinsic to a bustling urban area. Through the Chicago Term, students commute into city with their professors and experience the museums, landmarks, and other metropolitan offerings.

DYNAMIC FACULTY, CHALLENGING PROGRAM: North Central faculty have a passion for teaching. In fact, the college has been singled out and honored for its faculty's devotion to the undergraduate classroom experience. They all work to foster a community of learners who are dedicated informed, involved, principled, and productive citizens and leaders over a lifetime. With its small class sizes, the college fulfills its student-centered mission by recognizing the individual needs of students who are at different stages of life and who come from different ethnic, economic, and religious backgrounds. Professors augment their educational programs with work experiences and research opportunities, providing their students the practical skills necessary for a true understanding of their future careers.

NAPERVILLE: Naperville, often ranked as one of the best places to live in the country, has a national reputation. It is a top-rated suburban community of about one hundred and forty thousand. The affluent suburb offers internship and networking opportunities for North Central students, but the possibilities extended far beyond the professional sphere; an array of opportunities to shop lie two block north, and a beautiful park on the DuPage River borders the campus.

---

https://www.northcentralcollege.edu/

P: (800) 411-1861

PRIVATE

STUDENT PROFILE

2,733 undergraduate students

95% of undergrad students are full time

47% male – 53% female

10% of students are from out of state

80% freshman retention rate

67% graduated in 6 years

FACULTY PROFILE

142 full-time faculty

149 part-time faculty

14 to 1 student/faculty ratio

ADMISSIONS

7,307 Total Applicants

4,177 Total Admissions

599 Total Freshman Enrollment

57.16% of applicants admitted

ACT Ranges: C 22-27, M 21-27, E 21-27, W 7-8

TUITION & COSTS

Tuition: $35,241

Fees: $180

Total: $35,421

R&B: $10,089

Room: $6,999

Board: $3,090

Total: $45,510

FINANCIAL

$21,651 avg grant/scholarship amount (total)

$8,097 avg loan amount (total)

NORTHERN ILLINOIS UNIVERSITY

DEKALB, ILLINOIS

Northern Illinois University is centered on student success and growth. Through tremendous opportunities for study abroad, internships, and research, students gain a wealth of knowledge that can be applied to both personal and academic endeavors.

FIRST-YEAR EXPERIENCE (FYE): The First-Year Experience (FYE) at NIU is a collaborative academic plan between faculty and students. It aims to prepare students for successful academic and personal careers as undergraduates. About 60% of incoming freshmen enroll in UNIV 101, an introductory course that transitions students into college. There are approximately 19 students in each class—a small group setting that fosters peer interaction and engagement. Faculty cover topics such as: success tips, writing and oral communications skills, and how to utilize on-campus resources. Research has demonstrated that there are significant benefits to participating in UNIV 101; those enrolled in the course tend to have higher GPAs and are more likely to graduate on time.

SECOND-YEAR EXPERIENCE: The Second-Year Experience (SYE) is an extension of the first-year program. Sophomores involved in SYE build communities among their peers, both in and out of the classroom. The program also pushes students to define their academic and personal goals for the future. The Second-Year Experience also offers a living-learning option in which sophomores can live among one another in a community that shares common goals. The LLC functions under the direction of a Community Advisor who understands the academic and social needs of the students. Some of the awesome benefits to participating in the SYE LLC include: monthly dinners with faculty, quarterly service initiatives, and helpful presentations offered by Career Services.

THEMED LEARNING COMMUNITIES: Beyond SYE LLCs, Themed Learning Communities (TLCs) examine a specific theme through multiple perspectives. Students in TLCs take a series of linked courses, each of which takes a unique, different approach to the a common theme. There are only 25 students per TLC, allowing for individualized attention from faculty. Peer mentors are also available to help students work through their course material. There are tons of options to choose from, including pre-professional health, technology and social networking, and psychology.

RESEARCH ROOKIES PROGRAM: The Research Rookies Program is designed for freshman and sophomore students who wish to engage in research. Through the program, students are connected with faculty members in their area of study, working through a collaborative effort to tackle projects at the collegiate level. The Rookies program introduces participants to the process of developing and carrying out research efforts, gaining useful information throughout every step of the process, from writing a research proposal to reaching a conclusion.

NIU SERVICE: NIU regards service as an integral part of education and provides this opportunity to encourage students to make a positive impact on the lives around them. Huskie Service Scholars is a leadership program in community outreach and service. Scholars are divided into teams of three fellows under the supervision of a peer mentor. Together, they engage in a series of training sessions and reflection periods, ultimately completing 300 hours of meaningful service. Participants even receive a waiver of over $1,000 off their tuition. NIU also invites sophomores to serve in the less intensive (yet meaningful nevertheless) Sophomore Day of Service. In this one-day volunteer event, sophomores have the chance to give back to the community. They begin their experience with an orientation, helping them become acquainted to the details of their projects in order to provide the most impactful service possible.

---

http://www.niu.edu/

P: (815) 753-1000

PUBLIC

STUDENT PROFILE

15,027 undergraduate students

88% of undergrad students are full time

51% male – 49% female

72% freshman retention rate

50% graduated in 6 years

FACULTY PROFILE

883 full-time faculty

281 part-time faculty

15 to 1 student/faculty ratio

ADMISSIONS

17,099 Total Applicants

8,610 Total Admissions

2,259 Total Freshman Enrollment

50.35% of applicants admitted

SAT Ranges: CR 450-530, M 450-550, W 410-520

ACT Ranges: C 19-25, M 18-25, E 19-25, W 6-8

TUITION & COSTS

Tuition: (In) $9,169 (Out) $18,930

Fees: $4,830

Total: (In) $13,999 (Out) $23,760

R&B: $10,766

Total: (In) $24,765 (Out) $34,526

FINANCIAL

$9,112 avg grant/scholarship amount (total)

$7,682 avg loan amount (total)

OLIVET NAZARENE UNIVERSITY

BOURBONNAIS, ILLINOIS

Faith is at the heart of Olivet Nazarene University's superior academics, nationally competitive athletics, thriving social atmosphere, and countless ministry opportunities.

RESEARCH: Olivet students prepare for graduate school and their future careers through numerous opportunities for expanded scholarship and research. Math and science students, for example, work closely with faculty members on visionary, 10-week research projects through the Pence-Boyce Research Program as well as the Olivet Research Associates Program. They can even receive stipends that allow them to work full-time on their projects. During Scholar Week, students from all academic disciplines—along with faculty and other guests—are invited to present the results of their academic research projects during a weeklong series of lectures and discussions.

SERVICE: Service to the community is a central theme in many Olivet academic programs. Social work students organize an annual Christmas party and toy drive for children of jail inmates, while business students have created integrated marketing plans for small businesses in Swaziland and Haiti. Senior engineering students have traveled to South America to install self-designed water purification systems and, every year, physical science students conduct interactive astronomy shows in Olivet's all-digital planetarium for hundreds of elementary students.

HONORS PROGRAM: Olivet's Honors Program nurtures academically gifted students to become the Christian scholars and servant leaders they were meant to be. The Program's highlights include one-on-one mentored research with a professor of choice, exclusive study abroad opportunities, a presentation of research at an Honors Research Symposium, and numerous community service and cultural event opportunities.

4+1 PROGRAMS: Students have the opportunity to accelerate their work toward a graduate degree with Olivet's 4+1 programs. In just five years, students can earn both a bachelor's degree and a master's in either business administration or organizational leadership. An accelerated program in engineering also offers a bachelor's degree and a master's in engineering management. This is a great opportunity to save both time and money in the pursuit of a rewarding career.

LIFE OUTSIDE THE CLASSROOM: The quality of Olivet is about far more than what happens in the classroom; the University's outlets for spiritual and personal growth are just as spectacular! Attending on-campus events, traveling and working throughout Chicago, or working out in the University's state-of-the-art fitness center, Olivetians can be found doing just about everything! Olivet students participate in more than 80 clubs and organizations, including 30 intramural sports, the 195-member marching band, two orchestras, 28 musical ensembles, and theatre groups. Among their student-led organizations are nearly 20 ministry groups through which they can serve their community and grow together as compassionate Christians. Olivetians worship at summer camps for junior high students, play checkers with veterans at a nursing home, build houses with "Habitat for Humanity," and more. During the spring and summer breaks, Missions In Action groups travel in the U.S. and abroad to extend the love of Christ. As active community members, these students are constantly enacting change and enjoying endless fun events.

CAMPUS MINISTRY: Weekly chapel services, the student-led Party with Jesus, and local churches offer students, faculty, and staff the opportunity to worship and grow side-by-side. Chapel services, held in the 3,046-seat Centennial Chapel, regularly feature renowned spiritual, business, political, and other leaders who offer their wisdom to educate and inspire the ONU community.

STUDENT SUCCESS: No matter their destination after graduation, Olivet graduates find success in every sense of the word. Olivet has a worldwide network of more than 37,000 alumni who live in 50 U.S. states and 30 countries. As educators, medical professionals, musicians, engineers, pastors, lawyers, missionaries, and business professionals, Olivetians are living out the "Olivet difference" in their homes, workplaces, churches, and communities.

http://www.olivet.edu/

P: (800) 648-1463

PRIVATE - CHRISTIAN

STUDENT PROFILE

3,389 undergraduate students

90% of undergrad students are full time

40% male – 60% female

43% of students are from out of state

77% freshman retention rate

61% graduated in 6 years

FACULTY PROFILE

136 full-time faculty

306 part-time faculty

17 to 1 student/faculty ratio

ADMISSIONS

4,133 Total Applicants

3,165 Total Admissions

734 Total Freshman Enrollment

76.58% of applicants admitted

SAT Ranges: CR 460-580, M 470-570, W 430-562.5

ACT Ranges: C 20-27, M 19-26, E 20-27, W 7-8

TUITION & COSTS

Tuition: $31,950

Fees: $840

Total: $32,970

R&B: $7,900

Room: $3,950

Board: $3,950

Total: $39,889

FINANCIAL

$20,623 avg grant/scholarship amount (need)

$3,203 avg loan amount (need)

SAINT XAVIER UNIVERSITY

CHICAGO, ILLINOIS

Saint Xavier University is a distinguished, four-year private institution founded by the Sisters of Mercy in 1846. As Chicago's oldest Catholic university and the first Mercy college in the United States, Saint Xavier provides a quality educational experience to 4,000 students at its Chicago and Orland Park campuses with more than 40 undergraduate programs.

SERVICE: One of the core values of Saint Xavier University is service, and as such SXU features programs and classes that encourage students to make the most of their education while benefitting others. These engagement initiatives take the form of study abroad programs, internships, community service projects, and student-driven research, all of which ensure a well-rounded experience that immediately puts their skills to good use. The University is particularly dedicated to serving its community through the Mercy mission of service, including the S.T.A.T. program and the Mercy Volunteer Corps. Developed in 2008, students in S.T.A.T. (Service Through Action Team) have come together to make nearly 5,000 lunches for distribution to food pantries, ministries, charities, and schools. Students have also been called to serve in the Mercy Volunteer Corps to aid people who are economically poor or marginalized. Volunteers commit to compassionate service, simple lifestyles in community, and spiritual growth.

STUDENT ACTIVITIES: At Saint Xavier, students can find dozens of ways to get involved through more than 40 clubs and organizations. Extracurricular involvement allows students to share their interests with others while developing lifelong friendships while also reinforcing the active, collaborative learning environment in the classroom. Students can play club sports, participate in student government, or even host a radio show. Whatever interests or special talents students have, there is probably a group available to cater to them. And if there isn't, students are encouraged to band together and start their own. SXU's community is enlivened by student-run ethnic and cultural organizations; faith and spiritual organizations; social, political, and special interest clubs; club sports; student media; student government and activities programming; leadership groups; and more!

OPPORTUNITIES FOR EVERYONE: While record numbers of SXU students are taking advantage of the University's new and expanding residential facilities, well over half of all SXU students are commuters. Thanks to the Commuter Services Program, however, this diverse population is connected to one another, on-campus activities and events, and all the benefits that the University strives to make available. But no matter their living arrangements, all Saint Xavier students are often lured off campus to enjoy downtown Chicago's world-class museums, shopping, restaurants, theaters, and more. The city is an inexhaustible source of cultural enrichment, recreation, and inspiration, and through the "Discover Chicago" program, SXU makes it easy for students to take advantage of its urban treasures. This program offers free access to a wide range of attractions and events, including visits to the Chicago Art Institute and Chicago Bulls home games.

EDUCATION FOR EVERYONE: Current students and SXU graduates consistently identify their professors as the best part of their academic experience. SXU faculty are trained as research scholars and recognized as experts in their field of study—of full-time faculty, nearly 90 percent have the highest degree in their discipline. Not only are they experts, but they're also distinguished by their dedication to teaching undergraduates and taking full advantage of their 13:1 student-to-faculty ratio. SXU is made up of five academic divisions, each with a unique mission and academic focus. These divisions include The College of Arts and Sciences, The Graham School of Management, The School of Education, The School of Nursing, and The School for Continuing and Professional Studies.

---

http://www.sxu.edu/

P: (800) 462-9288

PRIVATE - CATHOLIC

STUDENT PROFILE

2,954 undergraduate students

88% of undergrad students are full time

35% male – 65% female

4% of students are from out of state

72% freshman retention rate

48% graduated in 6 years

FACULTY PROFILE

153 full-time faculty

213 part-time faculty

13 to 1 student/faculty ratio

ADMISSIONS

7,883 Total Applicants

5,886 Total Admissions

622 Total Freshman Enrollment

74.67% of applicants admitted

SAT Ranges: CR 460-520, M 490-530

ACT Ranges: C 19-23, M 19-24, E 17-24

TUITION & COSTS

Tuition: $32,250

R&B: $11,060

Total: $43,310

FINANCIAL

$20,004 avg grant/scholarship amount (need)

$4,078 avg loan amount (need)

TRINITY CHRISTIAN COLLEGE

PALOS HEIGHTS, ILLINOIS

Trinity Christian College has been changing students' lives since 1959, having been begun by a group of entrepreneurs who wanted to develop Chicago-area Christians who would put their faith into action, not just believe. As a smaller college, Trinity provides students with individualized attention, harnessing an extensive network throughout Chicago in order to make a difference in the world. Trinity faculty help students discover their passion and develop it into incredible achievement. Through a Biblically informed liberal arts education, the College community endeavors to provide an environment of Christian integrity and love, enhancing and supporting the entire learning experience.

COMMUNITY PARTNERSHIPS AND SERVICE-LEARNING: Trinity's community believes strongly that service is not something to be done exclusively in the summer or over spring break; rather, it should be woven into the fabric of their lives. At the core of the Office of Community Partnerships and Service-Learning (OCPSL) is a strong college-organization relationship with valued partners. Trinity seeks to equip local organizations with dedicated, responsible student volunteers and interns. It's with these partners that the College prepares its students to be "active members of a community based on the Biblical requirements of justice, humility, and love".

WORLDVIEW SERIES: Trinity's WorldView series is an annual community and college series for film, word, and current events and music. Students are exposed to a wide variety of interesting topics by thought-provoking speakers who offer critical insights, challenged to think deeply about issues that are crucially relevant to society.

CAMPUS MINISTRIES: The Chaplain's Office facilitates and leads various ministries with the help of the student ministry leadership team. This team is made up of student ministry leaders, student worship scholarship recipients, and peer ministry scholarship recipients. It meets weekly with the Chaplain to review ministry activities, grow in spiritual formation, learn leadership skills, and encourage one another in prayer and by mutual accountability. Worship ministries on Trinity's campus include the chapel program, Sunday Night Worship, Men's and Women's Ministry, Prayer Ministry, and Outcry, a student-led praise and worship group.

TRINITY BUSINESS NETWORK: The Trinity Business Network (TBN) is committed to providing Christ-centered business learning opportunities for Trinity Christian College students, alumni, and friends. To fulfill this mission, TBN hosts regular speaking engagements with local and nationally known business people, small group discussions, educational workshops, and seminars. These opportunities are always free to Trinity students, providing them unique insights and access to top business professionals.

STUDENT RESEARCH: One of the key highlights in Trinity research is the opportunity for students to present their discoveries at both a local and national level. Each spring, Trinity students are able to present their work during the annual OPUS celebration, a school-wide recognition of achievement and performance. Students have also been invited to present their work at the National Conference for Undergraduate Research (NCUR), held annually at various universities around the country. Being able to present on a national level is a rich opportunity for students to showcase their work to their peers, hone their presentation skills, and network with the top graduate schools in the nation.

CHICAGO NETWORK: Trinity's proximity to Chicago, the nation's third largest city, is a distinct student advantage. Trinity's extensive network of alumni, friends, and partners provides students with unique experiences that can't be matched at other institutions. Students bring their coursework to life with excursions both in and around the city, and guest speakers and experts in every field are accessible for lectures and various speaking engagements. Internships and field experiences are nearly unlimited, and the opportunities for weekend exploration and fun never stop.

---

http://www.trnty.edu/

P: (708) 239-4708

PRIVATE - CHRISTIAN

STUDENT PROFILE

1,085 undergraduate students

83% of undergrad students are full time

35% male – 65% female

53% of students are from out of state

83% freshman retention rate

58% graduated in 6 years

FACULTY PROFILE

70 full-time faculty

86 part-time faculty

11 to 1 student-to-faculty ratio

ADMISSIONS

884 Total Applicants

569 Total Admissions

160 Total Freshman Enrollment

64.37% of applicants admitted

SAT Ranges: CR 418-618, M 450-600

ACT Ranges: C 20-27, M 18-26, E 20-27

TUITION & COSTS

Tuition: $28,200

Fees: $475

Total: $28,675

R&B: $9,680

Total: $38,355

FINANCIAL

$15,990 avg grant/scholarship amount (need)

$4,640 avg loan amount (need)

UNIVERSITY OF ST. FRANCIS

JOLIET, ILLINOIS

The University of St. Francis in Joliet, Illinois, is a Catholic university rooted in the liberal arts. USF is a welcoming community of learners who are challenged by Franciscan values and charisma. Everyone is engaged in continuous pursuits of knowledge, faith, wisdom, and justice, proving to be mindful of the tradition that emphasizes compassion and peacemaking. USF strives for academic excellence in all programs, preparing women and men to contribute to the world through service and leadership.

DUNS SCOTUS: USF students are those who want to be engaged and active within their campus community. Whether they be freshmen or transfer students, residents or commuters, all USF students have countless opportunities to get involved and make a difference. Duns Scotus, USF's honors society, is a particularly notable way in which students can showcase their passions as hard-working, thoughtful intellectuals. This society challenges students to excel academically while exhibiting an inspiring life driven by the Franciscan tradition. Students in the Dun Scotus program receive annual scholarships and housing discounts so that they may direct all their focus on what matters most: their scholarship.

STUDENT RESOURCES: The College of Business' "Small Business Incubator," located at USF's downtown St. Bonaventure Campus, allows Entrepreneurship students to work with developing businesses develop their own "startup" company. College of Nursing students utilize the SIM Lab and Skills Lab, getting hands-on experience in simulated hospital environments before working with real patients. USF even offers a cadaver lab to give biology and pre-health sciences students the opportunity to expand their understanding of anatomy through hands-on dissection. For College of Education students, the annual Chrysalis Retreat gives students time to reflect on themselves and their passions to become teachers.

AN INVITING HOME: USF is located in the historic Upper Bluffs area on the west side of Joliet. Surrounded by historic homes, USF's main campus features SMART classrooms, a digital audio recording studio, a SIM nursing lab, and a state-of-the-art library. USF's downtown St. Bonaventure campus is the home to the Art & Design program; the St. Francis Art Gallery, which features both student and professional art exhibits; and a new building that contains a mock-trial courtroom and educational space for the Criminal & Social Justice, Political Science and Recreation, and Sport & Tourism programs.

STUDENT ACTIVITIES: Clubs and organizations, including USF's nationally competitive Mock Trial team, provide students with extra outlets for them to pursue their passions and interests, all while preparing them for real-world, professional responsibilities. Once prospective students visit USF, they quickly discover how they might fit into the university's close-knit community and make the most of their spectacular resources. Students are encouraged to take on leadership roles in the many campus clubs and organizations, and internationally known guest speakers, researchers, and performers are invited to campus each semester for further enhancement of the educational experience.

CERTAIN SUCCESS: USF students are well prepared to pass professional examinations. USF nursing students have program-wide pass rates of nearly 100% on the NCLEX examination, and accounting students and future teachers also have high levels of success in achieving their certifications. These test results stand as testament to USF's ability to prepare students for professional success as worldly contributors of service and leadership. USF has a network of 44,000 alumni nationwide in all 50 states and 8 foreign countries. Among USF's alumni are influential CEOs, attorneys, doctors, nurses, teachers, and social workers who all strive to make a difference both locally and globally. The Career Services staff helps students achieve such prestigious positions with résumé assistance and mock interviews. They also connect USF students to alumni, creating an amazing network of USF scholars.

http://www.stfrancis.edu/
P: (800) 735-7500

PRIVATE - CATHOLIC

STUDENT PROFILE

1,762 undergraduate students

77% of undergrad students are full time

32% male – 68% female

10% of students are from out of state

81% freshman retention rate

56% graduated in 6 years

FACULTY PROFILE

106 full-time faculty

234 part-time faculty

11 to 1 student/faculty ratio

ADMISSIONS

1,509 Total Applicants

763 Total Admissions

216 Total Freshman Enrollment

50.56% of applicants admitted

SAT Ranges: CR 460-520, M 460-530, W 430-530

ACT Ranges: C 21-25, M 20-25, E 20-25

TUITION & COSTS

Tuition: $28,220

Fees: $570

Total: $28,790

R&B: $8,770

Total: $37,560

FINANCIAL

$19,425 avg grant/scholarship amount (total)

$6,977 avg loan amount (total)

WHEATON COLLEGE

WHEATON, ILLINOIS

A Wheaton education prepares students for lives that are wholly dedicated to serving Christ and His kingdom. The College is largely tied to the Christian church, the values of which are implemented in every facet of its experience. Wheaton is concerned with the success of its students—success that can be used to perpetuate and best live out those Christian values. Professors and staff have been referred to as "Godly" faculty members that are highly dedicated to perpetuating Christian values, working very hard to give students an education that both benefits society and leads to a meaningful Christian life.

THE IMPORTANCE OF THE CHRISTIAN CHURCH: The values of the Christian Church are prioritized at Wheaton. Serving the needs of the Church is paramount regardless of profession. And, with a heart for progression, faculty and staff work to advance the Kingdom of God through education and practice. Students are encouraged to come together through love and commitment to Christ, as both the educational and personal aspects of Wheaton College come together to make an inclusive community, bound together by service and perpetuation of Christian ideals.

FUNDING FOR EXCELLENCE: The Faculty Global Research Awards provide professors the opportunity to bring new cultural perspectives to the classroom through various funded research efforts. These funds make it possible for recipients not only to bolster and change their course curricula, but they also facilitate travel and research projects in which they often invite their students to take part. Students can benefit more directly from school funds through such grants as the International Internship Travel Grant and the Global Scholar award. These allow students to venture out into the world without worrying as much about finances, enabling them to focus on life-changing work experience or research in a different country.

A DIVERSE COMMUNITY: Wheaton embraces diversity, recognizing its importance in creating the ideal community—one where many backgrounds come together to form the academic discourse. This commitment to diversity is highlighted in the Community Covenant, which calls upon every Wheaton student and faculty member to collaborate with others in work, service, and worship. As a supportive campus of Christian scholars, Wheaton fosters an atmosphere that promotes both spiritual and intellectual growth.

STUDENT ACTIVITIES: Wheaton has several clubs and organizations for students to choose from. These clubs range from service initiatives to special interest groups. While there are numerous options, students also have the chance to charter their own clubs to expand the scope of the community's focus. The College Union also helps bond the community by organizing campus-wide events catered to every student in the College. Concerts and dances make Wheaton burst with activity!

THE VALUE OF A LIBERAL ARTS EDUCATION: A liberal arts degree enriches the whole person, catering to and influencing every aspect of the individual. With this type of degree, students enter the workforce with a well-rounded repertoire of skills. They are prepared to handle any situation, no matter the circumstance. Ultimately, Wheaton recognizes one very important fact: an education should not be geared toward one specific thing; instead, it should encompass a plethora of ideas that spans across all disciplines.

THE CAREER DEVELOPMENT CENTER AND WHEATON IN NETWORK (WIN): The Career Development Center and online Wheaton in Network (WiN) tool connects members of the Wheaton network to one another through various postgraduate inquiries and career interests. All members of the Wheaton community are invited to take advantage of the Center's services, provide their insight, and use their personal networks to connect others to opportunities.

http://www.wheaton.edu/
P: (630) 752-5000

PRIVATE - CHRISTIAN

STUDENT PROFILE

2,463 undergraduate students

98% of undergrad students are full time

47% male – 53% female

70% of students are from out of state

95% freshman retention rate

89% graduated in 6 years

FACULTY PROFILE

219 full-time faculty

102 part-time faculty

11 to 1 student/faculty ratio

ADMISSIONS

1,971 Total Applicants

1,390 Total Admissions

605 Total Freshman Enrollment

70.52% of applicants admitted

SAT Ranges: CR 600-710, M 600-700, W 590-700

ACT Ranges: C 27-32, M 26-31, E 27-34, W 8-9

TUITION & COSTS

Tuition: $32,950

R&B: $9,200

Room: $5,410

Board: $3,790

Total: $42,150

FINANCIAL

$20,255 avg grant/scholarship amount (need)

$4,858 avg loan amount (need)

ANDERSON UNIVERSITY

ANDERSON, INDIANA

Anderson University offers more than 50 majors, including the new addition of computer engineering, information security, national security studies, and sport marketing in the 2016-17 academic year. Notably unique majors that are full of experiential and service-learning experiences include nursing, engineering, music education, dance, and finance.

FIRST-YEAR EXPERIENCE: Anderson University's First-Year Experience introduces students to a well-rounded liberal arts curriculum through a series of engaging activities. Every first-year student builds upon a sturdy foundation that consists of Raven 101 (a registration and advising event), new student orientation, a first-year seminar, a critical-thinking seminar, and a peer-mentoring program. The First-Year Experience's peer-mentoring program divides students into small groups that are led by teams of faculty and student mentors who aim to provide help wherever it is need.

UNDERGRADUATE RESEARCH: Undergraduate research and internships are intrinsic to every major at AU. Each spring, students work closely with faculty for a scholars' day research project to be presented on campus. These projects showcase the in-depth process of organizing abstracts, hypotheses, research, focus groups, and surveys.

LIFE OF FAITH AND SERVICE: It is a part of Anderson University's mission to educate its students for lives of faith and service to both the church and their society. In the last 50 years, for example, over 24,000 students have participated in the Tri-S program (Study, Serve, Share), which is designed to let students learn from other cultures while serving in communities around the world. Through Tri-S, students explore other cultures while participating in work camps, service, or ministry projects. In 2017-18, Anderson University students will travel to Trinidad, Greece, the Dominican Republic, Costa Rica, Guatemala, London, Paraguay, Zambia, Jamaica, Scotland, Grand Cayman, Nicaragua, Uganda, China, India, New Zealand, South Africa, Ireland, Romania, Hungary, and Germany. Tri-S also offers domestic opportunities to serve, hauling students around the United States for meaningful service. Examples of American Tri-S projects have included urban ministry in such cities as Philadelphia and New York City as well as work projects in the Native American communities of South Dakota and Oklahoma.

OUTLETS FOR SUCCESS: Anderson's close proximity to Indianapolis not only allows faculty members to maintain critical networks in the professional field, but it also offers opportunities for students to secure internships that often turn into jobs. IndyMix, a gathering of panelists from leading and cutting-edge Indianapolis businesses, is a significant example of the direct contact students have with the professional world beyond AU's borders.

LIBERAL ARTS EDUCATION: Anderson University's liberal arts education requires that students not only master their chosen fields of study, but also gain a broad understanding of the world around them. The liberal arts core curriculum sharpens students' skills in written communication, speaking and listening, quantitative reasoning, Biblical literacy, and personal wellness—part of AU's commitment to offer courses that complement every area of study. In addition to their core requirements, students choose between six categories of courses, which include Christian Ways of Knowing, Scientific Ways of Knowing, Civic Ways of Knowing, Aesthetic Ways of Knowing, Social and Behavioral Ways of Knowing, and Global/Intercultural Ways of Knowing.

LEARNING FROM THE BEST: Through a recent speaker series, students had the opportunity to witness valuable, real-world applications of their studies, hearing from experts in the sciences and national security studies as well as other successful AU alumni. Other renowned, annual lecture series conferences hosted by Anderson University include the Newell Lectures in Biblical Studies, the Indiana Faith Writing Conference, and the York Children's Literature Festival. Additionally, the School of Music, Theatre, and Dance hosted a conference for the American College Dance Association in 2016.

ANDERSON UNIVERSITY

http://www.anderson.edu/
P: (800) 428-6414

PRIVATE - CHRISTIAN

STUDENT PROFILE

1,760 undergraduate students

91% of undergrad students are full time

40% male – 60% female

25% of students are from out of state

75% freshman retention rate

54% graduated in 6 years

FACULTY PROFILE

129 full-time faculty

148 part-time faculty

11.4 to 1 student/faculty ratio

ADMISSIONS

2,620 Total Applicants

1,562 Total Admissions

422 Total Freshman Enrollment

59.62% of applicants admitted

SAT Ranges: CR 440-550, M 450-570

ACT Ranges: C 20-26, M 19-25, E 20-25

TUITION & COSTS

Tuition: $28,500

Fees: $150

Total: $28,650

R&B: $9,550

Total: $38,200

BALL STATE UNIVERSITY

MUNCIE, INDIANA

BALL STATE UNIVERSITY

http://cms.bsu.edu/

P: (765) 289-1241

Ball State is committed to education with an innovative approach. Students are given a wide range of opportunities to explore their passions through immersive and experiential learning methods. Ball State's unique entrepreneurship program, as well as its many impact and service initiatives, make the University an ideal environment to learn and grow.

FRESHMAN COMMON READING AND WRITING: During summer orientation, students are given a book that they are all assigned to read by the time they start school. This reading experience gets every student off on the same foot and has them begin their first semester already with something in common. Each year, a new book is chosen to focus on theme that faculty want to implement in the curriculum. The author of the year's book even visits campus to give a lecture to the students, allowing them to get an in-depth analysis from an expert. Freshmen also complete a common writing experience that pushes them to practice foundationally important writing skills at the college level.

CORE CURRICULUM: The Core Curriculum at Ball State is all about developing the skills that every student should possess by the time they graduate. It is about both individual growth as well as learning to work within a community. When both of these roles are assumed, students become engaged and active members of society. They are taught to think critically, communicate effectively, and pursue answers through thoughtful inquisition and research.

STUDY ABROAD: Ball State offers several different study abroad options, offering class credit through most programs and proving to be especially helpful for those aiming to graduate on time. There are five different types of study abroad programs that range in length, credit, and cost: international internships, direct enroll, exchanges, and study abroad consortia. Ball State also offers faculty-led study abroad trips, which are much shorter in length in order to benefit students who cannot afford to study abroad for an entire semester. No matter what a student's time and course restraints may be, they are likely to find a way to gain life-changing experiences in the country of their choice.

IMMERSIVE LEARNING: Immersive learning is a unique characteristic of Ball State's education. Faculty lead projects and programs that promote an astute application of academic theories. Students are given the chance to apply their knowledge to real-world situations, bringing classroom theory to tangible practice in the field. This approach to education has yielded great results, with nearly 1,500 immersive experiences being completed each year.

CHRISTY WOODS: The lush Christy Woods serves as a natural classroom for the students and members of the Ball State community. This outdoor teaching laboratory features a rich forest filled with several plant species and wildlife. Ball State has two greenhouses, an indoor classroom, and an outdoor interpretation area within Christy Woods.

LIVING LEARNING COMMUNITIES: Living Learning Communities (LLCs) give students the chance to interact with peers who share similar interests and academic goals. LLCs also allow the learning process to extend beyond the classroom and into the residence halls. They promote greater interaction with faculty and accessible academic support. Students involved in an LLC generally have better grades and enjoy living and learning with their peers. Just a few of the examples of Ball State LLCs include groups centered around Business, Communication, Emerging Media, Theatre and Dance, Nursing, Education, and more.

PUBLIC

STUDENT PROFILE

16,602 undergraduate students

89% of undergrad students are full time

41% male – 59% female

82% freshman retention rate

61% graduated in 6 years

FACULTY PROFILE

1,048 full-time faculty

228 part-time faculty

14 to 1 student/faculty ratio

ADMISSIONS

22,147 Total Applicants

13,399 Total Admissions

3,503 Total Freshman Enrollment

60.50% of applicants admitted

SAT Ranges: CR 510-600, M 500-590, W 490-580

ACT Ranges: C 20-24

TUITION & COSTS

Tuition: (In) $8,836 (Out) $24,354

Fees: $662

Total: (In) $9,498 (Out) $25,01

R&B: $9,656

Total: (In) $19,154 (Out) $34,672

FINANCIAL

$10,754 avg grant/scholarship amount (total)

$7,242 avg loan amount (total)

BUTLER UNIVERSITY

INDIANAPOLIS, INDIANA

At Butler, liberal arts courses exercise students' ability evaluate and communicate the skills that are essential for a job in any field. Butler University educates a graduate not simply to make a living, but to make a life of purpose. Butler University is located just a few miles from downtown Indianapolis, which has been ranked as the best city for new grads. Broad Ripple Village, near Butler's campus, is a neighborhood with trendy restaurants, shopping, and nightspots.

ENRICHED OFFERINGS: Butler has been lauded for its academic and campus resources. The University offers its students such beneficial opportunities as the first-year experience, study abroad, internships, service-learning, and research projects. These resources have been praised for their contributions to student success in recognition of their hands-on approaches to learning.

CORE CURRICULUM: The Core Curriculum is the foundation of Butler's educational experience. Students are taught to consider both their role in the classroom as well as their citizenship within the global community. The goal of Core is to develop a sense of community while teaching students to think critically and communicate effectively. Ultimately, students should come to appreciate the learning process as an ongoing adventure that continues after graduation. Butler professors recognize the importance of Core, not just for its content, but for its potential to engage. Through active involvement, students gain such necessary skills as critical and higher-level thinking, effective communication, and conceptualization.

OUTSTANDING PROGRAMS, OUTSTANDING FACULTY: With 60 academic programs that span over 6 colleges, students have several options to choose from. There are also pre-professional programs in areas of engineering, law, medicine, and veterinary medicine. Butler hires faculty who are actively engaged in their fields of study. Professors are researchers and scholars, practicing and exercising their talents through creative inquiry. Butler faculty create a solid foundation for students to work from. The educational experience offered by the University is grounded in the liberal arts and tied to professional studies. Students learn to integrate the two components into a framework of educational discovery.

STUDENT ACTIVITIES: Butler students have over 150 clubs and organizations at their disposal. Over 94% of the student body participates in some club or group, and nearly 33% of students are involved in Greek life. There are also plenty of opportunities to give back to the community; Butler connects its students with several organizations, many of which focus on mentoring the community's youth. The Programs for Leadership and Service Education (PULSE) is a resource available to assist any club or group, supporting students with the means to carry out the goals of their organizations. It is also the place to go to seek information regarding upcoming events and activities and serves as a great tool for getting involved. Staff members are happy to help students find their niche in the campus community.

INTERNSHIP & CAREER SERVICES (ICS): Internship & Career Services in an incredibly useful tool for students. The center focuses on the individual needs and goals of each student, working to provide them with the resources and guidance they need for postgraduate success. Through frequent academic advising and occasional counseling, students are guided through the rigorous process of selecting an area of study and, ultimately, a career path. ICS also offers self-assessments to help students better understand their talents and professional potential.

---

http://www.butler.edu/

P: (800) 368-6852

PRIVATE

STUDENT PROFILE

4,028 undergraduate students

99% of undergrad students are full time

40% male – 60% female

89% freshman retention rate

76% graduated in 6 years

FACULTY PROFILE

371 full-time faculty

11 to 1 student/faculty ratio

ADMISSIONS

9,943 Total Applicants

7,003 Total Admissions

1,025 Total Freshman Enrollment

70.43% of applicants admitted

SAT Ranges: CR 520-620, M 530-630, W 510-610

ACT Ranges: C 25-30, M 25-29, E 24-31

TUITION & COSTS

Tuition: $36,050

Fees: $960

Total: $37,010

R&B: $12,055

Room: $5,665

Board: $6,390

Total: $49,065

FINANCIAL

$15,747 avg grant/scholarship amount (total)

$9,214 avg loan amount (total)

DEPAUW UNIVERSITY

GREENCASTLE, INDIANA

DePauw University is a premier institution of higher education in which students are given endless opportunities to succeed both academically and personally. When it comes down to it, an education has to be about more than rote memorization and textbooks; true success comes from hands-on experience. Through DePauw's student engagement activities, students explore experiential opportunities that enhance their liberal arts education with an impact that extends beyond the classroom.

STUDENT RESEARCH: Undergraduate research is an incredible opportunity for students to explore the process of inquiry, methodology, and discovery. On top of the personal benefits, experience in research is considered an asset to both graduate schools and employers alike. At DePauw, research extends beyond the laboratory and into several disciplines, and every student who chooses to engage in research is assisted by a faculty mentor who helps them prepare for and connect to various research conferences in the broader community.

STUDY ABROAD: Semester-long study abroad is an incredible opportunity that affords students such benefits as a greater sense of independence, global citizenship and tolerance, and cross-cultural communication skills. During the Winter and May Terms, extended faculty-led study abroad programs allow experienced faculty to lead expeditions in foreign locations. Students are inspired and given many outlets through which to grow as they enjoy the mixture of exploration and high-quality DePauw lecture.

MANAGEMENT ACCELERATOR PROGRAM: The Management Accelerator Program is considered an Extended Studies credit that is open to sophomores, juniors, and seniors of all majors. The program, which takes place during Winter Term, explores the foundations of business and what it takes to make an organization run smoothly. No matter the field in which students study, they can all develop the foundational tools for understanding the business of their respective industry.

WINTER TERM IN SERVICE STUDENT LEADERS: Winter Term service initiatives are a great way for students to get involved over break. During a Winter Term service trip, students travel to a community in need and work to enact some positive change. In the past, students have assisted with construction projects, medical clinics, public health education, and much more. One outstanding example is the Servicio en Las Amèricas immersion program, which focuses on service with an emphasis on global citizenship. Students in the program spend two weeks in a Spanish-speaking country in which they perform various acts of service (while promising only to speak Spanish for the duration of the trip).

INTERNSHIPS: Internships allow students to gain both hands-on experience as well as firsthand knowledge of their specific industry. DePauw recognizes the incredible benefits of internships and works hard to provide students with several opportunities to get involved. Most students opt to complete an internship over the summer months and can receive a stipend through the Summer Internship Grant Program, even if their internships themselves are unpaid. Other students can work in short-term internships that take place in January. These opportunities are full-time positions and last for a maximum of four weeks. They offer a great preview of the actual demands of a specific career and allows students to get an immersive feel of their work environment.

CAREER SERVICES: Career Services is available to assist students with questions related to school, internships, and careers. It hosts a series of useful workshops and fairs throughout the year in order to help students develop their networking and interviewing skills. Career Service offers help in such areas as advising, connecting with alumni, graduate school advising, obtaining scholarships, and obtaining internships and jobs.

DEPAUW
UNIVERSITY
Est. 1837

http://www.depauw.edu/
P: (765) 658-4800

PRIVATE

STUDENT PROFILE

2,265 undergraduate students

98% of undergrad students are full time

46% male – 54% female

54% of students are from out of state

94% freshman retention rate

82% graduated in 6 years

FACULTY PROFILE

259 full-time faculty

43 part-time faculty

10 to 1 student/faculty ratio

ADMISSIONS

5,182 Total Applicants

3,356 Total Admissions

596 Total Freshman Enrollment

64.76% of applicants admitted

SAT Ranges: CR 510-620, M 550-670, W 520-620

ACT Ranges: C 25-29, M 24-29, E 25-31

TUITION & COSTS

Tuition: $43,950

Fees: $728

Total: $44,678

R&B: $11,700

Total: $56,378

FINANCIAL

$26,597 avg grant/scholarship amount (total)

$7,556 avg loan amount (total)

GRACE COLLEGE

WINONA LAKE, INDIANA

Grace College is an evangelical Christian institution in Winona Lake, Indiana. Grace prepares students by providing them a strong foundation in the liberal arts as well as the biblical values that promote service, compassion, and integrity.

FIRST-YEAR EXPERIENCE: The First-Year Experience at Grace is designed around a model that identifies particular keys to success. These keys include a steady transition into new academic and social environments, embracing personal and spiritual growth, and forming strong relationships with peers and professors. With such a strong foundation, students are more than able to persist through their first year of college.

GRACE CORE: At the heart of a Grace education are academically challenging courses that are specifically designed to foster a thirst for character, competence, and service. Every student at Grace completes a series of general education courses, the Grace Core, and thus enjoys a common experience that stretches across all the disciplines.

GO ENCOUNTER: Go Encounter trips are a unique part of Grace's general education core. Students spend this class developing a biblical lens for seeing the world and discussing ways to become more effective in cross-cultural interactions. By the end of the course, they get the chance to live out what they've learned on a 7- to 10-day experiential trip. This is just one of the exciting, immersive ways students can fulfill their "cross-cultural field experience" for the Grace Core's Global Perspectives requirement.

STUDY ABROAD: Grace's Study Abroad program opens students' eyes to the world beyond campus. Travel is an important part of a complete education in that allows students to understand other cultures and prepare to work and serve wherever they may be. Several majors and minors, including international business, intercultural studies, and languages, require study abroad in order to immerse students in the target culture and language.

HANDS-ON, KNEE-DEEP ENVIRONMENTAL SCIENCE PROGRAM: The Grace College Environmental Science program seeks to train young environmental studies professionals with a firmly grounded mindset of stewardship and service. In following God's command for stewardship, students serve the environment by conducting field research, founding wildlife preservation and clean-water initiatives, and even lobbying Congress. Whatever the realm, and whatever the passion, every student finds a place to develop their visions and hone their abilities through personalized training, instruction, and mentoring from caring and passionate environmental faculty.

HEALTH AND COUNSELING CENTER: Grace's Health and Counseling Center is dedicated to promoting, maintaining, and restoring students' physical and emotional health. All the services offered are founded upon biblical principles, incorporating medical knowledge, psychological acuity, and research. Physical and mental health services are available to every Grace College undergraduate student.

CHAPEL: Chapel reflects the heart of God and, therefore, the heart of campus—a community of faith, grace, and worship. At Grace, students examine their lives to see how God has wired them as well as how to uncover their passions, dreams, and shortcomings. Grace's chapel is frequently visited by authors, musicians, and leading voices for such global concerns as poverty, hunger, clean water, human trafficking, pornography, and modern-day slavery. Chapel services are planned and led by Grace College students and directed by the Dean of the Chapel and Community Life.

APPLIED LEARNING: At Grace, students complete 12 "field" credits of Applied Learning. These include: job shadowing, internships, study abroad, cross-cultural experiences, student teaching, student leadership positions, and more. This serves as an opportunity for students to get their hands dirty and let the world at large become their classroom. These experiences are crucial to helping students see the spectrum of jobs available within their best-fit career options. They also prepare students for service and generate career-ready graduates.

http://www.grace.edu/
P: (574) 372-5100

PRIVATE - CHRISTIAN

STUDENT PROFILE

1,614 undergraduate students

94% of undergrad students are full time

42% male — 58% female

37% of students are from out of state

61% freshman retention rate

84% graduated in 6 years

FACULTY PROFILE

46 full-time faculty

69 part-time faculty

22 to 1 student/faculty ratio

ADMISSIONS

4,093 Total Applicants

3,219 Total Admissions

400 Total Freshman Enrollment

78.65% of applicants admitted

SAT Ranges: CR 470-590, M 460-580

ACT Ranges: C 21-27

TUITION & COSTS

Tuition: $23,930

R&B: $8,782

Total: $32,712

FINANCIAL

$5,285 avg grant/scholarship amount (need)

$3,588 avg loan amount (need)

INDIANA WESLEYAN UNIVERSITY

MARION, INDIANA

Indiana Wesleyan University is a Christ-centered academic community committed to changing the world by developing students in character, scholarship, and leadership. Over 3,000 students learn, live, and thrive on IWU's 350-acre residential campus, and more than 10,000 adult learners study at education centers in three different states as well as online.

NEW STUDENT ORIENTATION: Known as NSO, New Student Orientation is a week-long immersion experience in which first-time freshman and transfer students are introduced to the IWU campus and integrated into college life. The week allows for students to become acclimated to their new home, meet new friends, and familiarize themselves with the campus before the semester officially starts.

UNDERGRADUATE RESEARCH: IWU is known for providing its undergraduates with real-life research opportunities—especially in the Division of Natural Sciences. Over 20 students participate in the Hodson Summer Research Institute every summer. They work alongside faculty members to conduct full-time, original research for eight weeks, addressing cutting-edge areas, including glial cell regulation of neuronal signaling in the retina and rescue mechanisms for bone cancer drug side effects. Many students continue their research into the following semester.

GLOBAL EDUCATION AND STUDY ABROAD: IWU seeks to be a truly great Christian university that serves the world. Part of this vision includes its drive to facilitate regular opportunities for students to study or serve abroad. Every year, hundreds of IWU students travel to various countries like Scotland, Israel, Germany, Italy, and more. Immersed in a new culture, each student has the chance to foster a global mindset, prepare for their career, and develop cultural responsiveness.

THE WRITING CENTER: The Ink Well, IWU's writing center, seeks to aid students throughout the writing process. Trained writing tutors meet with students individually, free of charge, to help with anything from the ideation process to grammar corrections. Most importantly, tutors equip students with strategies to improve their writing.

FRIDAY NIGHT LIVE: The Friday Night Live comedy show features a talented cast of IWU students (and sometimes even professors) two exciting nights each year. Modeled after Saturday Night Live, the audience enjoys a night of several sketches that poke fun at current events around campus.

SPOTTED COW WEEKEND: Students bring a blanket and lounge on the lawn to enjoy the annual Spotted Cow Weekend spring music festival, which features a talented lineup of local bands.

FUSION: Students can volunteer to help plan and coordinate the high-energy FUSION event, a two-day high school youth conference held on the IWU campus. Special performances may include artists like Lecrae, Switchfoot, and NEEDTOBREATHE.

BOWMAN BOAT RACE: Residence hall teams create a cardboard boat that can withstand the water and compete in the Bowman Boat Race on the University pond.

CAREER DEVELOPMENT: The Career Development professionals at IWU are committed to working with students all the way from their freshman year through graduation to help them determine their life calling. They offer life coaching, career coaching, and personal and professional assessments, such as the Myers-Briggs Assessment and StrengthsQuest. In fact, IWU provides every applicant with a free StrengthsQuest assessment to determine their top five strengths.

ACCELERATE INDIANA INTERNSHIP PROGRAM: IWU students have a unique opportunity to apply for paid internships with start-up organizations and businesses across Indiana. These internships are available year-round and are funded by the Lilly Endowment, Inc.

https://www.indwes.edu/

P: (866) 468-6498

PRIVATE - CHRISTIAN

STUDENT PROFILE

2,782 undergraduate students

94% of undergrad students are full time

34% male – 66% female

45% of students are from out of state

82% freshman retention rate

64% graduated in 6 years

FACULTY PROFILE

163 full-time faculty

110 part-time faculty

14 to 1 student/faculty ratio

ADMISSIONS

3,323 Total Applicants

2,455 Total Admissions

683 Total Freshman Enrollment

73.88% of applicants admitted

SAT Ranges: CR 460-590, M 460-580

ACT Ranges: C 21-27, M 20-27, E 21-28

TUITION & COSTS

Tuition: $25,346

Fees: $180

Total: $25,526

R&B: $8,148

Total: $33,674

FINANCIAL

$3,664 avg grant/scholarship amount (need)

$4,077 avg loan amount (need)

TAYLOR UNIVERSITY

UPLAND, INDIANA

Intellect and spirit coexist harmoniously at Taylor University, a thriving community in which students experience the Christian ideals of truth and life. Students have the chance to take advantage of a unique leadership development initiative, a nationally recognized study abroad program, and cutting-edge scientific research opportunities, all while concurrently advancing their spiritual development in a caring Christian community.

SATISFIED STUDENTS: Taylor's liberal arts curriculum builds on the foundational belief that all truth has its source in God. The academic program includes a core set of general education requirements, including a senior-year completion of an integrative, interdisciplinary, general education seminar. According to The National Survey of Student Engagement, Taylor students rated their college experience significantly higher than their peers at other institutions in overall satisfaction with their entire educational experience, the quality of their relationships with other student and faculty members, and their enriching educational experiences. They also rated their experience significantly higher than their peers at other institutions in acquiring a broad general education, writing clearly and effectively, understanding of self, and developing a personal code of values and ethics. Taylor's faculty members are highly accessible to students, hosting frequent office hours and living within close proximity of the school itself.

INTELLECTUAL ENRICHMENT IN THE CLASSROOM: Taylor students enjoy the university's many strengths, including its nationally recognized study abroad program as well as its cutting-edge scientific research opportunities. Students may choose from more than one hundred undergraduate majors, the most popular of which include education, media communication, biblical studies, biology/pre-med, and psychology. Taylor also offers graduate-level programs including a Master of Environmental Science, a Master of Business Administration, a Master of Arts in Higher Education, and a Master of Arts in World Religions.

STUDY ABROAD: Taylor currently sends an average of 475 students abroad to such countries as Australia, China, the Czech Republic, Ecuador, Egypt, Ireland, and Israel. Taylor even supports its own Irish studies program, which invites freshmen to spend their first semester of college in Ireland. Students can also travel through Taylor World Outreach on week- or month-long mission trips for shorter excursions to breathtaking locations.

ACTIVE FAITH: Members of the Taylor faculty are noted for their ability to reconcile intellectual pursuits and faith, placing an emphasis on the integration of faith and learning, ideas and values, and discussion and student initiative. Each January, freshmen in the Honors Guild are part of a unique overseas learning experience in which their faith and intellect meet real-world experiences. Past trips have included Jordan, Northern Ireland, and South Africa.

A HEAD START TO SUCCESS: In addition to its impressive programs of study, Taylor offers many programs that are designed to challenge students to be good stewards and citizens regardless of their discipline. The university's summer honors program, called CRAM, invites high school students participate in coursework that requires deep thinking of the culture at large. Opportunities to grow as responsible adults continue from CRAM all the way through senior year.

FELLOWSHIP, FRIENDSHIP, AND FAITH: Student life at Taylor provides the chance to learn outside the classroom. The biblical concept of the Body of Christ is evident as students live, serve, and learn together. Whether they competing with their residence floor in the intramural flag football championship, work with Project Mercy alongside a team of fellow students in Ethiopia, or create an award-winning film for the Heartland Film Festival, Taylor students are engaged in a variety of events that contribute both to their growth as well as to the campus community. Chapel services, during which the entire student body gathers in worship, are held three times a week on Monday, Wednesday, and Friday mornings. Though attendance is not taken at chapel, students nevertheless fill the pews.

http://www.taylor.edu/

P: (800) 882-3456

PRIVATE - CHRISTIAN

STUDENT PROFILE

2,126 undergraduate students

87% of undergrad students are full time

44% male – 56% female

59% of students are from out of state

87% freshman retention rate

77% graduated in 6 years

FACULTY PROFILE

129 full-time faculty

84 part-time faculty

12 to 1 student/faculty ratio

ADMISSIONS

1,716 Total Applicants

1,460 Total Admissions

521 Total Freshman Enrollment

85.08% of applicants admitted

SAT Ranges: CR 490-640, M 490-640, W 490-600

ACT Ranges: C 24-30, M 23-29, E 24-32, W 8-9

TUITION & COSTS

Tuition: $30,030

Fees: $240

Total: $30,270

R&B: $8,497

Room: $4,462

Board: $4,035

Total: $38,767

FINANCIAL

$16,517 avg grant/scholarship amount (need)

$4,840 avg loan amount (need)

UNIVERSITY OF INDIANAPOLIS

INDIANAPOLIS, INDIANA

University of Indianapolis, founded in 1902, is a private liberal arts institution that offers 100+ undergraduate degree programs, 37 master's degree programs, six doctoral programs, and a variety of certificate programs. Personalized attention, experiential learning, and a student-to-faculty ratio of 12:1 are just the beginning of what makes University of Indianapolis unique.

FIRST-YEAR SEMINAR: As part of the liberal arts core, all freshmen at University of Indianapolis are required to choose a First-Year Seminar course, which provides in-depth focus in various disciplines to spark intellectual curiosity while introducing students to academic life.

UNDERGRADUATE RESEARCH: University of Indianapolis actively promotes research and scholarly activity by providing unique, in-depth opportunities for students in a variety of fields. Research at the University is collaborative, allowing students to participate in research groups with fellow classmates and a faculty advisor. Student research at UIndy has even culminated in published research articles in peer-reviewed scientific journals. Most Schools and Colleges within the University also provide financial support for undergraduate student research expenses as well as travel for professional meetings and conferences at which to present their research.

DIVERSITY & GLOBAL LEARNING: University of Indianapolis serves an inclusive student body and promotes cross-cultural and global understanding through its academic curriculum, scholarly lectures and programs, performances, travel and study abroad programs, international student programs, and student organizations. The University's dedication to cultural diversity and international exchange has made the campus a welcoming environment for students from more than 60 nations, and its partnerships around the world provide numerous opportunities for U.S. students to study abroad.

THE WRITING LAB: The Writing Lab aims to produce better writers, teaching writing techniques and providing helpful resources on how to develop a thesis, support the thesis, and provide clear organization for any kind of writing projects. Whether they need help on an essay, research paper, journal article, lab report, or job or graduate school applications. The Writing Lab welcomes writers at all levels who wish to develop confidence in their work and further refine their skills.

SERVICE-LEARNING: The University's Center for Service-Learning and Community Engagement connects students with volunteer opportunities that align with their education and career goals. Service-learning is woven throughout the course curriculum and mutually transforms both the academic landscape as well as the community, resulting in benefits including increased civic engagement, enriched student learning, enhanced sense of purpose, greater feeling of fulfillment, nurtured creativity, and promotion of problem-solving skills and social responsibility.

INTERNSHIPS & CAREER PLACEMENTS: UIndy's Professional Edge Center provides ongoing exposure to working professionals, connecting students and new graduates to internships, employment opportunities, and mentorships. The Center draws from its extensive network of industry professionals, including staff of the Indianapolis Chamber of Commerce, business and professional organizations, and an alumni base of more than 32,0000. From day one, the Professional Edge Center helps students—even those who haven't decided on a major—identify career pathways, interact with business professionals, and develop professional and interpersonal skills. The Professional Edge Center team is organized into sector experts, giving students the opportunity to work one-on-one with a career advisor who is dedicated to their field. This gives students a critical advantage over the competition, arming them with everything from field experience and job interview skills to ways to build their network while discovering more about themselves and the world around them. According to a recent student survey, 94 percent of grads said that the Professional Edge Center gave them a notable advantage in their careers.

UNIVERSITY *of*
INDIANAPOLIS.

http://www.uindy.edu/
P: (317) 788-3368

PRIVATE

STUDENT PROFILE

4,346 undergraduate students

83% of undergrad students are full time

38% male — 62% female

15.09% of students are from out of state

76.7% freshman retention rate

55% graduated in 6 years

FACULTY PROFILE

267 full-time faculty

306 part-time faculty

13 to 1 student/faculty ratio

ADMISSIONS

7,301 Total Applicants

6,291 Total Admissions

995 Total Freshman Enrollment

86.17% of applicants admitted

SAT Ranges: CR 440-550, M 450-570

ACT Ranges: C 20-26, M 19-26, E 18-25

TUITION & COSTS

Tuition: $26,920

Fees: $500

Total: $27,420

R&B: $10,362

Total: $37,782

FINANCIAL

$8,390 avg grant/scholarship amount (need)

$4,565 avg loan amount (need)

BRIAR CLIFF UNIVERSITY

SIOUX CITY, IOWA

Briar Cliff University provides an outstanding education, offering more than 30 majors for undergraduates as well as an array of graduate and online degree-completion programs. Because a majority of Briar Cliff's classes are taught by full-time faculty and not adjunct or graduate instructors, students easily connect with their professors, forming close relationships as they work side-by-side on research projects and build outstanding professional networks.

FIRST-YEAR EXPERIENCES: "Franciscan Life," Briar Cliff's First-Year Seminar, introduces incoming students to the cultural and historical foundations of Briar Cliff University through an exploration of the school's Catholic Franciscan traditions. The course also familiarizes students with the academic expectations, skills, and demands of college life at Briar Cliff.

UNDERGRADUATE RESEARCH: Briar Cliff students have the distinct and rare honor to conduct undergraduate research alongside their professors. Through their collaborative work, students get to bulk up their résumés and graduate school applications as well as form close relationships with valuable professionals to add to their networks. In addition to one of the region's only educational cadaver labs, Briar Cliff is home to fully equipped laboratories that complement students' nursing, kinesiology, chemistry, and biology studies.

COMMON INTELLECTUAL EXPERIENCES: Briar Cliff's liberal arts education blends each student's major studies with a general education program that exposes them to all the intellectual, emotional, and religious foundations one needs to be fully equipped for the world's diverse challenges. The four components of Briar Cliff's General Education include Intellectual Foundations, Competencies, Service, and Franciscan Core. Together, these requirements ensure every student a fully rounded education that perfectly supplements their choice of major.

STUDY ABROAD & TRAVEL OPPORTUNITIES: BCU encourages student participation in both national and international travel experiences. These experiences immerse students in new cultures and stretch them to understand new perspectives and ideas. Recent trips abroad have included France, Italy, Tanzania, Costa Rica, Chile, Guatemala, and Honduras.

WRITING-INTENSIVE COURSES: Briar Cliff has a host of writing courses that develop students' skills as communicators and critical thinkers. Their college experience begins with Introduction to College Writing, which offers many chances to practice essay planning, writing, and revision on a variety of topics. Creative Writing introduces students to the craft of creative written expression in a variety of literary genres and encourages practice as they refine their arti. Communication courses teach students how to write for different media types. At Briar Cliff, students have access to a wide range of writing-intensive courses that all share the common value of helping students think critically and communicate effectively.

MENTORING PROGRAM: Briar Cliff's student mentor program establishes a consistent foundation of support throughout the campus community. It is a symbiotic system of students helping other students, whether that be through academic or emotional support. Peer mentors, course mentors, writing mentors, social mentors, tech mentors, and research mentors ensure that every student has someone to turn to for any help throughout their lives in college.

SERVICE LEARNING: Service is a core component of the Briar Cliff experience. As a foundation of the University's education, service activities help students to develop a lifelong willingness and sense of responsibility to contribute to the communities in which they live. Academic departments individually define the service component for their majors, creating a unique array of opportunities for students to apply their studies to real-world change. The minimum requirements for each service component must include either a 10-hour service project or a service-learning experience.

https://www.briarcliff.edu/

P: (712) 279-5200

PRIVATE - CATHOLIC

STUDENT PROFILE

972 undergraduate students

81% of undergrad students are full time

52% male – 48% female

5% of students are from out of state

79% freshman retention rate

44% graduated in 6 years

FACULTY PROFILE

64 full-time faculty

58 part-time faculty

14 to 1 student/faculty ratio

ADMISSIONS

1,491 Total Applicants

226 Total Admissions

210 Total Freshman Enrollment

15.16% of applicants admitted

SAT Ranges: CR 420-490, M 440-540

ACT Ranges: C 18-24, M 16-24, E 16-23

TUITION & COSTS

Tuition: $28,650

Fees: $1,136

Total: $29,786

R&B: $9,086

Total: $38,872

FINANCIAL

$14,647 avg grant/scholarship amount (need)

$4,837 avg loan amount (need)

BUENA VISTA UNIVERSITY

STORM LAKE, IOWA

**BUENA
VISTA**
UNIVERSITY

Buena Vista University is dedicated to transforming students to succeed in both the academic and professional worlds through a groundbreaking, interdisciplinary liberal arts education.

FIRST-YEAR EXPERIENCE: In order to help students transition smoothly into the college lifestyle, BVU enrolls first-year students into University Seminar, a semester-long course that familiarizes students to both college-level coursework as well as their new peers. University Seminar directs its course materials around globally focused topics. BVU highly values a broad, worldly perspective, and so every student kicks off their time on campus with an engaging curriculum that introduces them to the University's standards. Easing into the rigor of college-level coursework, students complement their orientation experience with peer-building activities as well as a summer reading project. The shared exposure to new friends and new assignments makes each new BVU student feel more at home with others who understand them.

STUDY ABROAD: There are few better ways to express one's intellectual curiosity than by going on an academic adventure to a brand-new part of the world. Through Buena Vista's study abroad program, students are able to travel to their choice of one of twenty countries across six continents. Regardless of their majors, these students are bound to discover something new and valuable, complementing their studies with global perspectives. Students are able to take first-rate classes while abroad, participating in internships, enacting meaningful service projects, and even student teaching. Buena Vista's Study Abroad Coordinators work individually with each student in order to place them in the best possible program to fit their goals.

JANUARY INTERIM: Every spring semester, BVU students have an entire month to delve deeply into a topic of study during the University's January Interim program. Throughout the Interim, students have the chance to travel across the country or around the world for a month-long intensive to have an educational experience unlike any other.

HONORS AND DEAN'S FELLOWS: Students who excel academically do not go unrecognized. Through the Honors Program and Dean's Fellowship Program, BVU's most tenacious students are rewarded for their hard work with both academic and financial advantages such as grant funding for research projects, exclusive courses, and priority course selection. Honors students form close relationships with their professors as they conduct research that spans across multiple semesters. Dean's Fellows students are also honored with travel stipends and funds to pay for graduate school entrance exams and application fees. Students with these honors are often invited to exclusive events both on and off campus, reaping the benefits of their academic achievement with all the best intellectual opportunities.

STORM LAKE, IOWA: Located along the shores of the gorgeous Storm Lake, Buena Vista University welcomes its students into a safe, comfortable campus environment that is full of outlets for fun, adventure, and inspiration. Storm Lake can double as a spot for peaceful reflection as well as a site for incredibly fun outdoor recreation. BVU provides students with paddleboards, canoes, bikes, and more for all the adventure they crave. In addition to the beautiful natural atmosphere of Storm Lake, students can get their fill of recreation through the small yet bustling town right next to campus. Places to shop, eat, and hang out are certainly not limited.

INTERNSHIPS: The center for Career and Personal Development aims to provide students a strong foundation for postgraduate success. The staff is full of resources and connections to set students up with meaningful, hands-on opportunities that build résumé experience and improve their professional proficiency.

---

http://www.bvu.edu/
P: (800) 383-9600

PRIVATE

STUDENT PROFILE

864 undergraduate students

99% of undergrad students are full time

48% male – 52% female

28% of students are from out of state

78% freshman retention rate

50.18% graduated in 6 years

FACULTY PROFILE

76 full-time faculty

30 part-time faculty

10 to 1 student/faculty ratio

ADMISSIONS

1,372 Total Applicants

934 Total Admissions

223 Total Freshman Enrollment

68.08% of applicants admitted

ACT Ranges: C 19-24, M 18-24, E 19-24

TUITION & COSTS

Tuition: $32,210

R&B: $9,304

Total: $41,514

FINANCIAL

$21,958 avg grant/scholarship amount (need)

$5,333 avg loan amount (need)

IOWA

DORDT COLLEGE

SIOUX CENTER, IOWA

Dordt College is a vibrant, Christ-centered learning and living community that challenges students to think, question, and prepare to live out their calling in God's world. Students grow in knowledge and insight from their education in the classroom as well as in the Christian community outside the classroom walls. Faculty at Dordt College care about the students they're teaching and offer a challenging and supportive academic atmosphere.

A CO-CURRICULAR EXPERIENCE: The Dordt College learning experience includes much more than the time students spend in the classroom. The non-curricular aspects of college life play a vital role in students' education. Dordt uses the term "co-curricular" to describe the wide range of activities that develop and enhance what is taught in the curriculum. One such example of co-curricular learning takes place with meaningful service-learning. The College works to foster an attitude of service and loving obedience by planning social and devotional activities as well as community-building and service projects. Such activities are not considered mere additions to the academic task, but a rather critical part of developing Christian insight.

CROSS-CULTURAL EDUCATION: Dordt College is committed to increasing the ways in which classroom learning is enhanced by structured educational experiences outside the classroom. The college has included a cross-cultural component in its Core Program that requires students to explore another culture either through coursework, study abroad, or volunteer service. In addition, Dordt College has encouraged faculty to develop service-learning opportunities, which combine reading and research with planning and executing related service projects.

COMMON CORE: Professors at Dordt College are primarily committed to providing a good education to their students. Faculty are leaders in their fields who genuinely care about students as individuals. Knowing each of them by name and understanding their passions, dreams, and goals. Dordt's Core Program provides a foundational curriculum of history, philosophy, and theology, as well as various communication skills. Other core courses in language and the arts, the natural sciences, and the social sciences provide a broad context for more specialized studies. At the end of students' college careers, they take a capstone course that deals with contemporary issues, helping them find out how their undergraduate studies fit into a larger world context.

A THRIVING CAMPUS COMMUNITY: Dordt students have the opportunity to be involved in a wide variety of roles and activities on campus. Since 90% of students live right on campus, there are many opportunities to participate in activities including music, theatre, mentoring and small groups, worship, and more. Dordt also has opportunities for intercollegiate and recreational athletes, with state of the art indoor and outdoor facilities.

RESIDENCE LIFE: Community is more than a feel-good buzzword at Dordt. On Dordt's residential campus, students live side by side, from first-year students up to seniors. This gives juniors and seniors a chance to help set the tone for campus and become leaders in a wide variety of ways.

SUPPORT SERVICES: There are many support services on campus for students. The Academic Skills Center, available to all students at no cost, provides an unprecedented level of service to students through tutoring and homework help. Faculty and staff at Dordt are all committed to helping students succeed in their college careers, and the Career Development Office has a similar goal: to help students find great internships and employment opportunities both during and after their time at Dordt.

DORDT COLLEGE

http://www.dordt.edu/
P: (800) 343-6738

PRIVATE - CHRISTIAN

STUDENT PROFILE

1,385 undergraduate students

98% of undergrad students are full time

52% male — 48% female

59% of students are from out of state

81% freshman retention rate

68% graduated in 6 years

FACULTY PROFILE

84 full-time faculty

58 part-time faculty

15 to 1 student/faculty ratio

ADMISSIONS

1,342 Total Applicants

937 Total Admissions

365 Total Freshman Enrollment

69.82% of applicants admitted

SAT Ranges: CR 460-650, M 500-650, W 470-620

ACT Ranges: C 22-29, M 22-28, E 21-29

TUITION & COSTS

Tuition: $27,800

Fees: $480

Total: $28,280

R&B: $8,350

Total: $36,630

FINANCIAL

$14,773 avg grant/scholarship amount (total)

$7,274 avg loan amount (total)

DRAKE UNIVERSITY

DES MOINES, IOWA

Drake University is committed to providing an exceptional learning environment that prepares students for meaningful personal lives, professional accomplishments, and responsible global citizenship. The University is distinguished by collaborative learning among students and staff alike.

THE DRAKE CURRICULUM: The Drake Curriculum gives students a solid foundation from which they can individually build both their educational and personal journeys. This curriculum introduces students to a wide variety of ideas and problem-solving skills. It trains students to become critical thinkers who engage in higher-level conceptualization. There are three components to the Drake Curriculum, which include the first-year seminar, areas of inquiry, and a senior capstone.

FIRST-YEAR SEMINAR: First-year seminar classes are designed to engage students with exciting and unique subject matters right at the start of their educational experience. Seminar courses have 19 or fewer students, all of whom will live in the same building as one another. This structure is designed to encourage comfortable participation in class as well as meaningful relationships outside of it.

AREAS OF INQUIRY: As students progress through college, they choose classes that suit and support their majors. No matter the concentration, however, they must also take 1-2 courses within each of Drake's 10 "Areas of Inquiry." These designations, which range from Quantitative Literacy to Critical Thinking, ensure that all students of all majors have the same foundational skill set for high-level thinking and success.

THE SENIOR CAPSTONE: The Senior Capstone is a chance for each student to demonstrate all they have learned over their first three years in college. This culminating capstone requirement is structured differently for every major, playing out in the format of field experience to an individual research project.

STUDY ABROAD: Drake offers its students the option to study abroad as a part of its initiative to prepare all of its students as globally engaged and conscious citizens. The University has programs in over 60 countries, and students have the option to travel throughout a semester, full-year, or summer term.

FACULTY AND RESEARCH: Drake has 289 full-time faculty, 87% of whom hold terminal degrees in their respective fields. Faculty members at Drake are fully dedicated to the growth and development the each student. Drake's professors are not only distinguished scholars in their fields, but also accomplished researchers. And, to make the most of such a privilege, Drake affords its students the possibility to work with their professors on research projects as early as their first year. This collaboration between students and faculty members leads to a learning environment that benefits both parties.

CLUBS AND ORGANIZATIONS: Drake offers its students plenty of opportunities to get involved outside of the classroom. The University encourages all of its students to get take part in extracurriculars, recognizing the social and academic benefits that active involvement can bring them. There are over 160 clubs and organizations to choose from, the interests of which span from media clubs to governing organizations. Students can immerse themselves in the arts by seeing a play or going to an exhibit, or, for those interested in athletics, they may join one of several intramural and club sports teams. Students can also get involved in service-learning projects or participate in the Leadership Development Program.

DES MOINES: Drake is located near the city of Des Moines, affording students a number of social and professional opportunities that extend beyond the campus. Students are encouraged to venture into the city and enjoy the food, shopping, and cultural events that make the city thrive.

---

http://www.drake.edu/
P: (515) 271-2011

PRIVATE

STUDENT PROFILE

3,338 undergraduate students

95% of undergrad students are full time

44% male – 56% female

70% of students are from out of state

88% freshman retention rate

73% graduated in 6 years

FACULTY PROFILE

314 full-time faculty

166 part-time faculty

13 to 1 student/faculty ratio

ADMISSIONS

6,514 Total Applicants

4,356 Total Admissions

803 Total Freshman Enrollment

66.87% of applicants admitted

SAT Ranges: CR 520-670, M 550-690

ACT Ranges: C 24-30, M 24-29, E 24-31

TUITION & COSTS

Tuition: $33,550

Fees: $146

Total: $33,696

R&B: $9,596

Room: $5,150

Board: $4,446

Total: $43,292

FINANCIAL

$18,494 avg grant/scholarship amount (total)

$7,827 avg loan amount (total)

GRINNELL COLLEGE

GRINNELL, IOWA

GRINNELL COLLEGE

At Grinnell, faculty and students love to learn. They value thoughtfulness, and they have fun. Students design their own academic program with a faculty advisor, and Grinnell's residential community encourages students to thrive.

FIRST-YEAR TUTORIAL: First-Year Tutorials (FYT) are introductory seminar courses that explore a variety of topics. In the FYT, students are taught foundational skills like critical thinking, writing, reading, and class discussion. Tutorials also have the unique component of an entertainment budget, which allows students and professors to experience events and culture outside the classroom.

INDIVIDUALLY-ADVISED CURRICULUM: Grinnell students have the unique opportunity to design their own course of study. Aside from requirements within one's major, the only other required course at Grinnell is the First-Year Tutorial. This opens up a lot of doors for students to design an educational experience that creatively suits their needs and interests. Advisors work closely with students in order to help identify each individual's specific talents and weaknesses. Ultimately, advisors help students choose a major that aligns with their goals and abilities.

OFF-CAMPUS STUDY: Off-campus study allows students the opportunity to extend their educational experience beyond Grinnell. There are incredible benefits to participation, and nearly 60% of students choose to engage in some form of study. Students can search for programs based on either geography or theme. Some theme examples include Arts, Media, Music; Gender, Women's Studies, and Sexuality Studies; Global Economics & Regional Development; and Peace & Conflict, Human Rights, and Social Justice.

UNDERGRADUATE RESEARCH: If an undergraduate student chooses to pursue research, it is considered a Mentored Advanced Project. MAPs are student-driven, faculty mentored initiatives that range from papers to portfolios. All MAPs are monitored by faculty, and in some cases, projects are an extension of a professor's existing work. Students can choose to tackle a subject within their area of study or pursue an unrelated topic. Directed research is a little different than a MAP. In a MAP situation, the student takes a leadership role while a faculty member oversees their work. In directed research, students work on a project that has been designed and structured by a faculty member. In this type of working relationship, the student acts as an assistant or apprentice.

INTERNSHIPS: Grinnell's internship programs allow undergraduates to gain hands-on experience in conjunction with their coursework. Students can choose from the academic year program or the summer session. Both are eligible for credit. In the academic year program, students work 14 hours a week while still attending school. In the summer session, students can choose any location—domestic or international—and can pick between part-time and full-time work.

SERVICE-LEARNING AND CIVIC ENGAGEMENT PROGRAM: Service-learning is considered a transformational experience. Not only do students address the needs of the community, but they apply their knowledge to enact a positive change. Grinnell has a longstanding commitment to the service of others and therefore provides students and faculty with several ways to get involved. Curricular opportunities are available as service-learning courses. In such a service-learning class, students spend a portion of their time engaging in course material, class discussion, and reflection. The other portion of time is dedicated to actual, hands-on service in the community. Typically, the kind of service performed is directly related to course material in order to help students bridge the gap between theory and real-world application.

http://www.grinnell.edu/

P: (641) 269-4000

PRIVATE

STUDENT PROFILE

1,705 undergraduate students

98% of undergrad students are full time

45% male – 55% female

74% of students are from out of state

94% freshman retention rate

86% graduated in 6 years

FACULTY PROFILE

211 full-time faculty

55 part-time faculty

9 to 1 student/faculty ratio

ADMISSIONS

6,414 Total Applicants

1,598 Total Admissions

442 Total Freshman Enrollment

24.91% of applicants admitted

SAT Ranges: CR 640-740, M 660-770

ACT Ranges: C 30-33, M 27-33, E 30-34

TUITION & COSTS

Tuition: $46,574

Fees: $416

Total: $46,990

R&B: $11,408

Room: $5,388

Board: $6,020

Total: $58,398

FINANCIAL

$30,448 avg grant/scholarship amount (total)

$4,538 avg loan amount (total)

LUTHER COLLEGE

DECORAH, IOWA

Luther's education speaks for itself. Students have ample opportunities to conduct research with faculty members, participate in extensive study abroad programs, engage in internships, and contribute to highly successful athletic teams and music ensembles.

INTEREST MEETS OPPORTUNITY: Luther College offers more than sixty majors, pre-professional programs, and certificate programs. The most popular include biology, education, psychology, music, and such business-related fields as business administration/management, economics, and accounting.

A WELL-ROUNDED CURRICULUM FOR ALL: Through the Paideia Program, all LC students are required to take three interdisciplinary courses: a common two-semester sequence for first-year students and a variety of one-semester courses from which juniors and seniors may choose. Paideia is ancient Greek for "education," which implies both formal and informal learning. These courses include common readings, lectures, and small group discussions that encourage strong bonds between students and their professors.

STUDY ABROAD: LC students take full advantage of off-campus and experiential learning opportunities. Education majors may observe in actual classrooms as early as their freshman year, while more advanced students can observe school settings at international locations. With access over twenty programs around the world in countries such as Guatemala, China, Japan, Australia, and Norway, about 75% of all LC students study abroad at least once, whether they do so for a full academic year, a semester, or a one-month January term. All foreign language majors are required to take part in an intensive language immersion program for at least one semester abroad.

ACADEMIC SUPPORT: LC's Student Academic Support Center (SASC) offers a myriad of services to students, providing them with tools to reach graduation. The services offered include tutoring, learning-skills workshops, and supervised study group sessions.

STICKING TO ITS ROOTS: As a college founded by Norwegian settlers, LC honors its history by offering a Scandinavian studies major. Part of the modern languages and literature department, the Scandinavian studies major gives students the opportunity to learn the Norwegian language while studying Scandinavian culture, history, and economics. This unique program is rich with an unmatched curriculum that takes an interdisciplinary approach to understanding the complexities of Northern Europe and its relationship to the broader world.

A BEAUTIFUL CAMPUS IS JUST THE BEGINNING: LC's beautiful campus, designed by one of the nation's greatest landscape architects, inspires a thriving community in which students make use of great facilities while participating in over 140 organizations and activities. LC embraces diversity and challenges its students to learn in community, discern their callings, and serve the common good with distinction. Students, faculty, and staff work together for the development of a living and learning environment that encourages caring relationships and an understanding of the wholeness of life.

SUSTAINABILITY: LC students are environmentally conscious. The College's new environmental studies major has raised awareness about and brought attention to environmental issues on campus, leading to the planting of gardens on campus that provide fresh produce for the dining halls.

HEALTHCARE FOR THE COMMUNITY: Expressing interest in the local community beyond the campus, LC students, faculty, and staff have started a free clinic to support the area's need for lower-cost healthcare. The clinic provides unique opportunities for pre-med, nursing, and language students to serve and learn at the same time.

INTERNSHIPS: Internships arranged by the LC Career Center are readily available to help students gain professional experience in the Upper Midwest as well as across the country and around the globe. For example, Luther's Washington Semester has placed interns in such high-profile locations as the Smithsonian Institution, the White House, and the United States Senate.

---

http://www.luther.edu/
P: (800) 458-8437

PRIVATE

STUDENT PROFILE

2,337 undergraduate students

99% of undergrad students are full time

45% male – 55% female

66% of students are from out of state

85% freshman retention rate

77% graduated in 6 years

FACULTY PROFILE

182 full-time faculty

62 part-time faculty

12 to 1 student/faculty ratio

ADMISSIONS

3,896 Total Applicants

2,606 Total Admissions

624 Total Freshman Enrollment

66.89% of applicants admitted

SAT Ranges: CR 495-625, M 475-640, W 480-610

ACT Ranges: C 23-29, M 22-28, E 22-30

TUITION & COSTS

Tuition: $38,940

Fees: $250

Total: $39,190

R&B: $7,920

Room: $3,570

Board: $4,350

Total: $47,110

FINANCIAL

$24,650 avg grant/scholarship amount (total)

$8,343 avg loan amount (total)

NORTHWESTERN COLLEGE

ORANGE CITY, IOWA

At Northwestern College, strong academics and a firm Christian faith mean big opportunities to learn and grow. Students benefit from close relationships—with supportive faculty mentors who are leading Christian scholars as well as with peers who become lifelong friends. Highly ranked study abroad programs, extensive internship opportunities, and impactful research experiences with professors help expand students' learning and prepare them for their careers. Faith is integrated into the whole Northwestern experience, so students are empowered to follow Christ and pursue God's redeeming work in the world.

NORTHWESTERN CORE: The Northwestern Core features 14 to 16 credits of courses that all NWC students take. These include a First-Year Seminar that provides an introduction to the Christian liberal arts, 8 credits of classes that focus on the Christian story and tradition; and other courses the cover such learning themes as belief and reason, cross-cultural engagement, historical perspectives, and self and society. A culminating senior-year seminar ensures that students are prepared to apply what they've learned—both in their major and in Northwestern Core classes—to their future career and life of service and social responsibility.

CHAPEL AND CHRISTIAN FORMATION: Chapel services, held twice a week, bring the campus community together to learn about God, the world, and how to make a difference in it. Nationally known speakers such as Hugh Halter, Jerry Sittser, and Sarah Thebarge challenge students, as do area Christian leaders, faculty and staff, and other students. The student-led Sunday Night Praise & Worship service is a popular way to start a new week. In the dorms and apartments, nearly 500 students meet in small discipleship groups on a weekly basis to pray, study the Bible, and talk about how their faith integrates with what they're learning.

RESEARCH: Northwestern students have many opportunities to pursue research projects that lead to presentations at conferences and act as great preparatory work for graduate school. Many of these are even collaborative projects with professors. Through a grant from the Howard Hughes Medical Institute, first- and second-year biology students have the unique opportunity to conduct research on phages, which are viruses that infect bacteria. Outstanding student academic and creative work is displayed at Northwestern's annual Celebration of Research. In 2017, 67 students presented posters of their research to faculty, students, Board of Trustees members, and area residents.

SERVICE-LEARNING: Service-learning opportunities enable Northwestern students to put what they're learning into practice through serving God and others. Examples include public relations students preparing advertising materials for local businesses, social work majors surveying housing needs in Orange City, accounting students helping people file their taxes, kinesiology students developing personal health and fitness plans for women at a transitional housing facility, and English majors presenting book-talk presentations to high school freshmen.

FEELS LIKE HOME: Northwestern is known to be a place where students experience belonging and togetherness. In fact, 94% of NWC freshmen say they feel like they've already found a home in their first semester of college. 90% of students live on campus, and many stay around on the weekends; the community is bustling with numerous student-planned events, opportunities to cheer on peers at games and performing arts events, and the spontaneous fun that happens when everyone's looking for a study break. Student resident assistants and professional resident directors, each of whom are committed Christians, staff every wing and hall, so students are known, cared for, and challenged to be the best they can be. Unlike other colleges, where freshmen-only dorms are the norm, at Northwestern junior and senior leaders choose to stay in the residence halls to befriend and mentor underclassmen.

---

http://www.nwciowa.edu/

P: (712) 707-7130

PRIVATE - CHRISTIAN

STUDENT PROFILE

1,076 undergraduate students

97% of undergrad students are full-time

44% male – 56% female

52% of students are from out of state

82% freshman retention rate

64% graduated in 6 years

FACULTY PROFILE

82 full-time faculty

59 part-time faculty

11 to 1 student-to-faculty ratio

ADMISSIONS

2,199 Total Applicants

1,441 Total Admissions

283 Total Freshman Enrollment

65.53% of applicants admitted

SAT Ranges: CR 440-560, M 460-610

ACT Ranges: C 21-28, M 20-27, E 21-28

TUITION & COSTS

Tuition: $30,000

Fees: $200

Total: $30,200

R&B: $9,000

Total: $39,200

FINANCIAL

$7,373 avg grant/scholarship amount (need)

$5,110 avg loan amount (need)

UNIVERSITY OF DUBUQUE

DUBUQUE, IOWA

The University of Dubuque is a private University affiliated with the Presbyterian Church (U.S.A.). It was founded in 1852 by Dutch immigrant Adrian Van Vliet to educate German-speaking ministers who could communicate with incoming immigrants. In 1902, new programs emerged to form what is now the University of Dubuque. The University has since maintained a continual expansion in order to adapt to the world's ever-changing social, economic, and academic challenges.

FIRST-YEAR EXPERIENCE: The University of Dubuque's First-Year Experience eases students' transitions into collegiate academics and expectations. The first-year curriculum orients students to the rigor of upper-level coursework, all while building a community of new friends by way of the experiences they share with their peers. With the support of an enthusiastic community, new UD students are challenged to further build upon their gifts through academic inquiry, their social interactions, and spiritual exploration as they discover their place within a diverse campus community. To kick off the First-Year Experience, the Bridge Program is designed to assist new students who need additional assistance in transitioning to college life. This program bolsters students' success with study-skills classes, bi-weekly study labs, online tutoring, and peer mentoring.

THE DIAMOND EDUCATION MODEL: The University of Dubuque recently developed Diamond, an education model that focuses all classroom learning around four key principles: Academics, Stewardship, Vocation, and Community and Character. These features set the standards for committed faculty and staff involvement, exciting and relevant course content, and inspirational spiritual guidance. Diamond helps students reach their full potential by promoting an environment that is student centered and individually focused. Students are prepared to manage change by building confidence, developing flexibility, and thinking critically.

CAMPUS LIFE: The University of Dubuque's campus is home to approximately 2,300 students from 43 states and 22 countries. Its faculty and staff strive to create a learning environment that is just as welcoming as it is challenging. Students have the opportunity to participate in more than 60 student organizations and clubs, approximately 25 intramural sports, and 23 varsity athletic teams. They may also take on an ample selection of volunteer opportunities and attend multiple Chapel services during the week.

SPECIAL PROGRAMS AND OPPORTUNITIES: UD students are challenged with special programs that enrich, enhance, and extend their academic experiences. A few of the special opportunities that students have include single-course, experiential study throughout the abbreviated January Term (J-Term), long- and short-term study abroad, and the prestigious Scholar-Leader Honors Program. Through this Honors Program, driven students are pushed to sharpen their communication and leadership skills, training them to develop attributes that are highly valued in the professional world.

SMALL TOWN SETTING. BIG TOWN FEEL.: Nestled along the scenic Mississippi River, Dubuque is home to the National Mississippi River Museum & Aquarium, the Dubuque Museum of Art, a variety of shops and restaurants, event venues, and more. The city of nearly 60,000 boasts miles of trails for walking, hiking, biking, and many Mississippi waterway and byway activities.

RESEARCH FELLOWSHIPS: The Joseph and Linda Chlapaty Summer Research Fellowship and Butler Fellowship are two examples of the research opportunities available to UD students. These fellowships help prepare undergraduate students for their postgraduate pursuits, no matter their discipline of study. Each year, over 30 upperclassmen are awarded a fellowship to conduct research over the course of a summer. The University of Dubuque works hard to ensure that these awards cover the costs of research supplies and travel, giving students free reign to explore and inquire within their area of study.

UNIVERSITY *of* DUBUQUE
THE DIAMOND UNIVERSITY

https://www.dbq.edu/
P: (800) 722-5583

PRIVATE

STUDENT PROFILE

1,921 undergraduate students

87% of undergrad students are full time

62% male — 38% female

57% of students are from out of state

65% freshman retention rate

42% graduated in 6 years

FACULTY PROFILE

94 full-time faculty

283 part-time faculty

15 to 1 student/faculty ratio

ADMISSIONS

1,664 Total Applicants

1,258 Total Admissions

443 Total Freshman Enrollment

75.6% of applicants admitted

SAT Ranges: CR 380 510, M 360-490

ACT Ranges: C 17-22, M 16-23, E 15-22

TUITION & COSTS

Tuition: $27,400

Fees: $1,300

Total: $28,700

R&B: $9,350

Total: $38,050

FINANCIAL

$17,871 avg grant/scholarship amount (need)

$7,298 avg loan amount (need)

IOWA

UNIVERSITY OF NORTHERN IOWA

CEDAR FALLS, IOWA

UNI is nationally recognized for its high educational standards as well as its various avenues for students to live and learn together. It's clear that UNI students, faculty, staff, and alumni all take tremendous pride in their outstanding University. The last 140 years have been full of school-wide successes, and UNI looks forward to many more.

FIRST-YEAR CORNERSTONE: UNI's First-Year Cornerstone course allows students to spend a full year under the consistent instruction of the same professor while satisfying two Liberal Arts Core requirements in tandem. This course integrates topics of writing, speaking, civility, and student success within a vibrant classroom community. Students are also accompanied by a peer teaching assistant who attends the course with them, available to mentor and answer questions about the college experience.

STUDENT-FACULTY RESEARCH: Prospective college students are looking for a university at which they can be taught by knowledgeable and experienced faculty. At UNI, not only are 99 percent of classes taught by actual faculty members, but professors also invite many of their students to work alongside them in cutting-edge and groundbreaking research.

STUDY ABROAD: A student's UNI experience extends far beyond the campus border—really far—to places like China, Ireland, Costa Rica, and 60 other countries. UNI has 100 study abroad programs that last anywhere from two weeks to one year, and students can start their journey as early as the second semester of their freshman year.

SERVICE ABROAD: Students can take part in a unique summer service-learning experience through UNI's Camp Adventure Child and Youth Services program. Each year, Camp Adventure recruits, interviews, and trains nearly 1,000 students from universities across the country to serve as counselors at American military bases, British installations, and embassies throughout the world. Lives are changed, global awareness is increased, and leadership and human-relations skills are improved.

THE CENTER FOR EXCELLENCE IN TEACHING: The Center for Excellence in Teaching and Learning (CETL) at UNI is a great resource for faculty to make sure their classes are engaging. The center seeks to explore and enhance the practice of teaching and the culture of learning at UNI, offering opportunities for conversation to cultivate and value the diversity of possible teaching styles. Available to support the entire campus teaching community, the CETL promotes research-based pedagogies and practices that encourage student engagement and success.

CEDAR FALLS: UNI is located in Cedar Falls, a student-friendly town with just fewer than 40,000 people. The community frequently welcomes new restaurants, coffee shops, retail stores, and clubs. Most are a few blocks from campus or just a short drive away. The Cedar Falls area also has more than 100 miles of nature trails, a water park, and golf courses—everything a student needs for year-round fun. Cedar Falls is also within a few hours' drive of Des Moines, Chicago, Minneapolis, Kansas City, and St. Louis. This makes big-city internships and student-teaching experiences convenient and close by.

HEALTHY LIFESTYLES: Cedar Falls was recently named a Certified Blue Zones community®, recognized for its commitment to promoting a healthy, balanced lifestyle. People on and off campus are eating better, being more active, connecting with one another, and finding a greater sense of purpose. Together, their efforts to enrich their health create an even stronger bond between Cedar Falls and UNI.

CAPSTONE COURSES: College graduates should enter the world as educated citizens, so UNI's capstone courses push students to deal with complex issues from multidisciplinary perspectives. The program is designed to challenge seniors to link theory and practice through complex thought and problem solving. Their culminating courses engage them to work across a variety of different fields and develop skills associated with self-directed, lifelong learning..

http://www.uni.edu/

P: (319) 273-2311

PUBLIC

STUDENT PROFILE

10,169 undergraduate students

90% of undergrad students are full time

43% male – 57% female

8% of students are from out of state

80% freshman retention rate

68% graduated in 6 years

FACULTY PROFILE

631 full-time faculty

158 part-time faculty

17 to 1 student/faculty ratio

ADMISSIONS

5,394 Total Applicants

4,290 Total Admissions

1,916 Total Freshman Enrollment

79.53% of applicants admitted

SAT Ranges: CR 410-570, M 470-610, W 360-550

ACT Ranges: C 20-25, M 18-25, E 19-25, W 6-8

TUITION & COSTS

Tuition: (In) $6,648 (Out) $16,836

Fees: $1,169

Total: (In) $7,817 (Out) $18,005

R&B: $8,320

Room: $4,176

Board: $4,144

Total: (In) $16,137 (Out) $26,325

FINANCIAL

$4,905 avg grant/scholarship amount (total)

$5,696 avg loan amount (total)

BAKER UNIVERSITY

BALDWIN CITY, KANSAS

Baker University's academic reputation is built on its liberal arts tradition. Its professors challenge students while giving them the tools to rise to new heights. Baker offers more than 40 areas of study and encourages students to explore unique educational experiences through internships, study abroad, and research. With more than 75 student activities and organizations from which to choose, students have no trouble finding their niche. At Baker, every person matters and everyone is connected. Students either learn together, play together, or live together—in many cases, it's all three.

STUDY ABROAD: Baker offers a full range of study abroad options worldwide in almost any discipline. The most popular international experience is that of England's Harlaxton College, which has been recognized as one of the nation's top study abroad programs.

INTERNSHIPS: Nothing puts knowledge to the test like real-world experience, so professors and the staff at Career Services work diligently to help students land rewarding internships. Often times, these internships can lead full-time job offers after graduation. Baker students have interned with the FBI, Polygram Records, Sprint, Hallmark, NASCAR, PriceWaterhouseCoopers, and the U.S. Senate.

SERVICE-LEARNING: Through community service, Baker students develop their leadership skills while helping to create meaningful social change. Student-organized projects link the Big Event and the Martin Luther King, Jr. Day of Service reach beyond the campus and connect with such agencies as Habitat for Humanity and Harvesters Community Food Network. The fraternities and sororities on campus are also well known for their philanthropic efforts.

ORIGINAL RESEARCH: In classes of a dozen students or fewer, students get to work closely with professors, producing original research to present at regional, national, and even international conferences. Not only do student researchers discover fascinating data within their own fields, but they also get the chance to share the findings to other students, enlightening the Baker community with their scholarly contributions.

DEVELOPING LEADERS: Members of Mungano, Baker University's student-run diversity organization, regularly attend the Big XII Conference on Black Student Government. At this event, participants gain the tools and knowledge to become successful leaders for their organizations and communities. This emphasis on diversity works to build students' confidence for their lives beyond college, empowering them to succeed in fields that have a history of exclusion and marginalization.

MENTORING PARTNERSHIPS: The parMentor organization is a long-standing tradition that pairs the University's best and brightest with Baker alumni mentors. Board of Trustees members, alumni, and local business and community leaders are paired with students to help them develop and work toward their future careers.

AWARD-WINNING NEWSPAPER: In the past decade, the Baker Orange, the University's weekly student-run newspaper, has repeatedly received high distinctions from the Associated Collegiate Press, Kansas Associated Collegiate Press, and Society of Professional Journalists. Having been recognized with two Pacemaker nominates (one for the print edition and one for the Orange online), the Orange has earned its place in the ACP Hall of Fame. Several Baker Orange staff members also have earned the distinction of KACP journalist of the year.

SOCIAL JUSTICE AND SERVICE IN HAITI: An associate professor of sociology recently took 10 students to Haiti for 12 days as part of a Social Justice and Service in Haiti interterm class. The students worked on restoring earthquake damage, helped build a school, taught English and computer literacy, and worked with orphans. Such life-changing service is more than common at Baker, and professors and students are always making strong efforts to pursue social justice and community wellness.

http://www.bakeru.edu/
P: (800) 873-4282

PRIVATE

STUDENT PROFILE

847 undergraduate students

58% of undergrad students are full-time

45% male – 55% female

33% of students are from out of state

80% freshman retention rate

54% graduated in 6 years

FACULTY PROFILE

59 full-time faculty

26 part-time faculty

12 to 1 student-to-faculty ratio

ADMISSIONS

899 Total Applicants

699 Total Admissions

238 Total Freshman Enrollment

77.75% of applicants admitted

ACT Ranges: C 20-25

TUITION & COSTS

Tuition: $27,600

Fees: $350

Total: $27,950

R&B: $8,230

Total: $36,180

FINANCIAL

$18,673 avg grant/scholarship amount (total)

$7,206 avg loan amount (total)

BETHEL COLLEGE

NORTH NEWTON, KANSAS

Bethel College (BC) is a private, coeducational, four-year liberal arts college affiliated with Mennonite Church USA. Bethel sets a goal to integrate faith and learning while opening up the experience for internships, undergraduate research, study abroad, and other hands-on opportunities. With only about 500 students, BC offers a student-centered education.

A MISSION OF EXCELLENCE: Bethel's mission is "to be a diverse community of learners committed to searching for authentic faith and academic achievement, providing rigorous instruction in the liberal arts and selected professional areas, and inspiring intellectual, cultural, and spiritual leaders for church and society." The College offers 17 degrees in the arts and sciences, the most popular of which are education, business, and nursing. The low student-to-faculty ratio of nine-to-one and small average class size of 14 mean that professors work closely with their students to ensure their learning, growth, and development.

CORE CURRICULUM: BC's academic curriculum is focused on helping students develop their intellectual, cultural, and spiritual leadership for the church and society. The General Education program provides a broad understanding of the social and natural world through the perspective of the liberal arts and sciences, helping students develop basic capacities in essential academic skills. Integrated into the General Education, biblical and religious studies courses enhance students' ethical perspectives while merging their intellectual and spiritual values. BC students develop authentic, meaningful relationships with any and all of God's children, enhancing their ability to make mature and reflective moral commitments.

CAMPUS MINISTRIES: Spiritual life activities include Bible study groups, praise and worship services, hymn sings, and weekly chapel services. Bethel's new Agape House, dedicated to campus ministries, provides a homey atmosphere for numerous spiritual life activities. In addition, experiences on the field, in the lab, on the stage, or in the chapel prepare BC students to reason clearly in new situations. It is a Bethel student standard to be able to communicate with precision and persuasion, even in completely unfamiliar situations.

SERVICE-LEARNING: Service-learning is highly encouraged on the Bethel campus, and with access to scholarships that are directed toward service, students are able to direct their entire focus to compassionate action. As more than passive spectators, BC students develop a strong sense of social responsibility while gaining experience in community support. BC emphasizes a true concern for the less fortunate, focusing, in addition, on the pursuit of peace and justice. Through their experiences, Bethel College students build practical peacemaking and conflict-resolution skills, communicating successfully with others of different backgrounds to create solutions amid societal conflict. BC students also strive to live in harmony with the natural world, caring for God's creations and working to reduce its exploitation. Bethel College students learn to act as environmentally careful citizens through an understanding of how their choices influence the environment on campus, in the community, and throughout the world.

A WELCOMING COMMUNITY: Though Mennonites represent the largest single denomination at Bethel, more than half of BC students come from non-Mennonite backgrounds. BC students welcome and engage people who identify differently, gaining a wealth of knowledge and perspective that enriches their personal growth. They are prepared for life with a deepened appreciation for the human experience as they confront a diverse global community.

STUDY ABROAD: BC students can choose to study abroad at 19 colleges and universities in such countries as France, Germany, Spain, England, China, Japan, India, Ecuador, Mexico, Costa Rica, Australia, Austria, and Northern Ireland. Most notable is the student exchange program with the university in Wuppertal, Germany, a partnership that dates back more than 50 years.

---

http://www.bethelks.edu/
P: (316) 283-2500

PRIVATE - CHRISTIAN

STUDENT PROFILE

483 undergraduate students

97% of undergrad students are full time

49% male — 51% female

46% of students are from out of state

63% freshman retention rate

58% graduated in 6 years

FACULTY PROFILE

37 full-time faculty

38 part-time faculty

10 to 1 student/faculty ratio

ADMISSIONS

833 Total Applicants

409 Total Admissions

110 Total Freshman Enrollment

49.10% of applicants admitted

SAT Ranges: CR 380-435, M 425-475, W 340-440

ACT Ranges: C 19-25, M 17-24, E 17-25

TUITION & COSTS

Tuition: $24,200
R&B: $7,760
Room: $3,940
Board: $3,820
Total: $31,960

FINANCIAL

$16,369 avg grant/scholarship amount (total)

$5,848 avg loan amount (total)

EMPORIA STATE UNIVERSITY

EMPORIA, KANSAS

EMPORIA STATE
U N I V E R S I T Y.

Since its founding in 1863, Emporia State has been "preparing students for lifelong learning, rewarding careers, and adaptive leadership." The University provides high-impact, real-world learning opportunities, internships, and research projects promote rewarding collaboration between students and their professors.

HONORS COLLEGE FIRST-YEAR SEMINAR: The Honors College's first-year seminar is optional for any student but a critical part of the Honors College curriculum. The course enriches the overall first-year experience while preparing Honors students for success in their program's rigorous coursework. It integrates adaptive leadership principles that give students the skills to mobilize others and encourage their peers to take on challenges in relationships, communities, the nation, and the world.

UNDERGRADUATE RESEARCH: At Emporia State, students don't have to wait to perform research alongside a professor. One example of the research opportunities available as Emporia is the ESU Summer Undergraduate Research Program (ESURP), which supports student/teacher research projects in all disciplines. In 2017, 15 projects were funded in biochemistry/molecular biology, social sciences, earth science, biology, mathematics, business administration, international business, marketing, secondary social science education, Spanish and English, political science, and history. The program includes grants up to $7,000 and is supported by the Kansas IDeA Network of Biomedical Research Excellence, the ESU Honors College, ESU Research and Grants Center, Office of the Provost, College of Liberal Arts & Sciences, School of Business, and The Teachers College. Such widespread support makes innovation more than common at ESU.

STUDY ABROAD: Students at Emporia State have many options to study abroad, the choices of which range from over 60 countries for year-, semesters-, or shorter-length, faculty-sponsored trips. Study abroad programs include student teaching opportunities in Paraguay, field study in England, applied sociology and service-learning in Uganda, a Japanese Language immerse course, and more!

DEVELOPING TOMORROW'S LEADERS TODAY: Emporia State works closely with the Kansas Leadership Center to incorporate leadership practices into the curricula campus-wide. The School of Business takes the mission one step further through the Koch Center for Leadership and Ethics, which aims to engage the ESU community in an ongoing discussion of ethical leadership both in their personal lives and the workplace.

E-EXPERIENCE: ESU offers a peer-led summer experience for incoming freshmen, giving them an early introduction to college life. During the two-day, one-night experience, students live in the residence halls, explore the campus and the Emporia community, and develop relationships with other students, both new and returning.

PHILANTHROPIC SPIRIT: ESU students are serious about giving back to the Emporia community, having enacted 17,695 service hours in the recent academic year. Service projects range from packing food bags for schoolchildren in food-insecure homes to painting a mural at a local law enforcement agency.

MAIN STREET FESTIVALS: ESU has a strong partnership with Emporia Main Street. Each August, Emporia Main Street organizes the Welcome Back Students Block Party, which features games, prizes, food, and activities for students and the broader community. Other festivals occur during the year, including a Cinco De Mayo celebration of Hispanic heritage; The Glass Blown Open, the largest disc golf tournament in the world; and the Dirty Kanza 200, a 200-mile bike gravel race through the Flint Hills of Kansas. Each of these events end in a block party, held only steps from ESU.

https://www.emporia.edu/
P: (877) 468-6378

PUBLIC

STUDENT PROFILE

3,578 undergraduate students

94% of undergrad students are full time

38% male – 62% female

10% of students are from out of state

71% freshman retention rate

44% graduated in 6 years

FACULTY PROFILE

252 full-time faculty

23 part-time faculty

18 to 1 student/faculty ratio

ADMISSIONS

1,702 Total Applicants

1,488 Total Admissions

665 Total Freshman Enrollment

87.43% of applicants admitted

ACT Ranges: C 19-25, M 18-25, E 18-25

TUITION & COSTS

Tuition: (In) $4,893 (Out) $18,106

Fees: $1,286

Total: (In) $6,179 (Out) $19,392

R&B: $8,391

Room: $4,836

Board: $3,555

Total: (In) $14,570 (Out) $27,783

FINANCIAL

$5,870 avg grant/scholarship amount (need)

$6,250 avg loan amount (need)

FRIENDS UNIVERSITY

WICHITA, KANSAS

Friends University, a Christian university of Quaker heritage, equips students to honor God and serve others by integrating their intellectual, spiritual, and professional lives.

STUDY ABROAD: Friends students have the chance to take their education on the road with dozens of study abroad opportunities throughout the year, allowing them the chance to dig deep and embrace their sense of adventure. Both undergraduate and graduate opportunities are available in such locations as Mexico, China, Cuba, Africa, Europe, and South America. These may range from a few days to several weeks with experiences that include setting up computer systems for third-world hospitals, performing jazz music in Cuba, or discussing spirituality in Brazil.

COMMON INTELLECTUAL EXPERIENCE: All students complete a general education program that builds their essential skills and prepares them for a diverse and constantly changing work environment. The courses provide a strong foundation for future coursework and develop skills in such areas as critical thinking, analysis, verbal and written communication, and peer collaboration.

COLLABORATIVE ASSIGNMENTS AND PROJECTS: Friends University students have many opportunities to partner with outside organizations on assignments and projects. Computer Science students obtain real-life experience by building data-based systems for nonprofit organizations and local businesses. Graphic arts students design logos and communication materials for local organizations, while marketing students develop and implement marketing plans that give them hands-on experience working with external clients.

RESEARCH AND SPECIAL STUDY OPPORTUNITIES: Students have opportunities to pursue research and take short-term learning trips with faculty members in various departments. Sociology students have worked with faculty to conduct research for Big Brothers and Big Sisters. Psychology students regularly present research they have conducted at several conferences throughout the academic year. Students from a Marine Ecology class have traveled to the Gulf of Mexico to study beach organisms, and General Ecology class students have traveled to the Missouri Ozarks to learn about caves and cave animals.

FRIENDS EXPERIENCE: The "Friends Experience" seminar course helps first-year and new transfer students learn how to be successful in their new lives on campus, both socially and academically. It connects students with campus resources and provides them with information on topics such as academic success skills, four-year graduation plans, managing financial matters, and developing positive relationships.

A BEAUTIFUL CAMPUS: Walking onto the Friends University campus in Wichita, students notice lush gardens, scents of flowers and freshly cut grass, beautiful and well-maintained buildings, and plenty of woodland creatures that skitter throughout centuries-old trees. But Friends University is so much more than just a pretty face. It's a place where tradition flourishes even more persistently than the blooms that decorate Rose Window Plaza. Homecoming, the spring Cherry Carnival, and the Christmas clock-tower lighting are just a few of the age-old traditions that keep the Friends University community thriving and connected throughout the years.

CAPSTONE COURSES AND PROJECTS: Many majors offer a final capstone course or project that requires students to integrate the knowledge and skills they have learned throughout their studies into one complete product. These courses and projects help prepare and advance students further toward employment. Examples include: contributions to a senior art exhibition in the community; computer science work with real-life clients for data-related projects; forensic practice in real cases and mock trials; and student teaching experiences within an actual school district. Nicole Ensminger, a 2014 graduate of the Master of Health Care Leadership degree program, used her capstone project to establish protocols that hospitals could use to identify victims of human trafficking. As a result, she was put in charge of this new program at Via Christi Health. Her protocols are even being implemented in other hospitals across the nation.

http://www.friends.edu/
P: (316) 295-5100

PRIVATE - CHRISTIAN

STUDENT PROFILE

1,266 undergraduate students

81% of undergrad students are full time

48% male – 52% female

30% of students are from out of state

64% freshman retention rate

43.6% graduated in 6 years

FACULTY PROFILE

68 full-time faculty

177 part-time faculty

11.4 to 1 student/faculty ratio

ADMISSIONS

713 Total Applicants

387 Total Admissions

163 Total Freshman Enrollment

54.28% of applicants admitted

SAT Ranges: CR 410-460, M 400-530

ACT Ranges: C 18-24, M 17-24, E 18-24

TUITION & COSTS

Tuition: $25,650

Fees: $180

Total: $25,830

R&B: $7,590

Room: $3,680

Board: $3,910

Total: $33,420

FINANCIAL

$8,273 avg grant/scholarship amount (need)

$4,178 avg loan amount (need)

KANSAS WESLEYAN UNIVERSITY

SALINA, KANSAS

At Kansas Wesleyan University, students learn in a small, vibrant, and caring environment that nurtures academic, spiritual, moral, and social growth. Students can pursue both their academic and personal interests. This "Power of AND" accentuates the Kansas Wesleyan's emphasis on learning outside the classroom.

THE WESLEYAN EXPERIENCE: First-year students participate in a Wesleyan Experience course, a dynamic and interactive learning experience that is designed to promote social interaction both in and out of the classroom. They learn and apply new skills that help ensure their academic success, explore the history and traditions of KWU, and establish important relationships with the faculty and staff.

THE WESLEYAN JOURNEY: It is critical for today's college students to have a global perspective, but KWU understands that studying abroad for a full semester is not an option for all students. Because of this, every academically qualifying student who has been at KWU for four semesters can get academic credit while participating in a service-learning course for free or at a low cost. These Wesleyan Journeys, take place during breaks in such places as Costa Rica, Germany, Florida, and New York City.

RESEARCH EXPERIENCES: Research experiences enhance learning for the more than 50% of KWU students who are pursuing degrees in science-based fields. An increasing number of the University's students are even attaining competitive placements in National Science Foundation-funded Research Experiences for Undergraduates (REU). Their trailblazing projects include developing a new methodology for searching encrypted data, building a molecule to selectively target cancer cells, and creating a simulated reality that is controlled by hand motions.

CAMPUS MINISTRIES: The Campus Ministries team is committed to awakening and equipping students for Christ through student-driven community, discipleship, and local-to-global service. The weekly "Tuesday Night Alive" programs are some of the most highly attended events on campus. Their student-centered, student-led service includes upbeat music, dancing, and guest speakers from the community. The Salina University United Methodist Churches, as well as the thriving campus community, traditionally welcome students back to school each year with a "Worship on the Lawn Service" on the quad.

KWU CARES: KWU is invested in helping students achieve their best. KWU Cares is a committee of caring administrators and faculty members that supports the academic and personal well-being of students. If students are underachieving in the classroom, not attending class, or having personal concerns, KWU Cares is ready and available to provide solutions to help get them back on track.

PROFESSIONAL CONNECTIONS: Kansas Wesleyan University has been an integral part of the Salina community for 130 years. Partnerships with local businesses, agencies, and organizations provide unique experiences for students within any of the more than 40 innovative programs. Guest lecturers in business classes include experts and entrepreneurs who lead national and global companies located in Salina (Philips Lighting, Schwan's/Tony's Pizza, Great Plains Manufacturing). In addition, the University hosts numerous speakers throughout the year, highlighted by a Media Reflections series and an Intersections program. Speakers have included such guests as Cheryl Brown Henderson (of the landmark Brown vs. Board of Education court case) and Jane Elliott (who performed the famous Blue Eyes/Brown Eyes experiment).

http://www.kwu.edu/

P: (785) 827-5541

PRIVATE - CHRISTIAN

STUDENT PROFILE

665 undergraduate students

93% of undergrad students are full time

52% male – 48% female

52.7% of students are from out of state

63.12% freshman retention rate

41% graduated in 6 years

FACULTY PROFILE

41 full-time faculty

79 part-time faculty

14 to 1 student/faculty ratio

ADMISSIONS

818 Total Applicants

504 Total Admissions

160 Total Freshman Enrollment

61.61% of applicants admitted

SAT Ranges: CR 430-520, M 480-550

ACT Ranges: C 20-24, M 18-24, E 18-24

TUITION & COSTS

Tuition: $28,000

R&B: $8,600

Room: $3,200

Board: $5,400

Total: $36,600

FINANCIAL

$8,978 avg grant/scholarship amount (need)

$4,608 avg loan amount (need)

OTTAWA UNIVERSITY

OTTAWA, KANSAS

Ottawa University is student-centered, value-priced, and technology-enabled. From its founding in 1865 in Ottawa, Kansas, Ottawa University has grown to an institution that serves approximately 5,000 students through a residential campus in Ottawa, a new residential campus in Surprise, Arizona, burgeoning online programs, and adult and professional studies campuses in Phoenix, Milwaukee, Kansas City, and the Louisville/Jeffersonville areas.

FROM TEXTBOOK TO TANGIBLE: When a F5 tornado destroyed the town of Greensburg, Kansas, Ottawa University students jumped to assist with recovery and rebuilding efforts. Students have also traveled to Israel, Kenya, Australia, and the Amazon for cross-disciplinary trips. They have performed in Carnegie Hall, participated in national forensics tournaments, and traveled to the Sundance Film Festival to work as movie critics. They have assisted with the Ottawa Tribe oral history project by conducting and transcribing interviews with senior tribe members, and they give of their own time and talents to conduct Braving Discipleship, a weekend spiritual retreat held on campus for area high school students. It is through such empowering experiences Ottawa University is making its mark on the world all throughout the year.

TOP-LEVEL, EASILY ACCESSIBLE FACULTY: With a student-to-faculty ratio of 18:1, personal engagement, direction, and collaboration define Ottawa's professor/student relationship. Teachers know their students by name (most of the staff do, too!), and each individual gets the personal attention needed to succeed. Through a wide range of service-learning projects and experiential learning opportunities, students can also engage directly in their education by completing dynamic projects that are particularly meaningful to them.

BRAND NEW, STATE-OF-THE-ART FACILITIES: To augment the teaching and learning experience at Ottawa University, a new library and student center recently opened on the Ottawa campus. Through the student center, students can broaden their academic exposure by speaking to top OU professors from across the country. And, to enhance the educational experience even further, other facilities and equipment are regularly upgraded, including the state-of-the-art Wenger music practice studios. Ottawa University is the only school in northeast Kansas to offer facilities of such a high caliber.

BEYOND THE CLASSROOM: In today's global society, students often hear, "The world is your classroom." At Ottawa University, that means traveling abroad, working with inner-city children, exploring the business practices of Indonesia, and gaining insight from their fellow classmates' diverse backgrounds and experiences. Other times, it means that the world is brought to the students through arts and cultural events, speakers, conferences, workshops, or weekly exploration sessions. Ottawa University believes that, by exposing themselves to a broad base of ideas, experiences, and people, students learn to achieve a better understanding of who they want to become.

ADAWE (SAY WHAT?): In 2008, Ottawa University established the Adawe LifePlan Center to serve as the epicenter for academic advising, counseling, and career services. Adawe (pronounced "a-dah-way") is an Ottawa word that means "to trade." Within the LifePlan Center, advisors facilitate educational exchanges and bring together a range of resources for collaborative mentoring. Tutoring services, experiential learning opportunities, workshops, personal counseling, spiritual exploration, academic advising, and career services are all available to students through the Adawe Center. The Center is also where students meet with personal success coaches and embark on their four-year process for developing "life plans," which encompass four key areas: self awareness, personal values, life-long practices, and career competencies. This unique concept is one way that Ottawa University delivers its promise to help students "prepare for a life of significance." So, when they cross the stage at graduation, students walk away with much more than a diploma; they also take with them a life-plan narrative, a career action plan, a working portfolio, a variety of career options, and a map for leaving an OU legacy

---

http://www.ottawa.edu/

P: (855) 392-0002

PRIVATE

STUDENT PROFILE

630 undergraduate students

97% of undergrad students are full time

60% male – 40% female

44% of students are from out of state

61% freshman retention rate

47% graduated in 6 years

FACULTY PROFILE

44 full-time faculty

3 part-time faculty

18 to 1 student/faculty ratio

ADMISSIONS

1,002 Total Applicants

410 Total Admissions

160 Total Freshman Enrollment

40.92% of applicants admitted

TUITION & COSTS

Tuition: $25,350

Fees: $854

Total: $26,204

R&B: $8,910

Room: $4,016

Board: $4,894

Total: $35,114

FINANCIAL

$18,040 avg grant/scholarship amount (total)

$8,508 avg loan amount (total)

ADRIAN COLLEGE

ADRIAN, MICHIGAN

With over 40 available majors and pre-professional programs, more than 80 student organizations, and 22 varsity sports, the opportunities to achieve and excel are limitless at Adrian College. AC students have been surging into the future through nearly 160 years of engaging education, applying their liberal arts studies into the College's innovative Institutes, directing plays at the historic Downs Hall Studio Theatre, and so much more.

CARING FOR HUMANITY AND THE WORLD: Students learn and live to foster compassion for humanity through various courses that involve outreach to the local and global community. For example, students have recently started a tradition to apply their knowledge and skills through a medical and dental outreach trip each December to Nicaragua. Through this "Global Health Experience," students work with medical professionals helping to organize, advertise, and assist in mobile health clinics that reach the neediest sections of the population.

CROSSING BOUNDARIES AND DISCIPLINES: For the past three years, Adrian College's "Model Arab League" course has offered students an opportunity to study international politics, hone their research and speaking skills, and travel to Washington D.C. to compete with other nationally recognized schools in a political simulation experience. Model Arab League is a program administered by the National Council on U.S.-Arab Relations in which participants learn about the politics and history of the Arab world as well as the arts of diplomacy and public speech. Numerous Adrian College students have recognized as "outstanding chairs" and "outstanding delegates" during the both Michigan- and nation-wide competitions.

THINKING CRITICALLY: The Honor's Program at Adrian College hosts a unique colloquium in which students embed themselves into 19th-century England and explore the beginnings of the evolution debate. Using a role-playing simulation pedagogy, called "Reacting to the Past," students take part in an interactive game as they play characters, research key debates around a topic, and present their perspectives.

DEVELOPING CREATIVITY: Upon her arrival at Adrian College in the spring of 2009, Dr. Jennifer Ellsworth brought over twenty years of business experience having worked at such internationally known companies as American Girl, Patagonia, and Williams-Sonoma. Dr. Ellsworth's know-how made it clear to her that her students would need more than basic theories and concepts–they would need real experiences directly tied to the world of business. She immediately took Adrian College's mission to heart and procured a seed donation for a fifteen-week project. She used this hands-on project to have her students develop, budget, market, and sell the "Downs Hall Holiday Ornament" in commemoration of the oldest building on the Adrian College campus. Since this class, every class has taken a project from conception to profit. Engaged learning at its best!

LEARNING THROUGHOUT A LIFETIME: Alumni get to spend Homecoming sharing their wisdom during the popular "Professor for a Day" program. This event is a testament to AC's engaged learning strategies, as it invites alumni to come and teach a class to current students, share life lessons, and give advice. It allows students and alumni to network and learn from one another so that they may better embrace the College's mission.

COMMUNITY EVENTS: The College celebrates numerous annual events that bring together both the campus and the greater community to engage in academic pursuits, raise awareness, enact service, and have fun! The events immediately begin with the noteworthy Community Plunge, during which freshmen help out around the city as a part of their Welcome Week activities. The fun continues with conferences, speakers, and student group activities that make the most of Women's History Month, Black History Month, Hispanic Heritage Month, and more. The annual Dance Marathon and Gift of Life Ball are other student-led events that raise awareness for various causes, and Military Appreciation Day honors student and community veterans. Ribbons of Excellence Day rounds out this chock-full calendar with a celebration of student research.

ADRIAN COLLEGE

http://www.adrian.edu/
P: (800) 877-2246

PRIVATE

STUDENT PROFILE

1,622 undergraduate students

95% of undergrad students are full time

52% male – 48% female

21% of students are from out of state

60% freshman retention rate

57% graduated in 6 years

FACULTY PROFILE

91 full-time faculty

90 part-time faculty

13 to 1 student/faculty ratio

ADMISSIONS

5,153 Total Applicants

3,189 Total Admissions

487 Total Freshman Enrollment

61.89% of applicants admitted

SAT Ranges: CR 460-540 , M450-530, W 460-540

ACT Ranges: C 19-24, M 18-25, E 18-24

TUITION & COSTS

Tuition: $31,870

Fees: $790

Total: $32,660

R&B: $9,740

Room: $4,680

Board: $5,060

Total: $42,400

FINANCIAL

$21,356 avg grant/scholarship amount (total)

$7,691 avg loan amount (total)

ALBION COLLEGE

ALBION, MICHIGAN

While students at Albion enjoy the privilege of a strong liberal arts education that is sure to help them in their career fields of choice, they benefit even further as they gain a surplus of useful skills and experiences. They develop their innate curiosity, their focus, and their sense of personal accomplishment. They emerge with the tools they need not just for success, but for a fulfilling life.

FIRST-YEAR SEMINARS: At the beginning of their Albion experience, students immediately go beyond the boundaries of the traditional classroom environment. Their choice of their first-year seminar range across unique topics like "The Far Side of Health;" "Orcs, Elves, and the Environment;" and "The Physics of Music." In small classes, and with opportunities for travel and field research, students explore areas they might never have otherwise imagined.

FURSCA: By participating through the Foundation for Undergraduate Research, Scholarship, and Creative Activity (FURSCA), students can build on their studies by discovering or creating something entirely new. As early as their freshman year, Albion students can work with a faculty member to approach a subject of their choice, develop a methodology, interpret their findings, and present their results. FURSCA even awards competitive grants to help fund outstanding projects. Recent research projects have explored crustaceans in Suriname's river systems, art and autism, the effects that the time of day can have on problem-solving, and many more complex topics. Student research in virtually every field of academia reaches its apex every spring at the annual Elkin R. Isaac Student Research Symposium. This event gives students the opportunity to present their research successes as well as to learn from others' findings. Classes are canceled specifically for this day-long, scholarly gathering, encouraging the entire community to learn something new.

STUDENT FARM: Albion students are able to educate others about the origins of their food with the help of the all-natural Student Farm near campus. Those who have a passion for conscious agriculture and sustainability can learn more and raise awareness as they plant, grow, tend, and harvest a wide range of produce on over 700 square feet of land. Student volunteers handle every aspect of the farm's operations and even sell their harvest crops to the College's dining halls.

BRITON BASH: The Briton Bash is a campus-wide, fall-semester kickoff event on the quad that introduces students to the many groups, clubs, and organizations available at Albion. Wrapping up with a picnic dinner, the day is full of fun events and community bonding that get students—both new and old—revved up for the upcoming year. One highlight of the Briton Bash in 2011 was the introduction of Brit, the first athletic mascot in the College's nearly 180-year history.

DAY OF WODEN: At the end of the academic year, students celebrate the Day of Woden on the last Wednesday of the spring semester. Classes are canceled, and students celebrate with everything from laser tag and human bowling to a climbing wall and a sundae bar. It is the perfect, hilariously fun tradition to say goodbye before the summer.

STATE-OF-THE-ART SCIENCE FACILITIES: Albion students learn from the best within outstanding facilities. The College's science complex, for example, was recently awarded silver certification under the U.S. Green Building Council's Leadership in Energy and Environmental Design (LEED) rating system. Student are also well equipped with the latest instrumentation in the Dow Analytical Science Laboratory as well as the 135-acre Whitehouse Nature Center.

INTERNSHIPS: All Albion students are encouraged to participate in at least one internship before they graduate. With the help of the Career Development Office, students can find experiences that provide them firsthand knowledge in their field of interest, new insight into day-to-day operations, and access to future job opportunities. In particular, the College has connections to well-established and prestigious internship programs all throughout Chicago, New York, Philadelphia, and Washington, D.C.

https://www.albion.edu/
P: (517) 629-1000

PRIVATE

STUDENT PROFILE

1,360 undergraduate students

100% of undergrad students are full time

50% male – 50% female

22% of students are from out of state

80% freshman retention rate

64% graduated in 6 years

FACULTY PROFILE

97 full-time faculty

47 part-time faculty

12 to 1 student/faculty ratio

ADMISSIONS

2,803 Total Applicants

2,227 Total Admissions

455 Total Freshman Enrollment

79.45% of applicants admitted

SAT Ranges: CR 500-590, M 420-570

ACT Ranges: C 22-27, M 20-26, E 21-27

TUITION & COSTS

Tuition: $40,570

Fees: $655

Total: $41,225

R&B: $11,610

Total: $52,835

FINANCIAL

$27,732 avg grant/scholarship amount (need)

$5,029 avg loan amount (need)

ALMA COLLEGE

ALMA, MICHIGAN

Alma College is at its best when it's working with students who don't have all the answers, but love to ask the questions. A beautiful residential college located in the middle of Michigan's Lower Peninsula, Alma College offers an individualized education through which each student is encouraged to identify their personal and professional goals and chart a path for the future. Alma does not prescribe a formula for success; rather, Alma helps students discover their options and open the right doors.

FIRST-YEAR SEMINAR: All incoming students begin their Alma experience by enrolling in a First-Year Seminar that allows them to study a topic alongside their new peers. These seminars illustrate the breadth of the liberal arts and vary in topic; some are introductions to academic disciplines, while others help develop study and time-management skills.

SPRING TERM: A highlight of Alma's general education is the popular Spring Term, a one-month immersion of a single course that offers learning experiences not typically available during the more traditional 15-week fall and winter terms. One might use this month to take an on-campus research course or travel to a foreign location to gain a more global perspective. With the help of the Alma Commitment's Venture Grant, Spring-Term travel courses can take students to explore marine organisms in Hawaii, study social change in China, examine medicinal plants in the Ecuadorian rain forest, or practice documentary-style photography in Spain.

GLOBAL EDUCATION: Alma encourages its students to look far beyond Michigan's boundaries. The Posey Global Leadership Program, for example, provides funding and opportunities for Alma students to travel anywhere in the world and complete a self-designed project. Since 2006, more than 280 Posey Global awards have been granted to students for research and service projects in 47 countries. 32 percent of students in Alma's 2016 graduating class reported studying abroad during their time at Alma. In cooperation with colleges and universities overseas, Alma offers international study and research opportunities in Australia, Austria, Ecuador, England, Germany, India, Italy, New Zealand, Peru, and Scotland.

UNDERGRADUATE RESEARCH: Alma undergraduates often design and undertake original projects that support their studies in their disciplines of interest. Almost half of Alma's students pursue an independent project under a professor's guidance, while another 10 percent work alongside faculty members in collaborative projects. These student researchers can even present their findings at regional and national scholarly meetings as well as the College's annual Honors Day. Other students can personalize their education by taking advantage of cooperative arrangements with urban teaching centers in Chicago, Philadelphia, and Washington.

STEM OPPORTUNITIES: In order to address the national demand for more graduates who are trained in the STEM fields, Alma has used generous funding to establish a groundbreaking initiative for student growth. Titled "e-STEM: Enhancing STEM Education and Practice," this program provides opportunities for students to engage in real-world research and learning in the academic disciplines of science, technology, engineering, and mathematics. A major component of the e-STEM initiative has been the development of the Dow Digital Science Center, a hub for collecting and storing data through remote sensing instrumentation. This technology immerses students in STEM research, linking environmental data from the remote sensors in the field to the Center for hands-on assessment.

THE ALMA COMMUNITY: Located in a community of 10,000, Alma College features a walkable campus made up of historic and contemporary buildings alike. The campus is only a block from downtown Alma and within two hours of Michigan's beaches and ski areas. Gratiot county and its surrounding neighborhoods feature plentiful parks, outdoor recreation opportunities, golf courses, and shops. The campus is also bordered by the 41-mile Fred Meijer Heartland Bike Trail.

ALMA COLLEGE

http://www.alma.edu/
P: (800) 321-ALMA

PRIVATE

STUDENT PROFILE

1,414 undergraduate students

97% of undergrad students are full time

43% male – 57% female

84% of students are from out of state

79.8% freshman retention rate

67% graduated in 6 years

FACULTY PROFILE

99 full-time faculty

64 part-time faculty

11.7 to 1 student/faculty ratio

ADMISSIONS

4,695 Total Applicants

3,184 Total Admissions

447 Total Freshman Enrollment

67.82% of applicants admitted

SAT Ranges: CR 420-590, M 460-593

ACT Ranges: C 21-26, M 20-26, E 21-26

TUITION & COSTS

Tuition: $38,348

Fees: $420

Total: $38,768

R&B: $10,642

Total: $49,410

FINANCIAL

$25,234 avg grant/scholarship amount (need)

$4,571 avg loan amount (need)

CALVIN COLLEGE

GRAND RAPIDS, MICHIGAN

With courage and wonder, Calvin students explore and appreciate the world that God has created. Founded by the Christian Reformed Church, Calvin College is a top-ranked liberal arts college that equips and empowers its nearly 4,000 students who come from around the globe. Students learn to think deeply, act justly, and live wholeheartedly as Christ's agents of renewal in the world.

LEADERS AND SERVANTS: Calvin programs provide students with meaningful, real-world experiences. For example, students in Calvin's community-based nursing program spend significant time not just in hospitals, but also in community organizations and neighborhoods. First-year engineering students design equipment for nonprofit organizations, while teams of senior engineers work on year-long design projects. Some of these projects have even led to patents and innovative products. For more than 25 years, accounting majors have volunteered to help low-income taxpayers file their tax forms through an IRS-sponsored program, Volunteer Income Tax Assistance. Every student is driven to apply their major to the benefit of others.

ACROSS THE GLOBE: Calvin's off-campus programs teach students that renewal is a worldwide effort. Students can spend semesters in 11 locales, choosing from more than 30 different off-campus courses during the January interim term. According to the annual Open Doors Report released by the International Educational Exchange, Calvin ranks second nationally among the nation's baccalaureate institutions for the number of students who study abroad. Calvin also ranks fifth in that same category for the total number of international students who study on its campus.

REAL-WORLD EXPERIENCE: With the support of Calvin's broad range of learning opportunities, 85 percent of students are shown to complete at least one internship before graduating. They have the tremendous privilege to take advantage of the vast network that the Calvin community has created, finding themselves working at companies like Airbus in Germany, the New York Stock Exchange, Wolverine Worldwide, Herman Miller, Zondervan, World Vision, and hundreds more. Each year, more than 120 students also work alongside Calvin faculty, conducting research in the sciences, arts, and humanities. A Calvin education is truly an experience in action.

THOUGHTFUL PARTICIPANTS: Calvin's biennial Festival of Faith & Writing invites conference participants and renowned authors for a weekend of education and renewal. It is also joined by the award-winning annual January Series, the Faith and International Development Conference, and a remarkable concert lineup. The guests who come to Calvin are always excited to impart their wisdom on such bright, inquisitive minds.

RESEARCH: Calvin professors regularly engage students in grant-funded research; nearly all faculty have been published in academic journals and/or presented their work at major conferences, many having received help from their undergraduates. In a recent year, 85 undergraduate students worked alongside 44 faculty members for 10 weeks of full-time summer research in the sciences. Collaborations like these are constantly giving students valuable experience and expertise. Such projects often lead to published reports and presentations in which students are even cited as co-authors.

SUSTAINABILITY INITIATIVES: Calvin faculty, staff, and students are breaking ground to develop strategies that protect the environmental resources that God has provided. One example of their efforts is the student-proposed Calvin Energy Recovery Fund, a revolving fund that is used to improve energy efficiency and reduce carbon dioxide emissions on campus. The cost savings from CERF projects are routed back into the fund to support future projects.

TANGIBLE TAKEAWAYS: Calvin's career center assists students as they prepare for careers after graduation through workshops, job fairs, internships, and on-campus interviews. These support systems are more than effective; 98% of recent survey respondents reported that they were professionally employed or in graduate school within one year of graduation.

---

http://www.calvin.edu/
P: (800) 688-0122

PRIVATE - CHRISTIAN

STUDENT PROFILE

3,788 undergraduate students

98% of undergrad students are full time

44% male – 56% female

45% of students are from out of state

86% freshman retention rate

73% graduated in 6 years

FACULTY PROFILE

262 full-time faculty

96 part-time faculty

13 to 1 student/faculty ratio

ADMISSIONS

3,824 Total Applicants

2,840 Total Admissions

944 Total Freshman Enrollment

74.27% of applicants admitted

SAT Ranges: CR 520-670, M 530-670

ACT Ranges: C 23-30, M 22-29, E 23-32

TUITION & COSTS

Tuition: $31,730

R&B: $9,840

Total: $41,570

FINANCIAL

$16,333 avg grant/scholarship amount (need)

$6,538 avg loan amount (need)

CORNERSTONE UNIVERSITY

GRAND RAPIDS, MICHIGAN

At Cornerstone University, students are more. More than a major. More than a degree. Each student is a story. At Cornerstone, students are encouraged to discover their unique gifts and abilities, pushed to think outside their comfort zones, and ultimately equipped to graduate with the skills needed to make an impact on the world for Christ. CU is a community of believers who are passionate about each individual's story. Students are mentored and supported by faculty and staff, and they develop friendships that last a lifetime and compel them deeper into their faith. At Cornerstone University, every student builds a life that matters.

TERRA FIRMA: Meaning "firm foundation" in Latin, Cornerstone's year-long Terra Firma orientation program provides new students a strong foundation for both academic and spiritual growth. Right when students move to campus, they are immediately connected with a small group of peers who walk alongside them throughout the entire first year at CU. Together, they enjoy off-campus outings, take part in a service-learning project in the Grand Rapids community, and learn about what it means to thrive in college.

GO STUDY: Students can spend a semester pursuing their passions by studying in the beautiful landscapes of Ireland, or they can trek through the rugged terrain of Hawaii during the two-week J-term. With over 30 study abroad programs in places like Australia, China, Oxford, and Dubai, Cornerstone students have a whole bunch of opportunities to add new context to their studies, all while earning college credit.

GO SERVE: Cornerstone sees the value in serving its community's brothers and sisters around the globe by returning to the same towns and villages year after year. On an annual basis, students have the opportunity to serve abroad by witnessing to the homeless in Chicago, mentoring and caring for abused and needy children in Guatemala, and sharing their love and compassion of Christ with other hurting families. These students seek to make an impact in this world for Christ.

CALLING MATTERS: Cornerstone is enlivened by a team of people who are passionate about helping each other discover their calling. The University's LifePath program provides purpose-guided academic and career planning to help students discover how God has gifted and equipped each of them with unique skills, abilities, and passions. Elements of the LifePath program include the Center for Career & Life Calling, which helps students discover and prepare for their postgraduate goals; Peer Advisors, who guide students through academic and personal challenges; and the Center for Student Success, which gives students the foresight to map out their four-year plan while at college.

INTERNSHIPS: Cornerstone believes that hands-on internship experiences not only bolster one's résumé, but also greatly prepare them for their career-field. With a campus located just minutes from downtown Grand Rapids—the second-largest city in Michigan—students are equipped to find an internship that fits their passions. CU students have obtained internships in such businesses and organizations as American Red Cross, Ford Motor Company, Kellogg Company, and the Department of Natural Resources.

WORSHIP MATTERS: At CU, students are supported and encouraged to grow in their faith. Cornerstone provides chapel services four times throughout the week for students to gather together in worship and learn from pastors and speakers from around the globe.

http://www.cornerstone.edu/

P: (800) 787-9778

PRIVATE - CHRISTIAN

STUDENT PROFILE

1,912 undergraduate students

78% of undergrad students are full time

40% male – 60% female

24% of students are from out of state

76% freshman retention rate

61% graduated in 6 years

FACULTY PROFILE

69 full-time faculty

337 part-time faculty

15 to 1 student/faculty ratio

ADMISSIONS

2,618 Total Applicants

1,910 Total Admissions

284 Total Freshman Enrollment

72.96% of applicants admitted

SAT Ranges: CR 482-588, M 472-588

ACT Ranges: C 20-25, M 218-25, E 20-26

TUITION & COSTS

Tuition: $26,490

Fees: $370

Total: $26,860

R&B: $8,810

Total: $35,670

FINANCIAL

$16,175 avg grant/scholarship amount (need)

$4,220 avg loan amount (need)

HILLSDALE COLLEGE

HILLSDALE, MICHIGAN

Hillsdale College was founded in 1844 by men and women who described themselves as "grateful to God for the inestimable blessings" of civil and religious liberty, "believing that the diffusion of sound learning is essential to the perpetuity of those blessings." Hillsdale is proud to continue its trusteeship of the intellectual and spiritual inheritance derived from the Judeo-Christian faith and Greco-Roman culture.

THE HONOR CODE: All students at Hillsdale College sign an Honor Code that animates student life: "A Hillsdale College student is honorable in conduct, honest in word and deed, dutiful in study and service, and respectful of the rights of others. Through education the student rises to self-government." Self-government is a challenge with the promise of a rich reward: liberty of the soul. A soul enjoys liberty when it is ordered—when its passions are ruled by reason and its habit is virtue. Virtus tentamine gaudet: Strength rejoices in the challenge. This truth, the motto of Hillsdale College, means that to be strong in virtue, one must welcome a challenge. In offering its students the challenge of self-government, Hillsdale College asks its students to act at all times worthy of the blessings of liberty.

THE LIBERAL ARTS CORE: A sound liberal arts education includes study in the humanities, the natural sciences, and the social sciences. There are eight specific courses that every Hillsdale student must complete: Physical Science; Core Principles in Biology; Great Books in the Western Tradition; Great Books in the British and American Traditions; The Western Heritage to 1600; The American Heritage; The U.S. Constitution; and Physical Wellness Dynamics. In addition, students are to complete at least one course from each offered group in the humanities, one in the social sciences, and one "Center for Constructive Alternatives" seminar.

THE COLLEGE FACULTY: The Hillsdale College faculty consist of 135 full-time members. No classes are taught by graduate students, allowing the closeness of the College community to facilitate worthwhile faculty mentorship both inside the classroom and during office visits after class. Each student has a faculty advisor who provides them academic and career counseling catered to their specific field of study. Hillsdale's faculty consider teaching their first priority, but many also work on compelling research and scholarly writing, Because they are able to explore and deepen their involvement within their fields, they often share valuable information on the national scene, in lecture programs, and in various media outlets.

STUDENT LIFE: Four national fraternities, three national sororities, and scores of social, academic, spiritual, and service organizations provide Hillsdale students with a diverse array of co-curricular opportunities. A resident drama troupe, a dance company, a concert and chamber choir, and a number of musical ensembles for a range of instrumentalists constitute the College's amazing performing arts organizations. The Student Activities Board and Campus Recreation Board also sponsor all-College events like Homecoming, the annual Garden Party and President's Ball, the Centralhallapalooza year-end celebration, Color Run, and more.

OFF-CAMPUS STUDY OPPORTUNITIES: In addition to a wealth of academic opportunities available on the Hillsdale College campus in Michigan, students also have a number of off-campus opportunities available to them. For example, students in the natural sciences can explore their interests at the College's G.H. Gordon Biological Station, a 685-acre field research laboratory located in the northern part of Michigan's Lower Peninsula. The James C. Quayle Journalism Intern Program places students from Hillsdale's Herbert H. Dow II Program in American Journalism in summer internships with a stipend provided by the College.

HILLSDALE COLLEGE

http://www.hillsdale.edu/
P: (517) 437-7341

PRIVATE

STUDENT PROFILE

1,482 undergraduate students

97% of undergrad students are full time

50% male – 50% female

65% of students are from out of state

94% freshman retention rate

83% graduated in 6 years

FACULTY PROFILE

127 full-time faculty

46 part-time faculty

10 to 1 student/faculty ratio

ADMISSIONS

1,934 Total Applicants

874 Total Admissions

377 Total Freshman Enrollment

45.19% of applicants admitted

SAT Ranges: CR 620-750, M 570-690

ACT Ranges: C 28-32, M 26-31, E 28-35

TUITION & COSTS

Tuition: $25,540

Fees: $1,202

Total: $26,742

R&B: $10,610

Total: $37,352

FINANCIAL

$7,275 avg grant/scholarship amount (need)

$5,701 avg loan amount (need)

KALAMAZOO COLLEGE

KALAMAZOO, MICHIGAN

As one of the oldest institutions in America, Kalamazoo College is sure to prepare its students for success. Collaboration with faculty and experiential learning opportunities groom students into intelligent and mindful leaders of tomorrow.

THE K-PLAN: The K-Plan is Kalamazoo's structure for its students' liberal arts education. Following four principles, the K-Plan is designed around depth and breadth in the liberal arts; learning through experience; international and intercultural experience; and independent scholarship. Upon graduation, students will have studied a variety of subjects across various disciplines, solidifying their interests and learning how to communicate themselves effectively across platforms. The K-Plan is specific to each student and tailored to their individual needs and interests. Through their general education, students are able to shape their college careers and make it their own, exposing their talents with the help of the College's academic and personal support.

SENIOR INDIVIDUALIZED PROJECT: The Senior Individualized Project (SIP), required of each student, is a final project that is meant to exhibit four years of growth. SIPs may pertain to any area of academia regardless of one's major, meaning that students are able to run in many directions to complete a truly innovative product. During the spring semester, Kalamazoo hosts several events to showcase student projects, allowing seniors to share their hard work as well as practice public speaking and performance.

STUDY ABROAD: The average Kalamazoo student studies abroad for six months, but options abound for everyone to travel the length of time that best fits their goals. Overall, nearly 80% of students study abroad, engaging in over 40 programs across 23 countries. While abroad, students take on Cultural Research Projects, which take them on adventures throughout a community, exploring and reflecting upon an activity that truly impacts their worldview.

CIVIC ENGAGEMENT AND SERVICE-LEARNING: Most Kalamazoo students are involved in the community through service-learning, which synthesizes education and volunteer efforts. This community-based education gives students the chance to apply academic theories to practice, enacting positive change in a truly impactful community initiative. All service-learning programs ask students to reflect and draw connections between their efforts and the needs of the local and global communities. At the core of service-learning is social justice, and students revel in their academic efforts to act as upstanding and thoughtful citizens.

SOCIAL JUSTICE LEADERSHIP: Kalamazoo values social justice and expects every student to appreciate the diversity of all people with tolerance and respect. The Arcus Center for Social Justice is the hub for service initiatives that aim to support those who have not received the respect they deserve, whether that be due to direct or historical acts of marginalization. Students and faculty can propose specific efforts and see that they are followed through, working to inspire unity, spark intellectual growth, nurture leadership, build community, and embrace change.

CAREER AND PROFESSIONAL DEVELOPMENT: Making decisions about one's career choice and postgraduate plans can be a daunting task for many. Kalamazoo recognizes that students need assistance with their future decisions and therefore seeks to provide each individual with helpful guidance. Students can receive one-on-one career counseling and attend workshops that aim to build the skills they need to land a job.

THE DISCOVERY EXTERNSHIP PROGRAM: The Discovery Externship Program links Kalamazoo students with alumni all over the world. Students who utilize this program have the opportunity to live and work with alumni in the Kalamazoo network—a priceless experience in which students gain industry knowledge and connect to the professional world that awaits them.

---

http://www.kzoo.edu/
P: (269) 337-7000

PRIVATE

STUDENT PROFILE

1,443 undergraduate students

99% of undergrad students are full time

44% male – 56% female

92% freshman retention rate

83% graduated in 6 years

FACULTY PROFILE

116 full-time faculty

20 part-time faculty

13 to 1 student/faculty ratio

ADMISSIONS

2,455 Total Applicants

1,759 Total Admissions

365 Total Freshman Enrollment

71.65% of applicants admitted

SAT Ranges: CR 528-680, M 550-690, W 550-650

ACT Ranges: C 25-30, M 24-29, E 25-31, W 10-11

TUITION & COSTS

Tuition: $42,510

Fees: $436

Total: $42,946

R&B: $8,886

Room: $4,335

Board: $4,551

Total: $51,832

FINANCIAL

$26,748 avg grant/scholarship amount (total)

$7,221 avg loan amount (total)

MICHIGAN TECHNOLOGICAL UNIVERSITY

HOUGHTON, MICHIGAN

Michigan Technological University is a leading research institution in technological advancement and innovation. The student-to-faculty ratio of 11:1 gives way to a collaborative environment in which student research leads to amazing discovery.

THE ENTERPRISE PROGRAM: The Enterprise Program brings together students of varying disciplines to work on real-world client projects. Each team functions like a company in which every individual brings something valuable to the table, bringing their skills together to engage in client projects that range from developing a service to creating a product. There are awesome opportunities available through Enterprise—some students get to create and test their own prototypes, while other teams get to work abroad. During the business process, participants have the chance to work with industry leaders, government organizations, members of the community, and faculty advisors. In the past, students have worked with companies like General Motors, Kimberly Clark, and The Department of Energy.

STUDY ABROAD: Studying abroad is an awesome way to learn about another country's culture, food, and language. Undergraduates who go abroad gain skills in cross-cultural communication, independent living, and problem solving. Because there are so many benefits to participation, Michigan Tech encourages all eligible students to seek out international opportunities during their undergraduate experience. Study abroad can take many different forms: semester, year-long, summer, and faculty-led programs. The semester/year-long programs are ideal for students who can afford to take the time away from their major and enrich their experience through a full, long-term immersion in such countries as Argentina, China, Denmark, Ghana, and Italy. There are also options, however, for those who need to fulfill their major requirements but nevertheless want to explore the world around them. Through summer and short-term, faculty-led programs, students can go on an abbreviated yet incredible trip to Greece, Israel, Japan, Norway, or Thailand.

FACULTY-LED STUDY ABROAD: Faculty-led programs, which generally last 2-3 weeks, take students on excursions around the world during the summer intersession. These experiences enable students to explore a new city while still receiving the amazing instruction from their Michigan Tech professors. With so many benefits to short, faculty-led travel, the Michigan Tech experience thrives far beyond campus walls. Examples of past faculty-led programs include an exploration of the English-Scottish border, an immersion in Spain's language and culture, and a joint exploration of both Paris and London.

RESIDENTIAL LEARNING COMMUNITIES: Residential Learning Communities (RLCs) offer students the opportunity to engage with peers who share similar interests and academic goals. There are countless benefits to participation, including: stronger academic performance, support from peers, and extra attention from peer staff members. One notable RLC is the Women in Engineering program, which is specifically designed for women interested in pursuing a career in engineering. The program tailors to the academic needs of its members, hosting activities that involve support and professional networking. Students in this RLC also have the opportunity to get involved with the Society of Women Engineers. Other examples include a Forest Resource & Environmental Science RLC, which supports students whose studies pertain to the natural world, and the First-Year Experience RLC, which allows freshmen to join and bond with a community of other students who are transitioning into the college lifestyle.

http://www.mtu.edu/

P: (906) 487-1885

PUBLIC

STUDENT PROFILE

5,697 undergraduate students

94% of undergrad students are full time

73% male – 27% female

87% freshman retention rate

65% graduated in 6 years

FACULTY PROFILE

484 full-time faculty

49 part-time faculty

12 to 1 student/faculty ratio

ADMISSIONS

5,386 Total Applicants

4,063 Total Admissions

1,277 Total Freshman Enrollment

75.44% of applicants admitted

SAT Ranges: CR 540-670, M 560-690, W 500-630

ACT Ranges: C 24-29, M 25-29, E 23-29

TUITION & COSTS

Tuition: (In) $14,630 (Out) $30,788

Fees: $300

Total: (In) $14,930 (Out) $31,088

R&B: $9,857

Room: $5,486

Board: $4,371

Total: (In) $24,787 (Out) $40,945

FINANCIAL

$7,728 avg grant/scholarship amount (need)

$4,618 avg loan amount (need)

NORTHERN MICHIGAN UNIVERSITY

MARQUETTE, MICHIGAN

NORTHERN MICHIGAN
UNIVERSITY

Northern Michigan University believes that a well-rounded individual is one who draws on a wide range of experiences. For that reason, Northern embraces not only the incredible academic experiences that happen in its classrooms, but also the passions that its students pursue beyond the walls of the lecture halls.

FIRST-YEAR SEMINARS AND EXPERIENCES: NMU's First-Year Experience (FYE) is a learning community initiative that helps new students develop strategies to maximize their academic success, utilize campus resources, and cultivate positive relationships with other students and faculty. FYE is designed to help all first-time, full-time students successfully manage the transition to college. With FYE's block scheduling, freshmen are even able to reserve spots in classes before orientation. In most cases, students share the same course schedule with about 20 others, creating an immediate cohort of peers that are perfect for study groups and a general sense of belonging on campus.

COMMON INTELLECTUAL EXPERIENCES: Through the General Education Program, the faculty of Northern Michigan seek to help students develop the skills necessary for becoming independent, lifelong learners and effective citizens of a challenging and rapidly changing world. This program is designed to complement all students' academic majors by integrating knowledge derived from multiple perspectives. It stresses the development of problem-solving skills and intellectual creativity through the exploration of a broad range of disciplines and fields.

COLLABORATIVE ASSIGNMENTS AND PROJECTS: Working as part of a team is an increasingly common requirement in today's businesses and organizations, and NMU students enter the workforce having engaged in plenty of collaborative learning throughout their years at college. Northern's campus thrives on collaboration, and many classes require or encourage group projects, critiques, and research with faculty and fellow students. For instance, Invent@NMU employs students as engineers, graphic designers, project managers, and public relations and marketing specialists to help entrepreneurs launch their products. The TEAM Business club gathers students from different majors to work with regional organizations to overcome their challenges, and the NMU Constructors take on projects to help community groups.

UNDERGRADUATE RESEARCH: Many people consider student research to be reserved for the graduate level, but that is far from the case at NMU. The faculty at Northern are committed to providing undergraduates with hands-on research opportunities from the moment they step onto campus. Undergraduates have helped write psychology textbooks, created apps for Intel, worked on finding cures for ALS and brain cancer, and helped identify new species of crabs. There are so many remarkable ways in which undergrads develop as practiced professionals.

WRITING-INTENSIVE COURSES: As part of their General Education requirements, students fulfill the "Effective Communication" component through two courses, which may include composition, writing, and/or foreign languages. Additionally, a course to fulfill the "Human Expression" component includes analysis and evaluation of artistic, literary, or rhetorical expression. Through these and more, writing is emphasized in numerous courses across the curriculum, urging students to refine their communication skills so that they may succeed in developing and articulating their ideas.

LEARNING COMMUNITIES: The Honors Program at NMU provides academically talented students with a two- or four-year series of interdisciplinary and department-based courses, which are designed to complement students' undergraduate degrees regardless of major. The Honors Program is not an academic major in itself, but it rather substitutes specially designed courses to enhance the typical general education program. These substitute classes provide unique learning experiences to some of Northern's most academically motivated students.

http://www.nmu.edu/

P: (906) 227-1000

PUBLIC

STUDENT PROFILE

8,001 undergraduate students

88% of undergrad students are full time

45% male – 55% female

21% of students are from out of state

72.6% freshman retention rate

49% graduated in 6 years

FACULTY PROFILE

305 full-time faculty

151 part-time faculty

21 to 1 student/faculty ratio

ADMISSIONS

6,848 Total Applicants

4,937 Total Admissions

1,595 Total Freshman Enrollment

72.09% of applicants admitted

ACT Ranges: C 19-24, M 17-24, E 18-24

TUITION & COSTS

Tuition: (In) $9,324 (Out) $14,556

Fees: (In) $299 (Out) $64

Total: (In) $9,623 (Out) $14,620

R&B: $8,954

Room: $4,566

Board: $4,388

Total: (In) $18,577 (Out) $23,574

FINANCIAL

$5,202 avg grant/scholarship amount (need)

$4,084 avg loan amount (need)

SIENA HEIGHTS UNIVERSITY

ADRIAN, MICHIGAN

At Siena Heights, students do so much more than earn degrees. They develop interests into passions. They discover talents they never knew they had. They make friendships that last forever. Siena Heights University has dedicated almost a century to creating an educational environment in which students feel both instantly comfortable and infinitely challenged.

STUDY ABROAD: The University offers a faculty-led Spanish-language immersion that plunges students into a full semester of an authentic experience in Costa Rica. Students speak the language and absorb the culture as they live, learn, and grow. They are also able to travel to such locales as eastern Europe and Italy and may apply for a scholarship to attend the annual Fanjeaux Seminar in France. This 16-day summer seminar was designed to inspire students who attend any of the 18 Dominican colleges and universities in the U.S. Participants spend 13 days in Fanjeaux in the south of France and three days in Paris. Weekday mornings are spent in seminars, and afternoons and weekends are spent on tours to places of historical and cultural significance. For Siena Heights students, the world is easily within reach.

RESEARCH: Undergraduate research is not an uncommon experience for Siena Heights scholars. For example, Environmental Science majors/minors have traveled to Florida's Ponce Inlet and the Indian River Lagoon, the most biodiverse estuary in North America. They commonly embark on excursions like this in order to research the current environmental issues that impact particular habitats and species. Subsequent research has involved tours of local conservation/preservation sites that see how said habitats are protected. Each spring, Siena Heights hosts a campus-wide Scholarship Symposium at which these pursuits and other research projects are presented and honored.

ONE-ON-ONE INTERACTION: At Siena, effectiveness in the classroom is exhibited by plenty of one-on-one interaction. The University's small size allows professors to know their students personally, participating actively to help each of them them reach their goals and aspirations. Faculty also share the benefit and wisdom from their own considerable accomplishments; Siena professors conduct scientific research, publish literature, and excel in their fields of expertise.

STUDENT SUCCESS: Siena's professors would be intimidating if they weren't some of the the most personable people one could meet. Faculty put student success first, getting to know each student's personal strengths and struggles. Additionally, faculty even work closely with one another so that they may foster interdisciplinary experiences. If a political science professor recognizes a student's love for writing, she may recommend a literature course on Orwell. A sculpture professor could spark a student's interest in theatre set design. When learning is based on real relationships, there's no limit to where it can lead.

COMMON DIALOGUE DAY: Unique to Siena Heights, the University annually conducts a traditional day for discussion and debate on campus. Dubbed "Common Dialogue Day," this event is open to the entire community and features several presentations that all focus around the year's academic theme. Classes are canceled for the day, encouraging all students and faculty to contribute to the dialogue and hear from noted guest speakers and other Siena thought-leaders.

MAKING A DIFFERENCE: After four years at Siena Heights University, students graduate raring to make a difference. A Siena education teaches students to engage in the world around them and contribute to their communities. To Siena students and faculty, service isn't just another activity or résumé-builder—it's a way of life. Through the Siena Serves program, students can participate in alternative spring break trips in Florida, Jamaica, and New Orleans.

VOLUNTEER OPPORTUNITIES: At some universities, a special week is set aside for volunteer work. By those standards, every week of the Siena academic year is special. Volunteers have a variety of opportunities to serve: some can visit Hope Community Center to help senior citizens with disabilities, and some groups may even drop by "Daily Bread" to provide lunch for those in need.

---

http://www.sienaheights.edu/
P: (800) 521-0009

PRIVATE - CATHOLIC

STUDENT PROFILE

2,492 undergraduate students

53% of undergrad students are full time

42% male – 58% female

13% of students are from out of state

72% freshman retention rate

37% graduated in 6 years

FACULTY PROFILE

96 full-time faculty

2 part-time faculty

12 to 1 student/faculty ratio

ADMISSIONS

1,777 Total Applicants

1,377 Total Admissions

305 Total Freshman Enrollment

77.49% of applicants admitted

SAT Ranges: CR 420-510, M 460-540

ACT Ranges: C 18-26, M 17-24, E 17-24

TUITION & COSTS

Tuition: $23,320

Fees: $430

Total: $23,750

R&B: $9,710

Total: $33,460

FINANCIAL

$16,259 avg grant/scholarship amount (total)

$7,042 avg loan amount (total)

WESTERN MICHIGAN UNIVERSITY

KALAMAZOO, MICHIGAN

Midway between Chicago and Detroit, the city of Kalamazoo thrives with both urban resources and rural landscapes, enriched with numerous cultural festivals, arts venues, and major science and research centers. Most notably, it is the proud home of Western Michigan University, a top-notch public research institution that supports active learners across 149 undergraduate, 75 master's, and 32 doctoral programs. Its diverse population brings life to its academics, always collaborating with a mix of cultural viewpoints and a broad span of disciplinary perspectives.

RESEARCH: WMU is proud to provide the resources and financial support for its faculty to conduct research and pursue innovative technologies. And because faculty are so greatly focused on creating a fulfilling environment for their students, they commonly seek out undergraduates for help. Regardless of their academic focus, students have outlets to pursue creative projects and research in the lab or out in the field. Some academic departments offer courses designated for research, and the Undergraduate Research Conference opens up the space for students to share their experiences and findings with one another.

BRONCO BASH: The Western Michigan Community is sparked to life at the beginning of each year at Bronco Bash, an annual festival that riles students up for a great semester with their friends and faculty. Bronco Bash is loaded with performances by local musicians, fun activities, and food. It is a great way for returning students to reunite with their friends, and perfect for first-year students to meet their new peers and get acquainted with the student clubs that they can join while at school.

GLOBAL AWARENESS: Diversity is embraced as an important feature of WMU's forward-thinking college environment. In fact, WMU was the first American university to require all students to study the non-Western world, incorporating global awareness into its general education curriculum. The University commits to inclusion, providing a safe outlet for students of all backgrounds to share their experiences and explore new cultures. The "Get Globally Engaged This Week!" newsletter keeps students in the know about all cultural events on campus, maintaining a weekly schedule of activities, lectures, and discussions that explore issues and communities from all around the world. Students are also invited to study, intern, or volunteer abroad to expose themselves firsthand to communities beyond WMU's walls. Across over 40 countries, they can enact service and gain professional experience while earning academic credit and growing inspired for a lifetime of globally conscious citizenship.

INTERNSHIPS: Western Michigan University recognizes that internships are one of the most valuable experiences students can have to prepare for their postgraduate careers. With the help of Career and Student Employment Services, anyone in any field of study can find an opportunity that best utilizes their skills and trains them for their individual goals. Resources like the Career Zone and BroncoJOBS help students craft their résumés, prepare for interviews, and seek out employers through a career catalog that is full of opportunities for all areas of work.

SUSTAINABILITY: The Office of Sustainability strives to engage each WMU student in initiatives that enact positive change to the environment. Campus-wide projects include a Bike Stable to promote clean methods of transportation, a waste reduction program that conducts research and promotes recycling, and the Gibbs House, which is a new laboratory within a historic campus building that provides space for students to design new technology for sustainable living.

https://wmich.edu/

P: (269) 387-1000

PUBLIC

STUDENT PROFILE

17,984 undergraduate students

83% of undergrad students are full time

51% male – 49% female

78.6% freshman retention rate

52.7% graduated in 6 years

FACULTY PROFILE

934 full-time faculty

512 part-time faculty

17 to 1 student/faculty ratio

ADMISSIONS

13,612 Total Applicants

11,205 Total Admissions

2,930 Total Freshman Enrollment

82.32% of applicants admitted

ACT Ranges: C 19-25, M 17-25, E 18-25

TUITION & COSTS

Tuition: (In) $12,528 (Out) $15,420

R&B: $9,420

Total: (In) $21,948 (Out) $24,840

FINANCIAL

$5,295 avg grant/scholarship amount (need)

$4,098 avg loan amount (need)

MACALESTER COLLEGE

ST. PAUL, MINNESOTA

Macalester is a private liberal arts college dedicated to creating ethical leaders out of its students. The College promotes the values of multiculturalism and service to the community and encourages students to use the knowledge they gain to bring about positive change in the world around them.

FIRST-YEAR EXPERIENCE: The first-year experience at Macalester is fulfilled by a student's choice of one course. For some students, their first-year experience may serve as an introduction to a minor or major. For others, the course may act as a way to explore a new discipline. Some first-year courses even require that students live together, doubling as both an academic venture as well as a community-building residential experience.

STUDY ABROAD: More than half of Macalester students study abroad to experience entirely different cultures and their customs. With a selection of over 90 programs that span across 6 continents, each student is sure to find the adventure that is perfect for them. In the last four years, students spent an average of 15 weeks abroad in nearly 70 different countries.

COMMUNITY-BASED LEARNING: Community-based learning involves the integration of coursework into service. At Macalester, students can work closely with faculty and local community partners to organize projects that are focused on community needs. This method of learning is beneficial to all participants: students have the opportunity to apply what they have learned to make a positive change, the community profits from the service itself, and professors have the chance to guide their students through thoughtful initiatives while raising social awareness about topics that matter to them.

UNDERGRADUATE RESEARCH: Under the guidance of their professors, Macalester students can conduct their own original research projects, taking advantage of the College's resources to supplement their education. In some cases, students even go on to have their work published. Professors also invite their students to join and assist with their research projects, treating undergraduates as extraordinarily helpful, knowledgeable peers as they pursue high-level topics.

CIVIC ENGAGEMENT: Service to society is recognized as an integral part of the undergraduate experience. As a responsible institution, Macalester pushes students to participate in the community as active and thoughtful citizens. The Civic Engagement Center works in partnership with the community and responds to the needs of different organizations, bringing students in touch with some of the most pressing issues of the community right outside the College's walls.

SPECIALTY AND LANGUAGE HOUSES: Specialty Houses are available to students who wish to live with peers who share interests similar to their own. These residences foster smaller community environments within the larger campus structure. There are currently eight Specialty Houses, including All-Gender House, Arabic House, Cultural House, Eco House, Healthy Living Community, Interfaith House, Summit House, and Veggie Co-Op. Students can even live in a Language House, an immersive experience in which residents speak the language of their designated home and explore the culture and customs of the country they are studying. A few native speakers also live in the house and help students with their speaking skills. The current language houses offered are Spanish, Chinese, French, German, Japanese, and Russian.

INTERNSHIPS: Macalester's Academic Internship Program coordinates off-campus work opportunities for students. Internships are extremely beneficial; not only do students gain hands on experience, but they also learn valuable information about their desired industry. Macalester encourages every student to pursue internship opportunities, recognizing such an experience as a vital part of an undergraduate education. The College offers several services in order to prepare students for the job, including résumé assistance and help in securing an internship. Additionally, students are called to apply their academic experience to service-learning and other courses that integrate some form of community-based initiative.

MACALESTER COLLEGE

http://www.macalester.edu/
P: (651) 696-6000

PRIVATE

STUDENT PROFILE

2,172 undergraduate students

98% of undergrad students are full time

40% male – 60% female

68% of students are from out of state

95% freshman retention rate

90% graduated in 6 years

FACULTY PROFILE

215 full-time faculty

56 part-time faculty

10 to 1 student/faculty ratio

ADMISSIONS

6,030 Total Applicants

2,353 Total Admissions

583 Total Freshman Enrollment

39.02% of applicants admitted

SAT Ranges: CR 620-730, M 620-720, W 630-720

ACT Ranges: C 29-32, M 27-32, E 29-34, W 8-10

TUITION & COSTS

Tuition: $48,666

Fees: $221

Total: $48,887

R&B: $10,874

Room: $5,810

Board: $5,064

Total: $59,761

FINANCIAL

$31,734 avg grant/scholarship amount (total)

$6,073 avg loan amount (total)

ST. OLAF COLLEGE

NORTHFIELD, MINNESOTA

St. Olaf is a liberal arts college grounded in Lutheran tradition. Its faculty and staff make a campus-wide effort to support the growth of each student through personal educational experiences, including study abroad, residential learning, and community service.

STUDENT GOALS: St. Olaf recognizes that an undergraduate experience consists of more than class and homework. College is about student development, both academic and personal. Involving oneself in extracurriculars is vital to growth, and St. Olaf considers its community the perfect place to participate and grow as well-rounded citizens. Within its mission, St. Olaf has defined 8 learning goals for students: Self-Development, Vocational Discernment, Critical Thinking, Integration and Application, Broad Knowledge, Specialized Knowledge, Communication and Collaboration, and Responsible Engagement.

ACADEMIC CIVIC ENGAGEMENT: Embracing the value of academic civic engagement, St. Olaf provides students with tons of opportunities to get involved. This educational practice, often referred to as service-learning, allows students to make an impact on the community as part of their coursework. Through organized projects, students and faculty come together to integrate academics into service, drawing connections between their schoolwork and the needs of the less fortunate. Often times, these community-based courses push students to recognize their privileges and use their positions in society to enact real change.

INTERNSHIPS: St. Olaf strongly recommends that each student complete an internship experience prior to graduation. Those who have interned have already begun to develop useful skills, making themselves much stronger candidates for potential postgraduate positions. Oftentimes, employers use internships as a recruiting tool, recognizing the hands-on experience as a valuable asset to their company. St. Olaf has plenty of resources to help students find and secure intern positions, including the useful Online Alumni Directory. With this tool, students can reach out to St. Olaf community members to network and get in touch with exclusive employment opportunities.

THE PIPER CENTER FOR VOCATION AND CAREER: The Piper Center for Vocation and Career offers guidance and advice for students looking to navigate their career options and plans for after graduation. It works individually with students looking for help, aiding them as they identify their skillset and the career that might be best for their talents. Most importantly, the Piper Center strives to prepare every student for life after college, whether that be in a career or professional school. Students have access to one-on-one career coaching, internship and networking opportunities, and assistance with résumé building and interview tactics.

INTERNATIONAL AND OFF-CAMPUS STUDY: International and off-campus study mixes academics with experiential learning throughout different locales around the world. While away from campus, students encounter the social constructs and cultures that inhabit their destinations, allowing them to grow as engaged and thoughtful members of a global society. The College has also designed some abroad programs to integrate faculty instruction in order to provide the amazing opportunity to learn from St. Olaf professors, all while while discovering a new city. In a way, the faculty-led programs preserve the St. Olaf education by allowing the same caliber of education to thrive even off campus. Faculty-led abroad options have included Biology in South India, Environmental Science in Australia, Global Semester, Mediterranean Semester, and Term in China.

---

http://wp.stolaf.edu/

P: (507) 786-2222

PRIVATE

STUDENT PROFILE

3,046 undergraduate students

99% of undergrad students are full time

43% male – 57% female

93% freshman retention rate

87% graduated in 6 years

FACULTY PROFILE

248 full-time faculty

91 part-time faculty

12 to 1 student/faculty ratio

ADMISSIONS

7,571 Total Applicants

2,723 Total Admissions

763 Total Freshman Enrollment

35.97% of applicants admitted

SAT Ranges: CR 560-710, M 580-700

ACT Ranges: C 26-31, M 26-33, E 26-31

TUITION & COSTS

Tuition: $42,940

R&B: $9,790

Room: $4,720

Board: $5,070

Total: $52,730

FINANCIAL

$26,917 avg grant/scholarship amount (total)

$6,587 avg loan amount (total)

UNIVERSITY OF MINNESOTA MORRIS

MORRIS, MINNESOTA

A University of Minnesota Morris degree garners respect, because the campus is known for attracting students who are serious about learning. Young people come to Morris with an exceptional amount of innate curiosity. Students grow in the small town of Morris, which is bursting with a lot of charm. With access to fishing, boating, camping, canoeing, hiking, biking, and many community festivals, students fall in love with the small-town feel.

STUDY AND TEACH ABROAD: Study abroad is an incredible opportunity to explore and experience another part of the world. Study abroad options at Morris range in program type and duration. In addition to traditional study and exchange programs, Morris also offers select education students the incredible opportunity to gain teaching experience abroad. Student teachers learn how instruction styles differ in foreign locations as well as the challenges that face students across the world. The program is a great way for education students to explore the culture and history of a new place while also gaining practice in their chosen field. The countries associated with the program include Austria, Ghana, Ireland, Italy, New Zealand, Poland, and Spain.

UNDERGRADUATE RESEARCH: Undergraduate research is one of the most challenging and rewarding experiences a student can have. Research involves many skills, including creative inquiry, methodology, interpretation, proper citation, editing, discovery, and in some cases, presentation. In other words, students who engage in research benefit from the experience and get to develop these skills on an advanced level. Morris provides undergraduates with the opportunity to engage in research, whether that be as part of a group or an individual pursuit. Morris students also have the chance to share their research during the annual Undergraduate Research Symposium. During the event, students present their work to the campus, visiting families, friends, and community members. The Symposium is a great way for students to practice their oral presentation skills as well as articulate the details of their work.

COMMUNITY ENGAGEMENT: While academics and extracurriculars are important parts of the undergraduate experience, another vital component is community engagement. Service to others continues to be an engaging and positive experience for students and faculty alike. There are several different ways to get involved, and UMM works hard to connect students to opportunities both in and out of the classroom. For example, "Tutoring, Reading, and Enabling Children" (TREC) is an awesome initiative that allows UMM students to work directly with local pre-K through 6th grade students. TREC students are, first and foremost, tutors and mentors. They are responsible for the educational and personal support of the children they are assisting. Not only do UMM students serve TREC in the classroom, but they work with students in afterschool programs. The continued support is a way to make a stronger impression on the students, and thus encourage their good performance in school.

HONORS AT MORRIS: The UMM Honors Program is designed for academically gifted students. Members of the Honors community are given coursework and tasks that more appropriately challenge their abilities. Aside from advanced course material, Honors students also take part in research, internships, global exchange, co-curricular activities, and plenty more. The program takes a holistic approach to its students so that each member graduates as an advanced, well-rounded, independent thinker. In general, interested students apply during spring semester of their freshman year, and if admitted, begin the program the fall of their second year.

---

http://www.morris.umn.edu/
P: (320) 589-6035

PUBLIC

STUDENT PROFILE

1,856 undergraduate students

92% of undergrad students are full time

46% male – 54% female

14% of students are from out of state

77% freshman retention rate

65% graduated in 6 years

FACULTY PROFILE

104 full-time faculty

2 part-time faculty

12 to 1 student/faculty ratio

ADMISSIONS

3,619 Total Applicants

2,164 Total Admissions

416 Total Freshman Enrollment

59.80% of applicants admitted

SAT Ranges: CR 500-660, M 510-640, W 490-620

ACT Ranges: C 22-28, M 22-27, E 21-28, W 21-25

TUITION & COSTS

Tuition: $11,896

Fees: $950

Total: $12,846

R&B: $7,804

Room: $3,642

Board: $4,162

Total: $20,650

FINANCIAL

$10,431 avg grant/scholarship amount (need)

$3,742 avg loan amount (need)

UNIVERSITY OF ST. THOMAS

ST. PAUL, MINNESOTA

Inspired by Catholic intellectual tradition, the University of St. Thomas educates students to be morally responsible leaders who think critically, act wisely, and work skillfully to advance the common good.

TALKING CIRCLES: Talking Circles is a first-year retreat that takes students around the community to provide service and enact change. The name of the retreat comes from the Native American tradition of the "talking circle," which was a gathering of members to discuss their current issues and possible solutions. Taking place at the end of January, the retreat encompasses three days of inspiring action that continue to remind freshmen of the University's mission.

COMMUNITY-BASED RESEARCH PROGRAM: The Community-Based Research Program is open to students of all majors and disciplines. It aims to recognize undergraduate research that that has in collaboration with community partners, honoring students who enhance their education while making a positive impact on the world around them. Those who choose to participate in C-B Research receive a stipend of $4,000 and commit to 400 hours of inspiring work.

STUDY ABROAD: Study abroad is a highly rewarding experience that provides incredible benefits to students as they explore other cities and cultures. Those who participate gain skills in cross-cultural communication and independence as well as a better understanding of the world's diversity. St. Thomas' study abroad programs range in focus and duration, allowing students to choose the experience that best fits their interests and schedules. Students who opt to study abroad for a semester or longer can work with third-party providers to find a program, or they can choose to participate in either St. Thomas' Catholic Studies Semester in Rome or the London Business Semester. J-Term and summer programs are perfect for students who can't commit to long-term study abroad. Even if their time is limited, however, they still have access to nearly 60 programs both through the University and with third-party providers.

CIVIC ENGAGEMENT: Civic engagement allows students to give back to the community while integrating their service with their coursework and academic theory. Made possible by the Office of Civic Engagement, community-based learning splits students' class time between lecture, service, and reflection. Students and faculty work together to grow and reflect, allowing them to improve their community approaches every year in order to provide the best service and academic experience possible. UST offers service-learning opportunities during the year, J-Term, and summer.

FALL LEADERSHIP INSTITUTE: The Fall Leadership Institute (FLI) is an annual event for undergraduate students. This conference explores the foundations of successful leadership and examines ways that students can develop their own skills. FLI is highly collaborative, bringing students and faculty to work together as they find new solutions and break new ground. Some of the concepts covered at the conference include marketing, time management, and fiscal management.

THE CENTER FOR WRITING: Writing can be a daunting task, and many students find that they need extra help to master the skill of writing at the collegiate level. Tackling such a common area of concern, St. Thomas' Writing Center has been established to address the needs of students and prepare each individual for success. At the center, peer consultants work one-on-one with students to address the challenges that may arise at any stage of the writing process. Whether they need help with formatting, brainstorming, or articulating, St. Thomas students find that the Writing Center is prepared to assist them every step of the way. Ultimately, it is the Center's goal to teach every student to recognize their own potential through trial and error and thoughtful analysis.

http://www.stthomas.edu/

P: (651) 962-5000

PRIVATE - CATHOLIC

STUDENT PROFILE

6,143 undergraduate students

95% of undergrad students are full time

54% male – 46% female

21% of students are from out of state

89% freshman retention rate

76% graduated in 6 years

FACULTY PROFILE

464 full-time faculty

463 part-time faculty

14 to 1 student/faculty ratio

ADMISSIONS

5,436 Total Applicants

4,564 Total Admissions

1,435 Total Freshman Enrollment

83.96% of applicants admitted

SAT Ranges: CR 520-630, M 510-620

ACT Ranges: C 24-29, M 24-28, E 23-29

TUITION & COSTS

Tuition: $37,264

Fees: $841

Total: $38,105

R&B: $9,750

Room: $5,886

Board: $3,864

Total: $47,855

FINANCIAL

$19,279 avg grant/scholarship amount (total)

$8,539 avg loan amount (total)

CONCORDIA UNIVERSITY, NEBRASKA

SEWARD, NEBRASKA

Concordia University, Nebraska, a Lutheran, Christ-centered institution, is a fully accredited, coeducational university that currently serves more than 2,300 students. Concordia offers more than 70 undergraduate, graduate, and professional programs in an excellent academic and Christ-centered community that equips men and women for lives of learning, service, and leadership in the church and world. Just 25 minutes from Lincoln, Nebraska, and 75 minutes from west Omaha, students have easy access to service and social opportunities, culture, and entertainment in the city. They can even hang out with plenty to do right in Seward, Concordia's friendly hometown of around 7,000 people. Seward offers several coffee shops, boutiques, local and chain restaurants, a movie theater, a bowling alley, and other shopping and entertainment activities.

A STUDENT-CENTERED EDUCATION: Concordia University, Nebraska is a place where students can find their heart's calling and be equipped to answer it. At Concordia, the culture is about students. It's about serving others, being part of a vibrant Christian community, and maximizing one's gifts and talents. At Concordia, the foundation of a Christ-centered, Lutheran university is evident in the way classmates genuinely support each other as well as the way professors care about every aspect of students' wellbeing. The variety of programs at Concordia allow students to explore their passions with confidence. Most importantly, Christ consistently remains an integral part of Concordia's classroom environment, as professors tie Christ and service to others to their academic content. Concordia is a place where students can be themselves, share their opinions, and find their way—all with the loving support of a community that cares about their success. And that's what makes Concordia feel like home.

SEWARD, NEBRASKA: Concordia's hometown of Seward, Nebraska, makes it easy to adjust to college life by providing everything students need. Seward has the #1 lowest crime rate of 31 Nebraska cities with 5,000+ people, and it has shopping, coffee shops, bowling, a movie theater, a biking trail, and parks to keep students busy and engaged. In Seward, students are part of the community, and they can rest easy feeling safe and welcome. Students can also experience the entertainment and city life of Lincoln, less than half an hour away.

DEDICATED FACULTY: At Concordia University, Nebraska, professors go out of their way to make the college experience as rich and rewarding as possible. They are known among students for their welcoming and encouraging attitudes as well as the personal and academic support they are happy to offer. More than 80% of the full-time professors have the highest degree possible in their field of study, and they recognize that every student has unique talents, passions, and skill sets. Professors commit to working side-by-side with students to teach in a way that fits each individual's learning style and abilities. With many students at Concordia from around the country, the reassurance and guidance that students receive from their professors make Concordia feel like a home away from home.

LIFE OUTSIDE THE CLASSROOM: Christ is an integral part of Concordia's culture. Students have opportunities to serve their community in such locations as the Seward Youth Center and local grade schools. With student organizations, Bible studies, music ensembles, intramural teams, mission and service groups, art exhibits, and residence hall activities, there's always something to do.

CONCORDIA UNIVERSITY NEBRASKA

http://www.cune.edu/
P: (800) 535-5494

PRIVATE - CHRISTIAN

STUDENT PROFILE

1,255 undergraduate students

97% of undergrad students are full time

49% male – 51% female

55% of students are from out of state

76% freshman retention rate

59% graduated in 6 years

FACULTY PROFILE

63 full-time faculty

177 part-time faculty

14 to 1 student/faculty ratio

ADMISSIONS

1,380 Total Applicants

1,072 Total Admissions

347 Total Freshman Enrollment

77.68% of applicants admitted

SAT Ranges: CR 430-560, M 470-560

ACT Ranges: C 20-27, M 19-27, E 20-28

TUITION & COSTS

Tuition: $27,880

Fees: $600

Total: $28,480

R&B: $7,800

Total: $36,280

FINANCIAL

$17,144 avg grant/scholarship amount (need)

$4,488 avg loan amount (need)

CREIGHTON UNIVERSITY

OMAHA, NEBRASKA

Creighton is the only university in the country to offer education in seven health professions—medicine, dentistry, pharmacy, nursing, occupational therapy, physical therapy, and public health—as well as outstanding programs in arts and sciences, business, and law, all on one walkable campus. One of 28 Jesuit colleges and universities in the country, Creighton offers a purposeful education that is established on academic excellence, social justice, and personal growth.

SERVICE-LEARNING: In a recent academic year, Creighton students contributed more than 1 million collective hours of service locally, regionally, nationally, and internationally. Service-learning is incorporated into many Creighton courses and, every spring and fall, students of different ages, majors, and faiths come together for spring and fall break service trips. These students devote their entire vacation to visiting various communities, helping the less fortunate, and making a difference in the world. They make new friends and experience new cultures, all while promoting Jesuit values.

THE SCHLEGEL CENTER FOR SERVICE AND JUSTICE (SCSJ): The Schlegel Center for Service and Justice (SCSJ) is committed to building a community of faith in service for justice. In addition to SCSJ members' participation in the school's justice and peace studies program, the Center also sponsors ongoing disaster relief for organizations such as the International Federation of Red Cross and Red Crescent Societies, the American Red Cross, Catholic Charities USA, and Catholic Relief Services.

THE CREIGHTON EDGE: The Creighton EDGE provides students with a holistic approach to academic advising, the pursuit of advanced studies in graduate/professional school, and career planning. It features alumni networking, mentoring, and shadowing; a connection to portfolio-building internship opportunities; individual and group tutoring; academic coaching and academic counseling; and assistance with any issues that could impact students' ability to be successful.

RESEARCH: More than 100 faculty research projects are under way at Creighton on any given day, the vast majority of which involve undergraduate students. Creighton's Center for Undergraduate Research and Scholarship (CURAS) supports and encourages undergraduate research and scholarship across all disciplines. Traditionally, more than 400 undergraduate students enroll in research hours each year, and an estimated 100 additional students volunteer to work on research projects without pay or credit. Creighton faculty members are deeply involved in nationally recognized research projects and are constantly searching for ways to enhance teaching, contribute to a better society, discover new knowledge, and find ways to pass their benefits on to students.

OMAHA, NEBRASKA: One of the 50 largest cities in the country, Omaha offers live music and theatre, great dining, and an active nightlife. The combined Omaha metropolitan area has a population of more than 800,000 and includes 30,000 businesses—including 50 Fortune 500 companies—providing Creighton students with plentiful job and internship opportunities. Omaha boasts beautiful, tree-covered rolling hills, and the city is home to the Old Market, which includes shops, restaurants, pubs, and art galleries.

PURSUIT OF SUCCESS: Creighton students are highly motivated to succeed and use their gifts to make a difference in the world with the help of caring professors, state-of-the-art technology, and hands-on learning experiences. More than 98 percent of Creighton graduates are employed, involved in volunteer work, or attending graduate or professional school within nine months of graduation. More internships exist than there are students to fill them, meaning that every student has the chance to build their résumés with loads of useful experience.

---

http://www.creighton.edu/

P: (402) 280-2703

PRIVATE - CATHOLIC

STUDENT PROFILE

4,163 undergraduate students

94% of undergrad students are full time

43% male – 57% female

79% of students are from out of state

90% freshman retention rate

74% graduated in 6 years

FACULTY PROFILE

627 full-time faculty

289 part-time faculty

11 to 1 student/faculty ratio

ADMISSIONS

9,747 Total Applicants

6,870 Total Admissions

1,068 Total Freshman Enrollment

70.48% of applicants admitted

SAT Ranges: CR 510-630, M 540-650, W 510-620

ACT Ranges: C 24-29, M 24-29, E 24-32, W 8-9

TUITION & COSTS

Tuition: $34,810

Fees: $1,612

Total: $36,422

R&B: $10,294

Room: $5,850

Board: $4,444

Total: $46,716

FINANCIAL

$19,610 avg grant/scholarship amount (total)

$8,804 avg loan amount (total)

NEBRASKA WESLEYAN UNIVERSITY

LINCOLN, NEBRASKA

NEBRASKA
WESLEYAN
UNIVERSITY

Nebraska Wesleyan University is an independent, Methodist liberal arts college of roughly 2,000 students in Lincoln, Neb. The university's steadfast commitment to putting learning into action through internships, study abroad, service learning, and collaborative research has yielded tremendous outcomes for students and alumni. Nebraska Wesleyan has earned a national reputation for placing students in top graduate and professional school programs. NWU is also among the nation's leaders in Fulbright scholars, Academic All-Americans, and NCAA Postgraduate Scholarship winners.

SERVICE FOR EVERYONE: Nebraska Wesleyan students get involved on and off campus before their first semester even begins. Community service projects are a part of New Student Orientation. NWU's Student Involvement Fair (held during the second week of classes) lets people explore student groups and get involved early. Professors also integrate service-learning components into many courses, carrying a high level of engagement throughout the academic year.

INNOVATIVE STUDY: Nebraska Wesleyan University adopted an innovative general education curriculum in 2013. Moving away from a "cafeteria approach" in which students build their class schedules by choosing "a little of this" and "a little of that," Nebraska Wesleyan now offers a format in which students select an interdisciplinary "thread." Here, they explore universal topics from the perspectives of multiple academic disciplines. This approach to a liberal arts education helps students see more explicitly the connections between different fields.

INTENSELY INVOLVED: A strong community makes it possible for Nebraska Wesleyan students to put what they learn into action. BFA students in theatre, for example, participate in an average of six shows per year. Their shows are consistently embraced and well attended by the community. Additionally, 100 percent of NWU business students conduct internships due to their strong reputation with local, regional, and even national businesses. These businesses are eager to place—and hire—NWU students.

SCHOOL-WIDE SERVICE: The Nebraska Wesleyan community is so strong due to NWU students' commitment to providing it service. In honor of the university's 125th anniversary in 2013, NWU students led the charge to contribute 100 hours of community service each year. Despite their busy schedules, NWU students, along with faculty, staff, and alumni, reached their 12,500-hour service goal for the year in just eight months.

PREPARED FOR THE WORLD: An outstanding education, the right priorities, and the willingness to work hard combine to bring just about any goal within reach. An excellent education is why 95 percent of surveyed seniors say Nebraska Wesleyan "prepared" or "strongly prepared" them for employment or graduate and professional school. And the work ethic that students sharpen at NWU helps them get the maximum benefit from their education as they pursue their goals. Nebraska Wesleyan alumni quickly learn they can compete with anyone when it comes to solving complex problems. They respond to changing circumstances and work well in teams.

FACULTY OF EXPLORERS: NWU professors are tremendously dedicated to teaching undergraduates. While some universities prioritize professors' research and publications, teaching is the priority at NWU. "The faculty are here because they like to do that," said Kathy Wolfe, dean of NWU's College of Liberal Arts and Sciences. "If they didn't want teaching to be their first responsibility, they wouldn't be teaching at a school like ours."

---

http://www.nebrwesleyan.edu/

P: (800) 541-3818

PRIVATE

STUDENT PROFILE

1,811 undergraduate students

83% of undergrad students are full time

39% male – 61% female

14% of students are from out of state

79% freshman retention rate

62% graduated in 6 years

FACULTY PROFILE

115 full-time faculty

147 part-time faculty

11 to 1 student/faculty ratio

ADMISSIONS

1,689 Total Applicants

1,331 Total Admissions

440 Total Freshman Enrollment

78.80% of applicants admitted

SAT Ranges: CR 430-590, M 510-600

ACT Ranges: C 22-27, M 21-27, E 22-28

TUITION & COSTS

Tuition: $29,200

Fees: $600

Total: $29,800

R&B: $8,340

Room: $4,630

Board: $3,710

Total: $38,140

FINANCIAL

$17,491 avg grant/scholarship amount (total)

$7,772 avg loan amount (total)

WAYNE STATE COLLEGE

WAYNE, NEBRASKA

Wayne State College, long recognized for providing academic excellence in its small, friendly setting, has been the educational and cultural anchor of northeast Nebraska for more than 100 years. What began as an institution devoted to teacher education has transformed into the region's most affordable leading comprehensive college. More than 3,600 students and 120 faculty members call Wayne State home.

EDUCATION AND INNOVATION: With such innovative programs as NENTA (Northeast Nebraska Teacher Academy) and RHOP (Rural Health Opportunities Program), Wayne State students have extraordinary outlets through which to gain real-world experience that prepares them for success both in and out of the classroom. NENTA, for example, places highly qualified Wayne State College teaching majors to be substitute teachers in participating school districts. The programs benefits go both ways, granting students legitimate teaching experience while providing the schools insight from those who are learning the latest in curriculum and instruction. This kind of real-world experience makes Wayne State College teaching majors some of the most sought-after and employable students after graduation.

DEDICATED FACULTY: The focus of Wayne State educators lie not simply on teaching, but true, transformative learning. The College's top-notch faculty emphasize student engagement in their classrooms, which are all small enough to enable class discussion. Classes naturally foster engaged, challenging experiences, and students are able to recognize how much their professors care about their individual academic success.

SERVICE-LEARNING: It is more than common for Wayne State courses to introduce hands-on learning to students outside of the classroom. The College's Service-Learning program promotes, mobilizes, and supports the efforts for Wayne State to strengthen its academics through service to the surrounding community. Such opportunities give students a true sense of purpose in their studies, encouraging them to make the most of their Wayne State education as well as their lives beyond college.

STUDENT LIFE: Wayne State College clubs and organizations encompass a wide variety of interests. Art, politics, athletics, business, and multicultural affairs are just a few of the interests around which students gather and meet like-minded peers. These clubs and organizations can even sponsor on-campus events like guest lectures from nationally renowned speakers as well as off-campus adventures that truly immerse them in their fields of interest. Wayne State's clubs and organizations, intramural sports, student activities board, and NCAA athletics bring more than 400 student-centered activities to campus each year, packing the College calendar with a whole lot of fun.

PREPARATION FOR SUCCESS: A degree from Wayne State can be thought of in two ways. First, it's the piece of paper that signifies a student's comprehension of certain skills, data, and knowledge within their major. WSC students graduate ready to assume roles as teachers, trainers, laboratory assistants, business leaders, construction managers, graduate students, and more. But there's more to it than that. A Wayne State degree signifies that a student has replaced "an empty mind with an open one." What Wayne State does is open its students' minds to critical thinking and analysis. It gives its students the tools not only to make discoveries, but also to remain endlessly curious. By opening their minds and asking questions, WSC students are equipped to shape their futures, create their careers, and continue the lifelong process of learning.

---

http://www.wsc.edu/

P: (402) 375-7000

PUBLIC

STUDENT PROFILE

2,969 undergraduate students

91% of undergrad students are full time

43% male – 57% female

68% freshman retention rate

49% graduated in 6 years

13% of students are from out of state

FACULTY PROFILE

127 full-time faculty

93 part-time faculty

18 to 1 student/faculty ratio

TUITION & COSTS

Tuition: (In) $4,200 (Out) $8,400

Fees: $1,404

Total: (In) $5,604 (Out) $9,804

R&B: $6,420

Room: $3,120

Board: $3,300

Total: (In) $12,024 (Out) $16,224

FINANCIAL

$4,176 avg grant/scholarship amount (total)

$5,409 avg loan amount (total)

UNIVERSITY OF MARY

BISMARCK, NORTH DAKOTA

UNIVERSITY
of **MARY**

The University of Mary in Bismarck, North Dakota, was founded in 1959 by the Benedictine Sisters of Annunciation Monastery. The school began as a four-year undergraduate college of education and nursing and, since then, has expanded to offer 56 undergraduate majors, 14 master's programs, and 3 doctoral programs. The variety of programs offered gives students a strong liberal arts base for their chosen careers while maintaining a distinctive focus on servant leadership.

FIRST-YEAR SEMINAR: Among the University's more unique attributes is the first-year seminar, which is taught by the University's president himself, Msgr. James P. Shea. Along with select members of his cabinet, Msgr. Shea's course attempts to ignite students' interest in life's core questions: "Why am I here? What was I made for? Who am I to love? How can I live well?" His active work with the freshmen is coupled with a fine assembly of faculty in a variety of disciplines. Because the University of Mary is not a research institution, Mary's faculty are hired and trained specifically to teach. They engage with students in projects outside of class and make an engaged investment in their success.

GLOBAL STUDIES: Global Studies at the University of Mary offers students the chance to travel to the "Eternal City" of Rome, Italy; Milan, Italy; Peru; and more through faculty-led and service-oriented trips. Students can study for a full semester, go on adventures for a few weeks out of the summer, and even participate in service around the world throughout the winter and spring breaks. The University's Global Studies program combines its already outstanding education with life-changing opportunities to experience a different culture, befriend classmates, and put into action the Benedictine values.

DAY OF SERVICE: In the fall of 2014, students involved in Student Government created a campus- and community-wide Day of Service. Since then, this new tradition compassionate volunteer work has blossomed into a highly anticipated event. Thousands of students and faculty have contributed to the needs of the Bismarck-Mandan, ND, community. By serving charitable organizations and businesses within the local neighborhood, University of Mary has touched countless lives, including the students who came to serve.

RESIDENT SCHOLARS: With the intention to bridge the gap between residential life and academia, the University has recently launched a new "Residential Life Scholar" program. Through this initiative, first-year students are placed directly in touch with amazing support; they have the privilege of living within the same residential community as expert professors who hold terminal degrees in their fields. These Resident Scholars foster a community of learning outside of the classroom, contributing to a truly unique experiment in higher education.

ACTIVITIES OUTSIDE OF THE CLASSROOM: While the University of Mary strives to produce top-notch professionals prepared for the rigors of postgraduate life, students can go even further by participating in the Emerging Leaders Academy (ELA). Those with a desire to go beyond Mary's already robust internships and experiential learning programs are able to engage in a personally interactive experience with leaders in their chosen profession. Offered as an optional community, students in ELA take part in personal mentorships that develop their professional skills and networks on a highly individualized level. The program gets students on a fast track to making profound impacts in their careers, learning actively from those who are already doing so.

GUARANTEED SUCCESS: The University of Mary's broad offering of programs prepares students for a range of career opportunities. And with a placement rate of 99%, Mary graduates happily excel in obtaining employment and getting into graduate school. Mary offers several professional preparation programs, including such fields as business, education, nursing, physical therapy, other health science specializations such as respiratory therapy. Newly launched specializations in engineering (chemical, civil, electrical, mechanical, and petroleum) are also preparing students to succeed in the evolving workforce.

---

http://www.umary.edu/
P: (701) 355-8030

PRIVATE - CATHOLIC

STUDENT PROFILE

2,049 undergraduate students

83% of undergrad students are full time

36% male — 64% female

50% of students are from out of state

75% freshman retention rate

60% graduated in 6 years

FACULTY PROFILE

231 full-time faculty

23 part-time faculty

13 to 1 student/faculty ratio

ADMISSIONS

900 Total Applicants

861 Total Admissions

410 Total Freshman Enrollment

95.67% of applicants admitted

SAT Ranges: CR 450-600, M 460-580, W 440-575

ACT Ranges: C 20-26, M 19-26, E 20-26

TUITION & COSTS

Tuition: $15,440

Fees: $1,245

Total: $16,685

R&B: $6,136

Room: $2,840

Board: $3,296

Total: $22,821

FINANCIAL

$8,722 avg grant/scholarship amount (total)

$7,470 avg loan amount (total)

ASHLAND UNIVERSITY

ASHLAND, OHIO

ASHLAND UNIVERSITY

Ashland is part of a safe and supportive family of scholars and students, a place where a small-town feel is met with big-time athletics. It's a place where community service, real-world internships, and more than 100 social organizations help students become leaders. And with small class sizes, nobody disappears in the back of large lecture halls. At Ashland University, the accent is on the individual.

FIRST-YEAR SEMINARS AND EXPERIENCES: Ashland University offers Freshman Success Seminars (FSS) that are designed to help first-year students adjust to the academic, personal, and social demands of a diverse university setting. It supports future success by reinforcing study skills and focusing on learning techniques at the collegiate level. Throughout these courses, new Ashland students are given the chance explore their strengths and goals in order to face their four-year plan with confidence.

COMMON INTELLECTUAL EXPERIENCES: Ashland University's Undergraduate Core Curriculum is foundational to all undergraduate students' majors, acting as the central academic experience to unify students across all programs, departments, and Colleges. Through the Core, students are taught to embrace the four key elements of Ashland University's institutional mission: intellectual development and wisdom, ethical behavior and justice, preparation for living and working as citizens, and awareness of global responsibilities.

DIVERSITY/GLOBAL LEARNING: Ashland University is committed to incorporating diversity into its curriculum. Examples of the diverse courses offered include African American Literature; Literature and Gender; Race, Ethnic, and Minority Issues; French Women Writers; and Intercultural Communication. Many of the courses that emphasize diversity also fulfill requirements within the Core, thus proving to bolster a well-rounded student experience for all.

UNDERGRADUATE RESEARCH: Ashland University is much different than many other small-to-mid-size universities, as it allows students within most majors to conduct research under the close supervision of a faculty mentor. In fact, AU students have played a major role in a number of important research projects on campus, including an investigation of lead content in inexpensive jewelry and toys that led to at least 14 recalls by the Consumer Product Safety Commission. Students have even discovered high levels of cadmium in jewelry items that were some at major retail stores in Ohio, Texas, California, and New York. Following this report, Wal-Mart even pulled many suspect items from its store shelves.

WRITING-INTENSIVE COURSES: The Writing Studio, administered through the College of Arts and Sciences, primarily offers individual consultation for papers across the curriculum. Writing Assistants provide guidance and instruction in the following areas: understanding writing assignments and styles, writing essays and critical analyses, supporting theses, revising for structure and grammar, documenting research, and teaching proofreading strategies.

INTERNSHIPS/COOPS/PRACTICUMS: Internship and Co-op opportunities are extremely important at Ashland, supporting the University's Mission Statement that challenges students to develop intellectually and ethically, to seek wisdom and justice, and to prepare for the rigors of living and working as engaged global citizens. Ashland faculty realize that, in order for their students to be successful upon graduation, they must do their part in making learning opportunities available outside of the classroom. While most majors offer internship-based elective courses, students can also explore opportunities through Ashland's Student Affairs Division.

CAPSTONE COURSES AND PROJECTS/SENIOR EXPERIENCE: Most majors at Ashland University require a capstone course or a senior seminar as part of their curricula. These experiences provide students with the ability to implement and practice the methods they've learned in previous and concurrent courses, examining multiple objectives, synthesizing concepts, and evaluating ways to put knowledge into practice. Through their culminating work, students demonstrate their overall competence within their respective fields of study.

https://www.ashland.edu/
P: (800) 882-1548

PRIVATE

STUDENT PROFILE

3,559 undergraduate students

92% of undergrad students are full time

49% male – 51% female

7% of students are from out of state

80% freshman retention rate

62% graduated in 6 years

FACULTY PROFILE

174 full-time faculty

218 part-time faculty

12 to 1 student/faculty ratio

ADMISSIONS

3,443 Total Applicants

2,495 Total Admissions

627 Total Freshman Enrollment

72.47% of applicants admitted

SAT Ranges: CR 460-560, M 490-580

ACT Ranges: C 20-25, M 19-25, E 19-24

TUITION & COSTS

Tuition: $19,740

R&B: $9,746

Total: $29,486

FINANCIAL

$10,778 avg grant/scholarship amount (need)

$4,617 avg loan amount (need)

CAPITAL UNIVERSITY

COLUMBUS, OHIO

Capital University is a private institution located in the Columbus, Ohio, community of Bexley. Capital is about transforming lives and enabling students to impact and transform the world.

COMMON INTELLECTUAL EXPERIENCES: Capital University strives to fulfill students with a liberal education that enhances both their majors and their General Education experiences. A liberal education readies the mind and spirit for every arena of life—the workplace, the home, the market, houses of worship, and town halls. This is accomplished through an exploration of several modes of inquiry, increasing cultural literacy and challenging students to examine foundational ethical and cultural assumptions. It enables students to think critically and reflect their roles as citizens as well as the values of play, wonder, travel, and lifelong learning in a rich and rewarding life.

UNDERGRADUATE RESEARCH: Over the past decade, Capital University has increasingly recognized the benefits of student-faculty collaborative scholarship. The active involvement that faculty have with their students is truly impactful, enabling close, individually focused mentorships that enrich the entire college experience. Faculty involvement can manifest in many great ways, whether they act as mentors throughout independent student projects or take them on as assistants in their own scholarship pursuits, Capital professors prioritize their students' growth and experiences.

DIVERSITY/GLOBAL LEARNING: Capital University's Office of Diversity and Inclusion provides support to students from underrepresented populations as well as students who wish to explore cultures and ideas that are different from their own. The Office partners with a number of facilities across campus to provide academic support, celebrate diversity and cultures, and coordinate programs specifically for students of color and difference as well as their allies.

CONTINUITY ACROSS THE CURRICULUM: A priority of Capital's General Education curriculum is literacy and writing skills. Students are given the space to practice critical thinking and communicating their ideas in clearly written terms. All General Education courses are intended to incorporate the methods and goals of one another, thereby establishing continuity across the curriculum as a whole. Working in accordance with the University's Unified Theme program, students learn to grasp the five key elements of critical thought and argumentation; organization; clarity and style; mechanics; and documentation and formatting.

LEARNING COMMUNITIES: Capital University hosts five Learning Communities, as well as themed housing, in which students can elect to live with and participate in a community of learners who share an affinity for a common focus. The Honors program, nursing, music, service, and healthy living communities foster a supportive environment for students to grow alongside one another as they improve their focused skills and sharpen their interests. Students in Learning Communities take classes as a cohort while engaging in shared co- and extracurricular programming to enhance their classroom learning.

SERVICE-LEARNING, COMMUNITY-BASED LEARNING: Capital University's mission is rooted in service to others. Students live out the mission through their work in service-learning courses, community-based research, mentoring programs, short- and long-term service collaborations, and alternative break experiences. Through this mix of active learning experiences, students are able not only to serve, but also to immerse themselves in the community around them.

INDEPENDENT LEARNING: There are a number of curriculum-based mechanisms for students to engage in activities that enhance their individual learning experiences. One such unique opportunity is the 491: Individual Study course in which they are given the allotted time and resources to work on an independent study project.

---

http://www.capital.edu/

P: (614) 236-6101

PRIVATE

STUDENT PROFILE

2,654 undergraduate students

93% of undergrad students are full time

43% male – 57% female

10% of students are from out of state

76.2% freshman retention rate

63% graduated in 6 years

FACULTY PROFILE

159 full-time faculty

263 part-time faculty

12 to 1 student/faculty ratio

ADMISSIONS

3,718 Total Applicants

2,685 Total Admissions

671 Total Freshman Enrollment

72.22% of applicants admitted

SAT Ranges: CR 480-610, M 480-580, W 460-590

ACT Ranges: C 22-28, M 21-27, E 21-28, W 20-26

TUITION & COSTS

Tuition: $32,630

Fees: $200

Total: $32,830

R&B: $9,250

Room: $4,490

Board: $4,760

Total: $42,080

FINANCIAL

$21,700 avg grant/scholarship amount (need)

$4,704 avg loan amount (need)

DEFIANCE COLLEGE

DEFIANCE, OHIO

Defiance College (DC) is a comprehensive, private, coeducational college affiliated with the United Church of Christ. Founded in 1850, the 150-acre campus is located in Northwest Ohio, an area of picturesque farmland at the confluence of the Auglaize and Maumee rivers. Defiance offers associate, bachelor's, and master's degrees.

DRIVEN TO SERVE THE WORLD: At Defiance College, there is an institution-wide enthusiasm for learning. Guided by excellent faculty members, Defiance students build on their existing interests while developing new passions. They approach challenges with the habits of heart, mind, and spirit, driven toward doing good in the world. In nearly 40 programs of study, everything from accounting and education to restoration ecology and digital forensic science, Defiance students are able to grow in all kinds of ways. No matter their focus, their education is firmly rooted in and supported by the values of the College's mission: To Know, To Understand, To Lead, To Serve. Although they arrive with an astonishing range of ambitions and take off in every possible direction, each Defiance student is provided with a strong liberal arts foundation that emphasizes critical thinking and character building.

FIRST-YEAR FOUNDATIONS: Within the new core curriculum, all students are immediately introduced to an excellent way of thinking and working through the Foundations of Academic Inquiry course. This course prepares students with the proper skills they need to conduct strong research. Students are taught to understand the different types of sources, how to acquire and judge material, and how to use information to prepare and support their research.

UNDERGRADUATE RESEARCH AND PROJECTS: The challenging academic environment at Defiance College is enhanced by undergraduate research, creative expression, and real-world professional experience. A rich classroom environment based in the liberal arts is the centerpiece from which students form connections and discover new ways to view and explore the world. These students are engaged in collaborative research and scholarship with their faculty members, benefiting strongly from their access to the Honors Program, campus symposia, capstone projects within their major, and experience-rich Learning Communities.

SERVICE-LEARNING: DC is home to the McMaster School for Advancing Humanity, an innovative research program devoted to teaching, service, scholarship, and action to improve the human condition. Distinctive among colleges and universities across the U.S., the McMaster School utilizes Defiance College's nationally recognized model of service and civic engagement. Through the McMaster program, students and faculty apply their academic expertise to a real-world effort that impacts the lives of others. In recent years, participants have developed projects and established partnerships in Belize, Cambodia, Tanzania, and Panama. Many of these projects start and develop in team-building Learning Communities, which are groups of student researchers who meet on a regular basis to plan, work, and prepare for their research and travel.

PERSONAL SUCCESS PLAN: The Defiance experience starts right when students take their first steps on campus. They set themselves up for a fantastic collegiate experience by working on individualized strategic plans that help them map out the most efficient and fulfilling way to reach their goals in higher education. These Personal Success Plans go beyond academics and even helps to integrate cultural experiences, physical and emotional wellness strategies, social enrichment, and ethical and spiritual growth. Students enter college with an idea of how to make the most of their experiences and leave with a distinctive résumé that gives them an advantage when applying to jobs and graduate schools. DC students graduate with real-world experiences as well as the knowledge to move into their futures as informed and engaged adults.

http://www.defiance.edu/

P: (800) 520-4632

PRIVATE

STUDENT PROFILE

681 undergraduate students

84% of undergrad students are full time

53% male – 47% female

56% freshman retention rate

41% graduated in 6 years

FACULTY PROFILE

40 full-time faculty

49 part-time faculty

11 to 1 student/faculty ratio

ADMISSIONS

1,210 Total Applicants

789 Total Admissions

183 Total Freshman Enrollment

65.21% of applicants admitted

SAT Ranges: CR 395-460, M 390-505

ACT Ranges: C 19-24, M 17-24, E 17-23

TUITION & COSTS

Tuition: $30,400

Fees: $682

Total: $31,082

R&B: $9,850

Room: $5,490

Board: $4,360

Total: $40,932

FINANCIAL

$18,303 avg grant/scholarship amount (total)

$9,032 avg loan amount (total)

DENISON UNIVERSITY

GRANVILLE, OHIO

Denison's academic mission is to educate students to become independent thinkers and active citizens of a democratic society. Students enjoy the University's dynamic learning environment 24 hours a day. Denison University is set in the small town of Granville, Ohio. They can walk the streets of this quaint area and enjoy all the restaurants and shops that line the main street. Students can also enjoy the local bike trails, which traverse all throughout the beautiful community.

SERVICE-LEARNING: Service-learning is an integral part of the Denison experience and can manifest in one of three ways: extracurricular community service, co-curricular service-learning, or curricular service-learning. Co-curricular service-learning functions to increase awareness of important social issues, and curricular service-learning acts as a supplemental addition to an academic course. Whether they perform service in collaboration with an area of study in club or help others through a student-run organization or club, the entire Denison community is making daily strides in the service of others.

LIBERAL ARTS FRAMEWORK: At Denison, each student is recognized for their individual value. A Denison education means that no students hide in the back of the class, as they are all encouraged to make themselves known and take advantage of their educational experience. While each student does choose a specific major to study, Denison provides a liberal arts framework upon which to grow as well-rounded thinkers. Their holistically beneficial education begins with the First-Year Program, which is a mixture of academic and co-curricular experiences. This program teaches students incredibly important and valuable skills, including complex writing, higher-level thinking and conceptualization, and active participation. Students also get the added benefit of one-on-one academic advising and counseling.

STUDENT RESEARCH: Undergraduate Denison students are afforded countless opportunities to involve themselves in research initiatives, no matter their field of study. And, with the additional offering of the Gilpatrick House, student researchers can enhance and support their efforts with unique residential resources. Both summer-term and senior researchers are able to live in this House so that their groundbreaking work is given all the attention it deserves.

ENGAGEMENT OUTSIDE OF THE CLASSROOM: Denison recognizes that the best college experience is one that transcends the classroom. Because of this truth, the University provides plenty of extracurricular and social activities for students to explore, including 175 organizations that range from Greek life to service and leadership groups. These clubs make it easy for students to fall in love with their campus community, allowing them to be socially fulfilled and, therefore, academically driven.

SPIRITUAL LIFE: Denison welcomes students of all religions and faiths. There is an open invitation for all to practice their religious beliefs, voice their doubts, and express their ideas in faith and doctrine. With such a welcoming support for all religious affiliations, Denison encourages all of its students to collaborate and learn from one another's diverse perspectives.

PREPARING FOR SUCCESS: Denison students are equipped with all the tools necessary for their entrance into the workforce. Upon graduation, the majority of Denison students will have had some leadership experience, whether that had been in a class or through an organization. Denison grads are also excellent writers thanks to the University's emphasis on high-level written communication. Denison takes measures to encourage dialogue and participation between professors and students, thereby bolstering student success as a whole. Thanks to the outstanding caliber of student-faculty interaction, students are much more likely to engage in research initiatives with their professors and have a better grasp of their area of study when they enter the workforce.

---

http://www.denison.edu/
P: (740) 587-0810

PRIVATE

STUDENT PROFILE

2,254 undergraduate students

100% of undergrad students are full time

43% male – 57% female

65% of students are from out of state

87% freshman retention rate

80% graduated in 6 years

FACULTY PROFILE

235 full-time faculty

10 to 1 student/faculty ratio

ADMISSIONS

6,110 Total Applicants

2,926 Total Admissions

632 Total Freshman Enrollment

47.89% of applicants admitted

TUITION & COSTS

Tuition: $46,250

Fees: $1,040

Total: $47,290

R&B: $11,570

Room: $6,370

Board: $5,200

Total: $58,860

FINANCIAL

$29,846 avg grant/scholarship amount (total)

$6,241 avg loan amount (total)

HIRAM COLLEGE

HIRAM, OHIO

Hiram College prepares students to answer tough questions, solve complex problems, and communicate their ideas through a broad, interdisciplinary curriculum. Recognizing that learning doesn't just take place in the classroom, 100 percent of Hiram students complete an internship, research, or study abroad experience in order to connect what they learn in classroom to the real world.

FIRST-YEAR SEMINARS AND EXPERIENCES: The First-Year Program at Hiram locks down a sturdy foundation for all students adjusting to the new college lifestyle. Enrolling in a colloquium of their choice, students develop their communication skills and delve deeper into their passions. The learning communities in these colloquia are small, tightly knit groups of sixteen students each. By their second semester, they are ready and able to hone their skills and pursue research within any academic discipline across the arts, sciences, and humanities.

THE EMERGING SCHOLARS PROGRAM: Hiram College builds its curriculum and campus life around practices that have been shown to support student learning and success. For select students, the Emerging Scholars program works to give direction and extra support to help them succeed in their first year. By identifying these students early on, Hiram is able to guide and encourage them to persist and conquer their challenges.

WRITING-INTENSIVE COURSES: Writing has always been valued very highly at Hiram. The College was even one of the first schools in the United States to establish a Writing Across the Curriculum (WAC) program. Writing is incorporated into nearly every Hiram course, giving students the chance to practice communicating and presenting their ideas in any discipline.

HIRAM CONNECT: The Hiram Connect program gives students the opportunity to develop both personally and professionally throughout their undergraduate careers. Connect is an exhaustive plan that helps students obtain internships, go on study abroad trips, and apply their education to real-world contexts. Together, each of Hiram Connect's hands-on programs challenge students to discover what they want to do, who they are now, and who they want to become.

THE ACES PROGRAM: Hiram encourages students to further their intellectual growth by going to engaging extracurricular events. ACES (Academic and Co-Curricular Engagement Series) is an academic loyalty rewards program that enters students into weekly and monthly giveaway raffles as a prize for their attendance. This extra incentive pushes students to learn more outside of their classes while helping them get involved and out into the campus community. Through ACES, students are rewarded for their curiosity—both with points and prizes as well as with the friends they make at the events themselves.

COMMUNITY SERVICE: Sugar Day is an annual Hiram holiday during which classes are canceled for a full day of community service. Students, faculty, and staff all band together to bring their helping hands out into the Hiram community. Even when class is in session, however, the Terriers still jump to serve whenever they can. Students can help out during Hiram's Bread & Soup nights, weekly soup kitchens hosted at the beginning of each semester. There is always someone to help, and so there is always some way to serve.

CAPSTONE COURSES AND PROJECTS/SENIOR EXPERIENCE: Hiram College students showcase their knowledge through the completion of a capstone at the end of their senior year. Capstone projects begin their development with the help of faculty advisors who meet one-on-one with the students who select them. Together, these student-faculty teams brainstorm and outline a topic of research and analysis. And, after a few months of in-depth exploration, students create a strong, mature product that demonstrates who they have become as analytical academics.

http://www.hiram.edu/

P: (330) 569-3211

PRIVATE

STUDENT PROFILE

1,063 undergraduate students

85% of undergrad students are full time

50% male – 50% female

23% of students are from out of state

66% freshman retention rate

60.4% graduated in 6 years

FACULTY PROFILE

79 full-time faculty

55 part-time faculty

10 to 1 student/faculty ratio

ADMISSIONS

1,864 Total Applicants

1,074 Total Admissions

161 Total Freshman Enrollment

57.62% of applicants admitted

SAT Ranges: CR 450-590, M 430-578

ACT Ranges: C 20-27, M 19-25, E 19-26

TUITION & COSTS

Tuition: $31,440

Fees: $1,600

Total: $33,040

R&B: $10,190

Total: $43,230

FINANCIAL

$19,753 avg grant/scholarship amount (need)

$4,393 avg loan amount (need)

KENYON COLLEGE

GAMBIER, OHIO

Kenyon College seeks talented, driven individuals to join its academic community. Students enrolled at Kenyon collaborate with other students and dedicated faculty members, fostering an environment that promotes academic and personal success.

OFF-CAMPUS STUDY: Nearly 50% of every junior class studies abroad. Students can choose from 150 programs in 50 countries. Kenyon's approach to off-campus study involves careful planning and advising. Interested students work closely with faculty, returning students, and sometimes students who are natives of the country they'll be visiting. Off-campus study programs range from U.S destinations to cities around the world. Students should take careful consideration when selecting a program. The Center for Global Engagement is available to answer questions and assist in decision making. Some of Kenyon's most popular off-campus study destinations include: Australia, England, Italy, Denmark, Spain, and France.

THEMED HOUSING: Themed housing is a great option for students seeking to live among peers who share similar interests. All of Kenyon's themed house are self-directed and self-governed. This is accomplished through a set of rules and guidelines as well as a housing contract. Themed housing fosters strong community bonds and allows students to further explore their passions. Wellness housing promotes all aspects of a healthy lifestyle and observes seven aspects of wellness: physical, intellectual, emotional, social, spiritual, environmental, and occupational. This housing option supports the life-long pursuit of balanced living, both in body and mind. On top of the many resident options available at Kenyon, there are also Program Houses that explore disciplines. The current Program Houses offered explore topics of culture, environmentalism, feminism, LGBTQ, and farming.

GENERAL EDUCATION REQUIREMENTS: Kenyon's General Education requirements ensure that all students graduate with a well-rounded education. In order to receive a degree, students must complete a series of courses that cover the four academic divisions offered at Kenyon. They must also take a full year of a language and demonstrate their proficiency in that language. This way, they get a better understanding of another culture, learn the structure of another language, and gain experience with foreign text. And finally, they must satisfy a quantitative reasoning requirement. These classes, called QR courses, explore the application of graphic and numerical data. Students are exposed to statistics, mathematics, and the scientific method. Through their General Education, Kenyon students are equipped with the skills to take on any academic challenge.

SERVICE-LEARNING: Kenyon recently received a grant to establish a community engagement center, which is designed to implement programs and practices that engage students in experiential learning. This high-impact teaching method forms a bridge between course study and the greater community. The "Sense of Place" grant allows faculty to bring experiential methods into the classroom. When service becomes a part of the curriculum, students are able to apply academic theory to the needs of the community.

RESEARCH: Kenyon offers a select group of students the opportunity to remain on campus during the summer months to pursue their own research. Chosen students receive a stipend while they work through their projects. Faculty work in partnership with students and guide their work all the way through to presentations. Some students even go on to have their work published.

Kenyon College

http://www.kenyon.edu/
P: (740) 427-5000

PRIVATE

STUDENT PROFILE

1,711 undergraduate students

99% of undergrad students are full time

45% male – 55% female

93% freshman retention rate

87% graduated in 6 years

FACULTY PROFILE

194 full-time faculty

6 part-time faculty

10 to 1 student/faculty ratio

ADMISSIONS

6,644 Total Applicants

1,703 Total Admissions

492 Total Freshman Enrollment

25.63% of applicants admitted

SAT Ranges: CR 630-730, M 610-690, W 620-720

ACT Ranges: C 28-32, M 26-31, E 30-34, W 8-10

TUITION & COSTS

Tuition: $47,220

Fees: $1,920

Total: $49,140

R&B: $11,960

Room: $5,240

Board: $6,720

Total: $61,100

FINANCIAL

$33,907 avg grant/scholarship amount (total)

$6,200 avg loan amount (total)

MALONE UNIVERSITY

CANTON, OHIO

As a Christian university with a highly respected liberal arts core, Malone is deeply committed to intellectual enrichment in the context of the Christian faith. Affiliated with the Evangelical Friends Church, Malone integrates faith into the classroom as it perpetuates its belief that God works through His students in all aspects of life, not just in church.

STUDENT RESEARCH SYMPOSIUM: Students excel most when they study what they are most interested in. To promote the incredible possibilities of each student, Malone hosts the Student Research Symposium, a forum in which undergraduates have the opportunity to present their proudest independent work. Projects from nearly every discipline are put on display, flooding the forum space with new scientific findings and entertaining fine arts performances alike. Because the faculty love the Symposium just as much as students, they are readily available to aid and mentor their curious pupils throughout their research.

SPIRITUAL FORMATION OPPORTUNITIES: Spiritual Formation Opportunities (SFOs) ensure that Malone students grow in their continual journeys in service to God. Straying from the traditional chapel requirement at most Christian universities, Malone requires its students to attend at least twenty of the three hundred SFOs hosted on campus. Each SFO is a unique experience that approaches spiritual development with a fresh perspective. Students can choose to attend whichever SFOs interest them most, allowing them to growth in faith along the path that bests suits them. They differ in size, structure, and topic, exploring such activities as small Bible groups, large worship events, and guest lectures from wise Christian leaders.

GEN 100 - THE COLLEGE EXPERIENCE: Every first-year student at Malone is swiftly taken into the community with the help of Gen 100, a common learning course that aids in the transition from high school to college. Gen 100: The College Experience begins the first day of Orientation when students are introduced to their fellow classmates who will take the same course. Students quickly learn about Malone's culture as well as the general strategies they should have in order to become successful, college-level learners.

MALONE TRADITION: A highly unique, much anticipated Malone tradition is the annual Davenport Derby. This hilariously fun event kicks off each fall semester with sofa races down the street. Students get together in groups, dress up in costumes, and charge decorated couches on wheels in a race to win the Golden Couch Award. The entire student body is always thrilled to gather and cheer on their peers, reuniting with old friends and making new ones in the riotous community gathering.

SERVICE-LEARNING: Serving others is an integral part of Christian faith, and Malone wants to ensure that its students are addressing the world's needs beyond their usual reach. A large number of international partners host Malone service groups all around the world, bringing students directly in contact with those who need help, including refugees, impoverished households, and exploited workers.

CENTER FOR STUDENT SUCCESS: Academic advising is all inclusive at Malone University. The Center helps students find the appropriate core courses that both fulfill their general education requirements and bolster the knowledge they need for their individual majors. Undeclared students receive helpful guidance as well, as their faculty advisors brainstorm with them to find what majors best align with their interests and strengths.

---

http://www.malone.edu/

P: (800) 521-1146

PRIVATE - CHRISTIAN

STUDENT PROFILE

1,367 undergraduate students

86% of undergrad students are full time

40% male – 60% female

70% freshman retention rate

57% graduated in 6 years

FACULTY PROFILE

104 full-time faculty

81 part-time faculty

12 to 1 student/faculty ratio

ADMISSIONS

1,168 Total Applicants

804 Total Admissions

245 Total Freshman Enrollment

68.84% of applicants admitted

SAT Ranges: CR 478-563, M 458-550

ACT Ranges: C 19-25, M 18-25, E 19-26

TUITION & COSTS

Tuition: $27,104

Fees: $856

Total: $27,960

R&B: $8,948

Room: $4,524

Board: $4,424

Total: $36,908

FINANCIAL

$17,777 avg grant/scholarship amount (total)

$7,761 avg loan amount (total)

MARIETTA COLLEGE

MARIETTA, OHIO

Marietta College is the perfect fit for students who are naturally curious with a pioneering spirit to match. Marietta offers more than 40 undergraduate majors, all of which are rooted in the liberal arts. Students learn from and conduct serious research with talented faculty who are renowned in their professional fields and wholly dedicated to teaching. The undergraduate experience at Marietta fosters leadership skills and a passion for learning that lasts a lifetime.

LIBERAL ARTS FOUNDATION: Marietta College students hone their skills in communication, problem solving, and critical thinking through a variety of general education courses that are focused on primary areas of knowledge. This broad-based approach to learning prepares students to thrive in the ever-changing professional landscape as well as develop interests outside of their primary field of study.

UNDERGRADUATE RESEARCH: Students at Marietta are encouraged to pursue serious research projects. In addition to team research with their peers, undergraduates have many opportunities to conduct studies with their professors. Students often present posters at industry conferences and, every spring, Marietta College conducts an All Scholar's Day event for students to present and celebrate the research work they have completed throughout the academic year.

INTERNSHIPS: All Marietta College students are encouraged to participate in at least one internship while pursuing their degree. Students are able to obtain academic credit by partaking in an academic internship, which doubles as a learning experience that is shaped by reflection, goal-setting, and evaluation. These internships are performed under the mentorship of an instructor and supervisor within the workplace. By working with the Career Center on campus, students may find internships that are directly related to their specific interests, gaining valuable skills that make them highly marketable upon graduation.

LEADERSHIP: The McDonough Leadership Program prepares students to be leaders in their chosen fields. This program is based on a "Knowledge-Action-Growth" approach, so students are constantly expanding their knowledge of leadership skills as they practice them.

ENTREPRENEURSHIP: Marietta offers an Entrepreneurship minor to help students better understand how their major may be utilized in the business world. This minor serves students who are interested in starting businesses as well as for those who are dedicated to progressing their industries but prefer to work within established companies. Talented faculty help students look at ways they can improve their respective industries.

STUDENT LIFE: There's life beyond the classroom and lab, and at Marietta College, that life is thriving. Students forge lifelong friendships through the 22 exciting varsity sports teams as well as the many social organizations that are offered to the campus community. Every spring, the students get to enjoy a campus-wide celebration called Doo Dah Day, a tradition that dates back to 1974. This event is packed with plenty of food, games, and fun—there's even a hot air balloon landing on campus.

THE COMMUNITY: Marietta is a residential college nestled in the historic city of Marietta, Ohio. The 90-acre campus is a blend of New England-style brick buildings, updated classrooms and labs, updated athletic facilities, and breathtaking landscapes. Just steps from campus is a bustling downtown filled with unique shops, coffee houses, gourmet restaurants, and historic sites of significance.

http://www.marietta.edu/
P: (800) 331-7896

PRIVATE

STUDENT PROFILE

1,076 undergraduate students

100% of undergrad students are full time

63% male – 37% female

36.4% of students are from out of state

62.2% freshman retention rate

56.4% graduated in 6 years

FACULTY PROFILE

91 full-time faculty

59 part-time faculty

10 to 1 student-to-faculty ratio

ADMISSIONS

2,693 Total Applicants

1,652 Total Admissions

262 Total Freshman Enrollment

61.34% of applicants admitted

SAT Ranges: M 460-610, W 420-530

ACT Ranges: C 20-26, M 19-26, E 19-26, W 17-24

TUITION & COSTS

Tuition: $35,030

Fees: $1,010

Total: $36,040

R&B: $11,320

Total: $47,360

FINANCIAL

$189,393 avg grant/scholarship amount (need)

$4,733 avg loan amount (need)

MIAMI UNIVERSITY – OXFORD

OXFORD, OHIO

Miami University provides a rigorous collegiate curriculum. Students are given the opportunities of a large university while experiencing the personalized teaching and attention found at small colleges. The University's students make up almost half of the population of Oxford, Ohio. This tiny town has numerous activities for students to enjoy, from biking to shopping, and it is greatly supported by and supportive of its college student community.

UNDERGRADUATE RESEARCH: Miami has a longstanding commitment to undergraduate research. It has always encouraged its students to pursue research opportunities, whether they be within their specific fields of study or come as an extension of a professor's work. Through research, students gain skills that are valued both by employers and graduate schools alike; not only do they learn about the research process itself, but they gain hands-on practice with inquiry-based learning. Miami research extends beyond the laboratory and into such areas as the humanities, engineering, and business. Essentially, this means that there are opportunities applicable to all students' interests.

STUDY ABROAD: A large portion of Miami's student body studies abroad and earns credit while exploring the world around them. There are incredible academic and social benefits to study abroad, chief among them being a greater understanding of the global community. Not only do students gain skills in cross-cultural communication, but they also naturally develop a greater sense of respect, tolerance, and appreciation for unfamiliar cultures and perspectives. Miami has several different abroad options that range in duration and destination, but one of the more popular programs is Miami's own Dolibois European Center in Luxembourg. Directly learning from Miami staff, participating students are continually exposed to the same top-tier academics and community service that are so highly valued by the University.

COMMUNITY ENGAGEMENT AND SERVICE: The Office of Community Engagement and Service (OCES) is responsible for connecting students to service opportunities, both big and small. It functions through the observance of five "Guiding Principles:" Mutuality, Integrity, Equity, Preparedness, and Inclusion. These principles form a foundation from which all service initiatives grow. One of the most complex and effective forms of community engagement is service-learning, an academic course that draws connections between what is learned in class and what is needed in the community. This type of learning is dynamically charged as it pushes students to apply academic theory to real-world application. Most often, service-learning courses involve some degree of reflection, allowing faculty and students to assess their impact and learn how best to utilize their drives to serve in the future.

THREE-YEAR PATHWAYS: Select first-year students who enter Miami with previously completed credits are given the opportunity to earn their degree in just three years. The Three-Year Pathways track is open to students who have completed college-level courses while in high school. Beginning their academic journey at an advanced level, three-year degree candidates hit the ground running with a cost-efficient plan that sends them straight to their future careers.

COMBINED BACHELOR'S-MASTER'S PROGRAM: Miami currently has 22 programs that offer a combined bachelors-masters degree. Students wishing to pursue a combined degree option may declare their interest at any point during their undergraduate experience. Of course, the earlier the better, as the programs take planning and academic advising. In a combined degree program, students complete their undergraduate courses first and then spend extra time on campus to complete their master's through a shortened graduate-level curriculum.

http://www.miami.miamioh.edu/

P: (513) 529-1809

PUBLIC

STUDENT PROFILE

16,387 undergraduate students

98% of undergrad students are full time

49% male – 51% female

37% of students are from out of state

90% freshman retention rate

80% graduated in 6 years

FACULTY PROFILE

976 full-time faculty

16 part-time faculty

15 to 1 student/faculty ratio

ADMISSIONS

27,454 Total Applicants

17,980 Total Admissions

3,811 Total Freshman Enrollment

65.49% of applicants admitted

SAT Ranges: CR 550-650, M 590-690

ACT Ranges: C 26-30, M 25-30, E 26-32

TUITION & COSTS

Tuition: (In) $11,673 (Out) $28,373

Fees: $2,614

Total: (In) $14,287 (Out) $30,987

R&B: $11,644

Room: $5,994

Board: $5,650

Total: (In) $25,931 (Out) $42,631

FINANCIAL

$8,754 avg grant/scholarship amount (need)

$5,166 avg loan amount (need)

MOUNT ST. JOSEPH UNIVERSITY

CINCINNATI, OHIO

MOUNT ST. JOSEPH
UNIVERSITY

Mount St. Joseph University is a Catholic academic community grounded in the spiritual values and vision of its founders, the Sisters of Charity. The University educates its students through interdisciplinary liberal arts and professional curricula, emphasizing values, integrity, and social responsibility.

WORLDWIDE ENGAGEMENT: Independent study, faculty-led research projects, participation in national conferences, and an Honors Program are a few of the most popular ways in which students choose to customize their liberal arts education at the Mount. Study abroad programs can transport students near and far, whether that includes an immersive experience with the Cherokee people of North Carolina or formalized course work through Richmond—the American International University—in London, England. Students at the Mount can also embark on short, faculty-led trips. Each August, for example, a group of students join Dr. Jim Bodle and Dr. Elizabeth Barkley on a trip to New York City to learn about the role that non-government organizations play in helping the United Nations achieve its Sustainable Development Goals by the year 2030.

MULTICULTURAL PERSPECTIVES: Mount St. Joseph University hosts several events meant to broaden students' cultural perspectives and awareness. One such example include the Sacred Arts Tour 2016 in which Tibetan monks from Drepung Gomang Monastery created a Sacred Sand Mandala in the Mount's Studio San Giuseppe art gallery, exposing students to gorgeous and meaningful art they may not have otherwise experienced elsewhere.

HANDS-ON FACULTY: Faculty and staff at Mount St. Joseph University take each student's education seriously from the start and well beyond graduation. From the class-wide interdisciplinary studies foundation during freshman year to the culminating capstone projects in their senior year, Mount students are challenged and supported in every one of their educational choices. When they are not in the classroom, Mount faculty might be found on a site visit at a cooperative education location, providing a letter of reference for a student's graduate school admission application, or in the lab completing a research project with a group of students.

STUDENT ACTIVITIES: The choices for co-curricular learning are endless! Students are fully engaged with cooperative education, service-learning, leadership programs, internships, performing arts, fraternities, and student government. The Mount is a place for students to indulge their interests and discover new ones. Dozens of campus clubs, groups, organizations, and teams give everyone a chance to get involved in new hobbies, awesome events, and amazing activities. Their choices include ethnic and political groups, Greek life, academic and service clubs, jazz ensemble, intramural sports, and so much more. Movie nights, Springfest, and theatre performances are all on campus, bringing together the entire community together and making it easy to form new friendships.

TALENT OPPORTUNITY PROGRAM: The Mount commits to helping students grow in ways that are not exclusive to academics. The Talent Opportunity Program, known as TOP, emphasizes professional development while incentivizing students to prepare themselves for the global marketplace. For example, the bronze level of the program requires students to take the Foundations of Professionalism Course, participate in at least one leadership development opportunity or course, and attend a minimum of three TOP events. At the end of the 2016 academic year, 100 percent of gold-level TOP students had secured full-time employment or graduate school admission upon earning their undergraduate degree at Mount St. Joseph University.

---

http://www.msj.edu/
P: (513) 244-4200

PRIVATE - CATHOLIC

STUDENT PROFILE

1,207 undergraduate students

83% of undergrad students are full time

48% male – 52% female

20% of students are from out of state

73% freshman retention rate

52% graduated in 6 years

FACULTY PROFILE

93 full-time faculty

122 part-time faculty

11 to 1 student/faculty ratio

ADMISSIONS

1,029 Total Applicants

906 Total Admissions

249 Total Freshman Enrollment

88.05% of applicants admitted

SAT Ranges: CR 440-560, M 450-580

ACT Ranges: C 19-24, M 17-24, E 17-24

TUITION & COSTS

Tuition: $28,100

Fees: $1,000

Total: $29,100

R&B: $9,266

Total: $38,366

FINANCIAL

$15,762 avg grant/scholarship amount (need)

$3,775 avg loan amount (need)

UNIVERSITY OF DAYTON

DAYTON, OHIO

Challenging academics that ask the tough questions, selfless service aimed at improving the world, and having a blast within a tight-knit community are just a few of the everyday pleasures at the University of Dayton. Noted as one of the top 10 Catholic universities, the University of Dayton provides an education that challenges and inspires, encouraging growth through active engagement with the world.

FIRST-YEAR EXPERIENCE (FYE): To help students transition to college and maximize their resources, University of Dayton asks all first-year students to participate in the First-Year Experience (FYE). FYE includes a seminar course that offers an in-depth look at the university experience, the development of a personal portfolio and professional résumé, and access to personal academic advising.

A REAL DIFFERENCE: At the University of Dayton, learning doesn't happen just for the sake of learning; it's about making a real difference whenever possible, even as undergraduates. Recently, UD students have created solar-powered equipment to sterilize medical devices, designed cost-effective cargo planes using new composites, developed fitness programs for grade-schoolers, explored the complexities of urban education, and managed and invested nearly $11 million of the University's endowment.

GLOBAL EDUCATION: Whether they study on campus or abroad, University of Dayton students have the chance to receive a globally inspired education. Outstanding courses enrich students with worldly perspectives, and education abroad programs immerse students in entirely different cultures.

INTERNSHIPS AND RESEARCH: With a vast array of internship and cooperative education opportunities available to them, UD students earn a professional foothold in the world well before earning their diploma. Fortune 500 companies regularly recruit students on campus, and the University itself even hires undergraduates to work on cutting-edge projects at one of the best research organizations in the world: the University of Dayton Research Institute.

CAMPUS MINISTRY: Whether a student wants to make a difference in the life of a child, work toward social justice, spend a week helping others, or sleep under the stars during a wilderness retreat, they can find the experience that's right for them through Campus Ministry. Home to one of the nation's largest campus ministry programs, the University of Dayton sponsors more than 30 student-run service clubs, retreats, BreakOut trips, and more.

CAMPUS ACTIVITIES: With a campus so full of activities, there's never a shortage of things to do as a UD student. Students can paint themselves red and cheer on the Dayton Flyers or even join the action themselves—in fact, 70 percent of students participate in intramurals and club sports. Students can also host a show on Flyer TV, build and race a concrete canoe, march with the Pride of Dayton, or join any number of more than 180 clubs and organizations. On-campus entertainment like comedy troupes, concerts, and movies, as well as off-campus adventures like whitewater rafting, are offered regularly.

DAYTON, OHIO: The city of Dayton has no shortage of things to do. Located at the edge of campus, Brown Street offers a variety of shops and restaurants, while downtown bustles with a lively nightlife with coffeehouses, galleries, theatre, music, minor league baseball, and a laser-lit riverfront park.

FIRST-RATE OPPORTUNITIES: University of Dayton graduates consistently take jobs with the nation's best firms and are accepted into top graduate programs. Students are helped to prepare for their careers right away, as Career Services aims to provide cooperative education, internship connections, on-campus recruiting, career advising, and job-search strategies as early as their first semester.

---

https://udayton.edu/
P: (800) 837-7433

PRIVATE - CATHOLIC

STUDENT PROFILE

8,665 undergraduate students

95% of undergrad students are full time

53% male – 47% female

51% of students are from out of state

91% freshman retention rate

79% graduated in 6 years

FACULTY PROFILE

630 full-time faculty

392 part-time faculty

16 to 1 student/faculty ratio

ADMISSIONS

16,968 Total Applicants

9,760 Total Admissions

2,143 Total Freshman Enrollment

57.52% of applicants admitted

SAT Ranges: CR 510-620, M 520-630, W 520-610

ACT Ranges: C 24-29, M 24-29, E 24-30

TUITION & COSTS

Tuition: $39,090

R&B: $12,190

Room: $7,310

Board: $4,880

Total: $51,280

FINANCIAL

$20,068 avg grant/scholarship amount (total)

$8,375 avg loan amount (total)

UNIVERSITY OF MOUNT UNION

ALLIANCE, OHIO

The University of Mount Union, a private institution located in Alliance Ohio, offers a rigorous and relevant academic program that is grounded in the liberal arts tradition. Mount Union's nearly 2,300 students can select from 55 undergraduate majors, both broad-based and career-specific, as well as three graduate programs. Known for its excellent academics and personal approach, the institution boasts a 14:1 student-faculty ratio and a dedicated faculty of teacher-scholars, 87% of whom hold terminal degrees in their fields. Founded in 1846, the University is affiliated with the United Methodist Church.

INTEGRATIVE CORE: The Integrative Core (IC) is how Mount Union brings the liberal arts to life. This unique curriculum is a collection of foundational courses that ensure breadth of study and a well-founded experience. Extending throughout all four years of undergraduate study, the IC allows students to explore a variety of concepts and topics through four levels that build upon one another. It includes the First Year Seminar (FYS), which exposes new students to the expectations of college-level work and assists in the development of skills they need to succeed. The IC concludes with the Capstone Seminar, which provides students with an opportunity to work with their peers to address a real-world issue through problem solving in a team-focused environment.

RESEARCH: Each year, students have the opportunity to participate in SCHOLAR Day, which stands for Student Celebration Honoring Our Latest Academic Research. This campus-wide event showcases the academic excellence and scholarly research completed during the year through both formal and poster presentations. In addition, a number of students participate in independent or joint research annually with faculty members or fellow students.

STUDY ABROAD: Students have an opportunity to spend a week, a summer, a semester, or a whole year studying abroad. The University has partnerships with 56 universities in 29 countries. Internships and student-teaching experiences can be pursued through these study abroad programs, and short-term travel opportunities led by faculty are organized annually. In addition, some courses and academic programs have an incorporated global experience. Engineering students travel abroad to learn through field projects that address worldwide issues, and students in the Social Responsibility Class travel to Guatemala during Spring Break to complete various service projects in rural areas.

WRITTEN AND ORAL COMMUNICATION (WOC) PROGRAM: At Mount Union, all students develop oral and written communication skills across the curriculum both through the Integrative Core as well as within their majors and minors. In an effort to gauge communication proficiency, all students submit a WOC Portfolio—including samples of their written and oral communication work developed during their first two years on campus—that is evaluated by numerous trained faculty and staff. This portfolio allows students to reflect upon their abilities and receive valuable guidance toward further development.

THE REGULA CENTER FOR PUBLIC SERVICE AND CIVIC ENGAGEMENT: The Regula Center offers opportunities to get involved in community service initiatives. From organizing clothing drives to volunteering in local parks, service-learning is a hands-on experience. Annually, nearly 80% of students participate in community service through individual, class, organizational, or campus-wide initiatives.

INTERNSHIPS: Hands-on learning through internships with leading organizations provides students with the professional, practical experience that employers seek. Mount Union students have participated in unique internship experiences with organizations, including Amnesty International, Cleveland Cavaliers, Cleveland Clinic Center for Autism, Country Music Television, Firestone, Greenpeace, House of Blues, The Humane Society, Interpol, MTV Networks, Ohio Environmental Protection Agency, Pro Football Hall of Fame, Progressive Insurance, Sherwin-Williams, Smithsonian Institute, State of Ohio Crime Lab, U.S. Department of Treasury, U.S. Marshal Service, U.S. Secret Service, and Walt Disney World, among others.

https://www.mountunion.edu/
P: (800) 334-6682

PRIVATE

STUDENT PROFILE

2,140 undergraduate students

99% of undergrad students are full time

52% male – 48% female

24% of students are from out of state

79% freshman retention rate

59% graduated in 6 years

FACULTY PROFILE

135 full-time faculty

106 part-time faculty

13 to 1 student-to-faculty ratio

ADMISSIONS

2,525 Total Applicants

1,944 Total Admissions

659 Total Freshman Enrollment

76.99% of applicants admitted

SAT Ranges: CR 430-540, M 460-570

ACT Ranges: C 20-26, M 19-25, E 19-26

TUITION & COSTS

Tuition: $29,560

Fees: $330

Total: $29,890

R&B: $10,100

Total: $39,990

FINANCIAL

$16,964 avg grant/scholarship amount (need)

$5,888 avg loan amount (need)

WALSH UNIVERSITY

NORTH CANTON, OHIO

Walsh University is a fully accredited liberal arts and science university in North Canton, Ohio. The school offers more than 65 majors, eight graduate programs, and an accelerated-degree program for working adults. As a Catholic university that welcomes students of all faiths, Walsh's ultimate mission is to develop leaders in service to others.

SERVICE: Volunteer work is not simply encouraged at Walsh; it is an inherent component of the core curriculum. Walsh students build homes for Habitat for Humanity, tutor and mentor school children, prepare taxes for low-income families, distribute meals, and perform service work around the world.

STUDY ABROAD: Students actively participate in the global society through the University's Global Learning program. In addition to Walsh's own campus just outside of Rome, Italy, students have the opportunity to study abroad in various locations, including Uruguay, Haiti, Mexico, Uganda, Tanzania, London, and Beijing.

STUDENT COLLABORATION: In 2016, Walsh opened "The Garage," a student-directed business incubator in which students have the opportunity to develop enterprising skills. Together, they can create their own businesses or work on collaborative projects.

STUDENT AND FACULTY RESEARCH: A team of Walsh undergraduate students, professors, and alumni are collaborating on significant cancer-related research. This team has been able to synthesize the compound needed for hands-on practice and methods to determine purity and efficacy. Their work is currently setting the stage for important clinical trials. Opportunities to contribute to the real world are both endless and endlessly fulfilling.

MUSEUM STUDIES MAJOR: One of the only programs of its kind in the entire Midwest (and the first in Ohio), Walsh University's Museum Studies major provides a unique and hands-on experience for students who want to work in and manage museums. As an added benefit, Walsh has its own museum on campus: the Hoover Historical Center. Museum Studies students can combine their classroom instruction with real training at the Center as well as in other local museums, including the National First Ladies Library and Museum, the Professional Football Hall of Fame, the Canton Museum of Art, and the Massillon Museum. Walsh is also a partner with the prestigious Campbell Center for Historical Preservation in Mount Carroll, Ill. Walsh students can receive a full scholarship to participate in Campbell Center workshops and work with museum professionals from across the globe, all while earning classroom credits.

STUDENT RETREATS: Student retreats, such as the Discover Retreat for freshmen and the Shape Retreat for sophomores, challenge students to make new friends, reflect on changes within their lives, and enhance their leadership potential. These non-denominational retreats offer students some time away from the daily grind to focus on their personal enrichment.

CULTURAL EVENTS: Walsh hosts several cultural events, including the International Dinner, World Week, theatre performances by the Walsh Genesius Players, and music by the Walsh University Chorale. Campus groups and academic units also enliven the community by inviting world-renowned singers, musicians, artists, and speakers to campus throughout the year.

INTERNSHIPS: Students are encouraged to work in their fields of study during their time at Walsh through practica, internships, and other real job opportunities. In fact, internships are a mandatory component of every academic program. Walsh's on-campus Career Center assists students in finding a program that best suits their career goals, both during college and after graduation.

---

http://www.walsh.edu/
P: (330) 490-7090

PRIVATE - CATHOLIC

STUDENT PROFILE

2,342 undergraduate students

81% of undergrad students are full time

39% male – 61% female

12% of students are from out of state

78% freshman retention rate

60% graduated in 6 years

FACULTY PROFILE

145 full-time faculty

13 to 1 student/faculty ratio

ADMISSIONS

1,447 Total Applicants

1,162 Total Admissions

439 Total Freshman Enrollment

80.30% of applicants admitted

SAT Ranges: CR 440-550, M 460-560

ACT Ranges: C 20-25, M 18-25, E 19-25

TUITION & COSTS

Tuition: $26,300

Fees: $1,410

Total: $27,710

R&B: $9,920

Room: $5,260

Board: $4,660

Total: $37,630

FINANCIAL

$18,022 avg grant/scholarship amount (total)

$7,823 avg loan amount (total)

WITTENBERG UNIVERSITY

SPRINGFIELD, OHIO

For more than 160 years, Wittenberg University has developed students' individual gifts and talents by creating an active, engaged learning environment that provides an outstanding foundation for successful careers and meaningful lives. Through a range of courses designed to engage and inspire, Wittenberg's award-winning professors push students' thinking beyond what is comfortable and into what is important.

FIRST-YEAR PROGRAMS: First-Year Programs (FYP) help students build solid foundations for lifelong academic, personal, and professional success with support services that facilitate their transitions into Wittenberg. All first-year students enroll in a First-Year Seminar, the topics of which range from international business to modern political philosophy. With 25 students per course, students experience supportive and collaborative environments that prepare them for guaranteed achievement.

GLOBAL CITIZENSHIP: Believing that students can only understand the world through firsthand experience, Wittenberg offers a vibrant study abroad program that enriches global citizenship in over 40 locations. From short-term semester and summer programs to full-year options, Wittenberg's study abroad has allowed students to learn on safari in Kenya, traverse China's Silk Road, or follow Martin Luther's footsteps in Wittenberg, Germany.

ENGAGED LEARNING INSIDE THE CLASSROOM: With a student-faculty ratio of 13:1 and an average class size of 20, Wittenberg ensures a highly personal, hands-on education with classroom discussion, group-based work, and collaborative projects. Wittenberg offers generous funding opportunities to students conducting research, the findings of which are often presented at regional and national conferences.

ENGAGED LEARNING OUTSIDE THE CLASSROOM: At Wittenberg, learning extends beyond the walls of the traditional classroom and out into local archaeological digs, theatre performances at the Stratford Festival in Canada, and so much more. Through the WittEntrepreneurs Program, students from any discipline can launch, operate, and manage an enterprise on campus. At the Springfield Center for the Arts at Wittenberg University, students can learn about arts management and education. The possibilities are endless.

COMPASS - CENTER FOR STUDENT SUCCESS: Designed to ensure student success, the new, one-stop Compass center assists students in achieving their academic and professional goals from day one. At the center, students can learn more about such high-impact practices as internships, faculty-student research opportunities, mentoring, and community engagement options. Students have access to several services essential to their success, including financial aid counseling, academic advising, and class registration.

COMMUNITY SERVICE AND SERVICE LEARNING: Through Wittenberg's community service requirement, students learn about community needs and how to contribute. Every year, students perform more than 20,000 hours of service, benefiting nonprofit organizations from around the world. Wittenberg's chapter of the Fuller Center for Housing offers alternative spring break trips to repair and rebuild homes in the southern United States, and first-year students can participate in service-learning courses that engage them in meaningful and purposeful ways. Such active service connects concepts and theories to the practical, hands-on learning of "real-life" experience.

INTERNSHIPS: Wittenberg students in every major are encouraged to pursue an internship to help them identify and launch meaningful and rewarding careers. The local area makes work experience easy and fulfilling with its abundance of internship sites, the Springfield News-Sun, the Springfield Crime Lab, the Ohio Department of Natural Resources, and the Wright Patterson Air Force Base, among many others. And, through the clinical intern program, students can pair up with area physicians and health professionals to gain hands-on learning opportunities.

---

https://www.wittenberg.edu/
P: (877) 206-0332

PRIVATE

STUDENT PROFILE

1,736 undergraduate students

100% of undergrad students are full time

43% male – 57% female

75% freshman retention rate

64% graduated in 6 years

FACULTY PROFILE

122 full-time faculty

57 part-time faculty

13 to 1 student/faculty ratio

ADMISSIONS

6,487 Total Applicants

4,986 Total Admissions

493 Total Freshmen Enrollment

76.86% of applicants admitted

SAT Ranges: CR 490-610, M 490-610

ACT Ranges: C 22-28, M 22-27, E 22-28

TUITION & COSTS

Tuition: $37,230

Fees: $860

Total: $38,090

R&B: $10,126

Total: $48,216

FINANCIAL

$25,798 avg grant/scholarship amount (need)

$5,572 avg loan amount (need)

XAVIER UNIVERSITY

CINCINNATI, OHIO

Rich history and tradition, great opportunities for academic and social growth, and the promise of a rewarding future come with an Xavier degree. Xavier University provides a holistic education that is complemented with over 145 academic clubs, student organizations, campus activities, international study opportunities in six continents, a small student-to-faculty ratio, and an excellent reputation with employers.

STUDY ABROAD: International study opportunities at Xavier are constantly expanding. To date, students have studied abroad in 20 different countries, including Argentina, Australia, Costa Rica, Denmark, Panama, and South Africa. Study abroad can be completed on both short- and long-term time increments as well as over the summer or through direct exchange with foreign colleges or universities. Academic learning semesters in Ghana, Nicaragua, and Cincinnati's Over-the-Rhine neighborhood even allow students to grow spiritually through volunteer service.

A CAMPUS OF SUPPORT AND OPPORTUNITY: From the moment freshmen arrive on campus, Xavier's support services provide the guidance and support they need to stay on track. These services encourage students to get involved in on-campus activities, inform students of the University's services and resources, monitor and encourage academic progress, and help resolve any personal problems. Through the Manresa orientation program, upperclassmen help incoming freshmen learn everything they need to know about the University, including where to eat and how to find their first classes.

INTERNSHIPS: Xavier's location in Cincinnati provides the resources to help students gain meaningful career experience through local internships. 13 Fortune 1000 companies operate in Cincinnati, and students are able to intern with such famous employers as Procter and Gamble, Cincinnati Reds, and the Cincinnati Bengals.

RESOURCES: Xavier's academic resources ensure student success. The Mathematics Tutoring Lab provides assistance in both major and non-major courses, and the James E. Glenn Writing Center is happy to help students achieve the University's high standard of writing. The Learning Assistance Center also offers free tutoring services to all Xavier students—one-on-one tutoring is available in almost all academic subjects, study groups and drop-in tutoring sessions are offered in various subjects, and study-skills assistance is available for both individual and group study.

A WORLD OF SERVICE: At Xavier, the Jesuit mission to educate the whole person is apparent in a number of programs. A variety of campus activities give students the opportunity to participate in programs larger than themselves, facilitating in their personal growth while giving back to the local and global community through service. These activities are led by the incredibly compassion-driven Academic Service Learning and Community-Engaged Fellows Program. Campus Ministry also offers student liturgies, faith-sharing groups, and retreats for spiritual enrichment, and the Center for Faith & Justice sponsors over 25 clubs such as Pax Christi, Amnesty International, Muslim Students Association, Habitat for Humanity, and more.

AN INCREDIBLE FUTURE: The Xavier name earns graduates the respect of both graduate schools and employers alike. More than 1,100 jobs and internships are posted to the XU Career Services Center's online job board each year to help students easily identify internships and postgraduate positions, and such initiatives as on-campus recruiting and alumni networking, the Business Professions Program, and formal professional mentoring programs help prepare students for successful transitions to graduate schools and careers after graduation.

http://www.xavier.edu/
P: (877) 982-3648

PRIVATE - CATHOLIC

STUDENT PROFILE

4,548 undergraduate students

93% of undergrad students are full time

46% male – 54% female

54% of students are from out of state

83% freshman retention rate

74% graduated in 6 years

FACULTY PROFILE

363 full-time faculty

347 part-time faculty

11 to 1 student/faculty ratio

ADMISSIONS

10,661 Total Applicants

7,631 Total Admissions

1,150 Total Freshman Enrollment

71.58% of applicants admitted

SAT Ranges: CR 490-590, M 490-590, W 480-590

ACT Ranges: C 22-27, M 21-27, E 22-28

TUITION & COSTS

Tuition: $34,050

Fees: $1,030

Total: $35,080

R&B: $11,380

Room: $6,300

Board: $5,080

Total: $46,460

FINANCIAL

$20,389 avg grant/scholarship amount (total)

$8,350 avg loan amount (total)

DAKOTA WESLEYAN UNIVERSITY

MITCHELL, SOUTH DAKOTA

Dakota Wesleyan University is the model of the small university for the 21st century. The institution offers three undergraduate colleges—the Donna Starr Christen College of Healthcare, Fitness, and Sciences; the College of Leadership and Public Service; and the College of Arts and Humanities—each of which are designed to strengthen the connection between students' programs of study, graduate schools, and professional success.

ESTEEMED FACULTY: Although the first priority of Dakota Wesleyan University faculty is teaching, they are also experts in their fields: they are published authors on topics that range from Jewish legends to military history; they display their photographic work and publish poetry; they are quoted as experts by the media in the region and all across the country. No matter what major a student chooses, their opportunities for unique learning experiences are only as far away as the professor at the front of the room. Each instructor aims to steer their students toward meaningful, creative, and transformative experiences.

REAL-WORLD IMMERSION: Dakota Wesleyan students are guaranteed phenomenal access to immersive opportunities. With the help of the University, they apply their interests of study to real-world or replicated situations. For example, one biochemistry/psychology student has spent the past two years working with her professor to research the environmental causes of brain cell death, leading her to a career in neuropharmacology. The criminal justice department's forensics classroom is a crime scene, specially constructed by local law enforcement officers to replicate a real crime. And the presence of an elementary school on the Dakota Wesleyan campus means that education students have the opportunity to work in classroom settings from the very beginning of their college careers. In short, every student is aptly prepared for their fields.

SERVICE IN ACTION: A service-minded accounting student proposed to the administration the use of empty lab space to house the space-challenged Weekend Snack Pack Program, a local nonprofit that delivers food to elementary school children who are food insecure. Thanks to his work, the nonprofit is now able to store more food at its new location on campus. Members of a Dakota Wesleyan University service-learning team recently spent two weeks in Uganda and Rwanda to volunteer, gift livestock, and provide other services like agricultural advising and workshops for teachers. They talked to locals about their needs, built a church, and established a library with the assistance of the campus-based church community.

STUDENT ACTIVITIES: Because of its small size, DWU students are able to participate in intercollegiate or intramural athletics, music, theatre, student senate, political organizations, and more. Nearly every major offers a corresponding student organization or academic society, so there is sure to be something for everyone.

PORTFOLIO: Every student at Dakota Wesleyan University creates their own professional electronic portfolio in which they make a record of their coursework, campus leadership, and service activities. This portfolio really makes DWU students stand out to prospective employers and graduate schools. Perhaps more importantly, the portfolio allows students to reflect on their four-year experiences of personal growth.

GALLUP STRENGTHSFINDER: One of the tools that DWU uses with each student is the Gallup StrengthsFinder. The StrengthsFinder does not tell students what career they should pursue, nor does it tell them how to fix their weaknesses. Rather, it offers insight about where each person's gifts lie. Having this kind of self-awareness leads to fulfilling lives and careers.

http://www.dwu.edu/

P: (800) 333-8506

PRIVATE

STUDENT PROFILE

905 undergraduate students

77% of undergrad students are full time

43% male – 57% female

28% of students are from out of state

71% freshman retention rate

42% graduated in 6 years

FACULTY PROFILE

53 full-time faculty

82 part-time faculty

10 to 1 student/faculty ratio

ADMISSIONS

644 Total Applicants

479 Total Admissions

178 Total Freshman Enrollment

74.38% of applicants admitted

SAT Ranges: CR 353-521, M 423-508, W 368-502

ACT Ranges: C 18-24, M 17-23, E 15-23

TUITION & COSTS

Tuition: $24,550

Fees: $250

Total: $24,800

R&B: $7,200

Room: $3,200

Board: $4,000

Total: $32,000

FINANCIAL

$14,920 avg grant/scholarship amount (total)

$7,251 avg loan amount (total)

MOUNT MARTY COLLEGE

YANKTON, SOUTH DAKOTA

MOUNT MARTY
C O L L E G E

Mount Marty College is a private, Catholic, Benedictine, coeducational liberal arts college. Its primary emphasis is placed on the development of each person as a complete human being with intellectual, professional, and personal skills that make up a composite of moral, spiritual, and social values.

THE BIOMEDICAL RESEARCH INFRASTRUCTURE NETWORK: The MMC BRIN (Biomedical Research Infrastructure Network) program continues to have a profound impact on students' exposure and opportunities to conduct research. BRIN, funded by the National Institute of Health (NIH), was designed to earmark research funds for historically low-funded states in need of improved infrastructure. It also encourages undergraduate students to follow research careers by exposing them to bench research. Student involvement successfully leverages participants' BRIN experience and MMC education in their acceptance to graduate and professional schools. Statistically, MMC boasts the highest placement rate for BRIN students in graduate and professional schools among all BRIN partner institutes in South Dakota.

HANDS-ON EXPERIENCE: MMC students majoring in human service and psychology have received a broad range of hands-on experience through internship positions with organizations such as the Boys and Girls Club, Ability Building Services, Cedar Village Assisted Living, Yankton Child Protective Services and Court Services.

SERVICE TRIPS: Each year, MMC students have the opportunity to serve others beyond the local area through service trips organized through the Campus Ministry department. Recent service trips have included working with the less fortunate in Mississippi and Florida, helping Habitat for Humanity in Texas and Louisiana, and assisting with tornado clean-up efforts in Joplin, Missouri. These trips drastically alter students' perspectives with their inspiring lessons in gratitude.

EUROPEAN TOUR: Mount Marty College embarks on a comprehensive European tour on an annual basis. The focus and itinerary varies each year and includes stops throughout several countries. Students, faculty, staff, and family can all travel together and live out the core values of community and lifelong learning. Students can also earn college credit for the trip by enrolling in ART-260, Art & Architecture in Europe. This course engages the student in the study of the art, architecture, culture, and history of each country on the itinerary.

PADDLEFISH: Paddlefish is a national literary journal that is written and edited by MMC students and faculty. It is an open-submission magazine with original works of fiction, poetry, and nonfiction. Students work as editorial assistants for the national literary journal and meet and discuss craft with award-winning authors.

SERVICE: MMC students get involved in service not only on an individual level, but also as collective units through campus ministry organizations, academic clubs, athletic teams, and more. The scope and variety of service at MMC can be seen by each student's willingness to give back. Some examples of recent service include donations of venison to Hunters for Hunger, blood drives in coordination with the Siouxland Community Blood Bank, Adopt a Family, and a collection of donations of cold-weather gear for Make a Difference distribution.

THANKSGIVING BASKET PROGRAM: Students, faculty, and staff come together to participate in the Thanksgiving Basket Program. Through the program, campus clubs, organizations, and departments collect and donate baskets that contain all the fixings needed for a traditional Thanksgiving dinner spread.

SERVICE LEARNING: Service is an intrinsic component of many academic courses in a variety of majors at MMC. Through this avenue, students in the business and accounting programs volunteer with such organizations as the Humane Society, the Boys & Girls Club, the Literacy Council, Sack Pack Program, The Banquet, Habitat for Humanity, the Special Olympics, Youth Soccer Programs, and annual Free Tax Clinic.

---

http://www.mtmc.edu/

P: (605) 668-1545

PRIVATE - CATHOLIC

STUDENT PROFILE

1,047 undergraduate students

47% of undergrad students are full time

42% male – 58% female

34% of students are from out of state

69% freshman retention rate

46% graduated in 6 years

FACULTY PROFILE

46 full-time faculty

54 part-time faculty

11 to 1 student/faculty ratio

ADMISSIONS

408 Total Applicants

296 Total Admissions

112 Total Freshman Enrollment

72.55% of applicants admitted

ACT Ranges: C 19-25, M 17-26, E 17-24

TUITION & COSTS

Tuition: $22,336

Fees: $2,070

Total: $24,406

R&B: $7,326

Total: $31,732

FINANCIAL

$14,593 avg grant/scholarship amount (total)

$7,569 avg loan amount (total)

CARDINAL STRITCH UNIVERSITY

MILWAUKEE, WISCONSIN

Cardinal Stritch University began as a teaching institution for the Sisters of St. Francis of Assisi in 1937. Since then, it has developed over 60 undergraduate and graduate programs to provide a phenomenal education to a variety of students with a wide range of academic interests. Stritch majors provide a comprehensive education in the arts, science, business, education, and nursing in addition to many liberal arts programs.

FIRST-YEAR EXPERIENCE: Every student new to Stritch enrolls in a First-Year Experience course that is carefully designed to settle them in to campus and expose them to the intellectual and social opportunities that await them in college. This course captures students' attention with engaging close material that they get to study in an intimate setting, all while helping them grow comfortable and integrate into the entirely new college lifestyle. Not only do they get to learn from friendly, personally invested professors, but they also get to sit in on exciting lectures given by local and national leaders who greatly exhibit the Franciscan values that Stritch desires to employ.

LIBERAL ARTS CORE CURRICULUM: Cardinal Stritch University's CORE Curriculum grounds each student with a strong, foundational liberal arts education. Through the liberal arts, students are able to look at the world with multiple perspectives and approach challenges with intellectual sense of responsibility. The CORE exposes students to the value of understanding art and culture as well as the natural order of the world's processes. It is designed to give students the room to think critically, solve problems, and communicate them effectively through their writing. As scholars of Stritch's Franciscan tradition, students become not only profound scholars, but also compassionate community members of strong faith who pursue peace and justice.

STUDY ABROAD: One of the best ways to grow as an internationally conscious member of society is by travelling internationally to experience the world oneself. Stritch students have a variety of destinations to choose from, exploring other cultures for a semester, full year, or shorter periods in special intensive programs. Students are given the chance to thrive in different locations around the world, fulfilling their academic requirements while networking with international colleagues and immersing themselves in unfamiliar cultures. Long-term trips are great for completing courses at the same pace as one would at Stritch itself, while short-term programs have goal-driven and location-specific trips with once-in-a-lifetime research initiatives. Stritch also offers special, change-oriented trips, including service immersion programs that bring the University's Franciscan spirit and care to far-off locations in need.

SERVICE DAY: Stritch's annual Service Day, which usually takes in place in April, gives students, faculty, staff, and alumni the opportunity to demonstrate their commitment to the Milwaukee community. Classes are canceled for the day so that volunteers may travel to a number of non-profit sites within the greater Milwaukee area. Having originated as a project in a communications class, Service Day has blossomed as a university-wide tradition that now brings amazing acts of service to a number of different organizations. Past activities include tending to the ecology of the Schlitz Audubon Nature Center, caring for children at a local, intergenerational care center, and everything in between.

STUDENT SUCCESS CENTER: Through a variety of programs within the Student Success Center (SSC), the University supplies its students with the tools they need to balance their academic and professional lives in tandem with their social and spiritual growth. The SSC offers five programs: Academic and Career Advising, Student Support, Student Affairs, Mission Engagement, and Retention. Each program ensures that students are prepared to take on every challenge that may come their way at Stritch, as multiple representatives of different student-affairs areas work to give one-on-one guidance to anyone looking for it. The senior director of student success also aids in conflict resolution through the SSC, bringing peace and productivity to the Stritch community.

CARDINAL STRITCH
UNIVERSITY

http://www.stritch.edu/
P: (800) 347-8822

PRIVATE - CATHOLIC

STUDENT PROFILE

1,971 undergraduate students

89% of undergrad students are full time

35% male – 65% female

14% of students are from out of state

69% freshman retention rate

44% graduated in 6 years

FACULTY PROFILE

87 full-time faculty

425 part-time faculty

11 to 1 student/faculty ratio

ADMISSIONS

1,185 Total Applicants

579 Total Admissions

163 Total Freshman Enrollment

48.86% of applicants admitted

SAT Ranges: CR 438-543, M 480-570

ACT Ranges: C 20-24, M 18-24, E 19-24

TUITION & COSTS

Tuition: $28,844

R&B: $8,118

Total: $36,962

FINANCIAL

$14,821 avg grant/scholarship amount (need)

$4,152 avg loan amount (need)

CARTHAGE COLLEGE

KENOSHA, WISCONSIN

Founded in 1847, Carthage College is a four-year, private college of the liberal arts and sciences in Kenosha, Wisconsin. Carthage combines an environment of reflection and self-discovery with a culture of high expectation so that students may uncover and ignite their true potential. Ideally located midway between Chicago and Milwaukee, Carthage allows students the opportunity to learn in a professional context. Its beautiful campus—an 80-acre arboretum on the shore of Lake Michigan—is home to 150 scholars, 2,600 full-time students, and 400 part-time students.

UNDERGRADUATE RESEARCH OPPORTUNITIES: Undergraduate research is a priority at Carthage. It starts as early as freshman year in courses like Phage Hunters, an intensive genomics class for biology majors. Students use equipment that is otherwise reserved for faculty and graduate students at larger universities. Professors guide students in original research on campus and connect students to elite research opportunities across the country. Carthage students have conducted research for NASA for eight straight years, flying in zero-gravity conditions aboard NASA aircraft. Their research is real, contributing to the actual design of spacecraft and satellite systems. The team is also currently working on a new propellant-gauging technique that may change how fuel is measured in space.

CARTHAGE SYMPOSIUM: Professors regularly team up to teach single courses that tackle topics from both of their disciplines. These team-taught courses, at least one of which is required for students, are called Carthage Symposia. This exploration through two completely different lenses enriches student understanding and prepares them to be versatile thinkers in the face of complexity.

SENIOR THESIS: Carthage is one of the few schools in the country to require a senior thesis; every student must complete a major work of research, scholarship, or creativity to complete the degree. Theses can take the form of a research project, research paper, performance, or art exhibit.

STUDY ABROAD: January Term, or J-Term, is a favorite time of year for Carthage students. Many use this month to travel on faculty-led study tours to such destinations as South Africa, Vietnam, Sweden, Costa Rica, or Cuba. Carthage recently established its first international field station in Nicaragua at which two groups annually provide drinking water and medical treatment to some of the world's poorest residents. Other students stay on campus for unique course offerings. Carthage is ranked No. 4 in the country for student participation in short-term study abroad. This prestigious recognition is mostly due to J-Term, but many students also choose to study abroad for a full semester or year.

CARTHAGE IN CHICAGO: The new "Carthage in Chicago" program takes full advantage of Carthage's location just an hour north of Chicago. This semester-long program provides students the opportunity to hold full-time internships or complete major academic projects, take classes, and join in weekend activities, all while living in one of the world's most dynamic cities.

COMFORTING ENVIRONMENT: Carthage's home of Kenosha, Wisconsin, is a vibrant area with art galleries, museums, theatres, shopping, and restaurants. With its ideal lakeside location an hour from Milwaukee and Chicago, Kenosha offers small-town charm with easy access to world-class amenities.

COMMUNITY SERVICE: Carthage students love to volunteer in student organizations like Circle K, Carthage World Relief, Carthage United to Rescue Earth, Colleges Against Cancer, and Live.Love. Donate, a group started by Carthage students to promote organ donation. The Carthage chapter of ONE regularly wins the national ONE Campus Challenge, with titles in fall 2013, spring 2014, and fall 2014.

CARTHAGE COLLEGE

https://www.carthage.edu/
P: (262) 551-8500

PRIVATE

STUDENT PROFILE

2,863 undergraduate students

92% of undergrad students are full time

47% male – 53% female

70% of students are from out of state

77% freshman retention rate

59% graduated in 6 years

FACULTY PROFILE

158 full-time faculty

167 part-time faculty

12 to 1 student/faculty ratio

ADMISSIONS

7,165 Total Applicants

5,028 Total Admissions

752 Total Freshman Enrollment

70.17% of applicants admitted

SAT Ranges: CR 500-620, M 500-620

ACT Ranges: C 22-28, M 21-27, E 21-28

TUITION & COSTS

Tuition: $38,375

R&B: $10,460

Total: $48,835

FINANCIAL

$21,928 avg grant/scholarship amount (need)

$8,730 avg loan amount (need)

LAWRENCE UNIVERSITY

APPLETON, WISCONSIN

Lawrence provides a quality education, outstanding faculty, close faculty-student collaboration, and a tradition of excellence in music and the arts. It is unmatched by any other college of its size.

FIRST-YEAR STUDY: Freshman studies is Lawrence's introduction to liberal learning. It gives new students the chance to test ideas with which they may be unfamiliar and build an intellectual foundation not just for college, but for life. A part of the Lawrence curriculum since 1945, this program brings groups of fifteen students together for two-term, seminar-style courses on topics that range from Hamlet to contemporary film. Even the faculty stretch outside their disciplines—biology professors teach Shakespeare, while English professors teach about "selfish genes." One of the nation's most distinctive programs for freshmen, the program pushes students to increase their reading, writing, and speaking skills as they are introduced to the kind of cross-disciplinary intellectual inquiry that is the core of Lawrence's academic programming.

INDIVIDUALLY EDUCATED: After building a strong foundation in the liberal arts and sciences, students at Lawrence have extraordinary opportunities for enriching, individualized learning. In fact, nearly 90% of students take at least one course in which they are the only students in the class.

INTERDISCIPLINARY COURSES: Interdisciplinary studies allow students to cross the boundaries of their majors' departments and look at issues from different perspectives. Areas of exploration include biomedical ethics, cognitive science, education, ethnic studies, gender studies, international studies, linguistics, and neuroscience.

PROFESSORS WHO PRACTICE WHAT THEY PREACH: Lawrence prepares students for lives of service, achievement, leadership, and personal fulfillment. The University's professors are committed to granting students the development of intellect and talent, the acquisition of knowledge and understanding, and the cultivation of judgment and values.

STUDY ABROAD: More than half of students take advantage of Lawrence's offering of off-campus study programs both across the United States and around the world. Lawrence students study abroad on every continent but Antarctica, so there's something for everyone to explore! Tanzania, Hungary, and Italy are just a miniscule selection of programs offered through the University.

COMMUNITY SERVICE: One of the key components of a Lawrence education is student involvement within the community. LARY (Lawrence Assistance Reaching Youth) links University students with local schools to tutor at-risk children in a variety of subjects, and many music students, particularly those majoring in music education, mentor pre-college students in music. Lawrence students also volunteer in a wide range of other projects, including the American Cancer Society Relay for Life, Big Brothers/Big Sisters, Habitat for Humanity, Oxfam America, Project Home, and the Fox Valley Special Olympics.

BEAUTIFUL EDUCATIONAL RETREATS: The University offers a 425-acre estate on Lake Michigan for educational retreats. Björklunden was bequeathed to Lawrence University by Donald and Winifred Boynton of Highland Park, Illinois, with the understanding that it would be preserved as a place of peace and contemplation. Throughout the academic year, students expand their minds in this magnificent setting with a wide variety of study issues. Each year, Björklunden hosts more than one thousand students in over fifty seminars.

A VIBRANT NEIGHBORHOOD: Lawrence is located in the heart of Appleton, Wisconsin, in one of the fastest growing metropolitan areas in the nation. Downtown Appleton offers an eclectic mix of shops, restaurants, coffeehouses, museums, parks, and a new 2,100-seat performing arts center.

http://www.lawrence.edu/
P: (800) 227-0982

PRIVATE

STUDENT PROFILE

1,557 undergraduate students

97% of undergrad students are full time

45% male – 55% female

62% of students are from out of state

89% freshman retention rate

76% graduated in 6 years

FACULTY PROFILE

187 full-time faculty

31 part-time faculty

9 to 1 student/faculty ratio

ADMISSIONS

3,014 Total Applicants

2,057 Total Admissions

400 Total Freshman Enrollment

68.25% of applicants admitted

TUITION & COSTS

Tuition: $43,400

Fees: $300

Total: $43,700

R&B: $9,210

Room: $4,410

Board: $4,800

Total: $52,910

FINANCIAL

$27,144 avg grant/scholarship amount (total)

$7,015 avg loan amount (total)

MARQUETTE UNIVERSITY

MILWAUKEE, WISCONSIN

Marquette's challenging curriculum and commitment to excellence in all things helps produce some of the most talented and successful graduates in the nation. But that's just the beginning; Marquette works to develop in its students an intellectual curiosity that not only asks questions, but also demands right action. Such values align with the University's belief that the mind is nothing without the heart.

STUDY ABROAD: Marquette students have the option to study abroad on six continents, generally during their sophomore or junior year. Spain, France, and Mexico are particularly popular destinations for students looking to practice their foreign languages, while Ireland and Australia provide an English-speaking experience that is nevertheless filled with culture and adventure.

SERVICE: The University's urban location comes with numerous opportunities for students to volunteer. Each year, Marquette students perform more than one hundred thousand hours of community service in such programs as Big Brothers/Big Sisters, Habitat for Humanity, and the Senior Citizens' Prom. Advertising and public relations students help create information campaigns for nonprofit organizations, and accounting students offer volunteer tax-preparation services. The University also offers a service-learning program in South Africa in which students take classes and help community-based organizations to give voice to disadvantaged people. Nursing students take part in Marquette's HIV/AIDS program in Africa.

LIVE IT, LOVE IT: Marquette is located on a ninety-acre campus in an urban setting. With unlimited use of public transportation, Marquette students find it easy to enjoy Milwaukee's cultural, educational, and entertainment opportunities. The Lake Michigan shoreline is just two miles from campus.

RESIDENCE LIFE: As it has expanded through the years, Marquette has absorbed several nearby buildings—a hospital, the downtown Milwaukee YMCA, and several hotels—and converted them into attractive, comfortable residence halls. About 94 percent of students choose to live either on campus or directly adjacent to it. Themed housing options include floors that are dedicated to engineering, nursing, leadership, and honors scholarship.

INTERNSHIPS: Internships with Milwaukee-based companies and organizations play a major role in many Marquette students' educations. Notably, Marquette's Les Aspin Center for Government began as a single-student internship and has since grown into one of the nation's leading congressional internship programs. Sitting in the shadow of the Capitol Building in Washington, D.C., the Aspin Center provides living and classroom space for students interested in government. Students meet and discuss issues with officials from the Pentagon, the Department of State, and the Central Intelligence Agency. Participants have also worked in the White House, the Food and Drug Administration, the Department of Defense, and the Secret Service.

CAREER SERVICES: A Marquette education is designed to prepare students not only for their professions, but also for their lives beyond work. Marquette's Career Services department provides students with an extensive database of job listings and search engines as well as online advice about interviewing, résumés, and networking.

AFTER GRADUATION: While many Marquette graduates stay in the Milwaukee area, working for multinational firms like GE Medical, the Miller Brewing Company, Harley-Davidson, or Northwestern Mutual, a substantial number of students begin their careers in Chicago; New York; Atlanta; and Washington, D.C.

ALUMNI: Among Marquette's many notable alumni are Chicago Sun-Times executive editor John Barron; Tony Award-winning actor Anthony Crivello; comedian Chris Farley; Patrick Eugene Haggerty, founder of Texas Instruments; Rudy Perpich, former governor of Minnesota; and Miami Heat basketball player Dwyane Wade. Many other alumni contribute to their communities through their work in politics, medicine, scientific research, nursing, teaching, law, and literature.

http://www.marquette.edu/

P: (414) 288-7302

PRIVATE - CATHOLIC

STUDENT PROFILE

8,143 undergraduate students

98% of undergrad students are full time

47% male – 53% female

67% of students are from out of state

90% freshman retention rate

80% graduated in 6 years

FACULTY PROFILE

630 full-time faculty

522 part-time faculty

14.6 to 1 student/faculty ratio

ADMISSIONS

20,486 Total Applicants

15,202 Total Admissions

1,876 Total Freshman Enrollment

74.21% of applicants admitted

SAT Ranges: CR 530-640, M 540-660, W 510-640, E 8-9

ACT Ranges: C 24-30, M 24-29, E 24-31, W 8-9

TUITION & COSTS

Tuition: $38,000

Fees: $470

Total: $38,470

R&B: $11,440

Total: $50,380

FINANCIAL

$18,681 avg grant/scholarship amount (need)

$6,880 avg loan amount (need)

NORTHLAND COLLEGE

ASHLAND, WISCONSIN

Northland rests on the northern tip of Ashland, Wisconsin, surrounded by acres of forest and bordered by the Lake Superior lakefront. Embracing the natural world, Northland students and faculty make the most of their many outdoor opportunities. It is with the influence of such a goal-oriented College that Northland students continue to succeed and chase their dreams long after graduating.

STUDY ABROAD: Whether during the academic year or summer intersession, students can benefit from one of Northland College's many life-changing study abroad programs. Every student has the chance to continue their specific fields of study at universities across the globe. Kansai Gaidai University in Japan is a popular destination, a melting pot of culture that hosts over one hundred colleges from around the world for international education. Programs are also offered in such places as Costa Rica, East Africa, and the Middle East through the Center for Ecological Living and Learning, a nonprofit educational organization that encourages students to collaborate and plan new environmental initiatives. As part of the Higher Education Consortium for Urban Affairs (HECUA), Northland collaborates with over twenty other institutions to share and build relationships with students through a network of international organizations. Colleges in places such as Italy, Norway, and Ecuador also partner with Northland, hosting valuable, experiential internships.

OFF-CAMPUS LEARNING: Ringing true with Northland's love for the natural world, the College partners with environmentally focused education organizations so that students may pursue their studies while also immersing themselves in the great outdoors. Many academic adventures await any student wanting to deepen their knowledge in the most hands-on approach possible, including a three-week wilderness expedition to study navigation or a paddling trip in the Boundary Waters of northern Minnesota for an ecology-based literature course.

MAY TERM: With its unique term structure, Northland College makes it easy for driven students to take full advantage of as many academic opportunities as they please. The 4-4-1 academic year is comprised of two four-month semesters in the fall and winter as well as a shorter, one-month session in May. The longer sessions are structured similarly to the traditional semester format, while the May Term gives students a single month to concentrate on one particular learning opportunity. At many colleges and universities, students who choose to work in internships or study abroad must do so during the semester, piling up supplemental yet valuable experiences alongside their schoolwork. Northland's May Term, however, lets students choose to spend an extra month focusing on one subject. This spring session may be short, but its concentrated nature ensures that anyone taking on an internship, study abroad trip, or seminar series will get a comprehensive experience of their extended learning.

THEMED HOUSING: Theme Communities allow Northland students to live with purpose twenty-four hours a day. Every year, groups of students excitedly apply to live together within the same residence while they focus on a central theme. Themed housing allows like-minded students to live with their closest friends, all while raising campus awareness of issues important to them. Through a year of theme-specific outreach and education organizations, students in Theme Communities make a positive impact on the Northland campus and the world alike.

SENIOR CAPSTONE: Every Northland student finishes off their college career with a final capstone or thesis course. A senior capstone synthesizes four years of knowledge into a single project. These courses stretch students to exemplify their mastery of a topic and their ability to think at an advanced level. With courses dedicated to capstone development, seniors are guaranteed the time and resources to create something to be proud of.

https://www.northland.edu/
P: (715) 682-1224

PRIVATE

STUDENT PROFILE

518 undergraduate students

99% of undergrad students are full time

51% male — 49% female

53% of students are from out of state

70% freshman retention rate

58% graduated in 6 years

FACULTY PROFILE

53 full-time faculty

8 part-time faculty

9 to 1 student/faculty ratio

ADMISSIONS

852 Total Applicants

487 Total Admissions

128 Total Freshman Enrollment

57.16% of applicants admitted

ACT Ranges: C 21-28, M 19-26, E 20-27

TUITION & COSTS

Tuition: $31,980

Fees: $1,452

Total: $33,432

R&B: $8,485

Total: $41,917

FINANCIAL

$22,372 avg grant/scholarship amount (need)

$4,868 avg loan amount (need)

ST. NORBERT COLLEGE

DE PERE, WISCONSIN

Producing graduates with the requisite skills to succeed, lead, and serve in the world, St. Norbert provides students with a classic liberal arts education, teaching them to think critically, write clearly, and communicate effectively. Situated on a residential campus along the banks of the Fox River, St. Norbert offers an active, stimulating community environment that encourages students to learn and grow throughout their lives.

CENTER FOR INTERNATIONAL EDUCATION: St. Norbert is known as one of the best colleges in the northern Midwest, particularly noted for service-learning and its strong international programs. St. Norbert's Center for International Education is dedicated to creating and enhancing international activities. Known for welcoming students from around the world, St. Norbert provides opportunities for students to engage with and learn from students from approximately 30 other countries. About one in three St. Norbert students participate in study-abroad programs. St. Norbert partners with 50 international institutions of higher learning in 29 countries to offer study-abroad opportunities in 75 locations around the world.

SERVICE-LEARNING: Service-learning—promoted by the leadership, service, and engagement office—is so deeply ingrained in the culture of St. Norbert that students regularly volunteer their efforts to several major projects every year. One residence hall is devoted especially to service, with each section performing its own year-long project. Fall and spring break alternatives offer many opportunities for involvement beyond the campus. St. Norbert ranks among the nation's leading schools for student participation. St. Norbert was also admitted to the President's Higher Education Community Service Honor Roll with distinction for its strong institutional commitment to service and community partnerships by the Corporation for National and Community Service.

RESIDENCE LIFE: St. Norbert has a four-year on-campus residence requirement, which the college believes contributes to the students' focus on their education and co-curricular lives. The college offers a wide variety of living options, including all-freshman residence halls; an all-women's residence hall; themed housing for students interested in science, service, a particular foreign language, or other specific interests; and townhouses, carriage houses, and apartments for upperclassmen.

ALUMNI SUCCESS: St. Norbert students have achieved notable success in many different fields, especially in education. The late Robert John Cornell, a former member of the U.S. House of Representatives from Wisconsin, was a St. Norbert graduate, and twelve generals in the military graduated from St. Norbert's military science program. Furthermore, St. Norbert graduates enjoy a 93 percent placement rate for those seeking full-time employment or admission to graduate school. This success rate is a result of the excellent reputation of St. Norbert graduates in the workplace and in graduate schools. Alumni play a role, too, serving as a reference point for students' networking and placement.

PROFESSIONAL OPPORTUNITIES: Faculty-student research is common at St. Norbert, with numerous first-year students making two-year research commitments to a particular faculty or staff member through the college's Research Fellows Program. Internships also play an important role in building networks and professional experience. Some participate in internships while on study abroad trips, while others can take part in the Washington Semester at Catholic University. These experiences in the lab and throughout the workplace arm students with the skills to excel after they graduate.

http://www.snc.edu/

P: (800) 236-4878

PRIVATE - CATHOLIC

STUDENT PROFILE

2,096 undergraduate students

97% of undergrad students are full time

44% male — 56% female

23% of students are from out of state

82% freshman retention rate

73% graduated in 6 years

FACULTY PROFILE

140 full-time faculty

39 part-time faculty

13 to 1 student/faculty ratio

ADMISSIONS

3,814 Total Applicants

2,963 Total Admissions

601 Total Freshman Enrollment

77.69% of applicants admitted

SAT Ranges: CR 510-610, M 500-610

ACT Ranges: C 22-27, M 21-27, E 21-27, W 7-8

TUITION & COSTS

Tuition: $33,622

Fees: $615

Total: $34,237

R&B: $8,794

Room: $4,695

Board: $4,099

Total: $43,031

FINANCIAL

$19,435 avg grant/scholarship amount (total)

$7,979 avg loan amount (total)

UNIVERSITY OF WISCONSIN–LA CROSSE

LA CROSSE, WISCONSIN

UW-La Crosse is a public institution within the University of Wisconsin system. The University is hailed as a leading Midwest institution with vast opportunities in research and personal development.

THE FIRST-YEAR SEMINAR: The first-year seminar (FYS) focuses on one central question: "What does it mean to be an educated person?" Students contemplate this question as individuals and explore perspectives within their seminars as part of a group. The purpose of the FYS is to push students to consider how they learn and what it takes to be successful. In the seminar, students build upon their critical thinking and writing skills while collaborating with peers and faculty.

STUDENT-FACULTY RESEARCH: Undergraduate research is not only a valuable experience, but it also demonstrates to employers the researcher's skills in higher-level conceptualization and analysis. UW-La Crosse allows students to collaborate with faculty members on research projects as early as freshman year. Students who begin research early on receive the added benefit of truly grasping how they feel about an area of study as well as making a more informed decision about their choices of major. Sophomore and junior researchers benefit too, as they have the option to write for summer research grants. Sophomore and juniors may also include their experience on grad school and job applications.

EAGLE APPRENTICES: Eagle Apprentices selects 25 incoming freshmen to work with a faculty member on a research project. If chosen, students get to work side-by-side with faculty as they pursue a project within their own area of study. Students put in 2-3 hours a week for an entire semester. They even receive a stipend of $1,000, which increases to $2,000 if they return for a second year.

REQUIRED WRITING COURSES: UW-La Crosse recognizes writing as a valuable skill that all undergraduates should master. All students are therefore required to demonstrate competency in writing through one of two ways: two 200+ level writing classes or the completion of a major that incorporates writing-intensive courses. Most majors have writing within the program, so many can satisfy the requirement simply by completing their degree.

INTERNATIONAL EDUCATION AND ENGAGEMENT: International Education and Engagement (IEE) is the number-one campus resource for global opportunities. IEE supports and promotes global experiences that range from study abroad to international service, enabling the amazing opportunity to experience another country's culture, language, and customs. UW-La Crosse encourages its students to study abroad at some point during their undergraduate experience because of the countless benefits of participation. Travel develops students' cross-cultural communication skills, an appreciation for another culture, and multicultural tolerance.

EQUIPPED TO EXPLORE: International Education Ambassadors (IEAs) are upperclassmen who assist other students with questions pertaining to study abroad. Ambassadors are both international and domestic students that have experience advising underclassmen. UW-La Crosse even has affiliations with universities in several foreign locations, so they are able to check with IEAs to make sure that their destination is comfortable, fun, and right for them.

http://www.uwlax.edu/

P: (608) 785-8000

PUBLIC

STUDENT PROFILE

9,706 undergraduate students

95% of undergrad students are full time

44% male – 56% female

17% of students are from out of state

85% freshman retention rate

68% graduated in 6 years

FACULTY PROFILE

537 full-time faculty

66 part-time faculty

18 to 1 student/faculty ratio

ADMISSIONS

6,051 Total Applicants

4,841 Total Admissions

2,071 Total Freshman Enrollment

80% of applicants admitted

TUITION & COSTS

Tuition: (In) $7,585 (Out) $15,536

Fees: $1,247

Total: (In) $8,832 (Out) $16,783

R&B: $5,850

Room: $3,500

Board: $2,350

Total: (In) $14,682 (Out) $22,633

FINANCIAL

$2,909 avg grant/scholarship amount (total)

$6,528 avg loan amount (total)

UNIVERSITY OF WISCONSIN-STOUT

MENOMONIE, WISCONSIN

The University of Wisconsin-Stout, Wisconsin's Polytechnic University, combines applied learning with a liberal arts education, preparing students for successful and demanding careers in their respective industries. Ninety-seven percent of the university's undergraduate students are employed or pursuing graduate degrees within six months of graduation.

POLYTECHNIC APPROACH: UW-Stout's polytechnic designation and approach to comprehensive education is truly unique and driven in pursuit of excellent outcomes. A student who chooses to attend one of the 3% of universities in the United States, that are designated polytechnic—such as UW-Stout—enjoys a blend of both a traditional liberal arts education along with an emphasis on active, applied learning. They also immerse themselves in interdisciplinary collaborations to solve emerging real-world problems.

HANDS-ON EDUCATION: Students are immersed in a career-focused education as early their freshman year and immediately benefit from numerous opportunities to gain real-world experience. And, with twice as many labs as classrooms, there are multiple opportunities to participate in applied research. Through a broad array of undergraduate and graduate programs, many of which are uncommon in the Midwest, UW-Stout emphasizes a student-centered education on campus as well as online and at offsite locations through one of the largest distance education programs in the UW System.

UNDERGRADUATE RESEARCH: Undergraduate research is supported in a variety of ways at UW-Stout. The faculty-student Creative Original Research Experiences Committee (CORE) leads efforts to bring research experiences to the campus. University grants also support various aspects of student research, including dissemination and travel. The Office of Research and Sponsored Programs supports students as they participate in Research Day; Research in the Rotunda; the annual National Conference on Undergraduate Research; the UW System Symposium for Undergraduate Research and Creative Activity; mentorship programs; and the Journal of Student Research, which is published annually.

DIVERSITY/GLOBAL LEARNING: UW-Stout's award-winning Multicultural Student Services office coordinates support; intercultural and leadership development; and living and learning communities for African-American, Asian, American Indian, and Latino students. The office also coordinates pre-college programs for middle and high school students from low-income environments. The university offers study abroad programs in more than 40 nations; students can choose to study or intern for a few weeks or an entire semester. Participation in the National Student Exchange allows students to study elsewhere in the U.S., its territories, or Canada, all while paying the same UW-Stout tuition and fees.

COMFORTABLE LOCATION: Menomonie offers the charm and security of a small town, yet is within easy driving distance of the Minneapolis-St. Paul metropolitan area. The city is a "college town" with a variety of restaurants, retail options, and perfect venues for social gathering. The university participates in the quiet and pleasant life of the town, and local residents eagerly support Stout's educational, cultural, and sports activities.

AN IMPRESSIVE EMPLOYMENT RATE: UW-Stout's graduates are ready to hit the ground running in their professional careers. Fully 97 percent of the university's undergraduate students are employed or pursuing graduate degrees within six months of their graduation, and more than three quarters are employed in their field of study. Such an continuous achievement goes back more than a decade.

PRE-GRADUATION CAREER EXPERIENCE: Professional Career Services counselors provide exceptional guidance for students. Their outstanding network is clearly demonstrated through their career conferences, hosting two of the largest in the Midwest every year. Most majors require an internship or co-op experience, ensuring that students gain professional experience in their field before they take on the workforce. The Career Services team works with academic departments to connect students with more than 500 employers.

http://www.uwstout.edu/
P: (715) 232-1122

PUBLIC

STUDENT PROFILE

8,178 undergraduate students

83% of undergrad students are full-time

55% male – 45% female

38% of students are from out of state

73% freshman retention rate

54.2% graduated in 6 years

FACULTY PROFILE

401 full-time faculty

102 part-time faculty

19 to 1 student-to-faculty ratio

ADMISSIONS

3,445 Total Applicants

3,023 Total Admissions

1,588 Total Freshman Enrollment

87.75% of applicants admitted

ACT Ranges: C19-25 , M 18-25, E 18-24

TUITION & COSTS

Tuition: (In) $7,014 (Out) $14,760

R&B: $6,624

Room: $4,040

Board: $2,584

Total: (In) $13,638 (Out) $21,384

FINANCIAL

$4,719 avg grant/scholarship amount (need)

$4,596 avg loan amount (need)

UNIVERSITY OF WISCONSIN–WHITEWATER

WHITEWATER, WISCONSIN

UNIVERSITY OF WISCONSIN
WHITEWATER

Founded in 1868, UW-Whitewater is a premier four-year public university located in southeastern Wisconsin. One of 13 universities in the University of Wisconsin System, it has approximately 1,400 faculty and staff members. Students have the option of 50 undergraduate and 15 master's degree programs, an education specialist degree, and a doctorate of business administration.

THE FIRST-YEAR EXPERIENCE: The First-Year Experience at UW-Whitewater is comprised of over several different components. It begins with Plan-It Purple, the day-long summer registration program. At Plan-It Purple, new students not only register for class, but also have the opportunity to meet other new Warhawks and connect with an academic advisor. Next, students participate in Club U-Dub-Dub—the two-day fall orientation for new freshmen and transfer students. Club U-Dub-Dub helps new students settle into life at UW-Whitewater by providing opportunities for social acclimatization as well as assistance with the academic transition to college. Orientation ends with a free on-campus concert.

UNDERGRADUATE RESEARCH: UW-Whitewater's Undergraduate Research Program has a national reputation, with more than 260 students participating from all four colleges. Undergraduate research grants support faculty-student collaborative research and scholarly activities. Every year, UW-Whitewater undergraduate research students present their research in various disciplines at state and national conferences. Student researchers are even regularly included as co-authors with faculty in scholarly journals.

STUDY ABROAD: In terms of global learning, the Center for Global Education helps student access the wide variety of study abroad and travel-study experiences available to UW-Whitewater students. The center's mission is to facilitate experiences that help students become successful leaders; to that end, UW-Whitewater offers dozens of programs in more than 50 different countries. The university also offers qualified students financial aid for study abroad experiences. For example, College of Business and Economics students who participate receive a grant of up to $1,000 toward their experience, and the the College of Education and Professional Studies offers scholarship opportunities to students who wish to student teach abroad. The undergraduate and graduate programs host hundreds of international students on campus, aiding their sense of community through such events as a popular international dinner every year.

PEER MENTOR PROGRAM: As part of the first-year experience, new students are assigned a student leader, known as a Peer Mentor, during their first semester on campus. Peer mentors lead their new students through the two-day fall orientation, Club U-Dub Dub. They also act as assistant instructors in their students' New Student Seminar courses. Peer Mentors act as points of contact for new students throughout the fall semester, encouraging deep connections to their peers and the university through fun activities and informal gatherings.

LEARNING COMMUNITIES: New students are encouraged to participate in one of UW-Whitewater's many Learning Communities (LC)—an opportunity to live and study with other new students who share similar interests. Consisting of around 25 students, each LC is centered on an academic or goal-oriented theme. Students in each LC live in the same residence hall and enroll in several courses together (including the same New Student Seminar). LCs are also led by a faculty or staff member who share similar interests with these students, facilitating students' contacts with faculty outside the classroom setting. Approximately 30% of each incoming class participates in LCs at UW-Whitewater.

SERVICE: UW-Whitewater supports community-based and service learning through a variety of initiatives. Learning Communities participate in a day of service to the community each fall. The Program for Community-Based Learning coordinates partnership opportunities between the university and the community. It also oversees the funding of several Summer Undergraduate Research Fellowships in Community Based Research. In addition, the university sponsors a year-long faculty development program, known as the Community-Based Learning Fellows Program.

http://www.uww.edu/
P: (262) 472-1234

PUBLIC

STUDENT PROFILE

10,775 undergraduate students

93% of undergrad students are full-time

51% male – 49% female

19.9% of students are from out of state

81.4% freshman retention rate

57% graduated in 6 years

FACULTY PROFILE

438 full-time faculty

128 part-time faculty

21 to 1 student-to-faculty ratio

ADMISSIONS

6,228 Total Applicants

5,056 Total Admissions

2,220 Total Freshman Enrollment

81.18% of applicants admitted

SAT Ranges: CR 420-520, M 470-590

ACT Ranges: C 20-25, M 18-25, E 19-24

TUITION & COSTS

Tuition: (In) $6,519 (Out) $15,092

Fees: $1,143

Total: (In) $7,662 (Out) $16,235

R&B: $6,442

Room: $1,996

Board: $1,225

Total: (In) $14,104 (Out) $22,677

FINANCIAL

$5,466 avg grant/scholarship amount (need)

$4,223 avg loan amount (need)

VITERBO UNIVERSITY

LA CROSSE, WISCONSIN

VITERBO
UNIVERSITY

With a 1:11 faculty-to-student ratio and an average class size of 16, Viterbo students are known by name and receive personal attention both in and out of the classroom. Many programs feature guaranteed paid internships, study abroad, high-impact practices, and research opportunities that are sure to enhance the classroom experience. Viterbo also has a generous transfer-credit policy and bachelor's degree-completion programs specifically designed for busy adult learners. Viterbo's beautiful campus and close-knit community are located in La Crosse—a city nestled between scenic bluffs and the Mississippi River and named the top college town in Wisconsin.

EXPERIENTIAL LEARNING: A Viterbo education means much more than traditional books, classrooms, and computer labs; Viterbo offers hands-on learning. Just a few of the options available for students include: spending the night outside in February—a simple but profound gesture—to raise awareness about people experiencing homelessness; harvesting organic vegetables at the local community garden; and gaining nursing experience assisting the people with the Salvation Army.

STUDY ABROAD: Perhaps the most enriching and life-changing experience a student can have is studying abroad in another country. In addition to academics, students learn first hand about new places, people, and cultures while experiencing things that most people only see in books or on a screen. Viterbo students also have opportunities to join their classmates on week-long overseas trips during Christmas break. For example, a group of Viterbo theatre and musical theatre students recently traveled to London to learn more about the history and evolution of theatre. Meanwhile, a group of music students enjoyed European culture and opera over break.

UNIQUE SEMINAR COURSES: Knowledge should be acquired with purpose and meaning. Viterbo's unique core curriculum allows students to select seminar courses that align with their interests and are infused with Viterbo's mission: Franciscan Values and Traditions, Living in a Diverse World, Serving the Common Good, and The Ethical Life.

COMMUNITY SERVICE: Service is an essential component of a Viterbo education. Students can choose to help build a house with Habitat for Humanity, collect hats and mittens for those who are less fortunate, or stock the food shelves at the local food pantry. Viterbo also hosts Service Saturdays, which provide opportunities for students and employees to serve alongside various community organizations, connect with each other, and enjoy a post-service reflection meal. Viterbo campus ministry organizes spring break and summer service trips to Midwest cities, all with a focus to build community among trip participants and between participants and those they serve.

ACADEMIC RESOURCE CENTER: Viterbo offers the practical tools for success. The University's Academic Resource Center offers a wide variety of tutoring, academic counseling, test-preparation services, and academic workshops. Faculty members also give students personalized attention that truly helps them succeed. Better yet, the University also offers counseling services, extensive disability support, and health and safety services.

CAREER SERVICES: For many students, success is defined by the job they can land after graduation, and with a 99% placement rate, the Viterbo career services office helps students achieve just that. Career services offers assistance with interviews, résumés, internships, and securing gainful employment.

---

http://www.viterbo.edu/

P: (608) 796-3000

PRIVATE - CATHOLIC

STUDENT PROFILE

1,861 undergraduate students

80% of undergrad students are full time

28% male – 72% female

34% of students are from out of state

80% freshman retention rate

46% graduated in 6 years

FACULTY PROFILE

120 full-time faculty

204 part-time faculty

11 to 1 student/faculty ratio

ADMISSIONS

1,770 Total Applicants

1,107 Total Admissions

312 Total Freshman Enrollment

62.54% of applicants admitted

SAT Ranges: CR 430-490, M 370-530

ACT Ranges: C 20-26, M 19-26, E 20-26

TUITION & COSTS

Tuition: $25,460

Fees: $690

Total: $26,150

R&B: $8,510

Total: $34,660

WISCONSIN LUTHERAN COLLEGE

MILWAUKEE, WISCONSIN

At Wisconsin Lutheran College, students not only have small class sizes and a variety of academic options, but they also can work side-by-side with professors doing groundbreaking heart-disease research, teach in local schools as early as freshman year, travel to Zambia for a nursing clinical, take a British literature course in England, or conduct marine biology research in Grenada. Taught from a Christian perspective, courses at Wisconsin Lutheran College help students develop skills they'll need in their careers: critical thinking, communication, teamwork, and decision-making.

COLLEGE 101: As part of the College's core curriculum, all WLC students take two orientation courses. "The Idea of a Christian College" is a freshman seminar that examines the skills and attitudes essential for college success as well as the intellectual perspectives that are nurtured through studying the liberal arts. "Christian Life Planning" is a sophomore seminar that assists students with establishing goals and planning for both their careers and academic programs. These seminars also incorporate an annual Campus Read, giving students the chance to join in a common reading experience as well as attend a guest lecture from the author of the book itself.

PERSONAL ATTENTION: During their freshman year, students receive personalized academic coaching and participate in seminar classes designed to assist them with academic and career planning. Through the Freshman Mentoring Program, all freshmen are assigned a mentor who also acts as the teacher of their freshman seminar. Students meet weekly with their mentor to discuss a wide range of topics intended to provide an extended orientation to the college, self-analysis, career exploration, academic planning, and personal development.

UNDERGRADUATE RESEARCH: Each year, WLC students in a variety of academic programs work closely with their professors on research projects that help prepare them for graduate school, professional schools, and the workforce. Many students conduct independent research projects as part of their capstone experiences, presenting at the college's annual Undergraduate Research Symposium or at professional conferences both nationally and internationally. In 2013, two students presented the results of WLC's marine biology research in Grenada at the Association of Marine Labs' International Conference held in Jamaica. In 2015, research by a WLC student, alumna, and professor was published in the International Journal of Humanities and Social Science.

VIBRANT CAMPUS LIFE: The WLC experience goes far beyond the classroom. Campus life is full of energy and activity, bustling with social events, guest speakers, variety shows, Homecoming and Winterfest, open mic nights, art gallery openings, and fine arts performances. Students become part of a vibrant, fun community that is centered on the mission and vision of preparing Christian leaders.

STUDENT ACTIVITIES: Through student programming events, students can socialize with each other, help members of the community, and gain leadership experience both on and off campus. The college's annual Serving Hands; Serving Hearts event brings the campus community together in a common service project. Students and faculty can gather outside the classroom at events such as the monthly Afternoon Tea and the annual WLC Christmas celebration.

SUCCESS DURING AND AFTER COLLEGE: The Student Success Center exists to provide a high level of support for all students and faculty, offering academic tutors, writing tutors, and peer mentors. The Career Development Office assists WLC students as they pursue a fulfilling and appropriate use of their God-given talents. The office helps students bridge the gap between college and career, playing an active role in students' career-development process.

---

https://www.wlc.edu/

P: (414) 443-8800

PRIVATE - CHRISTIAN

STUDENT PROFILE

989 undergraduate students

93% of undergrad students are full time

43% male – 57% female

75% freshman retention rate

61% graduated in 6 years

FACULTY PROFILE

63 full-time faculty

92 part-time faculty

10 to 1 student/faculty ratio

ADMISSIONS

658 Total Applicants

594 Total Admissions

228 Total Freshman Enrollment

90.27% of applicants admitted

ACT Ranges: C 21-27, M 20-27, E 21-28

TUITION & COSTS

Tuition: $28,840

Fees: $300

Total: $29,140

R&B: $9,910

Total: $39,050

FINANCIAL

$17,109 avg grant/scholarship amount (need)

$4,067 avg loan amount (need)

EASTERN CONNECTICUT STATE UNIVERSITY

WILLIMANTIC, CONNECTICUT

EASTERN
CONNECTICUT
STATE UNIVERSITY

Eastern Connecticut State University is the state's designated public liberal arts university. A predominantly undergraduate institution, Eastern attracts and welcomes a diverse community of learners who are supported by a teaching-focused faculty in a residential campus that promotes intellectual curiosity, integrity, and social responsibility.

UNDERGRADUATE RESEARCH: At Eastern, students of all majors and class levels conduct research. Even as undergraduates, they can see their high-quality work published in academic journals and presented at local and national conferences, including Eastern's own CREATE conference to the respected Posters on the Hill and National Conference on Undergraduate Research. Students' research earns them awards, helps them obtain competitive internships, and admits them into prestigious graduate schools. With fellowships, project grants, faculty mentorships, connections to research conferences, and extensive laboratory space on campus, Eastern proves itself to be a comprehensive school for undergraduate research.

GLOBAL FIELD COURSES AND STUDY ABROAD: Every year, students take department-sponsored "global field courses" (GFC), which are culturally and academically immersive study abroad experiences led by Eastern faculty. These trips have taken students across all corners of the globe ever since the first GFC program in biology went to the Caribbean in the late 1960s. Most recently, Eastern biology students went to Costa Rica; communication students studied throughout Eastern Europe; health sciences students went to Ghana; environmental earth science students went to Iceland; psychology students went to Ireland; and English students went to Italy.

SERVICE-LEARNING AND COMMUNITY ENGAGEMENT: Professors all across campus engage their students in community-based learning, recognizing the impactful educational experience that comes with working alongside community members and organizations. Recently, the town of Willimantic served as a laboratory for 236 students who participated in 23 service-learning courses with 13 faculty members from 10 departments. In that same year, nearly 1,200 students volunteered 20,025 hours in a variety of community service efforts.

ON-CAMPUS LEARNING VENUES: Among other top-notch locales on campus, students get an incredible learning experience in the 19-acre nature preserve; the planetarium; the campus radio station and television studio; the Center for Early Childhood Education; the new 118,000-square foot Fine Arts Instructional Center; and the high-tech labs of the 174,000-square foot Science Building.

CUSTOMIZED EDUCATION: Eastern students can design their own major through the University's Individualized Major option. Student-designed majors have included a variety of interdisciplinary fields of study, including Digital Multimedia, Psychology and Business Administration, Law and Society, Philosophical Methodology, Multimedia Writing/Production for the Deaf, Behavioral Biology, and French Women's Studies.

THE WARRIOR CUP: The Warrior Cup is an annual competition among all of Eastern's 13 residence halls. Students band together in an attempt to win the coveted Warrior Cup by earning points through their participation in University events activities.

CENTER FOR COMMUNITY ENGAGEMENT: Eastern and the town of Willimantic maintain a mutually beneficial relationship that only continues to strengthen thanks to the Center for Community Engagement (CCE). The CCE organizes numerous special events, such as the annual Day of Giving holiday meal, as well as semester-long service programs that affect long-term change, such as tutoring programs with Willimantic Public Schools.

---

http://www.easternct.edu/

P: (860) 465-5286

PUBLIC

STUDENT PROFILE

4,818 undergraduate students

89% of undergrad students are full-time

44% male – 56% female

11.8% of students are from out of state

76% freshman retention rate

54.4% graduated in 6 years

FACULTY PROFILE

199 full-time faculty

304 part-time faculty

15.6 to 1 student-to-faculty ratio

ADMISSIONS

5,863 Total Applicants

3,395 Total Admissions

1,013 Total Freshman Enrollment

57.91% of applicants admitted

SAT Ranges: CR 480-560, M 470-560

ACT Ranges: C 20-25, M 18-25, E 19-25

TUITION & COSTS

Tuition: (In) $5,424 (Out) $16,882

Fees: $5,495

Total: (In) $10,919 (Out) $22,377

R&B: $13,050

Room: $7,500

Board: $5,550

Total: (In) $23,969 (Out) $35,427

FINANCIAL

$5,743 avg grant/scholarship amount (need)

$4,301 avg loan amount (need)

FAIRFIELD UNIVERSITY

FAIRFIELD, CONNECTICUT

Fairfield University is a Catholic, Jesuit University established in 1942, rooted in one of the world's oldest intellectual and spiritual traditions. Located near the Connecticut shoreline just 60 miles northeast of New York City, Fairfield promotes a commitment to the Jesuit ideals of broad intellectual inquiry. Fairfield University fosters a strong sense of community among its students and offers an educational experience that encourages the pursuit of social justice, and cultivation of the whole person: body, mind, and spirit.

UNDERGRADUATE RESEARCH: Fairfield University is serious about providing every student with the opportunity to gain practical experience in their field of study. In fact, the university guarantees that every junior or senior in good academic standing will have the opportunity for an internship or research experience. Every summer, students collaborate with members of the faculty on research projects in a wide variety of academic disciplines. Students also get to co-author research with their professors. Fairfield students gain valuable research, scholarship, publication, and presentation experiences through a wide array of student-faculty, group, and independent opportunities.

WELL-ROUNDED CURRICULUM: The core curriculum requires students to take 60 credits in five areas, including mathematics and natural sciences; history and social/behavioral sciences; philosophy, religious studies, and ethics; English and the arts; and modern or classical languages and literature. Fairfield doesn't view the core as a checklist to get through, but rather as an important, integrated, and interdisciplinary component of well-rounded education. Fairfield has also developed a program that allows students to take interdisciplinary clusters of two or three thematically related courses. Clusters allow students to explore particular topics from a variety of different perspectives.

THE FIRST-YEAR EXPERIENCE: The First-Year Experience (FYE) program, a requirement for all incoming freshmen, is focused on teaching Fairfield's core Jesuit values, cultivating student self-discovery, and exploring the importance of community. FYE includes a course in the fall semester, designated campus events for students to attend throughout the fall, a mentoring program, and a community service component.

COMMUNITY SERVICE: Fairfield students are very committed to community service. Nearly one-third of all students engage in volunteer programs in nearby cities. Fairfield's community service programs are cutting edge and award-winning. The Corporation for National Service has praised Fairfield's Literary Volunteer Program, and The National Student Campaign Against Hunger and Homelessness has granted Fairfield three consecutive awards. Fairfield students were singled out from among 600 colleges and universities nationwide for their outstanding efforts.

ART FACILITIES: Fairfield's Arts & Minds Program serves as an important hub for students and visitors seeking entertaining and inspiring cultural events and activities. The Regina A. Quick Center for the Arts includes two theatres and an art gallery. The center regularly hosts performances that include musical concerts, ballet and jazz dancers, comedy, opera, plays, and other events. The Open VISIONS Forum is a popular lecture series that engages the 'life of the mind' with students and the Connecticut community. Its mission is to integrate the academic perspective of the university's students and faculty with topics of wide general interest.

LIVING AND LEARNING COMMUNITIES: Living and Learning Communities (LLCs) are available each year for Fairfield's undergraduate students. In addition to traditional residence hall options, the LLCs aim to transform the entire Fairfield University culture. The LLCs create a multicultural community across campus, building on Fairfield University's strategic vision of integrated learning through a variety of community housing programs. While each residential college has a particular focus, involved students are diverse in life experiences, hopes, desires, and interests.

http://www.fairfield.edu/
P: (203) 254-4000

PRIVATE - CATHOLIC

STUDENT PROFILE

3,970 undergraduate students

93% of undergrad students are full time

40% male – 60% female

76% of students are from out of state

89% freshman retention rate

82% graduated in 6 years

FACULTY PROFILE

288 full-time faculty

1 part-time faculty

12 to 1 student/faculty ratio

ADMISSIONS

10,767 Total Applicants

6,995 Total Admissions

966 Total Freshman Enrollment

64.97% of applicants admitted

TUITION & COSTS

Tuition: $44,250

Fees: $625

Total: $44,875

R&B: $13,520

Room: $8,280

Board: $5,240

Total: $58,395

FINANCIAL

$22,483 avg grant/scholarship amount (total)

$9,118 avg loan amount (total)

QUINNIPIAC UNIVERSITY

HAMDEN, CONNECTICUT

An education at Quinnipiac embodies the university's commitment to three important values: excellence in education, a student-centered campus, and a spirit of community. Quinnipiac's mission is to provide a supportive and stimulating environment for the intellectual and personal growth of its 6,500 undergraduate and 2,500 graduate, law, and medical students.

ESSENTIAL LEARNING OUTCOMES: Quinnipiac strives to provide its graduates with interpersonal and intellectual Essential Learning Outcomes through a coherent, purposeful integration of the full student experience. QU students acquire important skills valued by employers along with the aptitudes to creatively and responsibly solve problems and use technologies of today and tomorrow. Students are expected to become intentional learners who embody confidence and integrity, and who will emerge as informed leaders in their professions, in the communities where they live, and in their roles as global citizens in the 21st century.

GAINING EXPERIENCE BEYOND THE CLASSROOM: Students are encouraged to broaden their education and gain professional experience through internships or clinical experiences. The university works closely with each student to find placements that match the student's interests and future goals. Quinnipiac students have completed internships at Hugo Boss, the National Baseball Hall of Fame, the Yale's Child Life Program, The Tonight Show starring Jimmy Fallon, MTV, Good Morning America, ESPN, and more.

LIVING LEARNING COMMUNITIES: Quinnipiac currently offers five residential interest communities. Four living learning communities, all of which include academic courses, include Nursing, Global, 3+1 BS/MBA, and Honors. The Global Living community is a residential interest community for first-year students interested in learning about inclusion, cultural diversity, and individual identity through domestic and international immersion programs and experiences. The sole themed living community is LiveWell, which is a substance-free living environment that supports a healthy balance in students' everyday lives.

A WORLD OF LEARNING: Cultural immersion in a foreign country can be one of a college student's most memorable experiences. While traveling abroad, students develop a broader perspective of the world, themselves, their values, and their future. Quinnipiac provides several options for education abroad, including an arrangement with University College Cork in Ireland. Through agreements with other universities and international programs, Quinnipiac offers study abroad programs in a number of other countries, including Australia, France, the United Kingdom, Spain, Italy, Ghana, Canada, Costa Rica, South Africa, Nicaragua, Austria, and Germany. To provide flexibility for their course plans, students can choose to spend six weeks, a semester, or even an entire year abroad.

QUINNIPIAC POLLING INSTITUTE: Quinnipiac's students can get an up-close-and-personal lesson in current events by working as interviewers for the Quinnipiac Polling Institute, an independent research survey whose results are cited regularly by journalists, public officials, and researchers. The poll surveys individuals about political races, state and national elections, and issues of public concern, such as schools, taxes, transportation, municipal services, and the environment. Exact and thorough, results of the Quinnipiac Poll have been featured regularly in the New York Times, the Washington Post, the Wall Street Journal, and on national network news broadcasts.

CLUBS AND ORGANIZATIONS: There's always plenty to do on campus. The newly expanded Carl Hansen Student Center, on the Mount Carmel campus, is the hub of many student activities. The center is home to the student government office, a media center for the student-run radio and television stations, and the campus newspaper. More than 110 student clubs and organizations provide an excellent forum for meeting students with similar interests. Special events are also scheduled nearly every weekend, along with annual events like Parents and Family Weekend in the fall and the annual student Holiday Dinner before winter break.

http://www.quinnipiac.edu/
P: (800) 462-1944

PRIVATE

STUDENT PROFILE

6,982 undergraduate students

96% of undergrad students are full time

39% male – 61% female

74% of students are from out of state

87% freshman retention rate

76% graduated in 6 years

FACULTY PROFILE

391 full-time faculty

593 part-time faculty

12 to 1 student/faculty ratio

ADMISSIONS

22,745 Total Applicants

16,765 Total Admissions

1,903 Total Freshman Enrollment

73.71% of applicants admitted

SAT Ranges: CR 490-580, M 500-600, W 490-590

ACT Ranges: C 22-27, M 21-27, E 22-27

TUITION & COSTS

Tuition: $40,720

Fees: $1,550

Total: $42,270

R&B: $14,820

Total: $57,090

FINANCIAL

$21,226 avg grant/scholarship amount (total)

$10,870 avg loan amount (total)

SACRED HEART UNIVERSITY

FAIRFIELD, CONNECTICUT

Distinguished by its campus-wide commitment to personal attention, Sacred Heart University boasts an award-winning advising program, cutting-edge technology, championship Division I athletic teams, and nationally recognized community service initiatives.

HANDS-ON EDUCATION: Students in all majors engage in hands-on education both in and out of the classroom. The technologically advanced Martire Center for Business & Communications allows students to apply their skills to real-world settings with the help of SHU's finance lab and trading floor, full-size television studios, and motion capture lab. The new Center for Healthcare Education also features the latest technology available to health professions students, while students in the sciences can utilize the recently renovated laboratories and state-of-the-art computer labs.

SERVICE-LEARNING: Through a dynamic service-learning program, Sacred Heart students gain relevant experience while enacting the University's dedication to civic responsibility. Service-learning experiences are integrated into academic courses, giving students credit toward their degree while changing the lives of others in need.

STUDY ABROAD: Further from campus, students can participate in clinical and internship experiences in study abroad programs around the world. Sacred Heart's unique Freshman Fall Abroad program allows students to study abroad in Italy or Ireland during their first semester, setting the stage for the kind of engaged learning they're sure to receive throughout their college careers.

WELCH EXPERIENCE: A hallmark example of SHU's focus on active learning is the Welch Experience program for students in the Welch College of Business. This program includes faculty-led courses abroad, research opportunities, mentoring programs, specialized career services, and co-curricular activities that are designed to develop career awareness, business acumen, and leadership capabilities.

OFF-CAMPUS STUDY: The great teaching at Sacred Heart extends far beyond the traditional classroom setting. SHU's faculty enrich their students' experiences through trips abroad, shared volunteer experiences, and mentorships for sports teams. They also lead excursions to such locations such as Washington, D.C., and the New York Stock Exchange.

GREEK LIFE: Sacred Heart has a robust Greek life community whose participants engage in a unique balance of leadership, academic, philanthropy/service, and social opportunities. The entire campus benefits from events and programs organized by fraternities and sororities.

SERVICE: The SHU community is characterized by its dedication to serving others, as evidenced by an award-winning community service program. Each year, Sacred Heart students contribute around 53,000 hours of community service to the local community and go on service trips to Bangladesh, Dominican Republic, Costa Rica, Haiti, Mexico, and Colombia.

CAPSTONE PROJECTS: SHU's capstone experience challenges seniors to conduct research or lead creative projects that exemplify their thirst for discovery as well as the knowledge they gained throughout their years in college.

CAREER SERVICES: Outside the classroom, undergraduates in all majors participate in internships that are facilitated through the Career Development and Placement Center. Career counselors work with students one-on-one during their internship searches and introduce them to the "Pioneer Network," SHU's interactive career development system, which contains thousands of internship listings. Students get the opportunity to connect with potential employers through a variety of networking events on campus, such as career fairs and on-campus interviewing days.

---

http://www.sacredheart.edu/
P: (203) 371-7880

PRIVATE - CATHOLIC

STUDENT PROFILE

5,325 undergraduate students

90% of undergrad students are full time

37% male – 63% female

63% of students are from out of state

81% freshman retention rate

60% graduated in 6 years

FACULTY PROFILE

281 full-time faculty

521 part-time faculty

15 to 1 student/faculty ratio

ADMISSIONS

10,017 Total Applicants

5,731 Total Admissions

1,322 Total Freshman Enrollment

57.21% of applicants admitted

SAT Ranges: CR 486-622, M 497-632

ACT Ranges: C 22-28

TUITION & COSTS

Tuition: $36,920

Fees: $250

Total: $37,170

R&B: $14,140

Room: $9,900

Board: $4,240

Total: $51,560

FINANCIAL

$16,046 avg grant/scholarship amount (need)

$4,953 avg loan amount (need)

UNIVERSITY OF NEW HAVEN

University of
New Haven

As a recognized leader in experiential education, the University of New Haven employs a combination of internships, study abroad, faculty-led research, and academic service-learning to prepare students to be successful in their future careers.

STUDY ABROAD: UNH's study abroad program provides students with numerous opportunities to gain international experience. Choices include China, Germany, India, and Ireland, among other countries. UNH is one of only a few universities in the United States to offer freshman-year study abroad.

SPONSORED RESEARCH: The University promotes collaborative research among small groups of students or between students and faculty. Students receive valuable exposure to academic and professional circles by presenting their research at conferences and workshops held by recognized and prestigious associations.

PACE: College of Business students within the Personalized Academic Curricular Experience (PACE) work with their advisors to form a cluster of courses to take that are not from the College of Business but are nevertheless thematically related to the student's proposed field of work upon graduation.

CORPORATE CHALLENGE: Student groups who participate in the Corporate Challenge competitively perform field work on a case study with a local business organization. Their case studies are relevant to emerging issues in business while addressing real, ongoing business projects. Finalists receive awards, scholarships, and cash prizes.

ACTIVITIES: The University of New Haven is home to more than 170 clubs, professional and academic honor societies, a student government association, Greek life organizations, 16 Division II sports, and a number of intramural sports opportunities. The 58,000-square-foot David A. Beckerman Recreation Center houses three basketball and volleyball courts, a multi-activity court, two racquetball courts, and fitness equipment. Additionally, the campus center was recently expanded to add space for campus club events, student group meetings and programs, and new dining options.

PROFESSIONAL ENRICHMENT PROGRAM: Professional Enrichment seminars and forums focus on professional readiness and/or current work-related issues while giving students the opportunity to network with industry professionals.

JOB SHADOWING: Graduating seniors can accompany and shadow an industry professional throughout the day to get a firsthand impression of the workplace and career of interest.

STUDENT ADVISORY BOARD: Run by students and overseen by the dean, the Student Advisory Board provides information about all the special programs and opportunities that the College of Business has to offer. It also provides feedback and advice to the leadership team of the College of Business.

STUDENT AMBASSADOR PROGRAM: The Student Ambassador Program welcomes eligible business students who demonstrate academic accomplishment and professional expertise. Students serve as stewards to the community, ambassadors for the College to its alumni and business and community leaders, and role models for current students.

INTERNSHIPS: Each department in UNH's College of Arts and Sciences, College of Business, Tagliatela College of Engineering, and Henry C. Lee College of Criminal Justice and Forensic Sciences provides opportunities for their students to enroll in a three-credit internship.

---

http://www.newhaven.edu/

P: (203) 932-7000

PRIVATE

STUDENT PROFILE

5,002 undergraduate students

92% of undergrad students are full time

50% male – 50% female

61% of students are from out of state

79% freshman retention rate

54% graduated in 6 years

FACULTY PROFILE

282 full-time faculty

367 part-time faculty

16 to 1 student/faculty ratio

ADMISSIONS

10,748 Total Applicants

8,826 Total Admissions

1,244 Total Freshman Enrollment

82.12% of applicants admitted

SAT Ranges: CR 480-580, M 480-580, W 470-570

ACT Ranges: C 21-26, M 19-26, E 21-26

TUITION & COSTS

Tuition: $34,330

Fees: $1,320

Total: $35,650

R&B: $14,620

Room: $9,220

Board: $5,400

Total: $50,270

FINANCIAL

$20,209 avg grant/scholarship amount (total)

$11,535 avg loan amount (total)

UNIVERSITY OF SAINT JOSEPH

WEST HARTFORD, CONNECTICUT

The University of Saint Joseph (USJ) acts as a catalyst for distinctive success, propelling students forward with rigorous academics and experiential learning opportunities. Its exceptional faculty are focused on student accomplishment, and its impressive network of flourishing alumni enable students to explore and expand their potential. Reflecting values of personal integrity and responsibility, USJ's career-focused programs are designed to help students prepare for fulfilling, challenging, and meaningful futures.

FIRST-YEAR SEMINAR: The University of Saint Joseph's First-Year Seminar addresses the academic, social, and emotional challenges of the first year of college, all while acting as a springboard for students to develop their college-level critical thinking and skills. The Seminar encourages students to participate in University activities as well as interact actively with professors and other students both in and out of class. Led by engaged peer and faculty mentors, each First-Year Seminar class ensures that every student's first year at USJ is successful.

INTERDISCIPLINARY WRITING & REASONING: USJ's Interdisciplinary Writing & Reasoning program was founded on the belief that articulate communication is a crucial platform for critical thought. Because competent writing and communication are essential for success in the professional world, all USJ students are expected to hone their writing skills as part of their college careers. By the end of their time as undergraduates, they develop writing portfolios that showcase their growth.

CENTER FOR STUDENT RESEARCH AND CREATIVE ACTIVITY: USJ's Center for Student Research and Creative Activity commits to making education as engaging as possible. Its facilities and events enrich the University's curriculum, opening the doors to cutting-edge research and grant-funded projects that develop meaningful solutions to local and global issues. It also houses many resources that facilitate the creation students' original artwork, performances, and other works. USJ students can even present their research to the greater community during Symposium Day, an annual event that honors academic scholarship.

ON-CAMPUS LEADERSHIP POSITIONS: At the University of Saint Joseph, students with the enthusiasm to lead do not go unrecognized. As both a celebration of and workshop for their passion to make positive change, the University's annual Student Leadership Conference challenges students to discover and develop their potentials as leaders. Every club and organization sends its leaders to attend the Conference's sessions on communication, wellness, and programming, ensuring that USJ is a community aptly led by informed and creative students.

SERVICE LEARNING: In partnership with the Franciscan Center for Urban Ministry, USJ's Wellness Center promotes healthy living to those in need throughout Hartford. Among the Center's community outreach programs is the Manna Community Meals, an initiative that provides day shelter, meals, and other support services to the city's underserved population. USJ's naturally philanthropic students change lives, volunteering provide health screenings and education while practicing the skills they gain in the classroom.

STUDENT INTERNSHIP, FIELD, AND CLINICAL EXPERIENCES: Experiential education is a priority at USJ. 92% of USJ students graduate having with some kind of significant, pre-professional, and workplace-based experience. Their internships help them earn academic credit while expanding their real-world experiences and professional networks. Past internships offered to USJ students have included positions at major insurance companies, leading cultural institutions, major hospitals and healthcare facilities, business and financial services firms, educational institutions, and state agencies.

http://www.usj.edu/
P: (860) 231-5216

PRIVATE - CATHOLIC

STUDENT PROFILE

843 undergraduate students

86% of undergrad students are full time

1% male – 99% female

7% of students are from out of state

75% freshman retention rate

55% graduated in 6 years

FACULTY PROFILE

134 full-time faculty

167 part-time faculty

10 to 1 student/faculty ratio

ADMISSIONS

743 Total Applicants

647 Total Admissions

126 Total Freshman Enrollment

87.08% of applicants admitted

SAT Ranges: CR 430-560, M 400-540

ACT Ranges: C 20-24

TUITION & COSTS

Tuition: $35,220

Fees: $1,710

Total: $36,930

R&B: $11,095

Total: $48,025

FINANCIAL

$20,487 avg grant/scholarship amount (need)

$5,817 avg loan amount (need)

WESTERN CONNECTICUT STATE UNIVERSITY

DANBURY, CONNECTICUT

WESTERN CONNECTICUT

http://www.wcsu.edu/

P: (203) 837-9000

PUBLIC

STUDENT PROFILE

5,442 undergraduate students

80% of undergrad students are full time

47% male – 53% female

79% freshman retention rate

42% graduated in 6 years

FACULTY PROFILE

212 full-time faculty

367 part-time faculty

14 to 1 student/faculty ratio

ADMISSIONS

5,494 Total Applicants

2,199 Total Admissions

786 Total Freshman Enrollment

40.03% of applicants admitted

SAT Ranges: CR 440-540, M 440-540, W 440-550

ACT Ranges: C 18-24, M 18-25, E 19-24

TUITION & COSTS

Tuition: (In) $4,600 (Out) $14,886

Fees: $5,926

Total: (In) $9,077 (Out) $20,812

R&B: $11,106

Room: $6,432

Board: $4,674

Total: (In) $20,183 (Out) $31,918

FINANCIAL

$5,851 avg grant/scholarship amount (need)

$14,426 avg loan amount (need)

Western Connecticut State University changes lives by providing its students with a high-quality education that fosters their growth as leaders in a global society. To achieve this, the University offers undergraduate and graduate programs that weave together the liberal arts and professional education, instilling in them a desire for lifelong learning. It sustains a vibrant, inclusive campus that connects individuals through co-curricular programs, cultural events, and service to the community. In addition to its student-centered faculty who are passionate teachers and accomplished scholars, the University also helps connect students to internship, research, and experiential learning opportunities.

ENGAGING IN CLINICAL EXPERIENCE: Western education majors engage in clinical experience in community classrooms so that they may be prepared to meet the changing needs of tomorrow's learners. Nursing students can spend months in hospital settings, advancing their expertise. And social Work students engage in field experiences that are designated to provide them with direct experience under the supervision of a professional social worker. In many cases, students participate in a capstone course that requires them to integrate their professional values, knowledge, and skills within a case-study format. Regardless of their studies, Western students have an incredible opportunity to see their field in action.

ENGAGING WITH THE ENVIRONMENT: Western is having an important and growing impact on the preservation of Connecticut's largest lake, Candlewood. Students and science professors work together to monitor the lake for signs of zebra mussels, which have infected other local waterways. They are also able to participate in a study on a tick-borne illness, working with the CDC under a grant coordinated by WCSU's professor of Medical Entomology and Epidemiology.

ENGAGING WITH THE WIDE WORLD: For more than 25 years, Western has been a member institution of ISEP, a program that allows students to study anywhere in the world. Students study abroad for a semester, a year, or throughout short-term summer programs. Studying abroad raises global awareness, enhances academic learning, develops leadership skills, advances career opportunities, and facilitates personal growth.

FIRST-YEAR EXPERIENCE: The First-Year Experience program is designed to provide academic and cocurricular support as students transition into the college lifestyle. Faculty reach out to the wide range of students—recent high school graduates, transfer students, and non-traditional students—to help them identify the resources, skills, and procedures that will help them succeed. Both in and out of the classroom, faculty, staff, the administration, and peers work together to welcome first-year students to their new academic home.

INNOVATIVE PROFESSORS: Western's faculty members are dedicated teachers who are committed to meeting the needs of all their students. They regularly explore new pedagogies—like roleplaying or project-based learning—and work to develop approaches to ensure that their students understand online materials. Western also takes advantage of its location by developing courses that take students on trips to New York. More far-flung experiences involve faculty-led courses to Europe and Central America. In recent years, the Connecticut State University System has recognized several Western faculty as top teachers in the entire state system.

THE CENTER FOR BUSINESS RESEARCH (CBR): The Center for Business Research (CBR) in the Ancell School of Business engages students to conduct research for local and regional organizations. The CBR produces reports on projects under the direction of faculty and the company that requests the research. Examples of reports include comprehensive marketing plans, statistical surveys and interactive marketing, strategic management plans, e-commerce and website analysis, and advertising plans.

UNITY COLLEGE

UNITY, MAINE

Unity College is a leader in the environmental movement, focused on sustainability both in the classroom and in the real world. The friendly campus community is full of active learners—both students and teachers—who collaborate on various academic and research opportunities. Rigorous coursework and experiential learning opportunities prepare students for 21st-century environmental jobs and graduate school degree programs in a number of fields. Unity's alumni are environmental stewards, effective leaders, and responsible citizens.

TAKE ROOT AND GROW: All students begin their Unity experience with the Nova Program. Nova trips are four-day wilderness adventures that include community-building, small group discussions, and service projects. They are all designed to support the transition to life at Unity by emphasizing personal growth, social connections, and environmental stewardship.

CERTIFICATES: Students can earn several professional certifications, including Wilderness First Responder (WFR), Open Water SCUBA through the Professional Association of Diving Instructors, Forest Protection Officer with the U.S. Forest Service, Interpretive Guide through the National Association for Interpretive Standards, Teacher Certification for science (grades 7-12), and a Type II law enforcement commission.

SERVICE TRIPS: During the spring semester, students have the opportunity to participate in community service-based trips that are linked to specific courses. They can also participate in Alternative Spring Break, a shorter option for interested students to travel to a new location and help communities, organizations, and individuals in need. Other travel experiences have included a trip to Nicaragua studying culture, ecology, and environment as well as a trip to the Centre for Alternative Technology in Wales to learn more about renewable energy. 80% of Unity students complete an internship, and 88% participate in community service before graduating. Such experiences are extremely helpful in forming connections that help lead to employment.

GET OUTDOORS, GET REAL: The Unity College campus, 225 acres of fields and woodlands overlooking Lake Winnecook and the village of Unity, reflects the diversity of its student community. On the main campus, students can find the first and only Passive House-Certified student residence hall in the U.S., an organic garden that supplies food to the College's dining services; a student-run recycling program; a Sugar Shack for sap boiling and maple syrup production; and an Adirondack shelter that is used as an outdoor classroom. Just a short jaunt down the community trail is the Unity College Centre for Performing Arts, the Field of Dreams, and Unity Pond. Students can kayak, fish, play tennis, run the loop, and watch in awe a musical or theatrical show—all on the same plot of land.

DEAN'S CUP: Every year, students can participate in the Dean's Cup, a year-long competition among residence halls that celebrates diversity and a strong sense community involvement. Events include home-run derbies, chili cook-offs, karaoke contests, laser tag tournaments, and the final event: a Big Wheels race through campus!

CAREER RESOURCE CENTER: Unity's Career Resource Center assists students with internship and job searches as well as multiple career-building events, including grad school nights, résumé-writing workshops, and networking opportunities. Unity hosts the largest environmental career fair in New England each year, with more than 70 businesses and organizations in attendance.

http://www.unity.edu/

P: (800) 624-1024

PRIVATE

STUDENT PROFILE

665 undergraduate students

96% of undergrad students are full time

49% male — 51% female

69% of students are from out of state

66% freshman retention rate

54% graduated in 6 years

FACULTY PROFILE

44 full-time faculty

12 to 1 student/faculty ratio

ADMISSIONS

831 Total Applicants

756 Total Admissions

198 Total Freshman Enrollment

90.97% of applicants admitted

TUITION & COSTS

Tuition: $25,600

Fees: $1,200

Total: $26,800

R&B: $9,800

Room: $5,880

Board: $3,920

Total: $36,600

FINANCIAL

$14,716 avg grant/scholarship amount (total)

$8,293 avg loan amount (total)

UNIVERSITY OF MAINE

ORONO, MAINE

University of Maine is the flagship institution of the University Maine system. The University is focused on student success—an initiative achieved through world-class faculty members, state-of-the-art facilities, and a strong commitment to research.

FIRST-YEAR EXPERIENCE: UMaine's first-year experience is a transitional period for many students. The University welcomes new students to the campus community and offers a foundational structure to get freshmen on the right path. All freshman students are required to live on campus for their first year, placing them directly in touch with the lively social and academic activities that amp up campus life. Not only do on-campus students have better access to faculty and resources, but they naturally form strong bonds with their peers. Research has also demonstrated that living on campus can increase academic performance and overall satisfaction with their University experience.

THE FIRST-YEAR CENTER: The transition into college can be difficult for students, and many are likely to benefit from extra support. The First-Year Center is an amazing on-campus resource that helps students with any and all kinds of issues. Students can receive one-on-one assistance in areas like academic success, getting involved, and troubleshooting.

STUDY ABROAD: Through a direct exchange relationship, a student from UMaine can study abroad at a foreign, partner institution while an exchange student comes to study at UMaine. This abroad option is an immersive experience whereby participants learn side-by-side with local students. Direct exchange is ideal for independent students who are willing to step out of their comfort zone. Some of the program locations include England, Austria, Bulgaria, Turkey, and Wales.

RESEARCH ABROAD: Undergraduate research is an incredible way for students to further explore their passions and academic goals. While there are opportunities to research on campus, UMaine also allows select individuals to delve into hands-on work at a location abroad. In partnership with GlobaLinks Learning Abroad, UMaine is able to offer the EuroScholars Program, which is run by a group of renowned European Research Universities. Through the program, participants can gain international exposure while pursuing their field of interest

TRAVEL COURSES: Travel courses are faculty-led programs that involve both traditional classroom instruction as well as immersive site visits. Travel courses take place during winter break, spring break, and May term. Even though these excursions are short, students fall in love with the once-in-a-lifetime chance to experience another culture while receiving the education that only a UMaine professor can provide.

THE CAREER CENTER: UMaine's Career Service Center handles any and all inquiries regarding co-ops, internships, and anything related to future careers. Students are invited to stop by the office and utilize the many resources available, including workshops, one-on-one guidance, and career fairs.

MAINE MENTOR PROGRAM: The Maine Mentor program is an awesome networking resource that is available to both students and alumni. This program allows participants to search for and contact working alumni across many different careers. Especially beneficial for students, the network-building connections get them a firsthand look at different industries and career paths.

http://umaine.edu/

P: (207) 581-1865

PUBLIC

STUDENT PROFILE

9,297 undergraduate students

87% of undergrad students are full time

52% male – 48% female

35% of students are from out of state

76% freshman retention rate

55% graduated in 6 year

FACULTY PROFILE

541 full-time faculty

277 part-time faculty

16 to 1 student/faculty ratio

ADMISSIONS

11,044 Total Applicants

10,073 Total Admissions

2,047 Total Freshman Enrollment

91.21% of applicants admitted

SAT Ranges: CR 480-600, M 480-610, W 460-578

ACT Ranges: C 21-28

TUITION & COSTS

Tuition: (In) $8,370 (Out) $26,640

Fees: $2,240

Total: (In) $10,610 (Out) $28,880

R&B: $9,576

Room: $5,004

Board: $4,572

Total: (In) $20,186 (Out) $38,456

FINANCIAL

$8,916 avg grant/scholarship amount (need)

$4,512 avg loan amount (need)

FROSTBURG STATE UNIVERSITY

FROSTBURG, MARYLAND

Frostburg State University is a student-centered institution dedicated to providing transformative experiences as part of the educational journey. Such a foundation launches its graduates to professional success, achieved through not only strong academics and experiential education, but also personal attention from knowledgeable faculty and staff.

LEARNING COMMUNITIES: First-year students have a host of programs and resources at their disposal. Learning Communities get students in touch with mentorship opportunities with an experienced professor while also fostering close-knit friendships. These communities place students into residence halls that are dedicated to leadership, wellness, STEM subjects, or community service.

RESEARCH: Budding researchers see their projects through from inception to presentation. Many FSU faculty welcome student researchers to work alongside them or provide time to aid them in their own experiments. And, when they've made their conclusions, students can present their findings at a number of regional and international conferences as well as the College of Liberal Arts and Sciences' annual Undergraduate Research Symposium.

CAMPUS RESOURCES: Students of the natural sciences—from geography to ethnobotany—make use of the vast resources found in the Appalachian Mountains that surround Frostburg. The campus' close proximity to several state parks, forests, and wildlife-management areas also means that there are plenty of opportunities to volunteer or intern.

SERVICE-LEARNING AND LEADERSHIP: Service-learning and leadership development are hallmarks of the Frostburg State experience. Students can volunteer with Relay for Life, Beautify the 'Burg, ECHOSTARS, Alternative Spring Break, and many other events and organizations. Leadership opportunities abound, starting with a leadership retreat open to freshmen, and followed by the Sloop Institute for Excellence in Leadership for juniors and the President's Leadership Circle for seniors.

ARTS ON CAMPUS: Students of the arts can exhibit original artwork in FSU's Roper Gallery, broadcast themselves over TV or radio with FSU-TV3 or NPR-affiliate WFWM 91.9, and direct and perform in vibrant seasons of music, theatre, and dance.

ATHLETICS: Students can stay active and gain invaluable lessons in personal growth with Frostburg's 21 NCAA Division III sports teams. In addition, there are a growing number of club and intramural sports to choose from. FSU's student-athletes are known for maintaining healthy GPAs and volunteering for service projects.

CAREER & PROFESSIONAL DEVELOPMENT CENTER: FSU's diverse and rigorous academic programs give students the intellectual and experiential tools they need to excel as professionals. For students looking to take their education a bit further before graduation, or for any student wondering what to do with their future, the staff at the Career & Professional Development Center are raring to help. The Center helps create a culture on campus that actively supports, educates, and empowers students to make career decisions and gain skills relevant to their future in a rapidly changing, competency-based global workplace. Students can partner with the Center to take on internships, connect with employers, or just learn more to improve their prospects as graduates.

ACADEMIC SUCCESS NETWORK: The Academic Success Network includes a range of programs focused on student success and achievement. For example, its freshman monitoring program works to identify and address potential barriers to students' academic achievement, helping them create eight-semester plans of study to help them graduate on time.

http://www.frostburg.edu/

P: (301) 687-4201

PUBLIC

STUDENT PROFILE

4,961 undergraduate students

84% of undergrad students are full time

49% male — 51% female

5% of students are from out of state

76% freshman retention rate

51% graduated in 6 years

FACULTY PROFILE

267 full-time faculty

133 part-time faculty

16 to 1 student/faculty ratio

ADMISSIONS

3,913 Total Applicants

2,483 Total Admissions

933 Total Freshman Enrollment

63.46% of applicants admitted

SAT Ranges: CR 430-530, M 430-530, W 410-510

ACT Ranges: C 17-22, M 16-22, E 15-22, W 6-8

TUITION & COSTS

Tuition: (In) $6,214 (Out) $18,314

Fees: $2,274

Total: (In) $8,488 (Out) $20,588

R&B: $8,974

Room: $4,208

Board: $4,766

Total: (In) $17,462 (Out) $29,562

FINANCIAL

$6,872 avg grant/scholarship amount (total)

$8,716 avg loan amount (total)

LOYOLA UNIVERSITY MARYLAND

BALTIMORE, MARYLAND

Loyola University Maryland is a Roman Catholic, Jesuit private university dedicated to the education of the whole person. The ninth oldest Jesuit college in the country, LUM instills a broad base of knowledge, supported by a strong liberal arts core in its students.

MESSINA: Messina is a unique learning program offered to first-year students. Participants take two seminar classes, the topics of which are linked. Students are also involved in co-curricular activities that enhance the learning experience. Those who study through Messina live in proximity with one another so that they may highlight the intimacy of the program, thereby fostering a supportive community both in and out of the classroom.

INSPIRED FACULTY, ENCOURAGED STUDENTS: Students are bound to discover both their academic and personal potentials at Loyola. The University offers more than 30 undergraduate majors as well as 40 minors and several graduate programs. With a student-to-faculty ratio of 12:1, students receive individualized attention from their professors. Loyola values the individual spirit and pushes each student to discover their passions and talents.

ATHLETICS: Loyola is a highly athletic community, competing in the Patriot League as a Division I school for both men's and women's sports. Beyond varsity teams, students also have the option to join a club or intramural sport as well as take advantage of Loyola's Fitness and Aquatic Center. Classes are offered to help students get in shape, and there is enough exercise equipment to keep every student satisfied. Whether they are competitive, looking for fun, or just trying to stay in shape, Loyola students have an outlet for them.

BALTIMORE: The city of Baltimore is just a stone's throw away, and its vibrant lifestyle is open to the Loyola community. Students are encouraged to explore the city and take advantage of the many different cuisines and cultural attractions that line its streets. They can also reach out to the community and offer up their service to organizations and people in need.

GRADUATES OF HONOR: Loyola recognizes that a college education is a significant investment but one that is essential nevertheless. A college education equips students with the tools they will need to succeed, and Loyola works to integrate the values of academic excellence into every student's experience. Loyola aims to graduate confident scholars who foster an appreciation for both their liberal arts education and their specific discipline. More than this, the University wants its students to continue learning even after they earn their diploma. Learning should be a lifelong process, and Loyola inspires its students to consider their undergraduate educations as just the beginning of an incredible journey. Upon graduation, students are masters at critical thinking and effective communication. They are analytical and ethical. They are leaders and innovators. They are ready to take on the wide world ahead of them.

STUDY ABROAD: 60% of Loyola students study abroad during their undergraduate experience. The University highly encourages such an experience, noting the benefits of cross-cultural communication skills and the appreciation for diverse cultures. The majority of students study for a semester's length during their junior year, enriching their academic experiences with compelling information and adventures.

THE CAREER CENTER: The Career Center is available to everyone in the Loyola community, both before and after they graduate. It serves to guide career decisions and help individuals discover how best to seek out their passions and achieve their career goals. The Center works to incorporate Jesuit values into each career path, guiding decisions that are compatible with Loyola's mission and educational experience.

http://www.loyola.edu/

P: (800) 221-9107

PRIVATE - CATHOLIC

STUDENT PROFILE

4,068 undergraduate students

99% of undergrad students are full time

42% male – 58% female

86% freshman retention rate

81% graduated in 6 years

FACULTY PROFILE

384 full-time faculty

182 part-time faculty

11 to 1 student/faculty ratio

ADMISSIONS

13,867 Total Applicants

8,449 Total Admissions

1,033 Total Freshman Enrollment

60.93% of applicants admitted

SAT Ranges: CR 550-650, M 560-640

ACT Ranges: C 25-29, M 24-28, E 25-31

TUITION & COSTS

Tuition: $43,800

Fees: $1,400

Total: $45,200

R&B: $13,920

Room: $10,290

Board: $3,630

Total: $59,120

FINANCIAL

$22,245 avg grant/scholarship amount (need)

$5,520 avg loan amount (need)

MOUNT ST. MARY'S UNIVERSITY

EMMITSBURG, MARYLAND

The Mount is a contemporary Catholic university at which students learn to be individuals who are prepared to lead the global community. The new Veritas Program, along with more than 40 majors, minors, concentrations, and special programs, encourage students to discover the qualities about themselves and about the world that will allow them to lead fulfilling lives.

STUDY ABROAD: The Mount sponsors semester-long study abroad programs in Ireland, London, Ecuador, Florence, and Prague. Options for short-term sessions include China, Cameroon, and Russia. There are aslo summer programs available in locations like Costa Rica, Spain, France, and Austria.

SOCIAL JUSTICE: The Office of Social Justice at Mount St. Mary's University gives students the chance to put social justice-based education into action. By participating in local, domestic, and international service experiences, students become true agents of positive social change.

SERVICE-LEARNING: Service-Learning integrates experiences outside the classroom with an academic curriculum taught within the classroom. This kind of academically backed community involvement is offered in two ways: as a requirement for a particular course, or as an optional fourth credit. The fourth credit is awarded to students who complete a service-learning project in addition to their regular coursework.

ENGAGING WITH FACULTY: Independent study, honors, and research programs give students additional opportunities to work closely with faculty. Students present their work at the annual Scholarship, Performance, Arts, Research, & Creativity (SPARC) Festival as a way of making their engaged work public. And, of course, students in such programs as Education and Business have the opportunity to engage in extensive internships so that they may better understand the relationship between their classroom experience and the professional world. Students who come to the Mount know that they should expect a dynamic sense of engagement from outstanding professors.

CRUX: The Mount's outdoor adventures program, CRUX, empowers students to discover more about themselves and each other through hiking, climbing, caving, and rafting trips. World-class whitewater, pristine wilderness, meandering streams, breathtaking vistas, expansive trail networks, and magnificent cliffs are all nearby and ready for students to enjoy.

CAMPUS MINISTRY: The Center for Campus Ministry is one of the largest student life groups, hosting over 28 clubs and organizations as well as over 60 student leaders. Rooted in Catholic identity and embracing students of all faiths and denominations, Campus Ministry encourages the integration of faith, vocation, and leadership in the lives of all students.

LIFE OUTSIDE THE CLASSROOM: Typical on-campus events include comedians, hypnotists, movie premieres, bands, and late-night dance parties in 1808, the state-of-the-art nightclub. Along with these weekend events, the Office of Campus Activities plans some of Mount St. Mary's students' favorite traditions, like the annual crab feast, Christmas dance, homecoming, and spring blow-out day.

INTERNSHIPS: The Mount offers internships in every field of study, providing students with valuable experiences and marketable skills. One program of note "Mount in Washington," a special opportunity that allows students to spend a semester in Washington, D.C., in a credit-based internship. Through the program, students build their skills in critical thinking, problem solving, oral and written presentation, and interviewing.

http://www.msmary.edu/
P: (800) 448-4347

PRIVATE - CATHOLIC

STUDENT PROFILE
1,795 undergraduate students
94% of undergrad students are full time
46% male – 54% female
75% freshman retention rate
69% graduated in 6 years

FACULTY PROFILE
137 full-time faculty
1 part-time faculty
12 to 1 student/faculty ratio

ADMISSIONS
6,113 Total Applicants
4,105 Total Admissions
506 Total Freshman Enrollment
67.15% of applicants admitted

SAT Ranges: CR 460-570, M 450-560, W 450-560

ACT Ranges: C 18-24, M 17-24, E 17-24

TUITION & COSTS
Tuition: $36,250
Fees: $1,250
Total: $37,500
R&B: $12,400
Room: $6,070
Board: $6,330
Total: $49,900

FINANCIAL
$20,753 avg grant/scholarship amount (total)
$9,410 avg loan amount (total)

NOTRE DAME OF MARYLAND UNIVERSITY

BALTIMORE, MARYLAND

NOTRE DAME OF MARYLAND UNIVERSITY

http://www.ndm.edu/
P: (410) 435-0100

PRIVATE - CATHOLIC

STUDENT PROFILE

450 undergraduate students

97% of undergrad students are full-time

0% male – 100% female

15% of students are from out of state

68% freshman retention rate

50.5% graduated in 6 years

FACULTY PROFILE

105 full-time faculty

140 part-time faculty

7 to 1 student-to-faculty ratio

ADMISSIONS

773 Total Applicants

395 Total Admissions

101 Total Freshman Enrollment

51.10% of applicants admitted

TUITION & COSTS

Tuition: $34,800

Fees: $1,270

Total: $36,070

R&B: $11,500

Total: $47,570

FINANCIAL

$24,079 avg grant/scholarship amount (need)

$3,119 avg loan amount (need)

Notre Dame of Maryland University's approach to education has prepared thousands of high-level performers and creators of social change. The University is consistently responsive to the needs of a student body that's hungry to learn and a world that's hungry for knowledgeable, compassionate leaders.

GLOBAL LEARNING: NDMU is the first university in Maryland to be granted United Nations Non-Governmental Organization (NGO) Status. This classification for the institution offers NDMU students greater access to the U.N. and esteemed global leaders. Students can make regular trips to the U.N., participating in a range of international learning experiences. U.N. ambassadors are also brought to campus as part of NDMU's Visiting Ambassador Program, granting the opportunity to meet and learn from major influencers from around the globe.

STUDY ABROAD: Through Notre Dame's Office of International Programs, students can select from a diverse portfolio of semester and short-term study abroad opportunities all around the world. Short-term programs led by NDMU faculty themselves are also available, ranging from one to two weeks in length and offering additional academic credit. NDMU's program helps students develop an international perspective as well as a sense of global responsibility, building their intercultural and linguistic skills while fostering lifelong international friendships.

RESEARCH: NDMU's diverse educational environment offers students the opportunity to participate in research within their individual field of interest. Students work closely with faculty experts, conducting research and creating a path for their lifelong work. They can also participate in the annual Nancy Kreiter Research Day, a campus-wide celebration of student research at which their work is publicly presented to the community.

TRAILBLAZERS: NDMU's Trailblazer Scholars program provides academic enrichment and student support to first-generation college students. This program features a variety of workshops and mentoring activities that aim to empower students, connect them with college resources, help them integrate into college life, and immerse them in a supportive community of peers and faculty. It also provides high-impact experiences that collectively ensure first-generation students years of postgraduate fulfillment, steeping them in a comfortable environment of friends and mentors.

LEADERSHIP: The Transformational Leaders Program is offered to students who are enrolled in the Women's College. Embodying the University's commitment to the mission of its founders, the School Sisters of Notre Dame, this program is dedicated to educating women as future change-makers of world. The Transformational Leaders Program prepares students to be catalysts for positive social change, gaining expertise through a combination of interdisciplinary coursework, international study opportunities, professional development activities, and internship and service-learning experiences. Students in the Transformational Leaders Program earn a certificate in Leadership and Social Change, which can complement their degrees regardless of major.

WOW FESTIVAL: NDMU brings local, national, and international contributors to the stage during the WOW Festival to celebrate and discuss issues most important to women, including equal pay, race, gender equality, politics, activism, education, health, and more. Live music, entertainment, food trucks, speed mentoring, and a local marketplace are also highlights of the festival. These events are designed to be agents of change, providing a space for women to participate in discussion, education, and collaboration on the issues that most impact their lives.

CAREER CENTER: NDMU's Career Center provides expert guidance, timely resources, and career development to students and alumni so that they may achieve their career goals and become transformational leaders. The services provided by the Center include career counseling and coaching, career assessments, résumé assistance, mock interviews, and job-search guidance. Additionally, high-profile companies and businesses are often invited to campus to meet and interview students.

SALISBURY UNIVERSITY

SALISBURY, MARYLAND

Salisbury University (SU) is nationally recognized for academic excellence. Its creative curriculum emphasizes undergraduate research, study abroad, professional internships, and civic engagement. Located on Maryland's historic Eastern Shore, SU offers 43 undergraduate majors and 17 graduate programs, including a Doctor of Nursing Practice and a Doctor of Education program. With its award-winning faculty, a beautiful campus with national arboretum status, exceptional academic and athletic programs, and a dynamic administration, Salisbury is earning recognition as A Maryland University of National Distinction.

PACE: SU's 8,700+ students are active citizens locally, nationally, and internationally. Through the Institute for Public Affairs and Civic Engagement (PACE), students engage in the political process, intern for state and local governments, and attend national political conventions. Many PACE students are involved in intensive, multi-faceted, year-long civic experiences through the Presidential Citizen Scholars Program.

GLOBAL CITIZENS: A major part of the SU mission is to prepare global citizens. Education majors have taught elementary students in New Zealand, while others have studied children's literature in Ireland and Wales. Nursing students have provided aid and education to villagers in Africa, and business students have studied economics in France and South Africa. Other students have spent spring break helping with service projects in Costa Rica and Mexico. One philosophy professor even took a group to Japan to explore humanity's spiritual relationship with nature while hiking and maintaining pilgrimage trails. World leaders consistently visit campus; speakers have included Nobel Peace Prize winners and former presidents Lech Walesa of Poland, F.W. de Klerk of South Africa, and José Ramos-Horta of Timor-Leste.

COMMON INTELLECTUAL EXPERIENCES: In addition to the New Student Reader Program, SU's Sophomore-Year Experience program provides additional opportunities for students to have shared experiences in their second year. Throughout their time at SU, students are also encouraged to take advantage of the University's Cultural Laureate Program, which gives recognition to those who attend a certain number of SU-sponsored cultural events, such as performances, exhibits, and academic lectures.

INTERNSHIPS: SU's Career Services Office calls internships "the single most important thing you can do to gain career-related experience." Internships and practica are mandatory for some majors and strongly recommended for all. Students graduating from SU's Franklin P. Perdue School of Business, for example, are required to have an Applied Business Learning Experience (ABLE) that includes both a faculty-guided class and a work-site internship. In the Charles R. and Martha N. Fulton School of Liberal Arts, practicums are required for communication arts students, while political science students have internship opportunities with elected officials at the local, state, and national levels.

UNDERGRADUATE RESEARCH: Nationally lauded for its dedication to undergraduate research, SU offers students multiple opportunities to assist professors in research as well as perform their own independent studies. Findings are presented on campus during the annual Student Research Conference, and many student-scholars also speak at national and international conferences. SU has twice hosted the National Conference on Undergraduate Research.

CAPSTONE COURSES AND PROJECTS: Many majors and programs offer students the opportunity to complete capstone projects. Senior art majors, for example, may showcase their works in solo or group exhibitions on campus (which often also includes installation and promotion), while music majors often perform senior recitals. Similarly, the SU Honors College allows students to complete capstone projects related to their individual courses of study. All majors are invited to submit research papers and scholarly posters for presentation at SU's annual Student Research Conference.

http://www.salisbury.edu/

P: (410) 543-6000

PUBLIC

STUDENT PROFILE

7,657 undergraduate students

95% of undergrad students are full time

43% male – 57% female

19.40% of students are from out of state

84% freshman retention rate

67.9% graduated in 6 years

FACULTY PROFILE

411 full-time faculty

226 part-time faculty

16 to 1 student/faculty ratio

ADMISSIONS

8,307 Total Applicants

5,477 Total Admissions

1,329 Total Freshman Enrollment

65.93% of applicants admitted

SAT Ranges: CR 540-610, M 540-620

ACT Ranges: C 21-25, M 19-25, E 19-25

TUITION & COSTS

Tuition: (In) $6,846 (Out) $15,258

Fees: $2,518

Total: (In) $9,364 (Out) $17,776

R&B: $11,350

Room: $6,550

Board: $4,800

Total: (In) $20,714 (Out) $29,126

FINANCIAL

$6,043 avg grant/scholarship amount (need)

$4,252 avg loan amount (need)

ST. MARY'S COLLEGE OF MARYLAND

ST. MARY'S CITY, MARYLAND

As Maryland's public honors college, St. Mary's College offers the kind of liberal arts education and small college experience that are found at highly regarded private institutions while maintaining a commitment to the ideals of affordability, accessibility, and diversity. By combining such virtues of public and private education alike, St. Mary's College provides a unique alternative for students and their families. This special identity underpins the College's success and its reputation for excellence.

FIRST-YEAR SEMINARS: Incoming students are quickly immersed in the St. Mary's College experience via their First-Year Seminar courses. Students may choose from a vast selection of small, discussion-focused courses that are taught by professors from every discipline. Past seminar topics have included The Art of Political Protest, The Many Lives of Lincoln, and The Evolution of Altruism. The small class sizes and focused attention from faculty serve to foster students' ability to write, speak, research, and think critically.

WORLDWIDE LEARNING THROUGH RESEARCH: Research puts students in the driver's seat. At St. Mary's College, many students earn academic credit doing individual research and independent study projects in collaboration with a faculty member. First- and second-year students often join ongoing projects, while advanced students can pursue their interest under the mentorship of a favorite professor. The College's small size affords students the opportunity to play a significant role in research projects—all the way from design to execution. Recent projects have included The Effects of Family Dynamics on Aggression, Nondestructive Coral Health Monitoring, Improving Science Literacy Among Elementary School Children, U.S.-Cuban Relations: Where Do We Go From Here?, The Emergence of A Political Theater in South Africa, and Defining a New Internet Language.

STUDY ABROAD: Study Abroad is a serious subject at St. Mary's College. Unlike many colleges that expect students to sort out the details for themselves, St. Mary's designs unique international programs that organize truly explorative immersions in other cultures. Some of the most popular semester abroad programs include partnerships with Stellenbosch University in South Africa, China's Fudan University, Al Akhawayn University in Morocco, France's Sciences Po University, and James Cook University in Australia. There are also short-term study tours to Belize, India, Greece, Peru, England, and more.

THE ST. MARY'S PROJECT: The St. Mary's Project is a year-long, 8-credit, independently designed and executed course that serves as a capstone experience for a student's time at St. Mary's College. Working in close conjunction with one or more professors, the St. Mary's Project provides the opportunity to explore an idea or question that is particularly intriguing for the student. Many projects are interdisciplinary, bringing together threads from earlier classes that have taken all across the curriculum. And many projects are highly personal, involving creative or innovative work that ties together one's four years of study in a meaningful way. Past projects include "A Defect of the Confederation: The Crisis of Virginia's Western Cession;" "Geospecific 3-dimensional Databases for Real-Time Visual Simulation;" "Economic Aid for Women-Centered Cultures;" "A Miracle Manifested: A New Vision of Public Education;" and "Patients versus Patents: The Economics of Essential Medicines in Poor Countries."

SERVICE-LEARNING: Contributing to the strong sense of community that defines St. Mary's College, many students go beyond campus to contribute to their surrounding area. Students enact rewarding and impactful service by working in local schools, aiding those in need, and preserving the environment. Additionally, many departments even offer service-learning in conjunction with coursework, allowing students to earn academic credit while making a difference in their community. St. Mary's College students have completed service-learning projects with America Reads, Christmas in April, St. Mary's Hospital, and local schools. They also provide tutoring for the GED and at-risk youths.

http://www.smcm.edu/
P: (800) 492-7181

PUBLIC

STUDENT PROFILE

1,618 undergraduate students

98% of undergrad students are full time

42% male — 58% female

7% of students are from out of state

87% freshman retention rate

73% graduated in 6 years

FACULTY PROFILE

141 full-time faculty

54 part-time faculty

10 to 1 student/faculty ratio

ADMISSIONS

1,767 Total Applicants

1,413 Total Admissions

334 Total Freshman Enrollment

79.97% of applicants admitted

SAT Ranges: CR 510-640, M 490-610

ACT Ranges: C 23-29, M 22-30, E 22-28

TUITION & COSTS

Tuition: (In) $11,418 (Out) $26,566

Fees: $2,774

Total: (In) $14,192 (Out) $29,340

R&B: $12,442

Room: $7,184

Board: $5,258

Total: (In) $26,634 (Out) $41,782

FINANCIAL

$9,707 avg grant/scholarship amount (need)

$4,107 avg loan amount (need)

UNIVERSITY OF MARYLAND, BALTIMORE COUNTY

BALTIMORE, MARYLAND

UMBC is a dynamic public research university that combines teaching, research, and service to benefit the citizens of Maryland. As an Honors university, the campus offers academically talented students a strong undergraduate liberal arts foundation that prepares them for graduate and professional study, entry into the workforce, community service, and leadership.

STUDY ABROAD: Some of UMBC's students' most life-changing moments occur beyond UMBC's main campus itself; the University offers a wealth of opportunities to learn and serve abroad, and most students can even use their federal financial aid, institutional aid and scholarships, or state scholarships to fund their studies across the globe.

SERVICE-LEARNING: Service-Learning engages students in weekly service with a designated service placement. Through this sustained partnership, students build great relationships with those they serve. This collaboration gives students the opportunity to engage in formal and informal reflections of their service, allowing them to connect their inspiring work with their learning and academic growth.

INDEPENDENT RESEARCH: Not only can UMBC students conduct research in any discipline from day one, but they also find supportive faculty and an array of grants and awards to help make their projects successful. Students often present their research at URCAD (Undergraduate Research and Achievement Day), and some even contribute to papers published by their professors. From student-choreographed dance performances and studies of water systems in Kenya to historical profiles and innovations in engineering, students become fully engaged in interdisciplinary, hands-on research as early as their freshman year.

PROFESSIONAL FACILITIES: With its new, state-of-the-art facilities and venues, the award-winning Performing Arts and Humanities Building (PAHB) welcomes people throughout the greater Baltimore area to participate in UMBC's vibrant cultural life. The Proscenium Theatre and Black Box Theatre feature productions by UMBC's award-winning theatre department—one of the most frequently invited college theatre programs to perform at the Kennedy Center. Other PAHB venues, which host dozens of lectures and performances each year, include the visually striking and acoustically outstanding Earl and Darielle Linehan Concert Hall and the James T. and Virginia R. Dresher Center. These facilities enable UMBC to invite nationally known experts to speak to the community about topics in philosophy, history, culture, language, literature, and the arts.

GETTING INVOLVED: UMBC's friendly and energetic campus is home to nearly 4,000 students. Students enjoy living with direct access to the faculty, facilities, activities, and other services on campus, including a shuttle to downtown Baltimore. The University also offers more than 250 student organizations, ranging from kinetic sculpture and a cappella to groups that are centered on social, cultural, and academic interests. Opportunities abound for students to get involved both on and off campus, including arts and culture performances, volunteer outings, celebrations of student research, and pick-up games on the Quad.

SERVICE TO THE COMMUNITY: UMBC's BreakingGround initiative encourages and supports students to make practical, innovative contributions to the common good. For example, studies have created and produced the "Stories of Deindustrialization" radio series and "Mapping Baybrook" website after taking several courses that examined deindustrialization's impact on the relations between people, place, and community. Students also partnered with former Sparrows Point steelworkers and other Baybrook community members to document the cultural heritage of the local neighborhood.

INTERNSHIPS: Nestled between Washington, D.C., and Baltimore, UMBC provides easy access to an array of internships. UMBC students frequently intern locally at the Smithsonian, T. Rowe Price, Northrop Grumman, the Maryland Historical Society, The National Institutes of Health (NIH), Baltimore County School System, and Everyman Theatre. UMBC also has its very own on-campus research park, offering numerous internship and work opportunities in a variety of fields.

http://umbc.edu/
P: (410) 455-1000

PUBLIC

STUDENT PROFILE

11,067 undergraduate students

86% of undergrad students are full time

56% male – 44% female

7% of students are from out of state

87.2% freshman retention rate

63% graduated in 6 years

FACULTY PROFILE

533 full-time faculty

278 part-time faculty

19 to 1 student/faculty ratio

ADMISSIONS

10,812 Total Applicants

6,144 Total Admissions

1,518 Total Freshman Enrollment

56.83% of applicants admitted

SAT Ranges: CR 550-650, M 570-670

ACT Ranges: C 24-29

TUITION & COSTS

Tuition: (In) $11,264 (Out) $24,492

Fees: $125

Total: (In) $11,389 (Out) $24,617

R&B: $11,568

Total: (In) $22,957 (Out) $36,185

FINANCIAL

$8,415 avg grant/scholarship amount (need)

$4,256 avg loan amount (need)

WASHINGTON COLLEGE

CHESTERTOWN, MARYLAND

Washington College offers an outstanding liberal arts education with a strong focus on American heritage, self-designed interdisciplinary study, and hands-on learning. The campus's location on the Eastern Shore of Maryland and its enticing combination of a small-town environment with a nearby city city makes for an almost perfect setting in which to learn and grow.

GLOBAL PERSPECTIVES: Washington's dedication to connecting students to the world begins in the first year through the Global Perspectives: Research and Writing seminars. Being a contemporary citizen requires the ability to consider problems and issues from international and global perspectives. Therefore, Global Perspectives seminars offer a range of options that encourage thinking beyond national boundaries. Topics may include global warming, world hunger, nuclear proliferation, or post-colonial literature.

THE DOUGLASS CATER SOCIETY: WC's flagship academic enrichment program, the Douglass Cater Society of Junior Fellows, offers funding to students for a variety of self-directed projects. Requiring a GPA of 3.6 or better, membership in the Cater Society is highly competitive and offered only to students who achieve distinction among the school's top scholars. Recently funded internships offered through the Center have given students the chance to pursue work with International Policy in Washington, D.C.; the British Museum; the dolphin research program at the Kewalo Basin Marine Mammal Laboratory in Hawaii; the Philadelphia Theater Company; and the International Human Rights Commission in Geneva, Switzerland.

TRUSTED MOTIVATION: Students appreciate the College's emphasis on self-direction; it's not uncommon for professors to let students set class test dates and other deadlines. In return, they expect students to use their freedom wisely. This relaxed, egalitarian atmosphere promotes good discussion and collaborative learning, thus proving to be great practice for tomorrow's community and business leaders. When surveyed, 96 percent of students rank faculty accessibility as excellent, and WC alumni consistently cite "exceptional faculty" as the one factor that most enhanced their experiences at the College.

COMMUNITY SERVICE: The comfortable and relaxed atmosphere of the small, historic community of Chestertown, Maryland, is shared by WC's intimate campus. Nearly 80 percent of WC's students live on campus, and many choose to live in such themed residences as the Leadership and Service house in which students agree to perform community and campus service. Service organizations range from well-known programs like Habitat for Humanity, Amnesty International, and the Special Olympics as well as local environmental programs like Furthering Outreach in the Community and Environment (FORCE) and Neighbors for Good. The fraternity and sorority community at Washington is also active in service, sponsoring fundraising and other charitable events throughout the year.

CHESTERTOWN: Chestertown is located on the Chesapeake Bay's Eastern Shore, which is forty-five minutes from Annapolis and ninety minutes from Washington, D.C., Baltimore, and Philadelphia. Chestertown offers coffeehouses, art galleries, and a vibrant community theater. Local residents even attend WC's events, including lectures given by Senator John McCain, Ralph Nader, Plácido Domingo, and other top-notch speakers. WC also hosts other community events and fundraisers, and many students are greatly involved as members of local environmental clubs.

---

http://www.washcoll.edu/

P: (800) 422-1782

PRIVATE

STUDENT PROFILE

1,467 undergraduate students

97% of undergrad students are full time

43% male – 57% female

48% of students are from out of state

85% freshman retention rate

74% graduated in 6 years

FACULTY PROFILE

97 full-time faculty

56 part-time faculty

11 to 1 student/faculty ratio

ADMISSIONS

5,318 Total Applicants

2,960 Total Admissions

388 Total Freshman Enrollment

55.66% of applicants admitted

TUITION & COSTS

Tuition: $41,596

Fees: $996

Total: $42,592

R&B: $10,010

Room: $5,084

Board: $4,926

Total: $52,602

FINANCIAL

$23,114 avg grant/scholarship amount (total)

$7,024 avg loan amount (total)

ANNA MARIA COLLEGE

PAXTON, MASSACHUSETTS

Anna Maria College is a four-year, private, co-ed, Catholic liberal arts institution accredited by the New England Association of Schools and Colleges. Founded by the Sisters of Saint Anne in 1946, the College is located on a 192-acre campus in Paxton, MA, only minutes from the vibrant college-town of Worcester. Anna Maria College offers a variety of undergraduate and graduate degrees as well as both on-campus and online continuing education programs.

SUPPORTING GROWTH: AMC engages students by creating an environment that supports both academic achievement and personal growth. Anna Maria educates the mind and spirit with a Core curriculum that encourages students to pursue their minds, reach beyond their potential, and become valued members of the campus community and society as a whole. Through the efforts of the Student Affairs Office, programs and activities are developed to support student-led initiatives, community service projects, and other opportunities that allow students to become leaders in their own right. Many campus life programs and activities are planned and sponsored by the Student Council of the Student Government Association (SGA), which sets the tone for student leadership and engagement on campus.

SUPPORT SERVICES: AMC believes that it is the responsibility of the College to provide the resources and services necessary to support student success both in the classroom and in life. In addition to teaching small classes, AMC's dedicated faculty work closely with students to ensure that they are receiving the necessary academic support to succeed in the classroom and that they are taking the courses they need to graduate on time. The Advising Center, Learning Center, Health Services, and Counseling Center also contribute to students overall college experience with the academic advising, mentoring, tutoring, and counseling services available to anyone at no cost. The College has also invested in new learning technologies for the classroom and campus as a whole so that students are able to tap into the resources they need to achieve success. In addition, the Office of Residence Life provides a living-learning environment throughout the residence halls that is designed to support students' academic and social endeavors.

GET INVOLVED: In addition to athletic events on the College's new, all-purpose athletic field, AMC students enjoy a vibrant campus life through a variety of programs and activities. Clubs and activities vary by interest, but some of the available options include Spring Weekend, Student Leadership Night, dances with DJs and live bands, comedians, special concerts with popular musical artists, trips to sporting events, skiing, and other activities off campus. AMC also hosts student plays and concerts as well as student-led film series, seminars, and social events.

CAMPUS MINISTRY: The College's Campus Ministry program helps AMC maintain its mission to foster respect for others and the environment. Students love to provide service, participating in such organizations as the United Way Day of Caring, Earth Day activities, and Habitat for Humanity.

PREPARING STUDENTS FOR SUCCESS: AMC is a special place in which students have an opportunity to achieve excellence in all facets of their lives. The quality and tradition of AMC's Catholic education has a long history rooted in the mission of the Sisters of Saint Anne. The unique blend of AMC's liberal arts education, honors program, sports, and community service teaches students to reach far beyond their expectations. At AMC, students become leaders in the classroom, in on-campus clubs and organizations, and on the College's NCAA Division III sports teams.

---

http://www.annamaria.edu/
P: (508) 849-3360

PRIVATE - CATHOLIC

STUDENT PROFILE

4,065 undergraduate students

95% of undergrad students are full time

42% male – 58% female

74% of students are from out of state

91% freshman retention rate

73% graduated in 6 years

FACULTY PROFILE

603 full-time faculty

293 part-time faculty

11 to 1 student/faculty ratio

ADMISSIONS

8,398 Total Applicants

6,103 Total Admissions

1,025 Total Freshman Enrollment

72.67% of applicants admitted

SAT Ranges: CR 520-630, M 550-665, W 520-640

ACT Ranges: C 24-29, M 24-29, E 24-31, W 8-9

TUITION & COSTS

Tuition: $33,796

Fees: $1,564

Total: $35,360

R&B: $9,996

Room: $5,680

Board: $4,316

Total: $45,356

FINANCIAL

$19,280 avg grant/scholarship amount (total)

$7,744 avg loan amount (total)

ASSUMPTION COLLEGE

WORCESTER, MASSACHUSETTS

Founded in 1904, Assumption College is a Catholic institution sponsored by the Augustinians of the Assumption. Assumption offers undergraduate students 43 majors and 48 minors in the liberal arts, sciences, business, and professional studies. To prepare for the workforce, these driven learners revel in cutting-edge theory and best practices, conduct innovative research, and develop excellent communication and critical-analysis skills. Assumption graduates are known for their thoughtful citizenship and compassionate service to their community.

FIRST-YEAR PROGRAM: Assumption's Common Pursuit of Academic and Social Success (COMPASS) program offers first-year students the opportunity to become animated by living and learning within a small group of peers. COMPASS members choose from a variety of topics and themes, work with a team of faculty who serve as their academic advisors, and share a living environment and co-curricular activities related to their area of focus.

SEND PROGRAM: The Assumption SEND Service Immersion Program takes students to communities across the country and around the globe to help those in need during the winter, spring, and summer breaks for one or two weeks. At the end of each day, students reflect on their experiences to renew their spiritual commitment as well as to connect their experiences to the concept of social justice. When they return to campus, students are both humbled and inspired, gifted with new insight, compassion, and integrity.

STUDY ABROAD: Assumption students may choose to spend either a full year, semester, or shorter time abroad. In recent years, Assumption College students have studied throughout the world in locations like Australia, Brazil, England, France, Italy, Japan, and the Netherlands. The College even opened its own campus in Rome, Italy, in 2013. Students who take advantage of this College-owned campus are immersed in the very best of the classic liberal arts, a tradition that is woven into the fabric of Rome itself. Whether they study art, history, or politics, students who study abroad gain a deeper understanding of the world in which they live.

FACULTY/STUDENT COLLABORATION: Mentoring is an incredibly important part of an Assumption College education, as evidenced by a school-wide emphasis on faculty/student partnerships. Valuable research is performed at Assumption in a myriad of disciplines, yielding great advancements every day. But the value of student and faculty research extends beyond the data that they collect; these opportunities train the next generation of leading scholars, scientists, and researchers and provide them with the grounding for future exploration. By investing in the research—and researchers—of today, Assumption is funding the discoveries of tomorrow.

EXPLORING FURTHER: Students who enroll in honors courses are given the outlets through which to pursue the issues that fascinate them the most at the deepest levels. They ask questions, collect evidence, test answers, and arrive at new conclusions that help them flourish as leading scholars in their fields.

SUMMER STUDIES: Assumption offers a high-quality, personalized Summer Semester with courses offered both online and face-to-face. These courses are offered at a reduced cost yet still offer the same level of intellectual rigor as their fall or spring semester counterparts. Whether students attend Assumption or another college during the school year, the Summer Semester offers a great opportunity to accelerate a degree program, catch up, or simply take time to give extra focus to a particular course.

CAREER DEVELOPMENT: Assumption's Career Development & Internship Center works very closely with students to support their transition into the workforce, graduate school, or postgraduate service programs and aids the job search by posting numerous full-time and part-time job listings, internships, and volunteer opportunities. Advisors assist students right at the start of freshman year, helping them plan ahead for incredible futures.

ASSUMPTION COLLEGE

http://www.assumption.edu/
P: (508) 767-7285

PRIVATE - CATHOLIC

STUDENT PROFILE

1,979 undergraduate students

100% of undergrad students are full time

40% male – 60% female

35% of students are from out of state

83% freshman retention rate

72% graduated in 6 years

FACULTY PROFILE

144 full-time faculty

80 part-time faculty

12 to 1 student/faculty ratio

ADMISSIONS

4,769 Total Applicants

3,614 Total Admissions

570 Total Freshman Enrollment

75.78% of applicants admitted

SAT Ranges: CR 510-600, M 510-610

ACT Ranges: C 23-26, M 22-26, E 21-27

TUITION & COSTS

Tuition: $35,510

Fees: $650

Total: $36,160

R&B: $11,264

Room: $7,106

Board: $4,158

Total: $47,424

FINANCIAL

$21,066 avg grant/scholarship amount (need)

$4,957 avg loan amount (need)

BAY PATH UNIVERSITY

LONGMEADOW, MASSACHUSETTS

A Bay Path education empowers undergraduate women to become leaders in both their careers and communities with an innovative approach to learning that prepares for a constantly changing world. The University's experience is nothing less than transformational; its women-only undergraduate programs and coeducational graduate programs provide a cutting-edge, 21st-century education for learners at all stages of their lives and careers.

WELL - WOMEN AS EMPOWERED LEARNERS AND LEADERS: WELL is a one-of-a-kind program devoted to helping students find and use tools that will lead them to success both throughout and beyond their college years. Students in the WELL program are supported from their transition into college life to graduation. They tap into their strengths, challenge themselves to step out of their comfort zones, and think about their roles as leaders thanks to the help of expert guidance and support from WELL faculty. Through activities both in and out of the classroom, students are prepared with an understanding of what it means and what it takes to be a successful woman in today's complex world.

WOMEN IN STEM HONORS PROGRAM: Housed within the Center of Excellence for Women in STEM, the Bay Path University Women in STEM Honors Program (WiSH) offers a four-year curriculum that consists of integrated study and research for extraordinarily dedicated future scientists. Within this program, students experience hands-on, project-based research and link science to real-world applications. WiSH uniquely prepares women not only to enter scientific fields and excel within them, but to make a true and lasting impact on them. Participating students also receive great scholarship support through a renewable annual $2,500 scholarship.

STUDY ABROAD: No student should pass up the opportunity to study abroad; such a life-changing experience raises international awareness as well as a deeper understanding of other languages, cultures, and peoples. Today's professional world is a colorful blend of cultures and ideas, and it is through Bay Path's programs that students' multicultural growth is aptly nurtured. Students can study abroad in places such as Ireland, France, Italy, or Australia.

ENTREPRENEURIAL PROGRAM: The Bay Path Entrepreneurial Program is designed to prepare students for the creation and launch of new businesses and ideas. This program works to connect students with faculty, successful entrepreneurs, communities, organizations, and the world! At the core of the program is the belief that entrepreneurial skills can be taught, learned, and applied in all majors. Bay Path entrepreneurs are equipped to lead corporations, nonprofits, small businesses, and their own businesses.

HABITAT FOR HUMANITY: Bay Path actively works with Habitat for Humanity to help build decent and affordable housing for low-income families. in order to. This organization aims to provide some stability for families, working to empower them to reach their full potential and break the cycle of poverty.

BASHEVKIN CENTER FOR ACADEMIC EXCELLENCE: The Bashevkin Center for Academic Excellence assists all Bay Path University students in becoming more independent and successful learners. It helps students develop the vital skills they need to manage their time grasp difficult concepts in class. With free tutoring offered both on campus and online. The Center does all it can to set each student up for success.

---

http://www.baypath.edu/
P: (413) 565-1000

PRIVATE

STUDENT PROFILE

1,893 undergraduate students

75% of undergrad students are full time

0% male – 100% female

46% of students are from out of state

73% freshman retention rate

57% graduated in 6 years

FACULTY PROFILE

62 full-time faculty

337 part-time faculty

11 to 1 student/faculty ratio

ADMISSIONS

1,542 Total Applicants

924 Total Admissions

153 Total Freshman Enrollment

59.92% of applicants admitted

SAT Ranges: CR 425-550, M 420-515

ACT Ranges: C 19-25, M 18-24, E 18-25

TUITION & COSTS

Tuition: $32,739

R&B: $12,610

Total: $45,349

FINANCIAL

$21,203 avg grant/scholarship amount (need)

$4,886 avg loan amount (need)

BRIDGEWATER STATE UNIVERSITY

BRIDGEWATER, MASSACHUSETTS

Spread across 278 acres in Bridgewater, Massachusetts, Bridgewater State University is the place that 11,089 students call home. With an average class size of just 20 students, every course is guaranteed to foster fulfilling experiences. Bridgewater offers a broad range of academic opportunities, each of which challenges students to think critically, communicate effectively, and act responsibly with personal and professional ethics. Bridgewater is the tenth largest four-year university in Massachusetts, thriving with an active student life that spans across over 95 clubs and organizations. Its alumni network is just as expansive, amounting to more than 50,000 proud citizen-scholars around the world. Bridgewater also utilizes Connect—a regional partnership with other public higher education institutions—to introduce a diverse array of shared activities and programs for everyone to enjoy.

A PLACE FOR MORE THAN LEARNING: While learning in classrooms is an integral part of the college experience, Bridgewater State University goes the extra mile by giving students the opportunity to participate in its Undergraduate Research Program. This program pairs students with a faculty mentors in order to make original, intellectual, or otherwise creative contributions to their respective field. Not only does this create fantastic résumé material, but it can also help students stand out as professionals and gain deeper knowledge within their chosen disciplines. This research can manifest in many forms: through assistance with professors' projects, as an extension of a class project beyond traditional projects, as capstones or senior projects, or even as grant-funded summer experiences. These projects often culminate in impressive, original presentations at campus symposia.

AN ALL-ENCOMPASSING CURRICULUM: Bridgewater State University's Core Curriculum is designed to be skill-centered and outcome-based, offering a wide range of courses that allows students to shape their education in a way that best supplements their specific fields of study. Bridgewater's liberal arts education trains responsible, flexible world citizens who have the conceptual frameworks and methodologies to tackle any of life's challenges. Students demonstrate a strong proficiency in writing, logical reasoning, mathematical reasoning, and communication. Additionally, students also explore the arts and humanities, a broad variety of cultural perspectives, quantitative skills, government, and the natural, social, and behavioral sciences.

LIVING ALONGSIDE PEERS: Bridgewater State University makes meeting like-minded individuals easy through its Residential Learning Community Program. The objective of the RLC Program is to match students' academic goals with their co-curricular interests, all while fostering new friendships that make the college experience the best it can be. Some first-year communities include Leadership, Science & Math, Service-Based Learning, Women in Science and Math, and Lavender (Bridgewater's LGBTQIA+ community). After their first year of living and learning in these communities, they then have the opportunity to such upper-class RLCs as Honors, Social Justice, and the culturally rich Global Village.

HELPING OTHERS WHILE LEARNING: Bridgewater State is committed to providing students with opportunities to interweave meaningful teaching and learning experiences with community service. Service-learning opportunities are integrated into specific courses as well as individual course assignments, allowing students to utilize the tools they've acquired in the classroom to address real-world problems. Students can use these opportunities to reflect on how their service-learning teaches civic responsibility, collaborative work, and problem solving skills.

http://www.bridgew.edu/
P: (508) 531-1000

PUBLIC

STUDENT PROFILE

9,608 undergraduate students

83% of undergrad students are full time

41% male – 59% female

4% of students are from out of state

79% freshman retention rate

58% graduated in 6 years

FACULTY PROFILE

335 full-time faculty

19 to 1 student/faculty ratio

ADMISSIONS

5,868 Total Applicants

4,736 Total Admissions

1,528 Total Freshman Enrollment

80.71% of applicants admitted

SAT Ranges: CR 440-550, M 450-550

ACT Ranges: C 19-24

TUITION & COSTS

Tuition: (In) $910 (Out) $7,050

Fees: $7,993

Total: (In) $8,903 (Out) $15,043

R&B: $11,700

Room: $7,700

Board: $4,000

Total: (In) $20,603 (Out) $26,743

FINANCIAL

$5,409 avg grant/scholarship amount (total)

$7,083 avg loan amount (total)

COLLEGE OF THE HOLY CROSS

WORCESTER, MASSACHUSETTS

COLLEGE OF THE
Holy Cross

College of the Holy Cross is a selective liberal arts institution with a focus on discovery. Students are encouraged to explore their talents and intellectual capabilities, while applying their skills to improve the local and global communities.

MONTSERRAT: Montserrat is the First-Year Experience at College of Holy Cross. Its name, which refers to a mountain, symbolizes students' upward academic and personal journey. Montserrat invites each student to act as an engaging and lively member of the intellectual community. Students explore a broad range of topics that span over several disciplines, learning to become thoughtful in their approach. They ask questions and contribute to class discussion as they are pushed to pursue their own journeys of intellectual, spiritual, and personal growth. "The Cluster" is a component of Montserrat that organizes students into one of six groups, each of which is based on an interdisciplinary theme. Under the direction of faculty, Cluster groups come together throughout the year to engage in common texts, topics, and activities. Cluster-wide activities draw connections between disciplines and help the new classmates bond with one another. In the past, some of these Cluster-wide activities have included trips to museums, hiking a mountain, and seeing a theatrical performance.

WASHINGTON SEMESTER PROGRAM: Students have the option to participate in the Washington Semester, a highly competitive program that connects students from all disciplines to professional experiences. The program has three components: a seminar, an internship, and research. The seminar is a useful resource that pushes students to analyze their experience critically while tying their respective disciplines to their work. The internship provides hands-on learning through collaborations with professionals in their fields, thereby proving themselves valuable for potential employers. Finally, under the supervision of a faculty advisor, the research project acts as a tangible representation of their hard work and innovative curiosities.

STUDY ABROAD: There are 42 study abroad programs at Holy Cross and 29 host countries for students to choose from. There is also the choice to study through a full-immersion program—a culture-rich experience that forces participants out of their comfort zones. The Independent Cultural Immersion Project is required of all study abroad students, but should not be viewed as an academic burden. Instead, students are encouraged to view the project as an extracurricular activity and immerse themselves in some aspect of the local culture. This project can be fulfilled in three ways: a study abroad internship, a community-based learning project, or the development a hobby or passion that adequately engages them with the surrounding culture. These projects ensure that students get the most out of their time away from Worcester, plunging them into the the adventures that await them in the wider world.

THE CENTER FOR INTERDISCIPLINARY STUDIES: The Center for Interdisciplinary Studies is an awesome way for students and faculty to explore their interests across a wide range of disciplines. Students can work with faculty to design their own major/minor multidisciplinary program, a great way for their varying interests to collide and pave a whole new path to innovative scholarship.

SEMESTER AWAY: The Semester Away program allows students to expand upon their discipline by studying through another institution and utilize whatever exclusive resources are offered elsewhere. This is a great opportunity for students to experience another school's programs, culture, and social life. In the past, students have studied through such institutions as New York University, Boston University, and Union College.

http://www.holycross.edu/
P: (508) 793-2011

PRIVATE - CATHOLIC

STUDENT PROFILE

2,729 undergraduate students

99% of undergrad students are full time

50% male – 50% female

96% freshman retention rate

92% graduated in 6 years

FACULTY PROFILE

294 full-time faculty

48 part-time faculty

10 to 1 student/faculty ratio

ADMISSIONS

6,595 Total Applicants

2,442 Total Admissions

738 Total Freshman Enrollment

37.03% of applicants admitted

SAT Ranges: CR 600-690, M 620-690, W 610-700, E 8-10

ACT Ranges: C 28-31, M 27-30, E 28-33, W 8-10

TUITION & COSTS

Tuition: $46,550

Fees: $626

Total: $47,176

R&B: $12,748

Room: $6,878

Board: $5,870

Total: $59,924

FINANCIAL

$34,876 avg grant/scholarship amount (total)

$6,407 avg loan amount (total)

CURRY COLLEGE

MILTON, MASSACHUSETTS

Curry College provides rigorous and relevant academic programs to undergraduate and graduate students alike. Its rich blend of liberal arts and career-directed programs is enhanced by practical field experiences and co-curricular activities. Curry students have access to a wide range of co-curricular and extracurricular activities, including student newspaper and other campus media; performing arts programs such as theatre and dance; and intramural sports and NCAA Division III athletic teams.

GENERAL EDUCATION: At the heart of Curry College's undergraduate curriculum is the General Education (Gen Ed) curriculum. Gen Ed, required of all students, explores the liberal arts through a series of topical, real-world issues. The Gen Ed curriculum addresses the "Essential Learning Outcomes" and High-Impact Practices established by the Association of American Colleges and Universities. It prioritizes the development of skills needed to participate in the 21st-century economy: global knowledge, effective written and oral communication, critical thinking, information literacy, quantitative reasoning, intercultural sensitivity, teamwork, and ethical judgment

DIVERSITY: At Curry College, diversity is central to excellence in education, not a separate goal. The College believes that training students to become inclusive, empathetic citizens requires consistent learning throughout all four years of study. As a result, diversity plays a core role in both the College's Mission Statement as well as a guiding principal in core courses. Regardless of their program of study, students are encouraged to develop a deep respect for diversity in all its forms. By graduation, students are able to demonstrate a knowledge of the world's diversity and interconnectedness, identifying the similarities and differences among and between cultures, religions, genders, and value systems.

EXCEPTIONAL FACULTY: There are 122 full-time faculty members at Curry, 81 percent of whom hold terminal degrees in their fields. Additionally, the College annually hires highly qualified part-time faculty members and visiting lecturers to augment its teaching staff. Although they prioritize teaching, Curry's professors are also engaged in writing, research, and consulting. One-on-one faculty-student relationships provide many opportunities for personalized instruction and close interaction. The average class size is 20 students, and the student-to-faculty ratio is 10:1.

PROGRAM FOR ADVANCEMENT OF LEARNING (PAL): The internationally acclaimed Program for Advancement of Learning (PAL) at Curry College was established in 1970 as the nation's first college-level program for students with language-based learning differences. PAL is the longest-standing comprehensive support program designed to help intelligent and motivated students with language-based learning differences achieve at the college level. PAL faculty at the master's and doctoral level work directly with students to provide individual or small-group instruction, providing comprehensive support for intelligent and motivated students. Students even receive academic credit for enrollment in the program and are able to continue working with their PAL mentors for as long as needed.

INTERNSHIPS: Undergraduate internship experience is a key factor in job marketability after graduation. The Internship Program at Curry College offers students the opportunity to explore a variety of career paths. By learning about their interests, skills, strengths, and values, students are able to narrow down their career options to the fields that best suit their talents. They are able to work in consultation with faculty members to articulate their educational and personal goals while establishing the criteria for the evaluation of their field experience.

---

https://www.curry.edu/

P: (617) 333-0500

PRIVATE

STUDENT PROFILE

2,691 undergraduate students

75% of undergrad students are full time

45% male – 55% female

35% of students are from out of state

69% freshman retention rate

47% graduated in 6 years

FACULTY PROFILE

125 full-time faculty

365 part-time faculty

10 to 1 student/faculty ratio

ADMISSIONS

5,554 Total Applicants

4,871 Total Admissions

601 Total Freshman Enrollment

87.70% of applicants admitted

SAT Ranges: CR 420-510, M 420-520, W 410-510

ACT Ranges: C 18-22

TUITION & COSTS

Tuition: $35,740

Fees: $2,095

Total: $37,835

R&B: $14,970

Room: $8,030

Board: $6,940

Total: $17,065

FINANCIAL

$21,454 avg grant/scholarship amount (need)

$4,354 avg loan amount (need)

DEAN COLLEGE

FRANKLIN, MASSACHUSETTS

Dean College is a private college in New England that guides its students toward both academic and personal success. Its strong foundation of culture and tradition guarantee a meaningful living and studying experience for all who attend. For over 150 years, Dean has given its students a supportive academic environment that thrives on student engagement and exceptional teaching. "The Dean Difference" is exemplified through each student's commitment to their professional futures, social responsibility, and leadership.

THE DEAN DIFFERENCE: Dean College prides itself in "The Dean Difference." This College-wide commitment to success is a holistic effort that integrates academics with faculty support and community involvement. Whatever a student does on campus, they are acting according to The Dean Difference. Built into each class is a strong network of support, and supplemented by academic growth are a variety of meaningful service and community engagement activities. Through The Dean Difference, students find an interwoven sense of meaning behind everything they do as a Dean College scholar.

FIRST-YEAR COURSES: Unless they have exempting credits, each Dean College student begins their first year at school enrolled in both an English course and a mathematics course. These foundational courses build students' abilities to think critically and communicate their thoughts effectively. Through the entry-level composition course, students learn to organize their thoughts and write upper-level arguments, skills they need throughout their entire college careers.

STUDY ABROAD: Whether they travel for a small period of a couple of weeks or spend an entire semester or year abroad, Dean students have endless opportunities to study beyond the College's walls and out into the world. Students who wish to stay in the country have two fantastic options to study domestically. Dean College partners with the Washington Center in Washington, D.C., through which students can get hands-on internship experience with highly regarded government figureheads. Dean is also affiliated with the Disney College Program, a creative internship program that allows students to develop their problem-solving skills in either Disneyland or Disney World. Beyond the States, Dean College students can travel to study in a wide array of foreign countries, including Italy, Spain, Germany, New Zealand, Ireland, and even Australia. The College also partners with Regent's University London, offering students a life-changing university experience in the middle of downtown London. Regardless of one's area of study, they are bound to find a program that enriches their major, all while sending them on an exciting adventure.

COMMUNITY SERVICE AND INVOLVEMENT: Giving back to the local community is an important part of being a Dean College Bulldog. Community engagement is just one way that Dean students can interact with faculty and staff outside of the classroom, all while enacting meaningful change to the community around them. By participating service opportunities, students truly realize their ability to impact positively the lives of others.

INTERNSHIPS: Dean College's Office of Career Planning & Internships direct students closer toward their goals by offering many valuable services and resources that clarify the career-building process. Dean students and alumni alike have access to hundreds of jobs and internship opportunities through DEAN CareerLink, the College's exclusive online career management database. 100% of Dean students are guaranteed access to internships that bulk their résumés and provide them with employable skills. Every student completes an internship at some point throughout the academic career, working with such companies as The Boston Ballet, New England Patriots, Ralph Lauren, and UMass Medical Center. Through Dean's one-of-a-kind Center for Business, Entertainment, and Sports Management (The Center), students are given exclusive internship opportunities and job-shadowing days with multi-billion dollar companies such as The Kraft Sports Group, The Pawtucket Red Sox, and The Providence Bruins.

https://www.dean.edu/
P: (508) 541-1900

PRIVATE

STUDENT PROFILE

1,300 undergraduate students

87% of undergrad students are full time

50% male – 50% female

47% of students are from out of state

74% freshman retention rate

34% graduated in 6 years

FACULTY PROFILE

32 full-time faculty

134 part-time faculty

16 to 1 student/faculty ratio

ADMISSIONS

2,891 Total Applicants

2,571 Total Admissions

446 Total Freshman Enrollment

88.93% of applicants admitted

SAT Ranges: CR 370-490, M 370-490

ACT Ranges: C 16-21

TUITION & COSTS

Tuition: $38,090

Fees: $300

Total: $38,390

R&B: $16,346

Total: $54,736

FINANCIAL

$6,336 avg grant/scholarship amount (need)

$4,003 avg loan amount (need)

EMERSON COLLEGE

BOSTON, MASSACHUSETTS

A private, four-year college located in Boston, Emerson offers a unique perspective: a dedication to communication and the arts all within a liberal arts framework. Emerson College is located at the intersection of Boylston and Tremont streets in the heart of Boston, Massachusetts, directly next to the lush Boston Common and in the middle of the historic Freedom Trail.

WHERE LIBERAL ARTS MEET COMMUNICATION: Emerson embraces collaboration. The College strongly emphasizes the relationship between liberal arts and all the various fields of communication. Through this collaboration, students develop their skills as critical thinkers as they learn to challenge traditional conventions while synthesizing their new ideas into the world. Entertainment, writing, journalism, and all forms of media are best played out with a broad understanding of all fields of study and modes of thought.

BOSTON: Emerson is located in Boston, a noted historical and cultural hub. Students, on top of the many campus activities that Emerson offers, have the chance to enjoy a vibrant city life filled with museums and career opportunities. Students can enjoy cheering on the Red Sox at nearby Fenway Park, seeing live performances at the Boston Opera House, visiting the city's Aquarium or one of its many museums, or even attending a show at Emerson's very own Cutler Majestic Theatre.

LOS ANGELES-BASED RESIDENTIAL STUDY AND INTERNSHIP PROGRAM: Emerson opens up access for students to travel to Los Angeles and intern with over 1,000 sites in the media, marketing, and public relations industries. Those who choose to utilize this opportunity receive the benefits of working in the central hub of their chosen industry as they live and study with the same, high-level Emerson standards. Through Emerson, these driven students foster Boston scholarship, Los Angeles initiative, and vice versa.

TELEVISION, RADIO, AND FILM PRODUCTION: Emerson offers its students state-of-the-art production facilities that are fully stocked with high-tech equipment and gadgets. Students are given the opportunity to learn the ins and outs of the entertainment business while utilizing such a wealth of industry-standard gear. Emerson's facilities provide students with the hands-on experience they need to be successful in their chosen careers.

COMEDY, WRITING, AND PERFORMANCE: Emerson has recently introduced a minor in comedy. The minor is interdisciplinary, meaning that its course requirements are fulfilled through several departments. The comedy minor enhances the College's presence in the entertainment industry, giving students a more established skillset. Emerson has 8 comedy organizations on campus, affording students numerous opportunities to get involved.

MAKE IT HAPPEN: Emerson students learn to emulate and build off the work of their professors, all of whom are respected scholars in their fields. The College brings together academic theory with practice, bringing about new ideas and challenging traditional conventions through collaboration between students and faculty. Students explore their surroundings while building a repertoire of marketable experiences as they embody Emerson's belief that education is about stepping up and recognizing one's full potential. They are taught to make things happen, as professors motivate their students to challenge their surroundings and break out of their comfort zones.

ABROAD PROGRAMS: Emerson encourages many of its students to study abroad in order to develop a more worldly perspective. The College believes that these cultural experiences directly enrich one's professional skills through the exposure of different people, perspectives, and ideas. One standout study abroad program enhances this level of exposure by boarding its students in a 14th-century medieval castle. This semester-long program in the Netherlands is wholly immersive, inspiring students with the beautiful, historical architecture of the beautiful, historical country.

---

http://www.emerson.edu/
P: (617) 824-8500

PRIVATE

STUDENT PROFILE

3,808 undergraduate students

98% of undergrad students are full time

40% male – 60% female

100% freshman retention rate

80% graduated in 6 years

FACULTY PROFILE

202 full-time faculty

277 part-time faculty

13 to 1 student/faculty ratio

ADMISSIONS

8,618 Total Applicants

4,225 Total Admissions

915 Total Freshman Enrollment

49.03% of applicants admitted

SAT Ranges: CR 560-670, M 540-640, W 560-660

ACT Ranges: C 25-29, M 23-28, E 25-32, W 8-10

TUITION & COSTS

Tuition: $39,312

Fees: $732

Total: $40,044

R&B: $15,700

Total: $55,744

FINANCIAL

$19,097 avg grant/scholarship amount (total)

$11,163 avg loan amount (total)

FISHER COLLEGE

BOSTON, MASSACHUSETTS

Fisher believes that college is about more than just an education—it's about life-changing experiences. For over a century, Fisher has been changing lives by providing opportunities to students focused on the three most important aspects of a college experience: education, dedication, and life.

STUDY ABROAD: To encourage students to expand their global awareness, Fisher College offers a series of short-term study abroad programs. Most of these options occur during the summer months, allowing all students an opportunity to participate without adversely affecting their progress in completing their academic programs. Study abroad opportunities are currently offered in France, Austria, Italy, Australia, Ireland, Scotland, England, and Spain.

ALTERNATIVE SPRING BREAK: An equally life-changing and educational experience, Alternative Spring Break (and the Habitat for Humanity Service-Learning Program), allows students to embark on a week-long trip to help better communities throughout the United States. Fisher College has worked with Habitat for Humanity since 2010, traveling to Tampa, Florida; Macon, Georgia; El Paso, Texas; New Bern, North Carolina; and Gardena, California.

INTERNATIONAL STUDENTS: The Center for International Programs and Services (CIPS) supports a by creating a beneficial environment that fosters civility and respect. Fisher provides information, advice, and program support that altogether assist in students' initial transition and continued stay at Fisher. Aiming to facilitate the internationalization of the College, CIPS provides services and programs to support international students and develops activities that utilize their skills strengthen their contributions to the Fisher College community.

THE COMMON EXPERIENCE: The first year of college is full of new changes and experiences, and Fisher knows that the transition from high school can be daunting. The Common Experience is a semester-long course that bring students in touch with instructors and peers, gaining the skills and experience they need to achieve success throughout the first year of college. But this personalized attention does not stop after the first year; faculty and staff are ready to support all students throughout their entire journey at Fisher.

THE HONORS PROGRAM: The Fisher College Honors Program invites a select community of students to embark on a "Journey of Excellence" that provides them a wealth of opportunities to explore their chosen area of study. Through this rigorous program, students gain the sensitivity to test the moral and social implications of their future goals as well as foster respect for themselves and others in preparation for full and productive lives. The philosophy of the Honors Program is that well-educated individuals should seize the opportunity to apply their knowledge to the betterment of the communities from which they come and to those in which they plan to serve.

PHI THETA KAPPA: A chapter of Phi Theta Kappa (PTK), the national honor society for American two-year colleges, was established at Fisher College in 1965 with the chapter name Nu Omega. In order for students to be invited to this society, they must meet a certain GPA and be of good moral character. As Nu Omega members, students possess and exude recognized qualities of citizenship.

FISHER COLLEGE

http://www.fisher.edu/
P: (617) 236-8800

PRIVATE

STUDENT PROFILE
1,938 undergraduate students
64% of undergrad students are full time
29% male – 71% female
58% freshman retention rate
46% graduated in 6 years

FACULTY PROFILE
36 full-time faculty
145 part-time faculty
17 to 1 student/faculty ratio

ADMISSIONS
2,669 Total Applicants
1,873 Total Admissions
278 Total Freshman Enrollment
70.18% of applicants admitted

TUITION & COSTS
Tuition: $27,947
Fees: $995
Total: $28,942
R&B: $15,082
Total: $44,024

FINANCIAL
$16,909 avg grant/scholarship amount (total)
$7,420 avg loan amount (total)

MASSACHUSETTS

GORDON COLLEGE

WENHAM, MASSACHUSETTS

Theologian and missionary A. J. Gordon founded Gordon College in 1889 "to prepare the people of God to do the work of God" in bold and creative ways. More than a century later, such a mission remains its central commitment. With 38 major offerings, Gordon prepares students for faithful leadership in a wide variety of disciplines.

AN INFORMED AND INSPIRED EDUCATION: At Gordon, students have the freedom to pursue knowledge to the limits of their curiosity in an environment where Christian faith and bold academic inquiry inform one another. This dynamic interplay between freedom and faith is a defining characteristic of the Gordon experience. Gordon challenges students to make full use of their minds and hearts, trusting that faith in Christ will expand their knowledge and worldviews.

STUDY ABROAD: With a global education program that enables students to study around the world, Gordon students take full advantage of the many cultural opportunities available to them. In most cases, these programs come at no additional cost to students' regular tuition. Gordon has uniquely immersive programs in Italy, France, Romania, and more. Students can also choose from more than twenty programs sponsored by the Council for Christian Colleges & Universities or petition to spend a semester in countries of their own choosing. Gordon understands that gaining a global perspective is an important part of what it means to engage the world in faith, so the College works with students both on and off campus to make their global goals a reality.

UNDERGRADUATE RESEARCH: Student research opportunities at Gordon enable undergraduates to work directly with ancient manuscripts, high-tech instruments, and top-tier scholars. Many projects with Gordon faculty have yielded published peer-reviewed papers in psychology, philosophy, biology, and many other disciplines.

FELLOWSHIP: Gordon takes seriously its students' journeys of faith. Through a minimum of 30 Christian life and worship opportunities, students are encouraged to grow in the understanding and experience of their relationship with Christ. These opportunities include weekly chapels and convocations, special lectures, worship events, and service-learning excursions.

USING CHRISTIAN VALUES AS A SPRINGBOARD TO EXPLORE TRUTH IN ALL ITS DIMENSIONS: Notable among Gordon's 38 majors are Psychology, English Language and Literature, Business Administration, Communication Arts, and Biology. Teaching at Gordon focuses on critical thinking, strong communication skills, research, and an exploration of creative talents and social entrepreneurship. Due to their liberal arts education, graduates have the skills to be confident in many different environments.

EXPANSIVE CULTURE FOR ALL: Students have access to an array of extracurricular events and activities on and around Gordon's campus. Events range from prominent guest lecturers and debates to highly praised theatrical productions, local film festivals, and student-led coffeehouses. Nearby Boston also offers a world of cultural and intellectual experiences with its many museums, academic institutions, festivals, and concert venues.

INTERNSHIPS: The college's proximity to Boston, a global hub of innovation and progress, provides many opportunities for student internships and research experience. Whether at State Street Corporation or in a cancer research lab, Gordon students can gain access to the city's vast network of growing industries in finance, biomedicine, technology, publishing, and more. Many students have gained employment after college through the internships and research work they began at Gordon.

GORDON STUDENTS ARE PREPARED FOR ALL OF LIFE'S OPPORTUNITIES: A recent survey found that over 60% of alumni had enrolled in or completed graduate studies within ten years of their graduation from Gordon. Many Gordon alumni go on to earn graduate degrees from some of the best programs in the world at institutions like Harvard, Yale, Columbia, Tufts, and Cornell. Since 2006, seven Gordon graduates have received highly competitive Fulbright grants to study and teach in countries around the world.

GORDON
COLLEGE

http://www.gordon.edu/
P: (978) 927-2300

PRIVATE - CHRISTIAN

STUDENT PROFILE

1,694 undergraduate students

97% of undergrad students are full time

38% male – 62% female

66% of students are from out of state

85% freshman retention rate

69% graduated in 6 years

FACULTY PROFILE

121 full-time faculty

9 part-time faculty

13 to 1 student/faculty ratio

ADMISSIONS

1,832 Total Applicants

1,708 Total Admissions

441 Total Freshman Enrollment

93.23% of applicants admitted

SAT Ranges: CR 480-620, M 470-610, W 480-620

ACT Ranges: C 23-29, M 22-28, E 23-30, W 8-9

TUITION & COSTS

Tuition: $33,884

Fees: $1,502

Total: $35,386

R&B: $10,218

Room: $6,750

Board: $3,468

Total: $45,604

FINANCIAL

$18,906 avg grant/scholarship amount (need)

$4,805 avg loan amount (need)

LASELL COLLEGE

AUBURNDALE, MASSACHUSETTS

An innovator in education for over 150 years, Lasell is a comprehensive, coeducational college that enrolls more than 1,800 undergraduate students. Lasell complements traditional approaches with active learning experiences—a teaching method that the College calls "Connected Learning." Lasell College is committed to the idea of learning by doing through internships, service-learning, and challenging projects both in and out of the classroom.

CONNECTED LEARNING SYMPOSIUM: Each semester, Lasell College holds a Connected Learning Symposium that includes presentations, displays, exhibitions, and performances. Launched in the Spring of 2002, the Symposium showcases students' academic work within a Connected Learning environment. These end-of-semester events gather the Lasell community in celebration of the collaborative accomplishments of students and faculty, helping to further establish the relevance of teaching and learning beyond the walls of the classroom. The week-long Spring symposium culminates with Runway, an undergraduate and senior fashion show.

STUDY ABROAD: Lasell offers students further potential to connect classroom experiences to the real world through 75 extensive study abroad programs. Students have studied fashion in places like Paris and St. Petersburg, Business students have enrolled in programs in Ireland and China, and Literature and Theatre students have studied in London. For students looking to study off campus and stay Stateside, Lasell offers a semester-long internship program in Washington, D.C.

SERVICE-LEARNING: More than 90 percent of Lasell students complete a credit-bearing service-learning experience through the Center of Community-Based Learning. Merging coursework with service, students enact diverse forms of volunteerism. For example, some students have worked with the residents of a continuing care community, while others taught English to children in Papua-New Guinea. Lasell's international "Shoulder to Shoulder" programs are a collection of cultural immersion and service-learning excursions in which Lasell students learn about various social justice issues within a global context. Students live in the style of their host community while learning and working shoulder-to-shoulder with local partners.

HONORS PROGRAM: The Honors Program offers an intensive setting for intellectual and social development. It fosters independent thinking, social responsibility, enthusiasm for intellectual inquiry, and an overall appreciation for the power of ideas. The Honors Program aims to produce interdisciplinary thinkers and problem-solvers who live with a critical moral sensibility. Gaining the skills to research problems from a number of angles, these students develop the leadership strategies to organize action and implement solutions.

WRITING REQUIREMENT: Regardless of their major, students take two Writing-Intensive Courses that help them develop their writing skills in formats that are relevant to their programs of study. For example, Athletic Training and Exercise Science majors learn to write patient progress notes and scientific articles based on their own original research studies; Education majors learn to write lesson plans; and Fashion majors learn to write design statements.

RESEARCH ACROSS THE CURRICULUM: The Research across the Curriculum (RAC) program offers a range of research grant and credit opportunities at every level and in every field of study at Lasell, ranging from the arts and sciences to business and allied health. Through RAC work, students are challenged to demonstrate investigative skills, apply information literacy, and communicate empirical information effectively. Research-Intensive Course Grants provide faculty support to design and implement curricular changes in courses that incorporate new research projects or activities.

---

http://www.lasell.edu/

P: (617) 243-2000

PRIVATE

STUDENT PROFILE

1,815 undergraduate students

99% of undergrad students are full time

34% male – 66% female

44% of students are from out of state

75% freshman retention rate

52% graduated in 6 years

FACULTY PROFILE

87 full-time faculty

180 part-time faculty

13 to 1 student/faculty ratio

ADMISSIONS

3,171 Total Applicants

2,478 Total Admissions

490 Total Freshman Enrollment

78.15% of applicants admitted

SAT Ranges: CR 440-530, M 430-530, W 430-530

ACT Ranges: C 18-23

TUITION & COSTS

Tuition: $30,800

Fees: $1,200

Total: $32,000

R&B: $13,250

Total: $45,250

FINANCIAL

$20,004 avg grant/scholarship amount (total)

$7,406 avg loan amount (total)

NEWBURY COLLEGE

BROOKLINE, MASSACHUSETTS

Students don't just want to learn. They want to put ideas into action and connect the classroom to the real world. At Newbury, they are mentored, challenged, and encouraged to collaborate with other outstanding minds. All of this happens in a warm and friendly environment just minutes from downtown Boston. Students rave about their opportunities at Newbury, which guarantees them a great foundation for success both in their careers and throughout their lives.

CORE CURRICULUM: The General Education sequence at Newbury College is built to teach students how to communicate and apply their skills to an ever-changing world as well as how to become active thinkers and global citizens. It is designed to instill habits of the mind to face the challenges that inevitably show up in a range of career fields and personal communities. These Core courses open students' minds to the diversity of the human experience, empowering students to make ethical life decisions that contribute to the richness of their lives and the lives of others. These outcomes achieve information literacy, critical thinking, communication, knowledge, ethical awareness, and social responsibility.

INTERNSHIPS: With easy access to Boston and its infinite opportunities, Newbury students explore the work world long before graduation. As interns, students can go behind the scenes at five-star restaurants or hotels, gain firsthand knowledge at four-star accounting firms, or go pro with a dozen professional sports teams across Massachusetts. Newbury College students have access to tremendous resources through Career Services that help them secure their desired internship placements. One outstanding opportunity offered at Newbury is a 150-hour internship experience directly related to a student's major. This placement pairs them with an online course in which students and faculty across disciplines discuss their professional environments, projects, challenges, and successes in their respective workplaces.

STUDENT INVOLVEMENT IN SERVICE: The Office of Student Involvement provides excellent volunteer opportunities for students to enact change around the Greater Boston Area. Last year, Newbury students donated their time to Cradles to Crayons, served dinner and gave donations to underprivileged women at a homeless shelter, saved 83 lives through a Blood Drive, volunteered at the Boston Marathon, and served dinner at the New England Center for Homeless Veterans. Leaders in community service are also viable candidates for Newbury's scholarship program.

WRITING-INTENSIVE COURSES: In support of Newbury College's mission statement, faculty take advantage of their small class sizes to provide engaging, hands-on learning environments. Several years ago, Newbury College's professors made an intentional commitment to ensure that all of their courses—even math courses—include some type of writing assignment. Every academic major measures students' competencies through oral and written assignments in upper-level courses. And, through professional development initiatives, the College provides resources that make it easy for every professor to create quality writing assignments.

LEADERSHIP LLC: The Leadership Living Learning Community (LLC) provides opportunities for students to build their personal leadership skills through involvement in the Newbury Community. Members of the Leadership LLC aspire to develop their own philosophy of leadership, creating and contributing to campus traditions through civic engagement and programming. Members of the Leadership LLC have the unique opportunity to engage with faculty and staff from all different areas of campus. The Leadership LLC programming is based off The Social Change Model of Leadership Development. Students are encouraged to develop their own personal leadership philosophy, explore leadership in the community and how it connects to their major, interact with leaders in the Newbury community, and live in specialized housing.

---

https://www.newbury.edu/
P: (617) 730-7007

PRIVATE

STUDENT PROFILE

865 undergraduate students

90% of undergrad students are full time

45% male – 55% female

23% of students are from out of state

59% freshman retention rate

37.8% graduated in 6 years

FACULTY PROFILE

28 full-time faculty

65 part-time faculty

15 to 1 student/faculty ratio

ADMISSIONS

2,580 Total Applicants

2,040 Total Admissions

272 Total Freshman Enrollment

79.07% of applicants admitted

TUITION & COSTS

Tuition: $30,128

Fees: $1,280

Total: $31,408

R&B: $13,740

Total: $45,148

FINANCIAL

$19,878 avg grant/scholarship amount (need)

$4,074 avg loan amount (need)

NICHOLS COLLEGE

DUDLEY, MASSACHUSETTS

Nichols College is a college of choice for business and leadership education as a result of its distinctive career-focused and leadership-based approaches to learning, both in and out of the classroom. Founded in 1815, Nichols transforms today's students into tomorrow's leaders through dynamic, career-focused business and professional education. Nichols serves students who are interested primarily in a comprehensive business education that is supported by a strong liberal arts curriculum.

COMMUNITY SERVICE: Being a good neighbor is serious business. Nichols students, faculty, and staff have performed hundreds of hours of community service. Some examples of the community's astounding service includes helping elderly and lower-income area residents prepare their income tax returns; mentoring children at local elementary schools; working as volunteers for the Dudley Hill Cancer Awareness golf tournament; and serving dinner to residents of Jeremiah's Inn, a residential recovery program in Worcester, Massachusetts. Nichols students have also volunteered for Habitat for Humanity and the Community Harvest Project during "Alternative Spring Break" trips, providing housing and food to lower-income individuals and families.

FISCHER INSTITUTE: At Nichols, students can always find opportunities to expand their intellectual and cultural values beyond what they currently know. The school's Fischer Institute provides opportunities to further develop students through such community-building experiences as guest lectures from national and international speakers, campus community events, performing arts events, and faculty-led outings. These experiences diversify students' views of the world, bringing context to the social, political, and cultural events and ideas they are bound to encounter throughout their lives.

STUDENT ACTIVITIES: It's easy to feel at home on Nichols' friendly campus. With over 35 student organizations, students can easily meet friends with the same interests and make an impact while having fun at the same time. The student-run Campus Activities Board also holds dozens of events each semester, coming up with creative ways to hang out on campus. Fun events include outdoor movie nights. music events. game show-style competitions, and fun zipline courses!

EMERGING LEADERS PROGRAM: Nichols believes that leadership is a quality that everyone can learn and possess. The Emerging Leaders Program (ELP) is a four-year initiative that helps students develop their own leadership style, cultivating the leader within through structured study and practice.

PROFESSIONAL DEVELOPMENT SEMINAR: Nichols makes sure that professional development, skill building, and leadership education is woven throughout each student's undergraduate experience. The College's required four-year, award-winning Professional Development Seminar (PDS) is custom-designed by faculty to prepare students for their pursuits after college. It helps them succeed with job-hunting and -interviewing techniques, evolving every semester to stay current with workplace demands.

CAREER AND PROFESSIONAL DEVELOPMENT CENTER: With Nichols College's Career and Professional Development Center, students have the tools and resources they need to find the right careers for them. They are given plenty of help to present themselves on paper, in person, and online throughout their application processes to jobs, graduate schools, and more. Whether they are pursuing internships, on-campus positions, or full-time employment, Nichols College staff are there help every step of the way.

INSTITUTE FOR WOMEN'S LEADERSHIP: The Institute for Women's Leadership focuses on the issues and challenges that uniquely impact women's roles in business. It works to develop the leadership potential of all students while also serving as a helpful resource for women in the community at large.

Nichols College
Learn. Lead. Succeed.

https://www.nichols.edu/
P: (800) 470-3379

PRIVATE

STUDENT PROFILE

1,267 undergraduate students

91% of undergrad students are full time

64% male – 36% female

42% of students are from out of state

71% freshman retention rate

44% graduated in 6 years

FACULTY PROFILE

48 full-time faculty

38 part-time faculty

17 to 1 student/faculty ratio

ADMISSIONS

2,260 Total Applicants

1,881 Total Admissions

325 Total Freshman Enrollment

83.23% of applicants admitted

SAT Ranges: CR 420-510, M 440-530

ACT Ranges: C 14-22

TUITION & COSTS

Tuition: $32,070

Fees: $300

Total: $32,370

R&B: $12,235

Total: $44,605

FINANCIAL

$17,058 avg grant/scholarship amount (need)

$3,645 avg loan amount (need)

NORTHEASTERN UNIVERSITY

BOSTON, MASSACHUSETTS

Northeastern University's approach to education contains research, experiential learning, and active engagement. Northeastern gives its students the tools they need to succeed, both in the classroom and beyond. Students are developed into hard-working leaders who recognize their duties to the global community.

FIRST-YEAR EXPERIENCE: Northeastern's First-Year Experience is a preparatory program that welcomes students to campus and introduces them to the community. The FYE is both foundational and transformative, giving students the tools they need to succeed while helping them learn to put their new strategies into practice. Preparing students for their upcoming academic challenges, the FYE is guided by four main pillars: Personal Development, Academic Success, Experiential Learning, and Community Development.

SECOND-YEAR EXPERIENCE: The Second-Year Experience (SYE) is a continuation of the foundation that students establish in their first year. The goal of the SYE is to extend a focused sense of guidance, continuing to help students navigate their options and plans while they successfully conquer their second year of studies. The SYE exemplifies Northeastern's commitment to providing students with all the resources they need to lead accomplished college careers, offering a hands-on service that persists beyond the first year.

SERVICE-LEARNING: There are two components to service-learning: academic coursework and community-based service. These two elements feed off one another, helping students apply what they have learned to community service as well as gaining new perspectives and experiences from the volunteer work itself. More than 41,000 hours of service are completed every year, and over 1,100 students get involved. Northeastern has developed over 80 service-oriented partnerships in 3 countries, and its 73 different service-learning courses afford students plenty of opportunities to get involved. The Service Learning Advocacy Workshop opens up even more possibility, allowing students to ignite their own reforms and develop plans of action for change.

GLOBAL EXPERIENCE: Northeastern's experiential learning extends beyond campus to a number of destinations across the globe. While the courses offered through study abroad are fascinating, Northeastern's Global Experience is about more than studying; in some cases, students can conduct research or complete an international internship. Altogether, Northeastern students have completed global experiences in 128 different countries, exposing themselves to new cultures, new work environments, and new network connections.

STUDENT RESEARCH: Undergraduate research is alive and well at Northeastern. The University encourages students to showcase their work at the annual Research, Innovation, and Scholarship Expo. This is an amazing experience for Northeastern students, enabling them to share their work to the community, not just their professors. And their work in innovative research not only lets students discover new information critical to their fields, but it also demonstrates their marketable ingenuity and resourcefulness to future employers.

CO-OPS: Co-Ops allow students to gain real-world experience through the application of academic theories and concepts. In a recent academic year, for example, nearly 10,000 students participated in a co-op, the experiences of which were then directly associated with the University's postgraduate placement rates. 90% of students are enrolled in grad school or employed full-time within 9 months of graduation. Northeastern believes that preparation is the root of success, and it is through co-ops that students are positioned to accomplish great things well beyond graduation.

---

http://www.northeastern.edu/
P: (617) 373-2000

PRIVATE

STUDENT PROFILE

13,697 undergraduate students

100% of undergrad students are full time

50% male – 50% female

97% freshman retention rate

84% graduated in 6 years

FACULTY PROFILE

1,279 full-time faculty

403 part-time faculty

14 to 1 student/faculty ratio

ADMISSIONS

50,523 Total Applicants

14,388 Total Admissions

2,797 Total Freshman Enrollment

28.48% of applicants admitted

SAT Ranges: CR 660-740, M 680-770, W 640-730

ACT Ranges: C 31-34, M 27-34, E 27-34, W 7-9

TUITION & COSTS

Tuition: $44,620

Fees: $910

Total: $45,530

R&B: $15,000

Room: $8,010

Board: $6,990

Total: $60,530

FINANCIAL

$30,421 avg grant/scholarship amount (total)

$6,220 avg loan amount (total)

REGIS COLLEGE

WESTON, MASSACHUSETTS

Regis is a leading Catholic university that prepares students to succeed in an evolving, global world. Founded by the Sisters of Saint Joseph, Regis students benefit from the unique perspective of a values-based education that is integrated with cutting-edge technology and opportunities.

FIRST-YEAR SEMINAR: The First-Year Seminar (FYS) is an essential part of all incoming students' fall semester. FYS introduces new students to the Regis history and heritage, builds their academic and social skills, and engages them in a variety of co-curricular experiences and challenge-based learning projects. Faculty members from all across Regis lead the FYS and serve as their students' academic advisors throughout the entire year. Once the spring semester rolls around, students stay with their FYS classmates from the fall and enroll in a shared, linked course that meets one of the Regis Core Curriculum requirements. This allows them to maintain a sense of community while still moving forward with their degree requirements.

CLASSROOM WITHOUT WALLS: Regis is committed to providing an academic experience that is increasingly enriched by technological resources. Through the iPad initiative, all students are provided iPads to facilitate collaboration and enhance learning. The campus network provides access to campus apps and the internet through 24/7 wireless and wired connectivity, spanning across campus in all classrooms, learning spaces, residential halls, and exterior spaces. Over 98% of all current, full-time faculty are certified as online instructors through the Best Practices Seminar.

GLOBAL EXPERIENCES: Whether students are interested in a semester-, academic year-, or week-long trip, the Office of Global Connections provides personalized support to ensure that each student has an enriching global experience. Regis is directly affiliated with Regent's College in London, England; University College Cork in Cork, Ireland; Assumption College Rome in Rome, Italy; and Kyoto Notre Dame University in Kyoto, Japan. Students can also participate in faculty-led programs that supplement their coursework. Trips range from one to three weeks in length and have taken place in Italy, England, Cuba, and Belize.

OPPORTUNITIES FOR SERVICE: Regis students are encouraged to serve the community both on and off campus. Community service and outreach projects—sponsored by residence halls, class groups, and Regis itself—are an integral part of campus life. Regis students participate in awareness and fundraising events; work at shelters for the homeless and women and children; assist at Greater Boston Food Bank; and make an annual spring break trip to Villa El Salvador, Peru, and Jonestown, Mississippi, to serve while experiencing culture and developing their spirituality.

STUDENT EVENTS: The Office of Student Programming and Leadership sponsors many events throughout the semester, including musical and comedy performances, cultural and sporting events, a monthly "Pizza with the President," and other social get-togethers. Additionally, the office coordinates a number of Regis's traditional events, including Welcome Week, Regis Fest Family Weekend, Halloween, Senior Week, Spring Weekend, and the annual Christmas Tree Lighting.

ACADEMIC SUPPORT: The Academic Center for Excellence (ACE) offers comprehensive support services to empower Regis students of all abilities to enhance their academic development, achieve degree completion, and maximize their full potential. Services include academic coaching, writing assistance, tutoring support for courses with quantitative components, peer tutoring, and access to live online tutoring.

PREPARED FOR LIFE: 100 percent of Regis students participate in an internship or clinical placement before graduating, providing valuable real-world experiences and networking opportunities. Regis has educated leaders in law, medicine, management, education, communication, social work, and other professional fields. It has seen its graduates become economists, corporate officers, lawyers, college presidents, scientists, doctors, legislators, lobbyists, diplomats, foreign correspondents, artists, authors, teachers, nurses, graphic designers, programmers, and so much more.

http://www.regiscollege.edu/
P: (781) 768-7067

PRIVATE - CATHOLIC

STUDENT PROFILE

1,235 undergraduate students

78% of undergrad students are full time

21% male – 79% female

82% freshman retention rate

47% graduated in 6 years

FACULTY PROFILE

95 full-time faculty

15 part-time faculty

11 to 1 student/faculty ratio

ADMISSIONS

2,023 Total Applicants

1,704 Total Admissions

269 Total Freshman Enrollment

84.20% of applicants admitted

TUITION & COSTS

Tuition: $39,820

R&B: $14,740

Total: $54,560

FINANCIAL

$25,878 avg grant/scholarship amount (total)

$9,679 avg loan amount (total)

SPRINGFIELD COLLEGE

SPRINGFIELD, MASSACHUSETTS

Springfield College has been educating students in spirit, mind, and body for leadership in service to others since 1885. The College not only lives its mission of leadership through academics, clubs, and athletics, but also through community service both in local neighborhoods and across the world.

START OFF STRONG: Springfield College offers a first-year seminar course to help students transition into the college lifestyle and become part of the campus community. During this academic offering, students strengthen their critical thinking skills as they make decisions about the academic and cocurricular experiences they want to pursue as college students. The course provides a great foundation for the Springfield College education as well as the experiential support for the kind of skills that will prove to be beneficial in their college experience.

ACTIVE LEARNING: Springfield College students don't sit back and watch the world go by; they experience for themselves what it's like to work in their fields through fieldwork, internships, practica, and research. Learning at Springfield is an active process that ensures students to graduate with experience already on their résumés and, therefore, an advantage over others in the job market.

TALENTED FACULTY: Springfield College faculty members are experts who are seriously involved in student success. Many are nationally or internationally recognized authorities in their fields, and most hold the highest academic degrees and other certifications in their areas of expertise. With a student-to-faculty ratio of 13:1, Springfield College offers small classes and personal attention from extraordinary educators.

STUDY ABROAD: Blending an incredible education with immersive exposure to new cultures and languages, study abroad is undoubtedly the highlight of many students' college careers. Springfield College offers programs in Australia, China, England, France, Hungary, Ireland, Italy, New Zealand, Poland, Scotland, and Spain. Summer internships are also available in Dublin and London. Students can even embark on international and domestic trips to provide community service through a number of the College's service organizations.

DUAL-DEGREE PROGRAMS: Springfield College students are able to enroll in several dual-degree programs. For example, students in the physical therapy program earn both a bachelor of science and doctor of physical therapy within six years, while those in the occupational therapy program earn a bachelor of science and master of science in just five and a half years. Students in the physician assistant program earn a bachelor of science and master of science in six years. The College also offers a physician assistant program, an accelerated master of social work/juris doctorate program, and a six-year program for students interested in earning a bachelor's degree and law degree in conjunction with Western New England University School of Law.

EVENTS ON CAMPUS: The Springfield College campus is alive with cultural and arts events, presentations by field experts, a wide array of student organizations, and a vigorous schedule of sports and athletic events. The campus is also the site of national collegiate championships as well as the annual Spalding Hoophall Classic basketball event.

JOBS AND GRADUATE SCHOOL PLACEMENTS: A recent survey found that 96 percent of Springfield bachelor degree recipients are either employed or enrolled in graduate school within six months of graduation. Springfield's placement rate is 12 percent higher than the national average for schools of its kind and higher than the average of other colleges and universities in New England.

SPRINGFIELD COLLEGE

http://www.springfieldcollege.edu/

P: (413) 748-3000

PRIVATE

STUDENT PROFILE

2,147 undergraduate students

99% of undergrad students are full time

49% male – 51% female

87% freshman retention rate

72% graduated in 6 years

FACULTY PROFILE

190 full-time faculty

12 to 1 student/faculty ratio

ADMISSIONS

4,112 Total Applicants

2,638 Total Admissions

549 Total Freshman Enrollment

64.15% of applicants admitted

SAT Ranges: CR 460-560, M 470-580

ACT Ranges: C 20-26, M 20-26, E 20-25

TUITION & COSTS

Tuition: $33,970

Fees: $485

Total: $34,455

R&B: $11,540

Room: $6,280

Board: $5,260

Total: $45,995

FINANCIAL

$19,558 avg grant/scholarship amount (total)

$9,372 avg loan amount (total)

STONEHILL COLLEGE

NORTH EASTON, MASSACHUSETTS

Located just outside of Boston, Stonehill is a beautiful Catholic college that offers over 80 majors in the liberal arts, sciences, and business. Nearly 91% of students participate in internships, study abroad, research, practica, and field work, exemplifying the College's commitment to experiential learning.

COMMITMENT TO EXPERIENTIAL LEARNING: With a full-time undergraduate enrollment of 2,400, Stonehill offers more than 80 academic majors and minor areas of study in the liberal arts, sciences, business, and pre-professional advising programs. Stonehill's most popular programs are biology, biochemistry, English, political science, criminology, psychology, accounting, pre-law, and education. Stonehill is particularly unique for the internship and research possibilities it offers, reflecting its commitment to experiential learning.

STUDENT PROGRAMS: A vast majority of Stonehill students participate in hands-on learning experiences throughout their undergraduate career. Business students have interned at companies like Fidelity Investments and PricewaterhouseCoopers; English and writing students have had jobs in print media and public-relations firms; and science students have worked at hospitals in Boston and London.

THE STONEHILL UNDERGRADUATE RESEARCH EXPERIENCE (SURE): The Stonehill Undergraduate Research Experience (SURE) is an incredible opportunity for undergraduates. This unique program engages students in around 10 weeks of intense research during the summer with a professor, a stipend of up to $3,500, and the opportunity to co-publish and present at professional conferences.

CORNERSTONE PROGRAM: The core of Stonehill's liberal arts curriculum is the Cornerstone Program, an educational track that leads every student to examine the self, society, culture, and the natural world through courses in ethics, sciences, language, and more. Interdisciplinary Learning Communities are also ingrained in the Stonehill College experience, enrolling students in a combination of two academic courses from different disciplines. These team-taught seminars explore interrelated topics from both perspectives, providing an example of the importance of well-rounded thinking.

EASTON, MASSACHUSETTS: Stonehill is located in Easton, Massachusetts, a friendly residential community nestled between New England's largest capital cities. Ideally located just 22 miles from Boston, America's #1 college town, and 37 miles from Providence, Stonehill College is perfectly situated for internships, service opportunities, job prospects, museums, professional sports games, cultural events, and more. The beautiful, 384-acre campus features traditional landscaping, ponds, wooded trails, Georgian-style architecture, and award-winning student housing.

RESIDENTIAL LIFE: Stonehill is a residential college that over 90% of students call home. Undergraduates love to get involved through such organizations as the Stonehill Student Government Association (SGA)—one of the country's most active—as well as more than 60 student clubs and organizations, 20 competitive Division II varsity teams, and numerous intramural, recreational, and intercollegiate club sport programs.

THE OFFICE OF CAREER SERVICES: The Office of Career Services provides comprehensive career development for its students and alumni. The staff aim to help individuals achieve their academic and career goals through self-assessment, career exploration, internship and employment opportunities, advanced degree information, and the acquisition of lifelong career management skills. Collaborating with faculty, employers and alumni, Career Services provides programs and services that students can utilize to achieve their individual career goals.

http://www.stonehill.edu/
P: (508) 565-1000

PRIVATE - CATHOLIC

STUDENT PROFILE

2,400 undergraduate students

99% of undergrad students are full time

41% male — 59% female

89% freshman retention rate

87% graduated in 6 years

FACULTY PROFILE

183 full-time faculty

111 part-time faculty

12 to 1 student/faculty ratio

ADMISSIONS

5,892 Total Applicants

4,429 Total Admissions

656 Total Freshman Enrollment

75.17% of applicants admitted

TUITION & COSTS

Tuition: $38,550

R&B: $14,720

Room: $9,022

Board: $5,698

Total: $53,270

FINANCIAL

$24,372 avg grant/scholarship amount (total)

$7,938 avg loan amount (total)

SUFFOLK UNIVERSITY

BOSTON, MASSACHUSETTS

SUFFOLK
UNIVERSITY
BOSTON

http://www.suffolk.edu/

P: (617) 573-8470

PRIVATE

STUDENT PROFILE

5,185 undergraduate students

96% of undergrad students are full-time

45% male – 55% female

36% of students are from out of state

76% freshman retention rate

59% graduated in 6 years

FACULTY PROFILE

339 full-time faculty

345 part-time faculty

13 to 1 student-to-faculty ratio

ADMISSIONS

8,624 Total Applicants

7,271 Total Admissions

1,205 Total Freshman Enrollment

84.31% of applicants admitted

SAT Ranges: CR 450-560, M 460-560

ACT Ranges: C 20-25

TUITION & COSTS

Tuition: $37,128

Fees: $142

Total: $37,270

R&B: $16,576

Total: $53,846

FINANCIAL

$13,578 avg grant/scholarship amount (need)

$5,266 avg loan amount (need)

Founded in 1906, Suffolk University is a four-year, private university in the heart of Boston. Suffolk offers more than 60 undergraduate programs through the College of Arts & Sciences and Sawyer Business School. Its location in downtown Boston gives students unparalleled access to many opportunities in the Boston metro area, including prestigious internships and job placements. Upon earning their undergraduate degrees, students may pursue advanced studies at the College, the Business School, or Suffolk University Law School.

THE FIRST-YEAR EXPERIENCE: All undergraduates at Suffolk take a First-Year Experience course that's designed to make their transition to college life easier. SBS 100 and CAS 101 focus on academic skills and resources, personal development, career and professional preparation, and campus resources and involvement. Additionally, College of Arts & Sciences students take a Seminar for Freshmen in their first semester. Kept to a maximum of 19 students, each seminar offers an in-depth look at topics ranging from the Beatles' role as cultural avatars of the 1960s to global climate change, contemporary urban challenges, the meaning of life, and more.

AT HOME IN THE WORLD: Select freshmen have the chance to complete up to their first two years of undergraduate studies abroad at Suffolk University's Madrid campus, one of the only such opportunities in the United States. Students may also spend a semester, academic year, or summer at either Suffolk Madrid or one of the University's other study abroad offerings on six continents. Students in the Sawyer Business School may choose to investigate the business culture of another country on a Global Travel Seminar, while art and design students can explore masterpieces abroad on special study-tours.

ENGAGING RESEARCH: The University Honors Program features outstanding academic opportunities, mentoring, and special events from orientation through graduation. Honors students in the College of Arts & Sciences must complete an honors project in their senior year, which may take the form of an original work, fieldwork, or research with a faculty member. In the Sawyer Business School, honors students can focus on research in special Challenge Courses. Students all throughout the University pursue meaningful research projects as well. They can partner with professors to conduct polling for the nationally lauded Political Research Center, heal communities through the Center for Restorative Justice, and much more. Furthermore, the University's McNair Scholars Program inspires first-generation or income-eligible students to pursue research at the doctoral level.

COLLABORATIVE LEARNING: Suffolk's academic offerings reflect today's employers' demand for collaborative learning. Many of the largest classrooms in the University's newest academic building were built to promote team-based learning: students sit at communal tables instead of individual desks, enjoying the technological means to present each of their group's findings to the class. This approach applies equally to science students in the lab, marketing students working on case studies, and everyone else. Study groups for individual courses are also available through the Center for Learning & Academic Success.

AN EXCITING, URBAN UNIVERSITY: Boston is the quintessential college town, home to about 300,000 students from all over the globe. Its dynamic intellectual energy is unmatched by any other city. There are no real borders to the University's campus—Boston and Suffolk simply blend together to create a vibrant urban dynamic that students enjoy every day.

SENIOR YEAR SPECIAL OPPORTUNITIES: Regardless of their majors, students are encouraged to enhance their undergraduate studies during their senior year. They may choose to take capstone courses that synthesize their knowledge of their chosen fields or undertake theses for departmental honors. Entrepreneurship majors can work closely with successful alumni as part of their capstone experiences, while psychology majors take one of two specially designated capstone courses.

WENTWORTH INSTITUTE OF TECHNOLOGY

BOSTON, MASSACHUSETTS

Founded in 1904, Wentworth Institute of Technology is an independent, nationally ranked institution that offers career-focused education through 19 bachelor's degree programs. Areas of concentration include applied mathematics, architecture, business management, computer science, computer networking, construction management, design, engineering, and engineering technology. The Institute also offers master's degrees in architecture, civil engineering, construction management, facility management, and technology management.

HOTBED OF ACTIVITY: Accelerate, Wentworth's Innovation + Entrepreneurship Center, was conceived as a logical extension of Wentworth's already existing strengths and disciplines. Accelerate drives thought partnerships, interdisciplinary engagement, and out-of-the-box ideas among students, alumni, industry, and the Boston community. Being in Boston means that students are learning and working in the midst of one of the country's leading hubs of innovation, home to a thriving and fast-paced start-up ecosystem that includes research centers, venture capitalists, and business and technology experts.

COLLABORATION & PARTNERSHIPS: Wentworth collaborates with leading universities, corporations, and other partners on a wide range of projects. These opportunities provide students with hands-on experiences and valuable professional connections as they interact with and serve the needs of such partners as GE Aviation. Wentworth also makes it a priority to engage students in projects that benefit the institute's host community. The engine for such service-learning initiatives is the Center for Community and Learning Partnerships (CLP).

SERVICE-LEARNING: Infused throughout the Wentworth experience, the project-based Service-Learning program enriches learning, teaches social responsibility, and strengthens communities. Service-learning projects are executed through coursework under the direction of faculty, student clubs and organizations, co-ops with community organizations, or as a senior-year requirement. Students can also receive a certificate and academic recognition for their service-learning and community engagement work.

EPIC LEARNING: Wentworth is open to external collaborators of all sorts, such as new start-up businesses, major corporations, nonprofits of all sizes, and government bodies and agencies at all levels (federal, state, and local). The Institute is also interested in engaging learning opportunities wherever they arise. For instance, Wentworth's mechanical engineering students have refined the design of stoves produced by Aid Africa, a non-governmental organization (NGO) in northern Uganda.

FIRST-CLASS OPPORTUNITIES IN A WORLD-CLASS CITY: Boston provides Wentworth students with an expanded learning laboratory that is rich with resident experts and examples of excellence in a range of fields. Design students can visit the city's premier buildings, study its sites, and learn from local experts as part of their studio experiences. Engineering and construction students engage with the city's sophisticated culture of technology and its infrastructure, including the iconic Zakim Bridge, the widest cable-stayed span in the world.

COOPERATIVE LEARNING IN REAL-WORLD ENVIRONMENTS: Wentworth's cooperative education program (co-op) is one of the most comprehensive in the country, contributing to the firm basis for Wentworth's high placement rate for graduates among leading organizations—locally, nationally, and worldwide. At Wentworth, two semesters of co-op placements are required (and a third semester is optional). The simple reason for this is that the 21st-century economy moves too quickly to allow newly minted professionals time to get their feet wet and their hands dirty. Wentworth graduates hit the ground running and achieve career success because they already have extensive experience applying classroom knowledge to real-world situations.

WENTWORTH
INSTITUTE OF TECHNOLOGY

http://www.wit.edu/
P: (617) 989-4590

PRIVATE

STUDENT PROFILE

4,329 undergraduate students

89% of undergrad students are full time

81% male – 19% female

84% freshman retention rate

63% graduated in 6 years

34% of students are from out of state

FACULTY PROFILE

148 full-time faculty

219 part-time faculty

16 to 1 student/faculty ratio

ADMISSIONS

5,316 Total Applicants

4,393 Total Admissions

1,064 Total Freshman Enrollment

82.64% of applicants admitted

SAT Ranges: CR 480-590, M 530-630, W 470-570

ACT Ranges: C 22-27, M 23-28, E 21-26

TUITION & COSTS

Tuition: $29,320

Fees: $1,445

Total: $30,765

R&B: $12,840

Total: $43,605

FINANCIAL

$13,732 avg grant/scholarship amount (need)

$8,808 avg loan amount (need)

WESTERN NEW ENGLAND UNIVERSITY

SPRINGFIELD, MASSACHUSETTS

WESTERN NEW ENGLAND
UNIVERSITY

"Where do I see myself in four years?" is the question most students face as they enter college. With four Colleges—Arts and Sciences, Business, Engineering, and Pharmacy (as well as an additional School of Law)—Western New England University offers the academic opportunities of a university in a community that knows its students as individuals. With an emphasis on collaboration, leadership, and experiential learning, Western New England University's programs challenge students to dream big, take risks, and surprise themselves with all they can accomplish.

STUDY ABROAD: For many students at Western New England University, study abroad is a passport to a world of remarkable opportunity. Students gain new insights studying their discipline in the context of a foreign perspective, all while learning about other cultures' political and economic systems. Students have spent the semester or year in such destinations as Australia, China, England, Finland, Ireland, Italy, and Spain. The University also offers select seminar courses abroad to such locations as China, Iceland, Spain, Guatemala, Italy, and the UK. Through the Arts and Sciences Freshman Semester in London and Business Sophomore Experience Abroad program, students can spend the fall semester at London's Richmond University for the same cost (including airfare) as living on campus. Most classes are even taught by WNEU business faculty themselves.

LEARNING BEYOND THE CLASSROOM: The University's Learning Beyond the Classroom program helps students discover learning opportunities all around them. Combining in-class study with out-of-the-classroom activities, the program gives students hundreds of ways to gain new and valuable life experiences that can prepare them for future careers and community leadership roles. Subsequent opportunities to reflect on the service activity help students draw important lessons from their involvement as it relates to their academic work.

JOINT DEGREE PROGRAMS: Western New England University offers several joint degree programs. The school's 3+3 law and Six-year Engineering/Law programs offer a six-year course of study that leads to both an undergraduate and a law degree. Similarly, students can complete a five-year program that leads to both an undergraduate degree and an MBA, MSA, MSEE, or MSEEM. The University also offers two-year Pre-Pharmacy and Pre-Physician Assistant programs as well as a four-year PharmD degree.

FINAL PROJECTS: Many Western New England University students are required to complete projects that serve as stepping-stones to their first professional job. One student, for example, made a video for a local school for the deaf; she submitted the video to a local affiliate of ABC-TV and was offered an on-air reporter's job even while studying as a full-time student. Similarly, a mechanical engineering student who worked with United Technology on jet engines received an offer from NASA to work and earn her Ph.D. Western New England University also boasts a former biomedical engineering student who developed an apparatus during her Senior Design Project that surgeons then began using in open-heart surgeries a year later.

INTERNSHIPS: Every student is strongly encouraged to gain practical experience in internships. LEGO Systems, PricewaterhouseCoopers, and United Technologies are just a few of the more than 1,000 organizations that sponsor WNEU interns. The University has a partnership with a public radio station in nearby Albany, New York, at which students serve as reporters of the station and produce news segments that air throughout the Northeast. The station houses its Pioneer Valley News Bureau on campus.

CAREER DEVELOPMENT CENTER: Through its Career Development Center, the University has cultivated a network of alumni who serve as mentors for current students. Many alumni come back to campus to talk with students in classes or in formal mentoring programs. The Colleges of Business and Engineering also have alumni mentoring programs that match students with graduates in their disciplines.

Sidebar

http://www1.wne.edu/
P: (413) 782-3111

PRIVATE

STUDENT PROFILE

2,732 undergraduate students

94% of undergrad students are full time

60% male – 40% female

76% freshman retention rate

59% graduated in 6 years

FACULTY PROFILE

231 full-time faculty

124 part-time faculty

13 to 1 student/faculty ratio

ADMISSIONS

6,216 Total Applicants

4,982 Total Admissions

757 Total Freshman Enrollment

80.15% of applicants admitted

SAT Ranges: CR 470-570, M 500-600

ACT Ranges: C 22-26

TUITION & COSTS

Tuition: $31,200

Fees: $2,266

Total: $33,466

R&B: $12,688

Total: $46,154

FINANCIAL

$18,672 avg grant/scholarship amount (total)

$10,932 avg loan amount (total)

KEENE STATE COLLEGE

KEENE, NEW HAMPSHIRE

Keene State College prepares promising students to think critically and creatively, to engage in active citizenship, and to pursue meaningful work. As the public liberal arts college of New Hampshire, Keene State offers an enriching campus opportunity and achieves academic excellence through the integration of teaching, learning, scholarship, and service.

HANDS-ON EXCELLENCE: What happens in the classroom doesn't stay in the classroom. It gets put into action through travel, field research, conferences, student media, concerts, dances, and more; the sky's the limit for student involvement. Many students put their learning to use in more traditional arenas, but their opportunities to grow are best fostered through Keene State's resourceful hands-on programs, whether that be through undergraduate research or performance.

INTEGRATED STUDIES: Keene State's Integrative Studies Program is a college-wide curriculum that introduces every student to a broad understanding of a variety of fields. This program is a balanced survey of the arts and sciences, helping students in any major connect the dots to other fields of study and see how their focus ties in to the greater span of academia.

EXTRACURRICULAR ACTIVITIES: Keene State offers its students a bustling array of activities to pursue. Students have access to over 100 clubs, including sororities and fraternities, and are highly encouraged to get involved in organizations that allow them to express themselves and enjoy their lives outside of the classroom. The College believes that active engagement in social clubs helps students develop into stronger individuals; those who participate in extracurriculars are more likely to grow socially and maintain an excitement for their overall college experience. Between clubs, teams, and other activities, there's something for everyone—even the option to found a new group.

LIVING ON CAMPUS: First-year and sophomore students live on campus, as do many juniors and seniors. While the residence requirement is only applied to first- and second-year students, most see a great benefit in staying on campus throughout the entire collegiate experience. Living on campus puts students directly in contact with all the school has to offer, including two art galleries, frequent performances of many kinds, lectures, book discussions, and more. On-campus residency may be enhanced through participation in a Living-Learning Community. Living-Learning Communities are groups of students who live together, bound by common academic or social interests. Additional benefits include peer mentoring, special field trips, and networking opportunities.

COMMITTED FACULTY: Professors are primarily committed to the success of their students, aiming to provide the best undergraduate education that they can give to each student. They assist in research projects, lend advice regarding course material, and embrace the value that every individual brings to the classroom. More than half of classes have fewer than twenty students, and only one percent of classes exceed fifty. This ensures that students are able to interact one-on-one with their professors and get the assistance and wisdom that best supports their success.

OFF-CAMPUS LEARNING AND SERVICE: Keene State students learn and do amazing things far beyond campus walls. They put their hearts to work by performing over 100,000 hours of collective community service each year. These hours are racked up through all of the students' service work around the neighborhood, service-learning courses, internships that benefit this community and service-based trips across the country and around the world. No matter how—or where—they serve, Keene State students are always making a positive difference as they develop into responsible scholar-citizens. In addition to serving abroad, students are encouraged to participate in such global engagement opportunities as semester-long study abroad and faculty-led academic trips.

http://www.keene.edu/
P: (603) 358-2276

PUBLIC

STUDENT PROFILE

4,259 undergraduate students

96% of undergrad students are full time

44% male – 56% female

62% of students are from out of state

73% freshman retention rate

63% graduated in 6 years

FACULTY PROFILE

225 full-time faculty

238 part-time faculty

15 to 1 student/faculty ratio

ADMISSIONS

5,674 Total Applicants

4,469 Total Admissions

920 Total Freshman Enrollment

78.76% of applicants admitted

SAT Ranges: CR 440-550, M 440-550, W 440-540

ACT Ranges: C 19-24, M 18-24, E 17-24

TUITION & COSTS

Tuition: (In) $10,700 (Out) $18,800

Fees: $2,528

Total: (In) $13,228 (Out) $21,328

R&B: $10,712

Room: $6,372

Board: $4,340

Total: (In) $23,940 (Out) $32,040

FINANCIAL

$6,868 avg grant/scholarship amount (need)

$4,325 avg loan amount (need)

RIVIER UNIVERSITY

NASHUA, NEW HAMPSHIRE

One of the most affordable universities in the region, Rivier University prides itself on its small classes led by accomplished faculty who create an active, experiential learning environment. The University offers more than 50 distinctive degree programs, all of which are founded upon strong Catholic values. Founded in 1933 by the Sisters of the Presentation of Mary, Rivier University is a Catholic institution committed to its mission of transforming hearts and minds to serve the world.

EXPERIENTIAL LEARNING: At Rivier University, students are encouraged to be active learners. Through internships, student-driven research opportunities, and service-learning projects, students have an exciting opportunity to apply their learning in the real world as they answer the challenges of today's global economy.

INDEPENDENT RESEARCH: Many students, especially those studying the sciences, participate in independent research projects that deepen their understanding of what interests them most. Under the guidance of their instructors, students engage in each step of the research process, developing questions, predicting outcomes, conducting experiments or studies, and analyzing and reporting results. Through this process, students make original contributions to their studies and take ownership of the material in a unique way.

SERVICE-LEARNING: Service-learning gives students striking benefits that are similar to independent research with an additional impact through service to others. By integrating service into the curriculum, Rivier challenges students to connect their coursework to today's most pressing community needs, inviting them to discover meaningful solutions. While Rivier requires students to participate in an in-depth project that involves community service, students are nevertheless inspired to reach out and help others in many other ways beyond their requirements. By participating in service learning, students become engaged with the campus community as well as the wider communities that they assist, all while gaining a deeper and more informed understanding of the world around them.

GLOBAL ENGAGEMENT: The University emphasizes that global learning experiences are key to preparing students for the 21st-century workforce. Through coursework, service-learning, campus events, international faculty-led field experiences, study abroad, and internships, students develop a global perspective and expanded worldview that enables them to be successful in managing people, complexity, and change in any field.

INTERNSHIPS: Regardless of their major, students can take on rewarding internship experiences that cultivate their interests within a particular career field. Rivier students have participated in meaningful and practical experiences with local and regional corporations, social services agencies, and nonprofit organizations in various industries. These internships give students the chance to immerse themselves in many professional areas, using the training they have received in the classroom to impact the world. Whether these experiences include teaching in a local school district, working with patients at a well-respected healthcare facility, processing reports for a municipal police department, or engaging in any other aspect of work, internships give students a competitive edge in the job market.

EMPLOYMENT PROMISE PROGRAM: Rivier is so confident that its educational experience prepares students to succeed that it is willing to back it up. The University's Employment Promise Program is designed to enhance the career preparation and employability of students in all academic disciplines. This program demonstrates the University's confidence in its educational experience, which is marked by its distinctive academic programs, committed faculty, and active learning opportunities. The University promises that invested students will secure full-time employment within nine months of graduation and will offer twelve months of student loan repayment or tuition-free graduate study in up to six graduate courses if they do not.

http://www.rivier.edu/

P: (603) 897-8507

PRIVATE - CATHOLIC

STUDENT PROFILE

1,396 undergraduate students

56% of undergrad students are full time

20% male – 80% female

77% freshman retention rate

42% graduated in 6 years

FACULTY PROFILE

68 full-time faculty

135 part-time faculty

18 to 1 student/faculty ratio

ADMISSIONS

1,748 Total Applicants

1,002 Total Admissions

184 Total Freshman Enrollment

57.32% of applicants admitted

SAT Ranges: CR 440-520, M 440-530, W 430-520

ACT Ranges: C 18-22, M 16-19, E 14-21, W 2-8

TUITION & COSTS

Tuition: $28,800

Fees: $900

Total: $29,700

R&B: $11,310

Room: $6,060

Board: $5,250

Total: $41,010

FINANCIAL

$14,438 avg grant/scholarship amount (total)

$8,984 avg loan amount (total)

UNIVERSITY OF NEW HAMPSHIRE

DURHAM, NEW HAMPSHIRE

University of New Hampshire

The University of New Hampshire brings together the benefits of a smaller school educational experience with such bigger school perks as research and fieldwork. Students are united through interdisciplinary programs and are encouraged to give back to the community through shared and applied knowledge.

DISCOVERY: Discovery is the success-oriented core curriculum at University of New Hampshire. It exposes students to a range of disciplines and topics. By the time students graduate, they will have studied everything from humanities to physical and biological sciences. Discovery also equips students with such valuable skills as problem solving, critical thinking, effective inquiry, polished writing skills, and higher-level conceptualization. Within the core curriculum, there are certain requirements that each student must satisfy before they can receive their degree, including a first-year writing requirement that effectively prepares new college students for advanced writing assignments. Also incorporated into the core is the enlightening Inquiry 444 course, which directs students to approach one topic from many different academic perspectives. All inquiry courses embrace experiential learning, challenging students to engage actively with their course material. Inquiry seminars push students to expand their horizons and consider more than one interpretation of a subject or issue.

THE WASHINGTON CENTER INTERNSHIP: University of New Hampshire has for a long time sustained a relationship with the Washington Center. Through this affiliation, students have the opportunity to intern with one of the many businesses in Washington D.C. There are internships available across most disciplines, and participants work in government agencies, think tanks, major corporations, and more!

LIVING-LEARNING COMMUNITIES: Through Living-learning communities (LLCs), students gain academic support as they work with one another to achieve similar goals. LLCs are highly beneficial, especially during the first year of college, as participating students constantly profit from faculty interaction and support from their peers. LLCs foster personal growth as students learn to work both on their own and as part of a team. In addition to the freshman-exclusive Alexander Hall LLC, students can join themed residences that are built around communities of similar goals and interests. For example, students can enrich their home experience with the academically driven Making the Grade house or the adventurous Outdoor Experiential Education community. Living in such supportive environments, students find that their growth is furthered outside the classroom as much as it is within.

DAILY WALK-IN WORKSHOPS: The Advising and Career Center is an awesome resource available to all students. The center hosts daily walk-in workshops that focus on a specific skill or topic related to careers and internships. No appointment is necessary, and UNH encourages all students to drop by and see what the center has to offer. Some of the topics include: Starting your Résumé, Internships and Job Shadowing, LinkedIn 101, and Career Fair Prep.

UNH-MANAGED JANUARY TERM PROGRAMS: UNH offers several J-term programs for students looking to gain abroad experience and class credit over the month of January. Some of the programs available include "Building Rome in Italy," a course the explores the architecture and development of the Roman Empire; "Global Health in Ghana," an on-site assessment of the healthcare system in West Africa; and the "London Experience," which takes students on a tour throughout London's culture, architecture, and arts.

---

http://www.unh.edu/

P: (603) 862-1234

PUBLIC

STUDENT PROFILE

13,030 undergraduate students

97% of undergrad students are full time

46% male – 54% female

60% of students are from out of state

85% freshman retention rate

80% graduated in 6 years

FACULTY PROFILE

738 full-time faculty

416 part-time faculty

19 to 1 student/faculty ratio

ADMISSIONS

19,255 Total Applicants

15,137 Total Admissions

3,220 Total Freshman Enrollment

78.61% of applicants admitted

SAT Ranges: CR 500-600, M 500-610, W 490-590

ACT Ranges: C 22-27, M 22-27, E 21-30

TUITION & COSTS

Tuition: (In) $14,050 (Out) $27,320

Fees: $2,936

Total: (In) $16,986 (Out) $30,256

R&B: $11,218

Room: $6,620

Board: $4,598

Total: (In) $28,204 (Out) $41,474

FINANCIAL

$12,070 avg grant/scholarship amount (total)

$9,320 avg loan amount (total)

CALDWELL UNIVERSITY

CALDWELL, NEW JERSEY

Beautiful, affordable, and equipped with nationally accredited programs, Caldwell University is the only Dominican college in New Jersey and one of only 19 Catholic colleges in the U.S. that are guided in the tradition of St. Dominic. Caldwell offers nationally accredited programs, small class sizes, and outstanding personalized attention. With one of the lowest private college tuitions in New Jersey, as well as significant financial assistance to 90% of students, Caldwell University's education is a great value!

CLASS-WIDE EXPERIENCES: Caldwell University provides students with the support and tools they need to succeed. The "Freshman Seminar" and "Freshman Connect" are designed to ease the transition from high school to college, all while strengthening students' academic skills in controlled learning experiences. Then, through the "Second-Year Experience" program, students explore different majors, career options, and potential internship programs, gaining support and guidance to build their résumés, interviewing skills, and more.

SMALL CLASSES FOR HUGE OPPORTUNITIES: One of the strengths of Caldwell University is its size. Caldwell is committed to providing a learning environment designed to help students succeed. The student-to-faculty ratio is 12 to 1, and the average class size ranges from just 16 to 20 students. This allows for personalized attention and support to each and every student. And, since more than 80% of faculty have earned the highest degree available in their fields, they each have a breadth of experience that allows them to inspire their students. All courses are taught by professors themselves, not teaching assistants, in order to maintain a high quality of teaching that further enhances the value of a Caldwell University education.

CARES CENTER: At Caldwell University, each student's success is taken to heart. The CARES center combines advising, registration, and financial aid to serve students as much as possible. This center ensures every student the opportunity and means to complete their degree program, not only in a timely and efficient manner, but also in a way that is enriching and rewarding.

THE CITY RIGHT NEXT DOOR: Caldwell University offers students opportunities that extend far beyond the classroom. Because the University is in such close proximity to New York City, its students can easily visit museums, Broadway shows, cultural and business centers, and more. Faculty in business, the arts, music, and communication arts further enhance their course materials by taking routine trips into New York City. Students have even shadowed and interned with top professionals in the business world.

SERVICE-LEARNING: Service and community are all part of the discovery of Caldwell University. Through campus events, students strengthen their understanding of the needs of society gaining an enriched foundation for serving mankind as they enter the workforce. And, with the landmark Service Day event, classes are canceled so that students, faculty, and staff all get to volunteer their time throughout New Jersey. Each year, students get involved to support the needs of local shelters and food banks, volunteer at local community centers, or clean up local parks. Greek Life on campus is also dedicated to community service; sororities and fraternities work to "give back" to the community. Their activities have included fundraising for victims of natural disasters and participating in a 5k run for Caldwell University's nationally known Center for Autism & Applied Behavior Analysis. Through these types of events, students truly learn about the importance of community.

http://www.caldwell.edu/

P: (973) 618-3000

PRIVATE - CATHOLIC

STUDENT PROFILE

1,595 undergraduate students

86% of undergrad students are full time

29% male – 71% female

10% of students are from out of state

83% freshman retention rate

52% graduated in 6 years

FACULTY PROFILE

84 full-time faculty

11 part-time faculty

12 to 1 student/faculty ratio

ADMISSIONS

3,582 Total Applicants

2,271 Total Admissions

330 Total Freshman Enrollment

63.40% of applicants admitted

SAT Ranges: CR 420-530, M 430-550, W 420-530, E 7-8

ACT Ranges: C 19-23, M 19-25, E 18-22

TUITION & COSTS

Tuition: $29,950

Fees: $1,250

Total: $31,200

R&B: $10,965

Total: $42,165

FINANCIAL

$21,342 avg grant/scholarship amount (need)

$4,049 avg loan amount (need)

COLLEGE OF SAINT ELIZABETH

MORRISTOWN, NEW JERSEY

The mission of the College of Saint Elizabeth is to be a community of learning in the Catholic liberal arts tradition for students of diverse ages, backgrounds, and cultures. Founded in 1899 by the Sisters of Charity of Saint Elizabeth, the College of Saint Elizabeth has a strong tradition of concern for the poor, developing leadership in a spirit of service and social responsibility.

FIRST-CLASS EDUCATION: Great teaching and small classes are at the heart of a CSE education. The faculty are gifted educators who care about their students and work closely with them both inside and outside the classroom. Classes average 13 students, and the student-to-teacher ratio is 11:1. Such a compact environment allows the kind of intellectual give and take characteristic of learning take precedence at CSE. Students learn to think for themselves, examine ideas from all sides, and clearly and confidently defend their personal positions.

PERSONALIZED EDUCATION: The College's general education curriculum is designed specifically to promote success. Classes are targeted, integrated, and developmental, giving students more flexibility to double major and take electives within their majors. Students are assigned to learning communities comprised of approximately 15 students and two faculty members, one of whom also functions as an academic advisor.

CULTURAL EVENTS: Cultural and artistic events are constantly bringing energy and vitality to the CSE campus. Some of these events are generated through student-run clubs and organizations dedicated to specific cultures, while others are developed and presented by faculty and staff to bring some of the outside world into the CSE community. Events include international festivals, poetry readings, film screenings, concerts, dramatic productions, and dance performances.

ENCOURAGING THE ARTS: The Annunciation Center, dedicated in 2007, is home to the Dolan Performance Hall and the Therese A. Maloney Art Gallery, both of which host numerous art exhibitions, concerts, dance performances, and other events throughout the year. The outdoor Greek Theatre, built in 1932 as a recreation of the Theater of Dionysus in Athens, hosts performances every summer in collaboration with the Shakespeare Theatre of New Jersey.

SERVICE-LEARNING: The College of Saint Elizabeth understands that lessons instilled outside the classroom are just as valuable as those learned inside it. Service-learning provides the opportunity to take lessons learned in the classroom and use them to make a difference in the world. The Center for Volunteerism and Service-Learning offers year-round programs, courses, and events to foster the lifelong skills of service and leadership and displays CSE's commitment to civic engagement. Students participate with local community organizations with boots on the ground, building and refurbishing houses, holding events for children at risk, and visiting homeless resource sites. More global opportunities include trips both inside and outside of the U.S. to offer skills in building houses, working in health clinics, and tutoring.

EDUCATIONAL OPPORTUNITY: CSE believes that nothing should get in the way of a great education. Unfortunately, economic disparities, social stratification, and a variety of other factors have limited how accessible higher education can be for a great majority of Americans. As a small but nevertheless impactful effort to counter this fact, CSE has employed the Educational Opportunity Fund (EOF) to help economically disadvantaged students attend and acclimate to college. EOF not only makes tuition feasible for students who could otherwise not afford college, but it also provides extra advising and preparatory courses to make sure that students transition comfortably into college-level academics. EOF is a demanding yet incredibly beneficial program that gives the additional support some students need to make their dreams toward a degree and life-changing career more within reach. The EOF is an amazing representation of CSE's effort to educate and enable bright minds to reach their fullest potential regardless of whatever challenges come their way.

---

http://www.cse.edu/
P: (973) 290-4000

PRIVATE - CATHOLIC

STUDENT PROFILE

439 undergraduate students

99% of undergrad students are full time

0% male – 100% female

1% of students are from out of state

71% freshman retention rate

49% graduated in 6 years

FACULTY PROFILE

48 full-time faculty

108 part-time faculty

11 to 1 student/faculty ratio

ADMISSIONS

804 Total Applicants

508 Total Admissions

101 Total Freshmen Enrollment

63.18% of applicants admitted

SAT Ranges: CR 350-443, M 359-460, W 358-450

TUITION & COSTS

Tuition: $29,732

Fees: $1,956

Total: $31,688

R&B: $12,744

Total: $44,432

FINANCIAL

$17,140 avg grant/scholarship amount (need)

$4,617 avg loan amount (need)

DREW UNIVERSITY

MADISON, NEW JERSEY

Drew combines the best of the classical liberal arts tradition with innovative programming across the curriculum, upholding the highest intellectual standards. Drew offers the full range of traditional majors in the liberal arts. Additionally, students aren't far from New York City, meaning that they are directly nearby a hub of internship opportunities, weekend activities, and more.

FULL IMPACT: The educational experience at Drew University is a hands-on effort. With an average class size of 17, students learn in small settings that are designed to encourage their participation and active involvement. Drew University embraces "full-impact" learning, a style of education that inspires students to find their own answers to hard questions. Professors equip their students with the tools to succeed in their courses, but the responsibility to discover their full potential ultimately rests on the students themselves. Even after course material has been absorbed, students are encouraged to remain hungry for more.

WHY LIBERAL ARTS?: Drew is proud of its academic traditions and embraces the many benefits that a liberal arts degree affords. A college education should be about the growth of the entire individual, a process by which learning transcends disciplines and concentrated niches. While students do choose a dedicated area of focus, they also bolster their education with experience in several other subjects. This well-rounded education prepares them to solve the challenges of society while also acting as upstanding citizens of the global community.

ACTIVE LEARNING: Drew advocates for active learning, expecting students to participate and involve themselves with the subject matter. In order to immerse themselves in their fields of study, students become true practitioners of their interests. Many courses take students out into the field to apply their material to the real world, emphasizing the true, tangible value of their subjects. Some even incorporate supplementary service initiatives that benefit the wellness of the citizens of the surrounding neighborhood. Such a learning style allows students not only to see academic theory in action, but it also makes a positive impact on the local community.

AN INDIVIDUALIZED LEARNING EXPERIENCE: Drew's full-time faculty are not just professionals in their fields; they are first and foremost dedicated mentors to their students. Professors work in close collaboration with their students, enhancing each individual's educational experience. Because 72% of the classes taught at Drew have fewer than 20 students, students are guaranteed a meaningful and individualized college education. In such intimate settings, professors make is easy for students to step out of their comfort zones and think critically by utilizing their unique talents. They remind students that there are several reasons to learn, and they work to integrate the values of freedom, joy, career fulfillment, self-discovery, and society into their course material.

ATHLETICS: Drew's athletic affiliations include: NCAA (Division III), ECAC, Landmark Conference, MACFA, and IHSA. Students have the chance to cheer on their fellow peers at athletic events, or they may choose to get involved themselves. There are also club and intramural sports available for those who want a more casual experience on the field. For those who are simply interested in exercising, Drew also offers fitness classes that range in activity.

STUDENT ORGANIZATIONS: Drew provides access to several clubs and organizations, affording students numerous opportunities to be social outside of class and explore their hobbies. Club interests span from academic to athletic, providing plenty of options to choose from. It's also easy for students to create their own groups if they want a platform for other interests.

http://www.drew.edu/

P: (973) 408-3000

PRIVATE

STUDENT PROFILE

1,407 undergraduate students

98% of undergrad students are full time

39% male – 61% female

41% of students are from out of state

87% freshman retention rate

61% graduated in 6 years

FACULTY PROFILE

150 full-time faculty

101 part-time faculty

10 to 1 student-to-faculty ratio

ADMISSIONS

3,494 Total Applicants

1,997 Total Admissions

350 Total Freshman Enrollment

57.16% of applicants admitted

SAT Ranges: CR 520-640, M 510-610

ACT Ranges: C 23-28, M 22-28, E 22-29

TUITION & COSTS

Tuition: $38,668

Fees: $582

Total: $39,250

R&B: $14,108

Total: $53,358

FINANCIAL

$36,371 avg grant/scholarship amount (need)

$4,541 avg loan amount (need)

GEORGIAN COURT UNIVERSITY

LAKEWOOD, NEW JERSEY

Georgian Court University, established in 1908, provides a comprehensive education in the Mercy Catholic tradition. Located in Lakewood, NJ, GCU advances a curriculum that is broad enough to be truly liberal, yet specialized enough to provide in-depth preparation for careers or further study through 30 undergraduate degrees, 10 graduate degrees, and a variety of certificates.

FIRST-YEAR SEMINAR: The First Year Seminar (FYS) course introduces students to the total University experience. FYS includes a career development component that helps students focus on selecting an academic major, while exploring the ways that their strengths, talents, and interests inform their academic and career paths.

GLOBAL EDUCATION AND STUDY ABROAD: The Office of Global Education Program advances the University's mission to educate and empower students in a diverse global community by globally transforming the campus community in multiple ways. These initiatives include Travel Abroad and Study Abroad programs, International Student Exchange Programs, faculty exchanges and visiting professors, University-hosted international conferences and visitors, and international collaboration inside and outside the classroom.

INDEPENDENT RESEARCH: Georgian Court provides students with a wealth of research opportunities through its academic programming, including joint faculty-student research, grant-funded research, and independent study research. GCU students also participate in the annual Independent College Fund of New Jersey Undergraduate Research Symposium at which they present their research results to a panel of judges drawn from New Jersey's top industries, ICFNJ member institutions, and trustees.

MATH INDIVIDUALIZED LEARNING: The Assessment and Learning in Knowledge Spaces (ALEKS), provides students in need of mathematics remediation with an individualized learning experience tailored to their unique strengths and weaknesses. With the support of an instructor, students work at their own pace in a computer lab through the use of adaptive learning software. Assessment at the end of the course determines students' readiness for higher levels of math. Each week, students spend three hours in the lab during fixed class times as well as one hour at a time of their choosing. The program is designed to move students through developmental instruction that is individually paced to better ensure timely graduation.

LIVING-LEARNING COMMUNITIES: Living-learning communities offer students the opportunity to participate in shared learning experiences that are based around a specific theme. GCU's four communities are International Cultures, Gateway to the Arts, Outdoor Adventures, and Sustainability. Members of these communities work closely with a faculty coordinator and graduate assistant who plan and implement various programs, discussion groups, lectures, off-campus experiences, and other activities. Students benefit in many ways when they participate in a living-learning community; they enjoy a greater sense of community, personal attention and mentoring, enhancement of their intellectual development, built-in support systems, opportunities for leadership experiences, and specialized experiences for lifelong learning.

CRITICAL CONCERNS WEEK: Each year, GCU observes Critical Concerns Week to give special emphasis to issues addressed by the Sisters of Mercy, GCU's sponsoring organization. Since 2006, GCU has dedicated a week of scholarly study to these special concerns, including women's issues, the environment, immigration and identity, and nonviolence.

INTERNSHIPS: Internships help GCU students to transform their academic foundation into careers. The Office of Career Services helps get students in touch with internships, which combine supervised work experience with a structured academic plan. An internship may be full time or part time, paid or unpaid. The Office is readily available to utilize its outstanding network of regional employers, nonprofit organizations, and alumni for the internship placements.

http://georgian.edu/
P: (800) 458-8422

PRIVATE - CATHOLIC

STUDENT PROFILE
1,409 undergraduate students

94% of undergrad students are full time

26% male – 74% female

12% of students are from out of state

85% freshman retention rate

42% graduated in 6 years

FACULTY PROFILE
85 full-time faculty

175 part-time faculty

12 to 1 student/faculty ratio

ADMISSIONS
1,609 Total Applicants

1,198 Total Admissions

221 Total Freshman Enrollment

74.46% of applicants admitted

SAT Ranges: CR 420-510, M 430-530

ACT Ranges: C 17-23, M 16-22, E 15-22

TUITION & COSTS
Tuition: $30,158

Fees: $1,460

Total: $31,618

R&B: $10,808

Total: $42,426

FINANCIAL
$18,406 avg grant/scholarship amount (need)

$7,548 avg loan amount (need)

RAMAPO COLLEGE

MAHWAH, NEW JERSEY

Established in 1969, Ramapo College offers bachelor's degrees in the arts, business, humanities, social sciences, and natural sciences as well as in professional studies, which include nursing and social work. In addition, Ramapo College offers courses that lead to teacher certification at the elementary and secondary levels. Its broad offering of programs builds students up to be leaders in their fields.

FIRST-YEAR SEMINARS AND EXPERIENCES: Ramapo College incorporates a summer reading program that is academically linked to the First-Year Seminar (FYS) course. Students read a book over the summer and come to campus to discuss the book with their FYS classmates as its concepts are integrated into their coursework. This enables them to exercise their critical thinking, reasoning, analytical thinking, and writing and communication skills. Ramapo College offers approximately 42 first-year seminar experiences, each of which is designed to provide students with a strong foundation for lifelong learning and achievement through interdisciplinary and experiential learning. Seminars also promote diversity, inclusiveness, sustainability, student engagement, and community involvement.

COMMON INTELLECTUAL EXPERIENCES: The College encourages students to participate in a four-year Student Engagement Plan. This plan sets students up for success by incorporating the curricular and co-curricular activities that best support the needs and desires of students for each year of their Ramapo experience. With a solid plan for their college career, students are well prepared to enroll and engage in classes and events that fulfill all of their goals. The program ultimately supports crucial academic, social, personal, and community/civic outcomes.

UNDERGRADUATE RESEARCH: Many of the Ramapo's academic programs offer research symposia at which students may present their work. For example, the School of Theoretical and Applied Science sponsors an annual symposium, and students in the College Honors Program conduct research in fulfillment of programmatic requirements. In addition, Ramapo College students have presented their research at the annual regional student research conference, which was sponsored by the Council on Public Liberal Arts Colleges (COPLAC).

DIVERSITY/GLOBAL LEARNING: There are a variety of international education programs that may be utilized at Ramapo College, enabling students to study and intern abroad in more than 50 different countries. Ramapo also participates in the National Student Exchange program and attracts a wide variety of international students from more than 30 different countries, including Bulgaria, Nepal, and Myanmar. Many club and extracurricular activities on campus are designed to enhance student learning outside the classroom by tending to the intellectual and cultural climate on campus. Every year, the College hosts a World Expo fair at which students and faculty showcase the the diversity and cultures of different countries.

WRITING-INTENSIVE COURSES: Ramapo College offers Critical Reading and Writing courses that encourage students to think critically and express their ideas through written word. Communication and creative writing courses are also highly intensive, encouraging students to think outside the box. The Center for Reading and Writing provides support to students, regardless of ability, to help them achieve their goals in reading and writing.

LEARNING COMMUNITIES: Ramapo College offers students the opportunity to become part of various "Living Learning Communities" (LLCs) on campus. The purpose of this residential experience, specifically designed with undecided first-year students in mind, is to provide students the opportunity to integrate and apply their in-class experiences in a practical manner. Students in each LLC are grouped based on their similar academic, cultural, and social interests, fostering ongoing and lasting relationships. The LLC program also offers the opportunity for first-year students to connect with faculty to provide support and enhance their education right from the start of their experience in higher education.

RAMAPO COLLEGE OF NEW JERSEY

http://www.ramapo.edu/
P: (201) 684-7300

PUBLIC

STUDENT PROFILE

5,661 undergraduate students

88% of undergrad students are full time

45% male – 55% female

4% of students are from out of state

86% freshman retention rate

74% graduated in 6 years

FACULTY PROFILE

393 full-time faculty

32 part-time faculty

17 to 1 student/faculty ratio

ADMISSIONS

7,106 Total Applicants

3,783 Total Admissions

931 Total Freshman Enrollment

53.24% of applicants admitted

SAT Ranges: CR 490-590, M 500-610

ACT Ranges: C 20-26

TUITION & COSTS

Tuition: (In) $8,866 (Out) $17,731

Fees: $4,832

Total: (In) $13,698 (Out) $22,563

R&B: $11,640

Room: $8,020

Board: $3,620

Total: (In) $25,338 (Out) $34,203

FINANCIAL

$11,378 avg grant/scholarship amount (total)

$7,406 avg loan amount (total)

RIDER UNIVERSITY

LAWRENCEVILLE, NEW JERSEY

Rider University is a private, coeducational university located in Lawrence Township, New Jersey. Its motto, "In Omnia Paratus," promises to graduate students "in all things prepared." To ensure that its community understands the ins and outs of the world beyond campus, Rider attracts a diverse population of students and faculty that promotes new perspectives and problem-solving strategies. Rider University believes that one learns best in the company of others. Its vibrant and engaged learning community draws individual talents together to explore subjects, tackle problems, share ideas, embark on adventures, and create solutions.

STUDY ABROAD: Rider students have the option to study in one of twenty countries abroad. Locations abroad take place in a variety of exchange partner schools, direct enrollment schools, and Rider-affiliated study abroad institutions. Students in any discipline can benefit greatly from Rider's program, having easy access to world-class courses, exclusive internships, and fulfilling service-learning projects. What is experienced abroad translates seamlessly into Rider's transcripts, so taking the time to explore the world is nothing but beneficial. New perspectives, friendships, and academic potential await daring, adventurous Broncs.

HEALTH STUDIES INSTITUTE: Rider's unique Health Studies Institute asks its campus population to collaborate with one another in order to take an interdisciplinary approach to local and global health issues. Education, Innovation, and Outreach are the Institute's three main areas of focus, striving to take Rider's breadth of knowledge beyond the University's walls into order to bring valuable contributions to the future of healthcare.

THE GLASS MENTOR PROGRAM: Through the GLASS (General Liberal Arts and Sciences Students) Mentor Program, first-year students are supported through their transition into college with the help of upper-level student mentors. These mentors quickly become dear friends who help their freshmen mentees navigate the social and academic challenges that come with the new University environment. Such an overwhelming amount of support ensures that new students will easily melt in as part of the Rider community.

ISCAP DAY: Rider University hosts the Independent Scholarship & Creative Activities Presentations (ISCAP) Day in order to celebrate the creativity and innovative minds that thrive in the Rider community. It provides a forum for students and faculty to engage in interdisciplinary discussions about current academia and projects in the arts. Everyone at Rider University is encouraged to present their independent projects in the arts, sciences, and beyond to foster a well-rounded sense of scholarship. ISCAP Day is an extraordinary platform for students to give their efforts the exposure they deserve.

CAREER DEVELOPMENT AND SUCCESS: The Career Services Office at Rider University is equipped with the tools and resources that students need to succeed. It is proud to get students in touch with such highly esteemed organizations as CNN, Johnson & Johnson, VH1, and ABC News, launching them into hands-on experiences that give them a true feeling of what it's like to work in their fields of interest.

THE CRANBERRY CAVALRY: Once a Bronc, always a Bronc. Rider University alumni can stay connected to their legacy through the Cranberry Cavalry. This program is an engaging alumni network and student stewardship initiative that gathers Rider alumni and students to keep the University well maintained. As students and alumni give back to the school, they network with one another. The Rider family bolsters one another's future careers and pursuits, as they can trust that they have direct contact with others who have received the same high-quality education.

http://www.rider.edu/

P: (609) 896-5042

PRIVATE

STUDENT PROFILE

4,172 undergraduate students

88% of undergrad students are full time

43% male – 57% female

25% of students are from out of state

80% freshman retention rate

64% graduated in 6 years

FACULTY PROFILE

292 full-time faculty

309 part-time faculty

12 to 1 student/faculty ratio

ADMISSIONS

9,851 Total Applicants

6,798 Total Admissions

862 Total Freshman Enrollment

69.01% of applicants admitted

SAT Ranges: CR 450-550, M 460-560, W 450-540

ACT Ranges: C 19-25, M 19-26, E 18-25

TUITION & COSTS

Tuition: $37,650

Fees: $710

Total: $38,360

R&B: $13,770

Room: $8,910

Board: $4,860

Total: $52,130

FINANCIAL

$22,732 avg grant/scholarship amount (total)

$10,557 avg loan amount (total)

SETON HALL UNIVERSITY

SOUTH ORANGE, NEW JERSEY

A student-to-faculty ratio of 14:1 and an average class size of 20 provide a truly supportive educational environment; students enjoy hands-on guidance from a world-class faculty comprised of Fulbright scholars, leading researchers, industry leaders, and former ambassadors. Dozens of Seton Hall students have been chosen for highly selective national and international awards in recent years, including Rhodes, Fulbright, Pickering, and Udall scholarships.

SERVICE AND EXPERIENTIAL LEARNING: Every Seton Hall undergraduate student participates in at least one community service/volunteer project, and many students also participate in a career-based experiential education program prior to graduation. Career-based experiences include student teaching, clinicals, practica, field placements, and internship fieldwork.

STATE-OF-THE-ART TECHNOLOGY AND FACILITIES: Seton Hall places a major emphasis on the use of state-of-the-art technology and facilities, including the trading room at the Stillman School of Business and Sim Man, a portable and advanced patient simulator for College of Nursing students. Students can also get involved in the University's award-winning radio station, WSOU; produce their own programming on Pirate TV; or get hands-on experience by conducting focus groups in the brand-new Market Research Center.

AWARD-WINNING MOBILE COMPUTING PROGRAM: Offering a completely wireless campus, Seton Hall's award-winning Mobile Computing Program provides all incoming, full-time freshmen with a brand-new, fully loaded laptop. Incoming freshmen receive their laptops the summer before they enter Seton Hall, giving them the opportunity to become part of the Seton Hall community as early as freshman orientation. The laptops also allow faculty to integrate technology and cutting-edge learning into the classroom.

STUDY ABROAD: A Seton Hall education doesn't just take place on campus. The University is committed to providing students with a globally enriched perspective for today's increasingly interconnected world. The Office of International programs offers study abroad programs in Russia, Italy, Ireland, London, China, Cypress, and even Bermuda, to name just a few. Seton Hall has also had a relationship with universities in China since 1951, giving students and faculty the opportunity to live and learn within a new community that has long held the University's same values. For students who may pursue a career that has an international focus, the Whitehead School of Diplomacy and International Relations prepares diplomatic and business professionals to serve in public service, international business, law, technology, and the nonprofit sector. The School boasts an impressive faculty, including many current and former U.N. ambassadors and officials.

SOUTH ORANGE, NEW JERSEY: Seton Hall's 58-acre campus in South Orange offers students an abundance of opportunities both on and off campus. On campus, there are 14 varsity athletic teams that compete in the Big East Conference, over 100 clubs and organizations, over 20 intramural and club sports, and Greek life to keep students with all interests involved and entertained. Additionally, just a short, ten-minute walk from campus is the town center, which features bookstores, coffee shops, restaurants, and a movie theater. Once in town, students can hop on a train and arrive in the heart of New York City, the capital of fashion, finance, art, and entertainment, in under a half hour.

CAMPUS COMMUNITY GUIDED BY FAITH: The Seton Hall campus community is guided by faith and supported by a beautiful historic chapel on campus as well as a campus ministry office. All Seton Hall students take classes in ethics and learn in a community informed by Catholic ideals and universal values. They are engaged in learning about the importance of possessing integrity, compassion, and a commitment to helping others. This strong commitment is extended to everyone; Seton Hall welcomes students and faculty from all faiths.

http://www.shu.edu/

P: (800) 843-4255

PRIVATE - CATHOLIC

STUDENT PROFILE

6,090 undergraduate students

92% of undergrad students are full time

44% male – 56% female

84% freshman retention rate

63% graduated in 6 years

FACULTY PROFILE

503 full-time faculty

40 part-time faculty

13 to 1 student/faculty ratio

ADMISSIONS

14,108 Total Applicants

10,757 Total Admissions

1,406 Total Freshman Enrollment

76.25% of applicants admitted

SAT Ranges: CR 520-610, M 540-620

ACT Ranges: C 23-27, M 23-27, E 22-28

TUITION & COSTS

Tuition: $35,940

Fees: $2,132

Total: $38,072

R&B: $14,154

Room: $9,012

Board: $5,142

Total: $52,226

FINANCIAL

$22,476 avg grant/scholarship amount (total)

$10,774 avg loan amount (total)

THE COLLEGE OF NEW JERSEY

EWING TOWNSHIP, NEW JERSEY

The College of New Jersey is on a mission to keep the most talented students from NJ within their home state for their college education. The College combines the best practices of the finest private institutions with a public mission. TCNJ is located in the suburb of Ewing. Students can see shows, hear performances, observe an art gallery, and get involved in the local television and radio stations. Along with a slew of outdoor activities, Ewing offers countless outlets for both academic and personal growth.

THE FIRST-YEAR EXPERIENCE: The First-Year Experience (FYE) at TCNJ is an introductory program that explores the foundations of reading, writing, and critical thinking. The FYE is considered a transitional period in which students can get a feel for college academics and new social demands as they settle into their new home. This program is a mixture of classes and co-curricular activities that bring students together to promote a supportive environment. First-Year Seminars (FSPs) allow students to explore a topic of interest outside their major, designed to promote conversation and collaboration among students and faculty alike. TCNJ views this experience as a perfect introduction to college-level academics, and many students find the seminars useful for developing key reading, writing, and speaking skills.

COMMUNITY-ENGAGED LEARNING: The Community-Engaged Learning (CEL) component of the FYE commits each first-year student to a minimum of 8 hours of highly valuable service. TCNJ is dedicated to service and views helping others as an integral part of the undergraduate experience. CEL introduces students to the experience of volunteerism and community awareness, creating a drive of helpful citizenship that lasts throughout college. There are two different tracks for fulfilling the requirement: curricular and co-curricular. On the curricular track, students work with professors as an extension of their FSP. And on the co-curricular track, students engage in community service that is organized by interest or residence opportunities.

BONNER INSTITUTE FOR CIVIC AND COMMUNITY ENGAGEMENT: TCNJ's Bonner Institute is responsible for connecting students, faculty, and staff to service opportunities both in and outside of the campus. The Institute addresses a wide array of social issues, ranging from poverty to environmental needs. One component of the program is the Bonner Community Scholars Corps, a small group of highly committed students who receive academic scholarship for their engagement. Scholars are also responsible for motivating the campus community to get involved.

STUDY ABROAD: TCNJ has a plethora of study abroad options that range in both duration and destination. Each student is bound to find the program that best suits their needs and desires, as the College offers multiple options throughout the year. The College has designated programs for winter, summer, and semester trips, each of which offer similar benefits in cross-cultural communication, independence, and global education. Throughout the winter and summer sessions, faculty lead TCNJ students on intensive study abroad experiences to extend their fields of study beyond the home campus and into various destinations around the world. These short-term programs allow faculty to have their students focus intensely on one topic, all while guiding them along the journey of a lifetime.

THE HONORS PROGRAM: The TCNJ Honors program is specially designed to challenge academically gifted students. Participants enjoy an intimate community of intellectual leaders and peers, engaging in exciting, advanced coursework in small-class settings. They also benefit from graduate school preparation, access to exclusive fellowship opportunities, and an incredible advantage in the development of their leadership skills.

http://www.tcnj.edu/
P: (609) 771-1855

PUBLIC

STUDENT PROFILE

6,758 undergraduate students

96% of undergrad students are full time

41% male – 59% female

7% of students are from out of state

95% freshman retention rate

85% graduated in 6 years

FACULTY PROFILE

376 full-time faculty

498 part-time faculty

13 to 1 student/faculty ratio

ADMISSIONS

11,290 Total Applicants

5,495 Total Admissions

1,453 Total Freshman Enrollment

48.67% of applicants admitted

SAT Ranges: CR 550-640, M 570-670, W 550-650

ACT Ranges: C 26-30, M 25-30

TUITION & COSTS

Tuition: (In) $10,879 (Out) $21,810

Fees: $4,587

Total: (In) $15,466 (Out) $26,397

R&B: $12,497

Room: $8,621

Board: $3,876

Total: (In) $27,963 (Out) $38,894

FINANCIAL

$9,795 avg grant/scholarship amount (total)

$9,664 avg loan amount (total)

ADELPHI UNIVERSITY

GARDEN CITY, NEW YORK

Adelphi University provides students with a personalized, global learning experience that fully prepares them for successful, fulfilling careers. Adelphi students graduate with the knowledge and experience to compete and excel in their chosen fields as well as the skills to address the needs of their communities. With an ethnically diverse student body, hailing from 36 states and 47 countries, Adelphi provides an atmosphere that encourages both cultural exchange and personal and professional growth. Students also benefit from the rich intellectual and social opportunity of nearby New York City.

HIGH-IMPACT LEARNING: Internship opportunities are available for every type of student regardless of major. Through the signature Jaggar Community Fellows Program, students can be paired with nonprofit organizations across Long Island and New York City for 10-week, paid summer internships, or they can travel to their choice of more than 90 destinations in 40 countries through study abroad. Students can live and study in Europe, Asia, Latin America, Australia, or New Zealand for either one semester or a full year. They may also participate in a variety of short, faculty-led trips to Europe, Asia, and Central America as well as alternative spring break adventures to serve in such places as Costa Rica and the Dominican Republic.

FRESHMAN COMMUNITY ACTION PROGRAM: Even before they begin to take classes, Adelphi students understand their connection to the community. The Freshman Community Action Program (FCAP), for example, offers incoming freshmen experiential opportunities right from the start. To emphasize community service as a hallmark of an Adelphi education, FCAP engages first-year students with a week-long experience of volunteer work with local organizations. Adelphi has earned the Community Engagement Classification from the Carnegie Foundation and has been named to the President's Higher Education Community Service Honor Roll.

UNDERGRADUATE RESEARCH: Adelphi takes great pride in providing undergraduate students with a variety of opportunities to pursue original research. At its annual Research Conference, the University shows its enthusiasm by celebrating faculty-mentored research by students in virtually every discipline, from psychology to physics. Through its McDonell Fellowship Program, Adelphi even sponsors undergraduates to pursue full-time research during the summer. Honors College students are also eligible for sponsored summer research fellowships in any discipline, and undergrads in the Derner School of Psychology are supported through the yearlong Emerging Scholars Program.

FIRST-YEAR SEMINAR: One of the most exciting and intellectually challenging aspects of the first-year experience at Adelphi is the First-Year Seminar (FYS). Each year, faculty from across the University create seminar courses that are are related to topics they are passionate about. All seminars focus on the reading of college-level, theoretical material and it underlying questions, implications, and significance. Along the way, seminar participants become teachers themselves, leading class discussions and giving presentations. This focus on reading, writing, and public speaking reflects Adelphi's commitment to building effective citizens and leaders. Additionally, a first-year English composition course allows new students to hone the writing skills that are essential to clear thinking and communication.

SENIOR CAPSTONE: Adelphi is relentlessly dedicated to fostering the success of its students in college and beyond. All Adelphi undergraduates complete a capstone course or project as part of their major, which may manifest as a portfolio of creative projects, a senior seminar, or a significant research paper. The goal of this culminating capstone is to give students the chance to recognize and demonstrate their learning in a comprehensive and meaningful way.

http://www.adelphi.edu/
P: (800) 233-5744

PRIVATE

STUDENT PROFILE

3,313 undergraduate students

91% of undergrad students are full time

32% male – 68% female

7% of students are from out of state

83% freshman retention rate

68% graduated in 6 years

FACULTY PROFILE

320 full-time faculty

704 part-time faculty

11.8 to 1 student/faculty ratio

ADMISSIONS

11,863 Total Applicants

8,339 Total Admissions

1,226 Total Freshmen Enrollment

70.29% of applicants admitted

SAT Ranges: CR 500-600 , M 510-610

ACT Ranges: C 22-27 , M 22-27, E 21-28

TUITION & COSTS

Tuition: $34,000

Fees: $1,740

Total: $35,740

R&B: $14,052

Total: $49,792

FINANCIAL

$15,855 avg grant/scholarship amount (need)

$4,344 avg loan amount (need)

BINGHAMTON UNIVERSITY

BINGHAMTON, NEW YORK

Binghamton offers a wide array of personal and academic opportunities that range from international education to research initiatives. The University's commitment to student success is of paramount importance, and students are given the tools they need to excel and make a difference.

EMERGING LEADERS PROGRAM: The Emerging Leaders Program (ELP) is great for students who are seeking extra leadership experience. This certificate program spans over the course of a semester and connects participants with the University and community at large. ELP takes place throughout the first semester of college, allowing students to gain valuable skills very early on in their college careers. All students who participate are part of a "knowledge community" (KC), each of which is comprised of approximately 13 students. KCs are led by their own faculty advisors, professional staff program advisors, and peer mentors. ELP students are involved in a series of activities that promote success, gaining experience and building their network as they partake in leadership workshops.

GLOBAL GATEWAY: Binghamton students have the opportunity to study abroad, as early as the summer after freshman year and as late as the summer after graduation. There are plenty of programs to choose from, many of which allow students to take classes that offer transferable credit toward their major. Some programs include: "Chile–Doing Business in Emerging Markets," "Dominican Republic–Community Health," and "Morocco–Arabic Language and North African Studies."

CENTERS FOR SUCCESS: Binghamton offers many helpful resources that arm students with any supplemental assistance they may need in order to be the best student they can be. Binghamton's Public Speaking Lab, for example, provide the platform for students to develop their oral communication skills. PSL consultants work with students to increase their familiarity and comfort with oral presentations and public speaking. In this comfortable environment, students can excel as orators with the help of caring PSL staff. The Writing Center is another incredibly helpful department. Tutors are available to assist with any assignment across all disciplines and perform a wide array of services meant to help students with their progress. Tutors can help students better understand an assignment, develop a thesis, properly cite a source, and execute their arguments skillfully on paper.

CAREER SERVICES: Plenty of colleges and universities have career services offices, but Binghamton goes above and beyond. The Career Services office regularly holds career fairs and workshops on such relevant topics as interviewing skills and résumé building. These workshops are a great way for students to gain hands-on experience and build their confidence as future job hunters. In so many cases, students fear their first few interviews due to the new, intense levels of pressure that come with the job search. To combat the nerves, Binghamton calmly guides students through practice interviews and strategies.

INVOLVEMENT TRANSCRIPT: The Involvement Transcript is a record of all extracurricular activities in which students engage throughout college. This is a great way for employers to see how students have been active outside the classroom, showcasing their motivations as active citizens and community members. Students can include the activities in which they've acted as a leader, a volunteer, or even as a general member. No matter what, any out-of-the-classroom participation shows employers how their job candidates take advantage of their free time.

---

http://www.binghamton.edu/
P: (607) 777-2000

PUBLIC

STUDENT PROFILE

13,465 undergraduate students

97% of undergrad students are full-time

52% male – 48% female

8% of students are from out of state

91% freshman retention rate

81% graduated in 6 years

FACULTY PROFILE

689 full-time faculty

289 part-time faculty

20 to 1 student-to-faculty ratio

ADMISSIONS

30,616 Total Applicants

13,010 Total Admissions

2,661 Total Freshman Enrollment

42.49% of applicants admitted

SAT Ranges: CR 600-680, M 630-703

ACT Ranges: C 27-31

TUITION & COSTS

Tuition: (In) $6,470 (Out) $19,590

Fees: $2,583

Total: (In) $9,053 (Out) $22,173

R&B: $13,198

Room: $8,632

Board: $4,566

Total: (In) $22,251 (Out) $35,371

FINANCIAL

$8,551 avg grant/scholarship amount (need)

$4,987 avg loan amount (need)

CANISIUS COLLEGE

BUFFALO, NEW YORK

Canisius students receive a transformational education. They work with professors on world-changing research projects, participate in a rigorous academic curriculum, and actively create a better community on both a local and global scale. The College is not just a place from which to earn a degree, but rather a haven for success and true education. Students who are fascinated by the world and curious about their place in it are bound to thrive at Canisius.

SERVICE-LEARNING: As a Jesuit institution, Canisius College maintains a philosophy that is embedded with service to the community. And, with the economic and social issues that are typical of urban environments, the city of Buffalo has many areas of need to which students can contribute. In any given semester, faculty members can be found guiding hundreds of students from over 70 class sections at a time to apply their classroom learning to a wide variety of community-building endeavors. For example, business students have planned, organized, and managed a project to benefit a not-for-profit, while education students have transformed a barren elementary school courtyard into an urban oasis/outdoor teaching environment. Others have helped immigrants prepare for job interviews, tutored school children, and run workshops to prevent violence. The possibilities are endless.

RESEARCH: A junior biology major recently received an undergraduate research fellowship from the American Society of Plant Biology and presented his work at the group's international meeting, and another group of students produced a national award-winning video on Sri Lankan elephants. These successes are not at all unusual at Canisius; students in math, science, psychology, and other fields engage in meaningful hands-on research all the time. They regularly publish papers in professional journals and attend and present at major conferences. Field research has taken students to South Dakota, Ontario, Costa Rica, Bhutan, the Himalayas, the Galapagos Islands, and many other locales.

CAMPUS ENVIRONMENT: Canisius' environment and close-knit community encourages all to plunge in. There are more than 100 student organizations; 16 NCAA Division I athletic teams; numerous on-campus lectures, events, and activities; and countless off-campus diversions. It's no wonder that the majority of students live on campus; 85% of student residences are newly renovated, and all the outlets to have fun are surrounding all of the College's dorms, townhouses, and apartments! What's more, New York's second largest city of Buffalo is a vibrant college town. Live music and theatre, clubs, restaurants, shops, professional sports, museums, and the spectacular Frederick Law Olmsted-designed park are all right on Canisius' doorstep. Lake Erie beaches, Niagara Falls, and fabulous ski slopes are all nearby as well.

UNLIMITED POSSIBILITIES: At Canisius, students can choose from more than 125 majors, minors, and special programs, enjoying a flexible curriculum that can be catered to their overall goals. Dual and even triple majors are encouraged, the combinations of which range from mainstream to ingenious. Inspired students have mixed digital media arts with psychology, music with political science, biology with studio art, and English with European studies and international business.

STUDY ABROAD: Sure, most colleges offer study in foreign countries, but at Canisius the experiences are both varied and exceptional. Taking advantage of opportunities in more than a dozen countries, students can spend a few weeks or a whole semester abroad. A couple of examples include interning with Parliament in London and teaching English to school kids in Poland, France, or China. Some students can even extend their stay in Europe through their participation in EuroSim, an international competition that simulates the European Union. From pre-trip orientations to post-trip evaluations, Canisius offers extraordinary resources for students who wish to travel abroad.

http://www.canisius.edu/

P: (800) 843-1517

PRIVATE - CATHOLIC

STUDENT PROFILE

2,671 undergraduate students

95% of undergrad students are full time

46% male – 54% female

83% freshman retention rate

70% graduated in 6 years

FACULTY PROFILE

198 full-time faculty

227 part-time faculty

11 to 1 student/faculty ratio

ADMISSIONS

4,209 Total Applicants

3,661 Total Admissions

605 Total Freshman Enrollment

86.98% of applicants admitted

SAT Ranges: CR 470-580, M 480-600

ACT Ranges: C 21-27

TUITION & COSTS

Tuition: $33,282

Fees: $1,408

Total: $34,690

R&B: $12,766

Room: $7,500

Board: $5,266

Total: $47,456

FINANCIAL

$26,854 avg grant/scholarship amount (total)

$8,178 avg loan amount (total)

COLLEGE OF MOUNT SAINT VINCENT

BRONX, NEW YORK

The College of Mount Saint Vincent seeks to engage the development of the whole person. Every field of study emphasizes analytical skills; critical thinking; clear communication; and moral and religious thought—essentials for success in every profession. The Mount offers over 70 nationally recognized degree programs and course offerings, including majors and minors in the sciences and mathematics, humanities and the arts, social sciences, accounting, business, communication, education, and nursing, among others.

FIRST-YEAR EXPERIENCE (FYE): Individually paired with a faculty advisor, freshmen enjoy an introduction to college life through the Mount's freshman seminar course, FYE, while familiarizing themselves with their academic expectations and support systems. Students are also encouraged to immerse themselves in clubs, organizations, and other events through student activities. Finally, they also coordinate a community-building service project to help others beyond the Mount's walls.

CENTER FOR UNDERGRADUATE RESEARCH: Through the Center for Undergraduate Research, students produce original work that they may present at both national and international conferences. These incredible research experiences allow students to develop a range of skills, encourage them to develop their expertise in their area of study, and prepare them for graduate studies and future employment.

STUDY ABROAD: The Mount provides students the opportunity to study abroad in more than a dozen countries, including England, France, Greece, Italy, Peru, Spain, Turkey, and Vietnam. Students live and learn internationally to enhance their development as global citizens through a variety of semester-long and short-term programs. By studying abroad, they get to enrich their academic studies, expand their perspectives, gain valuable work skills, and build their intercultural competence.

SETON SERVICE AND LEADERSHIP PROGRAM: The Seton Service and Leadership Program welcomes Mount students to join a like-minded community of peers who serve together and foster important leadership skills. Students of all backgrounds find commonality in service as they engage in frequent spiritual and faith-based reflection to contemplate life's biggest questions.

MOUNT MENTORS: The College connects accomplished industry leaders with academically outstanding students through the Mount Mentors program. Providing students the opportunity to refine their professional skills and valuable networking resources, this program helps develop lasting relationships and emphasizes the transferability of skills outside the classroom.

STUDENT ACTIVITIES: Mount students immerse themselves in a diverse and supportive community that changes the way they think and helps them realize what matters most. The Office of Student Activities, Leadership, and Commuter Life plans numerous extracurricular events, trips, and activities. Not only does it host its own events, but it also provides discounted ticket to Broadway shows, games, concerts, and other events. Beyond the Office, the Mount's Student Activities offers more than 35 different clubs and organizations, covering such interests as community service, journalism, acting, creative writing, dance, art, cultural awareness, sports management, athletics, film and TV production, history, business, finance, and environmentalism, among many others.

SERVICE: Many Mount clubs support an array of community service initiatives, including A Moment of Magic Foundation and Be You Stay True. A Moment of Magic Foundation is a student-led nonprofit organization that invites volunteers to dress as popular characters and visit children in need—in hospitals, schools, camps, and social services agencies—throughout New York and beyond. Be You Stay True hosts a free annual basketball camp each summer as well as numerous skills competitions throughout the year in partnership with the Jr. NBA. The Mount also partners with local service agencies and supports some of the most disadvantaged populations across New York City. It is no wonder why Mount students are so highly recognized as impressive servants.

https://mountsaintvincent.edu/

P: (718) 405-3200

PRIVATE - CATHOLIC

STUDENT PROFILE

1,683 undergraduate students

94% of undergrad students are full time

30% male — 70% female

12% of students are from out of state

77.6% freshman retention rate

54.6% graduated in 6 years

FACULTY PROFILE

80 full-time faculty

165 part-time faculty

13 to 1 student/faculty ratio

ADMISSIONS

2,667 Total Applicants

2,471 Total Admissions

436 Total Freshman Enrollment

92.65% of applicants admitted

SAT Ranges: CR 400-490, M 380-490

ACT Ranges: C 17-22, M 16-22, E 16.22

TUITION & COSTS

Tuition: $35,620

R&B: $9,500

Total: $45,120

FINANCIAL

$22,229 avg grant/scholarship amount (total)

$7,655 avg loan amount (total)

CONCORDIA COLLEGE NEW YORK

BRONXVILLE, NEW YORK

Concordia College is a small, diverse, co-educational liberal arts college located in suburban Westchester County, New York. Concordia aspires to enhance the lives of students by weaving together academics, vibrant student life, experiential learning opportunities, co-curricular programs, and campus spiritual life into a tapestry of lifelong learning. Concordia is the perfect home for students who participate actively in their education, want to be involved in lots of activities, seek a broad-based education, and seek a supportive, Christian-based community.

A HOME OF BEAUTY: Concordia's beautiful, residential campus is set in the tranquil village of Bronxville. The century-old campus features nearly 30 buildings, including original "College Gothic" structures designed by the architect who designed Ellis Island, a world-class worship and performance hall, a state-of-the-art academic center and library, on-and-off campus residence halls, and awesome athletic facilities, all set in immaculately landscaped grounds.

NIGHTLIFE IN NEW YORK CITY: Concordia's proximity to New York City is one of its biggest advantages for students. The Student Life Office offers free bus shuttles directly into the heart of Manhattan, placing students directly near museums, Broadway, good food, and shopping. Various clubs also sponsor such city excursions as the annual trip Rockefeller Center during the holiday season and an excursion through Chinatown with the International Club.

SPRING WEEKEND: The annual Spring Weekend celebration is filled with many exciting events. Dozens of student-led and local bands are invited to take part in Band Bash, which is a full day of music, games, food, and festivities that last well into the night. The weekend also includes a Fashion Show organized by the Multicultural Club.

DIVERSE CURRICULUM: The curriculum at Concordia College New York is ideal for students who are interested in interdisciplinary or cross-disciplinary education. With New York City an arm's length away, Concordia has the ability to weave the appeal of the Big Apple into the advantages of a small school environment. Concordia students encounter a community in which questions are as important as answers. And with a curriculum where all fields of knowledge intersect, they gain real-world experiences that alter the course of their lives. The school's liberal arts philosophy is built on the history of human experience, supporting a Christian community in which the multicolored fabric of diversity thrives.

DEDICATED PROFESSORS: Concordia students enjoy individualized interactions with their professors in a small, supportive community. This is an institution in which educators focus on each student's interests and goals, supporting educational programs that are tailored to each student. Students can expect nothing but the best from their professors, all of whom are accomplished scholars dedicated first and foremost to their students. Whether they walk a student through a theory, help in landing an internship in the city, share a cup of coffee while chatting about finals, or help to organize a community service project, Concordia's faculty are available for guidance to anyone who aspires to become a person of confidence, character, and courage.

COMMITMENT TO RESPECT: Concordia aims to create an environment through which students' worldviews and perspectives are broadened to reflect a world that is increasingly shedding its boundaries. It is the College's desire that each student develop a global perspective on human issues and thereby be able to understand and appreciate the rich diversity of God's creation. In return, the College expects its student to adopt a healthy sense of respect for themselves and others as well as to develop a sense of reverence for God and His magnificent creation. It is this compassion for others, alongside this sense of wonder, that provides life with deep and lasting meaning.

http://www.concordia-ny.edu/

P: (914) 337-9300

PRIVATE - CHRISTIAN

STUDENT PROFILE

958 undergraduate students

84% of undergrad students are full time

32% male – 68% female

20% of students are from out of state

71% freshman retention rate

41% graduated in 6 years

FACULTY PROFILE

52 full-time faculty

96 part-time faculty

14 to 1 student/faculty ratio

ADMISSIONS

1024 Total Applicants

776 Total Admissions

74.77% of applicants admitted

SAT Ranges: CR 380-470, M 380-490, W 390-470

ACT Ranges: C 17-22, M 16-23, E 16-23

TUITION & COSTS

Tuition: $27,740

Fees: $1,065

Total: $28,805

R&B: $10,530

Room: $5,685

Board: $4,845

Total: $39,335

FINANCIAL

$19,844 avg grant/scholarship amount (total)

$7,117 avg loan amount (total)

D'YOUVILLE COLLEGE

BUFFALO, NEW YORK

D'Youville College is a community of thinkers and doers that is collectively committed to working for the common good. The College believes that students should learn how to think critically, work with others, be leaders, and communicate effectively in order to translate their education into a successful and meaningful career.

D'YOUVILLE CARES: Every year, students, faculty, and staff provide over 6,000 hours of community service to a diverse range of organizations that are helping to make the world a better place. Recent opportunities to care for the local and global community include medical mission trips to the Dominican Republic during winter break; pharmaceutical assistance at the local community center; and the annual Lending a Hand trip to support service organizations in New Orleans. Through these opportunities, students are living out the College's mission to lead compassionate lives.

STUDY ABROAD: Study abroad opportunities exist for all D'Youville students to travel to 7 major cities, including London, Florence, Dublin, Istanbul, Beijing, Buenos Aires, and Sydney. In addition, faculty-led study abroad programs can take students to places like Hungary and Ireland, and mission trips for faithful service travel to Haiti, the Dominican Republic, and more.

INTERPROFESSIONAL CLINICAL ADVANCEMENT CENTER: Students in D'Youville's healthcare programs can participate in a unique, hands-on learning experience in the Interprofessional Clinical Advancement Center. The Interprofessional Clinical Advancement Center is a research and academic project that uses professional actors to create real-life patient-care simulations for students. To date, over 1,500 health-profession students have graduated from D'Youville having utilized these resources to learn how to provide patient-centered care.

FACULTY MENTORSHIP AND RESEARCH: At D'Youville College, every professor aims to make their students successful in their careers. The accessible faculty, small classes, and comprehensive student-support programs set students up for success, no matter the challenge. And, with the help and guidance of their faculty mentors, students at every level—including undergraduates—can be involved in thought-provoking research. They have opportunities to conduct research alongside faculty; present research results at regional, national, and international conferences; participate in clinical settings to test new theories and practice; and learn the techniques for collecting, analyzing, and interpreting data for meaningful applications.

STUDENT ACTIVITIES: D'Youville offers 25 student-run organizations on campus, which include academically related organizations as well as cultural and recreational clubs. These groups of students sponsor a myriad of campus events and support travel to conferences and workshops. On-campus programs include the International Fiesta, Moving Up Days, Black History Month, and events that host guest speakers and entertainers. Additionally, the campus houses a professional theater at which students can watch performances for free.

LOCATION, LOCATION, LOCATION: D'Youville is minutes from the booming Buffalo Niagara Medical Campus. The Buffalo Niagara Medical Campus is a consortium of the region's premier healthcare, life sciences research, and medical education institutions. D'Youville students in the College's health care programs have the opportunity to participate in the innovative and cutting-edge efforts through clinical and fieldwork placements, and many others can even research alongside professors and real-world practitioners. D'Youville College is minutes away from a vibrant theatre district as well as the Allentown and Elmwood Village sections of Buffalo. The City of Buffalo is undergoing a rebirth, and D'Youville is located right in the middle of exciting developments. The surrounding towns host a variety of shops, art galleries, festivals, and restaurants. The Peace Bridge connection to Canada is 3 blocks from the campus, and the metropolitan area of Toronto is 90 miles away.

---

http://www.dyc.edu/

P: (716) 829-8000

PRIVATE PUBLIC

STUDENT PROFILE

2,292 undergraduate students

78% of undergrad students are full time

28% male – 72% female

9% of students are from out of state

80% freshman retention rate

FACULTY PROFILE

185 full-time faculty

121 part-time faculty

9 to 1 student/faculty ratio

ADMISSIONS

1,220 Total Applicants

891 Total Admissions

329 Total Freshman Enrollment

73.03% of applicants admitted

SAT Ranges: CR 460-550, M 460-560, W 440-530

ACT Ranges: C 21-25, M 19-25, E 19-24

TUITION & COSTS

Tuition: $24,370

R&B: $11,180

Total: $35,550

FINANCIAL

$15,026 avg grant/scholarship amount (need)

DAEMEN COLLEGE

AMHERST, NEW YORK

Daemen is built on a strong foundation in the liberal arts. It is a student-centered College with dedicated, highly qualified faculty who value personalized teaching and intellectual excellence. The College prepares students for 21st-century careers by offering rigorous academic programs that develop the liberal arts-based skills necessary for lifelong learning and intellectual growth.

STUDY ABROAD: In today's global economy, it makes sense to learn all one can about different cultures, political systems, and histories. International study is strongly encouraged with a generous selection of semesters abroad, summer programs, and accelerated January-term trips. Daemen's Global Programs office coordinates distinctive global programs in Europe, Asia, Latin America/ Caribbean, and Africa, all of which are designed to facilitate students' professional aspirations.

LEADERSHIP: Daemen College's LEADS Center serves as a clearinghouse for students aspiring to realize and develop their leadership skills. The LEADS program affords Daemen students the knowledge, skills, and experiences necessary to bring purpose, meaning, and integrity into their lives and the lives of others. The program emphasizes lifelong learning through interdisciplinary programs that provide and encourage the development of the self, ultimately fostering inclusive, collaborative relationships.

SERVICE-LEARNING: Daemen believes in "learning through service." Throughout their time at Daemen, virtually all undergraduate students engage in a number various service-learning activities. Students from every major and class level participate in short- and long-term projects that benefit the local, national, and global communities, working with environmental organizations, refugee groups, environmental agencies, nursing homes, hospitals and clinics, tutoring and mentoring programs in city schools, and more.

STUDENT-CENTERED: Daemen offers an innovative Plus Pathway Program to enhance its already astounding liberal arts degree. The +PLUS Pathways, outlets for experiential learning, are fully integrated into the individual curriculum so that every student can put their knowledge into action. Students focus on an interdisciplinary series of courses that are designed to prepare them for their future careers, learning to apply their critical-thinking, writing, and communication skills to real-world experiences.

LEARNING COMMUNITIES: Daemen offers core curriculum courses to freshmen in a format known as Learning Communities. This format allows students to move through the first year of their college career alongside small-group peers, promoting community bonding among people from different backgrounds and with different majors and extracurricular interests. In a learning community, a common topic, issue, or subject is studied from the perspective of two or more disciplines, making for a broader, richer learning experience.

RESEARCH THINK TANK: The Student/Faculty Interdisciplinary Think Tank offers students the opportunity to work with faculty members on significant research projects. Students who participate receive research scholarships and get acknowledged for their work through publications, showings, presentations, or other forms of public recognition.

CAREER SERVICES: Career Services works with students to create Individual Career Action Plans (iCAP), helping them find internships to gain real-world experiences in their areas of interest. Employers who are in contact with Career Services include those in business, the sports industry, the arts, government, health-related entities, nonprofits, educational institutions, and cultural organizations. These opportunities are local, national, and even international!

http://www.daemen.edu/
P: (716) 839-8225

PRIVATE

STUDENT PROFILE

1,884 undergraduate students

86% of undergrad students are full time

32% male – 68% female

58% of students are from out of state

79% freshman retention rate

55.5% graduated in 6 years

FACULTY PROFILE

143 full-time faculty

165 part-time faculty

12 to 1 student-to-faculty ratio

ADMISSIONS

3,175 Total Applicants

1,670 Total Admissions

478 Total Freshman Enrollment

52.60% of applicants admitted

SAT Ranges: CR 450-570, M 470-590

ACT Ranges: C 21-27

TUITION & COSTS

Tuition: $27,450

Fees: $540

Total: $27,990

R&B: $12,346

Total: $40,336

FINANCIAL

$11,070 avg grant/scholarship amount (need)

$4,671 avg loan amount (need)

DOMINICAN COLLEGE

ORANGEBURG, NEW YORK

DOMINICAN COLLEGE

Since 1952, Dominican College has fostered an environment that cultivates unique bonds and lifelong relationships. It is a welcome community in which personal connections share center stage with academics. There are many reasons why students from all over the world choose Dominican College; the small, personal classes translate into a highly individualized educational experience for each student, and its convenient location in the scenic Hudson Valley area, just 17 miles from New York City, feels like a home away from home.

DEVELOPING THE WHOLE STUDENT: Dominican College is committed to developing the whole student. It recognizes that a true education not only promotes critical thinking and informed judgement, but it also addresses emotional, physical, and spiritual development. For this reason, students can find a wide range of activities, including social clubs, honor societies, service organizations, campus ministry, and student chapters of professional organizations. Dominican College's NCAA Division II athletics program is recognized as one of the finest among small colleges in the region.

THE FRESHMAN YEAR PROGRAM: The Freshman Year Program makes the transition to College life easier. It is run by a select group of faculty, administrators, and peer mentors who provide one-on-one advising throughout the academic year, help new students to adjust to college life, and monitor their academic progress. Individualized attention is given to each new freshman who enters Dominican College, assisting them to form and solidify their aspirations for their education and career. Freshman Orientation, Freshman Convocation, the Freshman Seminar, and Freshman Interest Groups all form a sturdy foundation so that first-year students feel comfortable and supported as they embark on their new collegiate journey.

SERVICE-LEARNING: Service is central to the Dominican experience, and the College is bustling with students who have the energy, ability, and the desire to make a real difference in the world. Whether they are studying social work or athletic training, Dominican College students are making positive change with a commitment to social justice. Service-learning is an additional offering that couples community service projects with classroom learning, providing academic credit while engaging students with community beautification projects, assistance to people who are homeless, Sister Cities Project, Light the Night, Walk for the Cure, Relay for Life, and more.

CENTRALLY LOCATED: Dominican College's provides a wealth of entertainment and cultural opportunities just a short trip away. Its campus is less than 30 minutes from the world-class attractions of New York City: Madison Square Garden, Broadway, Museum Mile, and more are all within easy reach of the campus. The school is also a short distance from the military academy at West Point, the Meadowlands, and Yankee and Shea stadiums. Rockland County offers the quaint shops of Nyack and Piermont, art galleries, sporting events, theatre productions, and musical performances. In addition, the Palisades Center, the nation's second largest mall, is just down the road.

INTERNSHIPS: Internships provide a link to the world beyond college, offering the chance for students to gain practical experience in their fields of study. The College's location provides excellent access to internship and career opportunities throughout the metropolitan area. These experiences help students prepare for their postgraduate lives by giving them hands-on work in business, industry, non-profit organizations, and government. They expand the educational experience by presenting students with the chance to apply the theories they learn in the classroom to actual practice in the workplace.

http://www.dc.edu/
P: (848) 848-7800

PRIVATE

STUDENT PROFILE

1,552 undergraduate students

87% of undergrad students are full time

34% male – 66% female

71% freshman retention rate

46% graduated in 6 years

FACULTY PROFILE

75 full-time faculty

135 part-time faculty

16 to 1 student/faculty ratio

ADMISSIONS

1,959 Total Applicants

1,400 Total Admissions

365 Total Freshman Enrollment

71.47% of applicants admitted

SAT Ranges: CR 390-480, M 390-490, W 390-480

ACT Ranges: C 17-21

TUITION & COSTS

Tuition: $25,680

Fees: $770

Total: $26,450

R&B: $12,120

Total: $38,570

FINANCIAL

$17,712 avg grant/scholarship amount (total)

$6,708 avg loan amount (total)

ELMIRA COLLEGE

ELMIRA, NEW YORK

ELMIRA COLLEGE

A national, top-tier liberal arts college founded in 1855, Elmira College is proud of its longstanding reputation for academic distinction. From the very beginning, Elmira has placed its focus on academic rigor. It was, in fact, the first college for women to execute a course of study equal in rigor to the best men's colleges of the time. Today, as a co-educational institution, Elmira continues to excel with the same dedication to opportunity, challenge, and success.

FIRST-YEAR SEMINAR: Elmira College's First-Year Seminar (FYS) program is the foundational course for all entering freshmen. The FYS introduces students to the wider world of learning beyond that of the specialized training of their declared majors. This seminar focuses on sharpening students' skills in critical thinking and reading. While many of the nation's colleges only offer one general first-year course, Elmira students are able to build their FYS foundation with their choice from a wide variety of seminar topics, ranging from the natural sciences and the humanities to the fine arts and the social sciences.

UNDERGRADUATE RESEARCH: Throughout their years at Elmira College, students are actively engaged in undergraduate research alongside their classmates and professors. For example, business students construct business plans for real clients, including product and marketing strategies. And in science courses, students conduct undergraduate research with their professors and, many times, present at state, regional, and national conferences.

STUDY ABROAD: Elmira College partners with Regent's University London to offer a 12-week study abroad option in the heart of London, England. The Elmira College/Regent's University partnership provides students the chance to spend a term living and learning in one of the world's preeminent capitals, all while exchanging ideas with students from around the world and earning academic credit toward their Elmira degrees.

ACADEMIC WRITING PROGRAM: The Academic Writing Program at Elmira College is designed to help incoming students acclimate to college-level communication, a skill they must continue to develop in order to succeed both during and after college. Through classroom instruction, in-class writing workshops, and occasional one-on-one conferences with their instructors, students learn to become more independent writers and thinkers who are better prepared to take on any academic or professional challenge.

JULIA REINSTEIN '28 SYMPOSIUM: Each year, the Women's and Gender Studies Program organizes the weeklong Julia Reinstein '28 Symposium, made possible by a bequest from Elima alumna Julia Reinstein '28, a feminist, early lesbian activist, and strong supporter of women's issues. In cooperation with Students Against Sexism and Stereotypes (SASS), the Symposium annually features a different theme and keynote speaker.

SCHOOL SPIRIT: Elmira College values its many traditions. Love for the College's purple and gold colors, songs, shape (the Octagon), and flower (the Iris), connect students and alumni throughout the decades. When individuals link arms and sing the "Alma Mater" or participate in the beloved Mountain Day or Holiday Banquet, they are connecting to the spirit of Elmira College—a spirit that spans generations of Elmira College alumni, family, and friends.

COMMUNITY SERVICE AND INTERNSHIPS: Elmira College is committed to the ideals of community service, personal empowerment, and individual growth. To that end, each student completes a career-related internship and a minimum of 60 hours of community service. These programs provide students with hands-on experience that often results in postgraduate opportunities. Elmira students contribute nearly 16,000 hours of service each year, altogether strengthening students' personal growth and the connections between the College and its surrounding communities. The Office of Career Services annually hosts the Excellence in Community Service Luncheon, which highlights the importance of volunteerism and recognizes students and student clubs for their exceptional service and impact.

https://www.elmira.edu/

P: (800) 935-6472

PRIVATE

STUDENT PROFILE

1,252 undergraduate students

90% of undergrad students are full time

31% male — 69% female

44% of students are from out of state

79% freshman retention rate

63% graduated in 6 years

FACULTY PROFILE

67 full-time faculty

103 part-time faculty

12 to 1 student/faculty ratio

ADMISSIONS

2,387 Total Applicants

1,818 Total Admissions

258 Total Freshman Enrollment

76.16% of applicants admitted

SAT Ranges: CR 450-560, M 460-570

ACT Ranges: C 22-27

TUITION & COSTS

Tuition: $41,900

R&B: $12,000

Total: $53,900

FINANCIAL

$27,161 avg grant/scholarship amount (need)

$4,766 avg loan amount (need)

FORDHAM UNIVERSITY

NEW YORK, NEW YORK

Fordham University is a laboratory in which anyone can explore the deepest meaning and fullest measure of success. Through the Fordham experience, students acquire the knowledge, skills, confidence, and experience to succeed in their chosen field. The University offers both the firm foundation and the competitive edge that can make every student a leader at work and successful throughout their lives.

A COMMUNITY BUILT FOR EXCELLENCE: Strong orientation programs, special freshman seminars, and active faculty advising ensure a smooth transition to college life. Integrated learning communities in the residence halls on the Rose Hill campus give students the chance to collaborate with other students, staff, and faculty to design social, service, and educational activities and events throughout the year. Alternatively, the Lincoln Center campus features McMahon Hall, a 20-story complex that provides apartment-style living and great views of Manhattan. Fordham's state-of-the-art facilities also include one of the most technologically advanced libraries in the country.

WITHIN FORDHAM, WITHIN ONESELF: The best college experience is one that embraces a journey of self-discovery. At Fordham, every student has the opportunity to discover his or her true self through academics, service, spiritual reflection, and athletics.

TWO DISTINCT CAMPUSES: With its two distinct residential campuses—green and gothic Rose Hill, on 85 acres adjacent to the New York Botanical Garden and the Bronx Zoo, and cosmopolitan Lincoln Center, in the heart of Manhattan, across from the Lincoln Center for the Performing Arts— Fordham offers students virtually unlimited possibilities for learning and personal growth. Students often say, "New York is my campus. Fordham is my school."

THE OFFICE OF CAREER SERVICES AND INTERNSHIPS: Fordham attracts students from across the country and around the world, inviting all who is interested in and willing for a challenge the chance to live and learn in the global capital of commerce and culture. The University offers one of the most extensive internship programs in the country; students choose from more than 2,600 internship options in business, communications, education, government, healthcare, biomedical research, law, the arts, and other fields. The office of career services also offers workshops, career days, one-on-one career counseling, and on-campus interviews with major corporations. Students are known to compete for and earn prestigious fellowships and scholarships, including Fulbright, Truman, and Mellon scholarships. And each year, 4,000 students engage in community service, both locally and in distant corners of the world, through the University's award-winning global outreach program.

JESUIT EDUCATION: Fordham has a proud history rooted in the Jesuit tradition. Emphasizing cura personalis, a commitment to nurturing the whole person—mind, body, and spirit—Fordham challenges students to surpass their perceived limitations. This kind of education unites both heart and mind within and beyond the classroom.

WORLD-CLASS FACULTY: Fordham's world-class faculty are committed to teaching and research. In small classes, these scholars and mentors challenge students to develop to their full potential while giving each of them the individual attention he or she needs to excel. Every student also completes a rich core curriculum that spans literature, history, science, religion, the social sciences, and the arts. This curriculum is designed to nurture curiosity and inspire a lifelong love of learning.

LEADERS READY TO TRANSFORM THE WORLD: Fordham empowers students to pursue their dreams during and far beyond college. Through an extensive career-planning and -placement program, a large pool of proactive alumni, and a vast array of opportunities for real-world experiences, Fordham is proud to help its students find their place in the world.

---

http://www.fordham.edu/

P: (800) 367-3426

PRIVATE - CATHOLIC

STUDENT PROFILE

8,855 undergraduate students

94% of undergrad students are full time

44% male — 56% female

91% freshman retention rate

81% graduated in 6 years

FACULTY PROFILE

635 full-time faculty

14 to 1 student/faculty ratio

ADMISSIONS

42,811 Total Applicants

20,366 Total Admissions

2,211 Total Freshman Enrollment

47.57% of applicants admitted

SAT Ranges: CR 580-670, M 590-680, W 590-680

ACT Ranges: C 27-31, M 26-30, E 27-33, W 8-9

TUITION & COSTS

Tuition: $46,120

Fees: $812

Total: $46,932

R&B: $16,350

Total: $63,282

FINANCIAL

$25,564 avg grant/scholarship amount (total)

$8,427 avg loan amount (total)

HOFSTRA UNIVERSITY

HEMPSTEAD, NEW YORK

Every day on Hofstra's vibrant campus, dynamic students enrich, enlighten, and challenge one another both inside and outside the classroom. Hofstra's diverse and driven student body bring with them a wealth of knowledge, views, and experiences, thus enhancing the Hofstra experience for the entire campus community.

FIRST-YEAR CONNECTIONS: Hofstra's first-year seminars and clusters are designed to get students' college experiences off to a great start. At the heart of the freshman program are small classes taught by distinguished faculty from a range of disciplines. Not only do these courses introduce students to the intellectual and social life of the University, but nearly all of them also help satisfy the general education requirements for all majors.

DEDICATED FACULTY: Students are taught by Guggenheim Fellows and Fulbright scholars; Emmy Award recipients; prize-winning scientists; leaders in business, education, and the health sciences; and knowledgeable and insightful thinkers. Hofstra's 1,181 faculty members, 489 of whom are full-time, are experts in their fields and are dedicated to providing the foundation needed to succeed. Hofstra's faculty affirm the value of education; 93 percent of the full-time faculty hold the highest degree attainable in their fields. Plus, unlike many other schools, students at Hofstra learn from faculty, not graduate students.

UNDERGRADUATE RESEARCH: Hofstra faculty instruct students not only in content but also through methodical inquiry leads to new discoveries. Undergraduates engage in research at increasing degrees as they move from foundational courses to more advanced and closely defined topics. Serving as a capstone to a student's development within their major, Hofstra's undergraduate research is conducted in such places as the laboratory, the library, the studio, the stage, or the field. These projects can lead to graduate study or directly into professional life. Advanced research culminates in a public presentation of results on Undergraduate Research Day for the Hofstra community as well as at professional conferences.

STUDY ABROAD: Hofstra's Study Abroad program offers life-changing experiences that foster students' personal and academic growth. Students are challenged in new environments, developing lifelong friendships with new and exciting people from different backgrounds and cultures. They gain fluency in foreign languages and earn college credits, all while satisfying major, minor, or distribution requirements. Students also build their résumés and improve their knowledge of other cultures and international policy. Cultivating a global perspective of business, they learn how to communicate comfortably and socialize with people from other parts of the world.

LIVING-LEARNING COMMUNITIES: Hofstra offers eight thematic "living-learning communities" that are all associated with several first-year clusters and seminars, giving students the opportunity to live with many of the same classmates. They are joined together by a shared passion for such things as leadership, business, communications, math, science, and the arts. Students enjoy their class-based activities and events, but it is ultimately through the energetic living-learning communities that Hofstra students are intellectually stimulated and supported far beyond the classroom itself.

COMMUNITY SERVICE AND CIVIC ENGAGEMENT: Hofstra University has a strong focus on community service and civic engagement. The Office of Student Leadership and Engagement offers students many opportunities to volunteer for community service, and the Center for Civic Engagement at Hofstra encourages students to make a positive difference in the world through on-campus events, off-campus community partnerships, and curricular offerings. This center directs its attention to improving high school graduation rates, creating affordable housing for families, improving the health of area children, reducing bullying, increasing food security, and deepening grassroots democracy by protecting civil rights. Students can volunteer, take internships for academic credit, or become paid fellows.

http://www.hofstra.edu/

P: (516) 463-6700

PRIVATE

STUDENT PROFILE

6,810 undergraduate students

95% of undergrad students are full-time

45% male – 55% female

37% of students are from out of state

82% freshman retention rate

64% graduated in 6 years

FACULTY PROFILE

489 full-time faculty

692 part-time faculty

14 to 1 student-to-faculty ratio

ADMISSIONS

28,617 Total Applicants

17,806 Total Admissions

1,647 Total Freshman Enrollment

62.22% of applicants admitted

SAT Ranges: CR 530-630, M 540-630

ACT Ranges: C 24-29

TUITION & COSTS

Tuition: $42,900

Fees: $1,060

Total: $43,960

R&B: $14,930

Total: $58,890

FINANCIAL

$18,345 avg grant/scholarship amount (need)

$4,547 avg loan amount (need)

HOUGHTON COLLEGE

HOUGHTON, NEW YORK

Houghton College provides an experiential and transformative learning experience within a close-knit, highly-relational Christian community. Named one of the safest college campuses in the country, Houghton enrolls 1000+ diverse and deeply curious students from 39 states, 31 countries, and 30 different Christian denominations. Located in rural Western NY, Houghton's scenic location fosters deep reflection, close connections with people and with nature, and an ideal environment for focusing on what truly matters. With over 40 majors and programs and a newly designed general education curriculum, a Houghton education prepares students to meet the challenges of the 21st century. As a Christian learning community in the Wesleyan tradition, Houghton equips students to lead and labor as scholar-servants in a changing world.

CENTER FOR FAITH, JUSTICE, AND GLOBAL ENGAGEMENT: The Center for Faith, Justice, and Global Engagement is the face of Houghton's long-standing commitment to address social and economic needs, both locally and globally. The Center's annual symposium provides a forum for students to interact with world-renowned speakers, all of whom travel to Houghton to introduce different perspectives around a single, core issue. Together, students and speakers use their areas of expertise to collaborate and discuss such issues as hunger and extreme poverty, human trafficking, and climate change.

WRITING-ENRICHED COURSES: All Houghton students receive writing instruction through a set of foundational coursework in college-level writing as well as in other designated courses that require at least 20 pages of writing (including shorter papers that collectively add up to 20 pages). Since writing is essential in so many vocations, all students, no matter their majors, have at least three opportunities to receive writing feedback so that they may learn to improve their composition skills.

SPIRITUAL LIFE ON CAMPUS: Houghton students remain refreshed and motivated, uninhibited by the rigorous challenges that come with college. Routine is reinforced by the invigorating rhythms of Christian community. With grounding, campus-wide chapel services, and welcoming prayer services throughout the week, Houghton integrates faith, academics, and community. Spiritual formation is ingrained in the everyday Houghton lifestyle, connecting every interaction to God's presence. While much of the college's Christian rhythms are supported by Houghton's faculty, spiritual growth is ultimately driven by the active contributions of the students themselves. Students are welcome and encouraged to participate in chapel, lead devotionals, and travel all throughout the world in missionary groups. Other opportunities to nurse Houghton's spiritual health include the student-led "Mercy Seat" worship service every weeknight and the student-leader "Deacons Program."

VOCATION AND CAREER: A Houghton education is about preparing graduates for the fast-paced and ever-changing world of work. Work is not thought primarily in terms of "career," but of "calling." Houghton's Vocational Opportunities and Career Advising (VOCA) Center provides the resources and guidance that students need to integrate God's calling with their individual interests and goals. With the help of everything from alumni networking to career assessment, every student is able to find the way they may best serve in this changing world. More than just a career services office, the VOCA Center provides a unique approach to vocational and career planning by engaging with students throughout their first year of college, walking them through individually customized and comprehensive career development plans that are also available beyond graduation.

---

https://www.houghton.edu/
P: (800) 777-2556

PRIVATE - CHRISTIAN

STUDENT PROFILE

1,007 undergraduate students

99% of undergrad students are full time

35% male – 65% female

38.21% of students are from out of state

87% freshman retention rate

FACULTY PROFILE

75 full-time faculty

53 part-time faculty

11 to 1 student/faculty ratio

ADMISSIONS

792 Total Applicants

743 Total Admissions

238 Total Freshman Enrollment

93.81% of applicants admitted

SAT Ranges: CR 490-640, M 490-620

ACT Ranges: C 21.75-27, M 21-29, E 21-28

TUITION & COSTS

Tuition: $31,040

Fees: $200

Total: $31,240

R&B: $9,018

Room: $4,838

Board: $4,180

Total: $40,258

FINANCIAL

$11,583 avg grant/scholarship amount (need)

$4,558 avg loan amount (need)

IONA COLLEGE

NEW ROCHELLE, NEW YORK

In the tradition of the Christian Brothers and American Catholic higher education, Iona College is a diverse community of learners and scholars dedicated to academic excellence. Iona's students, faculty, staff, and administrators embody the values of justice, peace, and service.

LOCAL AND INTERNATIONAL SERVICE PROJECTS: At Iona, serving the greater community is at the heart of the school's mission. Iona believes that education is a valuable tool to improve the world; whether they plant a tree or volunteer at local soup kitchens, Iona students find that even the smallest acts of kindness and consideration can move the world. Iona students find ways to give back through campus services as well as through nationally recognized organizations, including Best Buddies, Habitat for Humanity, Christian Brothers Outreach, Project Family Soup Kitchen, and more. The Iona in Mission program also offers students once-in-a-lifetime opportunities to immerse themselves in different cultures and ways of life. This program is a way for students to exercise their passions and make profound differences in the world.

RESEARCH OPPORTUNITIES: From their first day on campus, Iona students are a part of the school's mission to move the world through rigorous projects and assignments. They work closely with highly acclaimed faculty in order to develop valuable skills for the future and conduct independent research to develop their critical thinking, analysis, and creative research techniques to succeed in any career.

MISSION & MINISTRY: The Office of Mission and Ministry provides students and the community at large with opportunities to build a caring environment of faith and compassion through volunteer service, immersion trips, faith-sharing groups, advocacy and social justice groups, and more. Students even have the opportunity to serve as Student Ministers. Student Ministers help develop programming for students and coordinate local service projects while acting as liaisons between the student body and the Office of Mission and Ministry.

LAPENTA-LYNCH TRADING FLOOR: The LaPenta-Lynch Trading Floor in the School of Business offers students a simulated trading environment that features 20 high-end networked trading desks and a continuous live data feed from Bloomberg. Students learn firsthand as they use the same technology and analytic tools used on Wall Street, building and tracking investment portfolios as if they were on an actual trading floor or in a corporate finance office.

COMPASS LEADERSHIP SERIES: The COMPASS Leadership Series is open to all students, including individuals who are interested in learning more about leadership, students already acting as leaders, and students who are interested in exploring their leadership potential. Through their participation in workshops, COMPASS leaders are exposed to various concepts of leadership that assist them in becoming more aware of themselves and the roles they play within their community. Ultimately, COMPASS enables students to identify and develop their unique styles of leadership.

CHALLENGED TO MOVE THE WORLD: Iona College is one of the most highly accredited institutions in New York with 10 college and program accreditations. Iona has a commitment to combining a career-focused education with a liberal arts curriculum, challenging and preparing students for success. Students gain a competitive edge with employers through real-world knowledge, ethics, and critical-thinking skills. An Iona education also gives students the global exposure they need to succeed in today's highly competitive world. Throughout students' academic careers, service-learning projects, and internships, they always have someone to encourage and challenge them to move the world.

---

http://www.iona.edu/

P: (914) 633-2000

PRIVATE - CATHOLIC

STUDENT PROFILE

3,271 undergraduate students

90% of undergrad students are full time

49% male – 51% female

25% of students are from out of state

77% freshman retention rate

66% graduated in 6 years

FACULTY PROFILE

174 full-time faculty

170 part-time faculty

15 to 1 student/faculty ratio

ADMISSIONS

9,587 Total Applicants

8,744 Total Admissions

842 Total Freshman Enrollment

91.21% of applicants admitted

SAT Ranges: CR 450-550, M 440-550

ACT Ranges: C 20-25

TUITION & COSTS

Tuition: $33,124

Fees: $2,200

Total: $35,324

R&B: $13,980

Total: $49,304

FINANCIAL

$19,975 avg grant/scholarship amount (total)

$19,975 avg loan amount (total)

KEUKA COLLEGE

KEUKA PARK, NEW YORK

Many students agree that attending Keuka College is like joining a new family. The growing campus community supports personal experiences in all facets of student life. Keuka professors may be accomplished contributors to their respective fields of scholarship, but they ultimately consider teaching their calling. They are enthusiastic to guide every student to their individual goals.

THE KEUKA COLLEGE WAY: At Keuka College, distinguished faculty (not graduate students) teach all of the classes. These professors hail from such nationally known institutions as Cornell University, Yale, MIT, Syracuse University, the University of California at Berkeley, University of Rochester, Princeton University, and Gallaudet University. With an impressive student-to-faculty ratio of 8:1, each Keuka College student will always get the personal attention he or she needs. Their professors know them by name and grow to be personally invested mentors.

STUDENT EMPLOYMENT: On a small campus of fewer than 1,000 students, there are plenty of work-study positions available. Without the College's student employment work force, Keuka would have to hire more than 100 full-time employees. Part-time jobs on campus allow students to explore interests, build resumes, and earn extra spending money. Work-study jobs range from serving as referees at intramural games or working at the circulation desk in the library.

SERVICE: Keuka College is nationally recognized for its commitment to service and community support. Named in the President's Higher Education Community Service Honor Roll, the College has received the highest federal recognition an institution can receive for its commitment to volunteering, service-learning, and civic engagement.

SUPPORT FROM THE BEGINNING: Faculty, staff, and upperclassmen within the Keuka College community are committed to helping new students succeed in academics, career development, and personal life. Every incoming freshman is assigned both a professional success advocate and an upperclassman mentor to discuss their personal and academic goals during their adjustment to college life. Each success advocate and mentor is trained to help students settle into school and connect with other resources on campus.

TEAMWORKS!: Keuka College is home to a ropes course right on campus for those who love the outdoors, adventure, and physical challenges. Since 1989, Keuka College's TeamWorks! adventure staff has been developing customized programs for school and college groups, nonprofits, church groups, and corporations to build teamwork and success strategies. Participants have the chance to explore the high and low elements of the Birkett Mills Challenge Course as well as a near-endless supply of ground, stationary, and portable activities. Those who join the TeamWorks! Adventure Club can participate in off-campus adventures, including whitewater rafting, rock climbing, cave diving, and more.

ACCESS TO ADVENTURE: Keuka College's beautiful, tree-lined campus sits on the shore of the majestic Keuka Lake, one of the cleanest freshwater lakes in the world. The Finger Lakes region is known for its stunning scenery, a picturesque setting full of hundreds of hiking trails and access to lakes, watersports, apple orchards, wineries, ski resorts, golf courses, horseback riding, and much more. With Keuka Lake State Park right down the road and the Watkins Glen State Park and Corning Museum of Glass just short drives away, there's no reason to way to get bored. Not only is Keuka surrounded by such a beautiful environment, but it is also only an hour away from the major metropolitan area of Rochester, NY, and the historic village of Penn Yan is only three miles from campus. There, students can enjoy go-karts, bowling, putt-putt, a movie theater, and hidden waterfalls.

KEUKA
COLLEGE
Believe in What We Can Do Together

http://keuka.edu/
P: (315) 279-5000

PRIVATE

STUDENT PROFILE
1,723 undergraduate students
77% of undergrad students are full time
26% male – 74% female
72% freshman retention rate
53% graduated in 6 years

FACULTY PROFILE
94 full-time faculty
6 part-time faculty
8 to 1 student/faculty ratio

ADMISSIONS
2,290 Total Applicants
1,756 Total Admissions
318 Total Freshman Enrollment
76.68% of applicants admitted

TUITION & COSTS
Tuition: $27,942
Fees: $750
Total: $28,692
R&B: $11,070
Room: $5,258
Board: $5,812
Total: $39,762

FINANCIAL
$20,222 avg grant/scholarship amount (total)
$9,021 avg loan amount (total)

LE MOYNE COLLEGE

SYRACUSE, NEW YORK

Established in 1946 by the Society of Jesus, Le Moyne College provides its students with a rigorous, values-based education that allows them to explore their potential through academics, experience, and service. It equips them with the intellectual skills necessary to succeed in the world as well as the will to use their abilities to promote a more just society. The nearly 500-year-old Jesuit tradition upon which the College was founded is alive and well today. Le Moyne's grounding in mission and values guides graduates to lives of meaningful success. Le Moyne's 160-acre, tree-lined campus is located in a residential setting 10 minutes from downtown Syracuse. Right outside the city are rolling hills, picturesque lakes, and the miles of open country for which Central New York is renowned.

EXCLUSIVE OPPORTUNITIES TO GROW: Students get involved in ways they would never have imagined. Some work alongside Dr. Martha Grabowski, the Distinguished McDevitt Chair in Information Systems, traveling to Alaska to help with oil-spill research. Some take trips to New York City with their professors, getting the most out of their core curriculum's "outside the classroom" experience. Some even take classes taught by the prestigious Dr. Doug Egerton, a history professor who is one of the nation's preeminent Abraham Lincoln scholars.

EXTENDED LEARNING OPPORTUNITIES: Every year, Le Moyne students immerse themselves in their educations through internships, study abroad opportunities, community service projects, and faculty-mentored research. It is through such exciting, hands-on opportunities that they discover who they are as fun-loving citizens who are driven and full of spirit. In time, they also find who they are to become: leaders, experts, and compassionate advocates for those in need.

OUTSTANDING HELP ALONG THE WAY: Le Moyne's outstanding faculty members are ready to help solve puzzling mysteries and answer striking questions. They can speak not only to their students' performances in the classroom, but also to their dreams for the future. No matter their field of expertise, Le Moyne's faculty are committed to helping students pursue their talents and interests in an environment characterized by academic excellence, generous service, and creative, responsible leadership.

STUDENT ACTIVITIES: The wide range of clubs, organizations, and activities on campus is a great expression of Le Moyne's commitment to "educating the whole person." There are more than 100 student organizations and clubs to choose from at Le Moyne, ranging from service and social action to visual and performing arts groups. Students are always forming new clubs on campus, ensuring that there is something for everyone and every interest. They are the driving force behind what is happening on campus, for the Le Moyne Student Programming Board (LSPB) is responsible for scheduling each and every social activity and special event.

ON-CAMPUS EVENTS: Campus life is strengthened by a wide-range of special events, including concerts, theatrical performances, art exhibits, dances, first-run films, trivia contests, and stand-up comedy shows. Students also participate in a number of annual campus events, including "Dolphy Day," "Earth Jam," a winter semi-formal, and the popular "Fall Fest."

ALUMNI SUCCESS: At Le Moyne, success is not just an outcome; it's a way of living. It's not simply what one does, but why, and for whom. It's setting goals. It's embracing the unknown, trusting in oneself, and never settling for second-best. It's the tireless, constant pursuit of the best possible version of oneself. Le Moyne is proud to foster outstanding communicators, collaborators, and critical thinkers who live their lives with meaning.

http://www.lemoyne.edu/
P: (800) 333-4733

PRIVATE - CATHOLIC

STUDENT PROFILE

2,877 undergraduate students

87% of undergrad students are full time

40% male – 60% female

88% freshman retention rate

68% graduated in 6 years

FACULTY PROFILE

172 full-time faculty

177 part-time faculty

13 to 1 student/faculty ratio

ADMISSIONS

6,877 Total Applicants

4,247 Total Admissions

634 Total Freshman Enrollment

61.76% of applicants admitted

SAT Ranges: CR 480-580, M 500-590

ACT Ranges: C 21-25, M 21-26, E 20-25

TUITION & COSTS

Tuition: $31,260

Fees: $990

Total: $32,250

R&B: $12,540

Room: $7,880

Board: $4,660

Total: $44,790

FINANCIAL

$20,894 avg grant/scholarship amount (total)

$8,824 avg loan amount (total)

LIU POST

BROOKVILLE, NEW YORK

Long Island University (LIU) was founded in 1926 in Brooklyn, NY, under the guiding principle of educating and empowering students from all walks of life. It has since grown into one of the nation's largest private universities.

STUDENT ORGANIZATIONS: At LIU Post, students find a vibrant community of passionate and driven people. Many students choose to participate in fraternal organizations (six sororities, six fraternities) and more than 70 student organizations. They can join the student government, jazz ensembles, the "Pioneer" campus newspaper, and more.

EXPERIENTIAL EMPLOYMENT: LIU Post is a national leader in student-powered entrepreneurship and engaged learning opportunities. In 2014, the Student-Run Business Committee worked with the campus community to launch four on-campus businesses that employ students into all levels of operation. LIU Post now has eight student-run businesses and other student employment opportunities. These ventures are all part of LIU's dedication to fostering entrepreneurship in its community as well as its commitment to provide students with real-world experiences.

COMMUNITY SERVICE: LIU Post believes in the power of community service. The LIU Cares initiative connects 20,000 students, 3,500 faculty and staff, and 200,000 alumni to service opportunities through volunteerism and community engagement.

STUDY ABROAD: LIU students can study abroad to take their classroom knowledge out into the world. Faculty-led Study Abroad also offers the opportunity for students to spend their summers or winters in different locations across the world, hosting courses that are are open to both current LIU students as well as visiting students from other colleges and universities.

SOMETHING FOR EVERYONE: With a broad and comprehensive catalog of majors and degree programs across nine academic units, LIU Post offers the flexibility to explore interests, discover intellectual passions, and embark on academic paths that lead students to careers of their dreams.

ESTEEMED FACULTY: LIU Post's faculty are passionate professionals who care about helping students achieve their full potential. Faculty are made up of Fulbright Fellows, conductors of award-winning research, scholarly residences at the world's top institutions, and much more.

THRIVING ARTS COMMUNITY: LIU Post is home to Long Island's cultural venue, Tilles Center for The Performing Arts, as well as nearly 30 student and faculty performance ensembles for music, theatre, and dance. LIU Post is alive with artistic opportunities in every desired medium.

THE LIU PROMISE: The LIU Promise is a commitment to providing the right tools, guidance, and support for student achievement. LIU students are immediately assigned an LIU Promise Success Coach who follows them all the way through graduation. These coaches are the point of contact for everything students need, from academic and career counseling to campus activities and financial aid.

LOYAL ALUMNI: Each of LIU Post's 200,000 alumni has made a mark on the world in his or her own way. From the beginning, LIU Post has been educating students who go on to gain both national and international acclaim for their accomplishments. It is not uncommon to see successful alumni on and around campus, sharing their experiences and insight with current students.

---

http://liu.edu/post
P: (516) 299-2323

PRIVATE

STUDENT PROFILE

3,443 undergraduate students

89% of undergrad students are full time

40% male – 60% female

14% of students are from out of state

72% freshman retention rate

49% graduated in 6 years

FACULTY PROFILE

278 full-time faculty

652 part-time faculty

12 to 1 student/faculty ratio

ADMISSIONS

6,371 Total Applicants

5,134 Total Admissions

530 Total Freshman Enrollment

80.58% of applicants admitted

SAT Ranges: CR 450-550, M 460-560, W 440-550

ACT Ranges: C 19-24, M 18-25, E 20-26, W 7-8

TUITION & COSTS

Tuition: $33,678

Fees: $1,868

Total: $35,546

R&B: $13,138

Room: $8,200

Board: $4,938

Total: $48,684

FINANCIAL

$9,758 avg grant/scholarship amount (need)

$4,856 avg loan amount (need)

MANHATTAN COLLEGE

BRONX, NEW YORK

MANHATTAN COLLEGE

Throughout its 150-years history, Manhattan College has been at the forefront of outstanding, comprehensive colleges. Through the years, the College has been guided by one constant: the Lasallian Catholic heritage upon which it was built.

DIRECT ACCESS TO ENRICHMENT: Manhattan College's welcoming campus in Riverdale, a residential neighborhood in New York City, fosters close bonds among fellow students as well as with their professors. Just thirty minutes from midtown Manhattan, the College provides easy access to the vast, enriching resources that this mecca of commerce and the arts has to offer. Manhattan College Jaspers enjoy a strong network that links students and alumni to each other in mutually beneficial ways.

STUDY ABROAD: In partnership with a number of educational institutions, including Lasallian schools overseas, the College offers many opportunities for study in other countries. Studying abroad is an extraordinary opportunity for intellectual, cultural, and personal growth for Manhattan College students, many of whom have never gone beyond the borders of the USA. Manhattan believes that educators have a responsibility not only to prepare students for careers, but to make them more knowledgeable, sensitive, and tolerant of other cultures. A Manhattan College student is sure to be an informed citizen of an increasingly interdependent world. As one student writes, "Living and studying in South Africa has allowed me to understand and appreciate a reality so different from my own—to witness firsthand the strength of people and their ability to overcome incredible hardships."

NEXT DOOR TO THE BIG APPLE: Thanks to their proximity to metropolitan New York, Manhattan students can enjoy all the city's cultural opportunities, including world-class museums, musical theatre and drama, concert halls, and sports events. They also include access to many seminars, special events, and internships.

ATHLETICS: The College's 19 varsity teams for men and women offer a full spectrum of athletic opportunities, including baseball, basketball, softball, volleyball, track and field, tennis, soccer, lacrosse, swimming, golf, and cross-country. Many clubs and intramural activities also complement the collegiate athletic program. Better yet, most varsity sports offer scholarships in addition to the College's academic need- and merit-based awards.

SERVICE: The office of Campus Ministry/Social Action foster spiritual development and an enhanced understanding of issues related to social justice. The Lasallian Outreach Volunteer Experience (LOVE) provides the opportunity for students to explore social causes while developing and reflecting upon their faith. Through participation in these programs, students develop value-based relationships with their peers as well as with people whose cultures are very different from their own. Opportunities are available during academic breaks in places like New Orleans, Ecuador, Mexico, Kenya, Texas, Maine, and Alabama.

A STRONG MANHATTAN COLLEGE COMMUNITY: Manhattan College has been expanding its academic offerings and facilities to accommodate a growing number of students from the northeast corridor and, increasingly, from other regions of the country. The approximately 80% residential students, as well as the commuters, enjoy a sense of belonging within the close-knit Manhattan community. Two new, state-of-the-art residences have been added on campus, and a planned Student Commons will soon serve as a hub for meetings, dining, student government, multicultural clubs, and other shared student activities.

ETHICAL GROWTH, NOT JUST INTELLECTUAL: Above and beyond their professional accomplishments, graduates from Manhattan College are able to demonstrate the kind of ethical grow that had been a major part of their education. Nowhere is this more poignantly apparent than in their contributions at the World Trade Center site. From the earliest days, Jaspers have always proven their ability and ethical standards as citizens of the world.

http://www.manhattan.edu/
P: (800) 622-9235

PRIVATE - CATHOLIC

STUDENT PROFILE

3,576 undergraduate students

95% of undergrad students are full time

54% male – 46% female

36% of students are from out of state

84% freshman retention rate

72% graduated in 6 years

FACULTY PROFILE

221 full-time faculty

217 part-time faculty

13 to 1 student/faculty ratio

ADMISSIONS

8,313 Total Applicants

5,557 Total Admissions

900 Total Freshman Enrollment

66.85% of applicants admitted

SAT Ranges: CR 490-580, M 500-610, W 480-590

ACT Ranges: C 22-27

TUITION & COSTS

Tuition: $35,600

Fees: $3,300

Total: $38,900

R&B: $14,430

Total: $53,030

FINANCIAL

$14,451 avg grant/scholarship amount (need)

MANHATTANVILLE COLLEGE

PURCHASE, NEW YORK

With an average class size of 17 students, Manhattanville College students can count on focused, personal instruction from faculty who are highly invested in the rewards of a liberal arts education: critical thinking, thoughtful expression, and creative collaboration.

FIRST-YEAR VALIANT EXPERIENCE: Manhattanville's welcoming first-year learning environment encourages students to become active participants in the College's mission to educate "ethical and socially responsible leaders for the global community." The first-year program equips students with a greater ability to identify and understand the ethical dimensions of problems, all while stimulating intellectual curiosity and increasing analytical ability.

RESEARCH OPPORTUNITIES: Throughout their careers at Manhattanville College, students in the physical and health science programs gain real-world experience by working on projects in research labs and completing a senior research project. Each student also receives assistance along the way, developing their skills with the help of faculty advisors and research mentors.

COMMUNITY SERVICE AND SOCIAL ACTION: Since Manhattanville's inception in 1841 as the Academy of the Sacred Heart, its community has perpetuated the mission, vision, and heritage of social responsibility. Students continue this engagement in social justice through the Duchesne Center for Religion and Social Justice, which provides many opportunities to help those in need. Programming includes community outreach and cultural, leadership, and spiritual initiatives across the Manhattanville College campus and beyond. Service experiences and programs are tightly linked to the academic curriculum to ensure that all students acquire the right skills as effective and responsible members of their communities.

STUDY ABROAD: Manhattanville College has relationships with more than 100 different international programs in many major countries, including Spain, Italy, South Africa, Japan, England, and Germany. The Study Abroad Office at Manhattanville guides students through the research, applications, and approval process for overseas study, aiming to make every student's experience as fulfilling as possible.

THE MENTOR PROGRAM: Manhattanville's Mentor Program, which emphasizes academic achievement and student leadership, connects incoming students with successful upperclassmen to help them with their transition to college. Mentors are assigned to oversee classes within the First-Year Program and are also available for individual support upon request.

SELF-DESIGNED MAJOR: Manhattanville College offers more than 50 different programs for undergraduate students to major and/or minor in; however, if students have interests that lie outside of or between existing areas, they can propose a unique, self-designed major or minor. Students receive guidance from faculty advisors through these areas of study, should they be approved by Manhattanville's Board on Academic Standards. Recent examples of self-designed majors include film directing, Italian studies, and youth advocacy.

QUAD JAM: Before students start the push for their final exams and research papers, the Manhattanville College community comes together for Quad Jam. This annual spring event brings several well-known musical acts to campus to perform throughout the day. There are also musical and dance performances from Manhattanville students themselves!

EMERGING LEADERS PROGRAM: Manhattanville College's Emerging Leaders program is a living-learning community geared toward first-year students who demonstrate leadership potential and a strong drive to become active leaders. Through Emerging Leaders, students receive transitional support while simultaneously acquiring skills to learn about their personal identity. They also learn about their leadership style and how to communicate effectively within a diverse group of people.

http://www.mville.edu/

P: (914) 323-5464

PRIVATE

STUDENT PROFILE

1,744 a students

98% of undergrad students are full time

34% male – 66% female

36% of students are from out of state

81% freshman retention rate

57% graduated in 6 years

FACULTY PROFILE

109 full-time faculty

208 part-time faculty

12 to 1 student/faculty ratio

ADMISSIONS

4,033 Total Applicants

2,989 Total Admissions

452 Total Freshman Enrollment

74.11% of applicants admitted

SAT Ranges: CR 480-580, M 480-570

ACT Ranges: C 21-26

TUITION & COSTS

Tuition: $35,570

Fees: $1,350

Total: $36,920

R&B: $14,520

Room: $8,680

Board: $5,840

Total: $51,440

FINANCIAL

$7,857 avg grant/scholarship amount (need)

$4,427 avg loan amount (need)

MOLLOY COLLEGE

ROCKVILLE CENTRE, NEW YORK

Molloy College, an independent Catholic college based in Rockville Centre, was founded in 1955 by the Sisters of Saint Dominic in Amityville, NY. The College serves a student population of approximately 4,900 undergraduate and graduate students, and was the only school in the nation to be named in the top 3 for value for two consecutive years by Money magazine. Molloy students can earn degrees in a variety of outstanding academic programs, including nursing, business, education, social work, music therapy, computer studies, and many more.

COMMITTED TO ITS MISSION: With a 10:1 student-to-faculty ratio, students enjoy the benefits of small classes and personal attention from their professors. Molloy's 85% retention rate is the best of all Long Island private schools and among the highest in the nation. Such an outstanding outcome comes from Molloy's outstanding promise. Even as it expands and renovates, Molloy remains committed to its core principles and the power of education to transform lives. Through the College's diversity of programs, personal attention from faculty, and commitment to improving both Long Island and the world, students graduate prepared to make a difference.

STUDY ABROAD: Molloy students possess the confidence needed to live and work in this fast-paced, ever-changing world. The College has expanded its International Education program, allowing students to travel from Rockville Centre to study in Belgium, India, Italy, France, Spain, Thailand, Japan, Australia, and many other locations. By immersing themselves other parts of the world, students gain knowledge while learning acceptance and understanding.

OUTSTANDING PROGRAMS: Molloy students can earn degrees in a variety of outstanding academic programs, including the liberal arts, social and natural sciences, nursing, business, education, social work, speech therapy, music therapy, and many more. Molloy's nursing and education programs are well known even beyond the New York metro region. The College has also earned recognition for its treatment of those with autism, with the music therapy and speech therapy programs providing tremendous support in that area. New programs include a New Media major, the Molloy/CAP21 B.F.A. program in musical theatre, and a four-year degree in Nuclear Medicine Technology. Additionally, the Business Division features classes taught by CEOs, CFOs, and other senior leaders from the business world.

TRADITIONS AND EVENTS: Molloy hosts several activities, including a variety of barbecues, an annual Halloween party, a Comedy Night, and much, much more. Additionally, Molloy has become a focal point for civic discourse in recent years. The school has hosted guest lectures from world leaders looking to assess critical and timely issues. Past speakers have included Secretary of State Gen. Colin Powell, New York Times best-selling author Malcolm Gladwell, and Newsweek editor Fareed Zakaria.

ALWAYS SOMETHING TO DO: Campus life in Rockville Centre is alive and vibrant. Students are comfortably housed in two new residence halls, and they find entertainment and outlets for creativity in the new student center, which includes a performing arts theatre. With a wide range of activities, including social events, charitable programs, and Division II athletics, there's always something to do, someone to meet, or somewhere to go.

AMAZING ATHLETES: Sports and academics go hand-in-hand at Molloy, where students are known for both their athletic and scholastic success. More than 60 percent of athletes record a GPA of 3.25 or higher, showcasing their strong dedication to everything they put their minds to. Molloy competes in the East Coast Conference with a winning tradition in a number of athletic programs. For example, the women's basketball team reached the Sweet 16 nationally, and the men's basketball, baseball, and soccer teams all made the conference finals.

---

http://www.molloy.edu/

P: (516) 323-4000

PRIVATE - CATHOLIC

STUDENT PROFILE

3,562 undergraduate students

81% of undergrad students are full time

27% male – 73% female

7% of students are from out of state

85% freshman retention rate

75% graduated in 6 years

FACULTY PROFILE

190 full-time faculty

533 part-time faculty

10 to 1 student/faculty ratio

ADMISSIONS

4,030 Total Applicants

3,100 Total Admissions

565 Total Freshman Enrollment

76.92% of applicants admitted

SAT Ranges: CR 490-580, M 490-590

ACT Ranges: C 21-26

TUITION & COSTS

Tuition: $28,000

Fees: $1,100

Total: $29,100

R&B: $14,250

Total: $43,350

FINANCIAL

$12,044 avg grant/scholarship amount (need)

$4,183 avg loan amount (need)

NIAGARA UNIVERSITY

NIAGARA UNIV, NEW YORK

Founded in 1856, Niagara University is a comprehensive institution, blending the best of a liberal arts and professional education, grounded in a values-based, Catholic tradition. With more than 80 majors, nearly 60 minors, six pre-professional options, and 4+1 combined master's programs, NU students are immersed in meaningful real-world learning opportunities from the moment they step foot on the University's beautiful campus.

CATHOLIC MISSION: Niagara strives to educate and enrich students with special attention to the Catholic and Vincentian traditions. The University's commitment to the Catholic faith allows students to experience the vision and reality of a service-oriented, value-centered education. St. Vincent de Paul's tradition of serving the poor is continued at NU, and more than half of NU's undergraduate students participate in research. Designed to make a difference in the lives of students, Niagara invites many to take advantage of study abroad, cooperative education, and internship programs.

LEARN AND SERVE NIAGARA: Learn and Serve Niagara is a program designed to promote the knowledge, values, and skills necessary for lifelong engagement in the pursuit of social justice. All major programs require the completion of Learn and Serve components for graduation. Courses with service-learning components are offered in every college and in almost every academic department, sending students on projects that range from working with the Niagara County District Attorney's Office in the domestic violence program to doing historical research for nonprofit agencies. Education majors serve as teachers' aides and provide tutoring for local children, while other NU students participate in Habitat for Humanity projects, just to name a few.

PRACTICAL EXPERIENCE: It's no fluke that NU graduates are so highly sought after by graduate schools and employers. Niagara graduates are ready for the real world because they've experienced the real world. Those types of real-world learning opportunities help Niagara alumni translate their practical education into top jobs within their career fields. To prepare students for their careers, professors assist students in finding internship placements and invite them to contribute to research in a variety of fields.

STUDYING ABROAD: For students who wish to study abroad, the University offers semester and summer programs in Chile, China, England, France, Ireland, Mexico, Spain, Thailand, and many other countries. For example, hospitality and tourism management majors have the opportunity to participate in a hotel management program in Peru and Italy, where students work alongside management at a hotel on Lake Como. In total, students may choose from more than 200 available programs in more than 30 countries.

GETTING STARTED: Niagara University Beginnings (NUB) is a one-credit seminar course required of all first-year students. It is designed to introduce students to the academic culture of Niagara, introducing students to how their specific field of study may integrate with the University, the general education curriculum, and student life as a whole. First-year students typically take their NUB course with other students in their major, enjoying an introduction to their field with an NUB instructor from their department. This way, students acclimate comfortably to college life, all while receiving a fitting introduction to their major.

CAREER SERVICES: NU's award-winning Office of Career Services prepares students to make a successful leap into the professional world. From job fairs and résumé critiques to practice interviews and alumni networking opportunities, staff members are committed to providing students with the hands-on resources necessary to get their lives after college on track. Career services are integrated into the student experience during all four years, with over 100 classroom presentations offered by staff members each year.

---

http://www.niagara.edu/

P: (716) 285-1212

PRIVATE - CATHOLIC

STUDENT PROFILE

3,045 undergraduate students

96% of undergrad students are full time

38% male — 62% female

9% of students are from out of state

81% freshman retention rate

67% graduated in 6 years

FACULTY PROFILE

165 full-time faculty

242 part-time faculty

12 to 1 student/faculty ratio

ADMISSIONS

3,359 Total Applicants

2,784 Total Admissions

625 Total Freshman Enrollment

82.88% of applicants admitted

SAT Ranges: CR 460-560, M 470-570

ACT Ranges: C 21-25, M 19-25, E 19-24

TUITION & COSTS

Tuition: $30,500

Fees: $1,450

Total: $31,950

R&B: $12,950

Total: $44,900

FINANCIAL

$20,970 avg grant/scholarship amount (need)

$4,984 avg loan amount (need)

PACE UNIVERSITY

NEW YORK & PLEASANTVILLE, NEW YORK

Pace University is committed to a hands-on approach to education and professional preparation, broad spectrum of academic programs, and diversity of valuable connections all throughout the state of New York and the surrounding NYC metro area. These opportunities proliferate among both of Pace's campuses, one of which lies in the heart of New York City, the other of which is located in the nearby suburban town of Pleasantville. As one first-rate University with two distinct campus environments, Pace is designed to be fit for absolutely anyone—the NYC campus is a thriving location for students who want to take advantage of the city as their classroom, while the Westchester campus fosters a close-knit sense of community and easy access to opportunities in the city and the surrounding area. Whether they study in the city or dwell in the comfort of a traditional campus environment, students who choose Pace find their niche and everything they need to succeed in their field of study.

The Pace Path: Starting freshman year, every Pace student works with an advisor to craft a customized four-year plan that helps them utilize as many resources for success as possible – on and off-campus. Each student's Pace Path builds upon his or her coursework and co-curricular activities (e.g. internships). Through a progressive development of their professional confidence and competence, the Path is designed to develop students into market-ready professionals at graduation. This flexible plan gives them an idea of when and how they reach particular milestones throughout their college career.

First-Year Learning Communities: All first-year students are immediately introduced to Pace's enthusiasm for interdisciplinary thought. In First-Year Learning Communities, students take a combination of courses with the same tightly knit group of peers, fostering new friendships while exploring diverse academic perspectives. Learning Communities' linked courses are intelligently combined to complement one another, teaching students how to approach topics of varied disciplines with well-rounded insight.

Professional Preparation: Success in the workforce is best attained with experience and, through the Pace Path, professional experiences are woven into a student's four-year plan, including internships, research with faculty, clinicals, student teaching, volunteer work, and study abroad. Students on both campuses take advantage of a multitude of professional opportunities in New York City or the metropolitan area. Whatever their future goals, students thrive in New York's international hub of business and innovation.

Activities for Everyone: Both of Pace University's campuses are bustling with activities that cater to any and all of students' interests. Social and cultural clubs are active with multiethnic and heritage-based celebration, fraternities and sororities, religious fellowship organizations, and societies for LGBTQ+ advocacy and support. Students can also dive deeper into their academic interests through collegiate societies like the Model UN, Pace Marketing Association, Criminal Justice Society or the Future Educators Association. Other clubs gather the resources for creative students to perform on stage or produce art in all forms of media. And, in addition to all of its opportunities for extracurricular involvement, Pace's Westchester campus is home to its NCAA Division II men's and women's varsity athletics teams.

Over 100 Majors and Combined Degrees: Pace offers students over 100 majors as well as combined Bachelor's + Graduate degree programs on both campuses, including Pre-Med and Pre-Law. While most majors are available on both campuses, the NYC campus is the exclusive home to the School of Performing Arts and such majors as Arts and Entertainment Management, Communications Sciences and Disorders, Art, Art History, Latin American Studies, Spanish, and Women's and Gender Studies. The Westchester campus is the exclusive home for the Nursing, Digital Cinema and Filmmaking, Digital Journalism, and Public Relations majors.

https://www.pace.edu/
P: (866) 722-3338

PRIVATE

STUDENT PROFILE
8,747 undergrads
87% are full time
41% male – 59% female
78% freshman retention rate
53% graduated in 6 years

FACULTY PROFILE
490 full-time faculty
14 to 1 student/faculty ratio

ADMISSIONS
17,038 applicants
14.283 admitted
2,128 first-year students enrolled
83.83% of applicants admitted

SAT Ranges: CR 470-580, M 470-580

ACT Ranges: C 21-26

TUITION & COSTS
Tuition: $39,728
Fees: $1,605
Total: $41,333
R&B: $17,938
Total: $58,271

FINANCIAL
$25,745 avg grant/scholarship amount (total)
$8,475 avg loan amount (total)

ST. JOHN FISHER COLLEGE

ROCHESTER, NEW YORK

St. John Fisher College has experienced significant enrollment and program growth, igniting fast-moving change to an already beautiful campus. It's a place where tradition and innovation continue to be joined hand-in-hand. The College stays true to the educational philosophy of its founders including liberal learning, high academic standards, and personal attention to each student.

FIRST-YEAR PROGRAM: The transition into college can be daunting, but Fisher's First-Year Program makes every new student feel like they are part of the family. The summer before students begin their classes, they get the chance to attend Great Beginnings, a summer orientation session that is fully loaded with information about what students can expect for their first few months at the College. Later in August, they kick off their fall semesters with a three-day Orientation full of activities just prior to the start of classes. Students connect with new friends, learn about campus resources, and enter college with a firm foundation of what life at Fisher is all about.

FRESHMAN SEMINAR: The Freshman Seminar and Research-Based Writing classes come as part of the first-year academic package. These courses familiarize students with time management, study skills, self-care, and upper-level writing that will be crucial throughout their college experience. The first-year curriculum includes Learning Communities, tightly knit groups of students who take two classes together around a specific theme. Taught by professors of differing disciplines, these Learning Community classes help students understand the value of approaching topics from different perspectives and across different fields of study.

STUDY ABROAD: With over 100 Foreign Study programs to choose from, St. John Fisher College students have the incredible opportunity to combine adventure and academics. Both summer- and semester-long trips all across the globe bring courses to life, immersing students in the cultures of their destinations and expanding their social and professional networks far beyond the Fisher campus.

THE TEDDI DANCE FOR LOVE: Fisher's longest-running student tradition, the Teddi Dance for Love, is a fun, inspiring event that exemplifies the College's commitment to service. It calls upon hundreds of students every year to raise money for Camp Good Days and Special Times, an organization that brings life-changing experiences to children diagnosed with cancer. A 24-hour dance marathon that features live performances and nonstop dancing, the Teddi Dance for Love helps children and families affected by cancer, all while creating memories that Fisher students will value for the rest of their lives.

SERVICE-LEARNING: The Center for Service-Learning and Civic Engagement helps incorporate community service into Fisher's academic courses. These acts of service help develop students' civic responsibility and compassion, all while enriching their education. Assignments, field trips, and workshops motivate students to think critically as they make a positive impact on their community. A small sample of service-learning opportunities include a sociology course that brings students in touch with elderly individuals so that they may discuss and analyze social trends of the human life course; a biology course that conducts research for the benefit of teenagers living with cancer; and an education course that provides literacy support to underprivileged children. It is through Fisher's service-learning program that courses come alive and allow students to see real results of their hard work.

CAREER CENTER: Fisher's Career Center staff are available to help students and alumni through every phase of their job searches. The Center hosts editing sessions to review students' résumés and cover letters, events that build their career networks, mock interview workshops that set them up for success, and so much more. Fisher's CareerZone acts as a hub for all the best resources, including job and internship postings, sample résumés, and strategy guides that make navigating the career-search process easy.

---

http://www.sjfc.edu/

P: (585) 385-8000

PRIVATE - CATHOLIC

STUDENT PROFILE

2,757 undergraduate students

95% of undergrad students are full time

40% male – 60% female

5% of students are from out of state

84% freshman retention rate

73% graduated in 6 years

FACULTY PROFILE

237 full-time faculty

214 part-time faculty

11 to 1 student/faculty ratio

ADMISSIONS

4,551 Total Applicants

2,937 Total Admissions

576 Total Freshman Enrollment

64.54% of applicants admitted

SAT Ranges: CR 480-560, M 490-590

ACT Ranges: C 22-26, M 21-26, E 20-25

TUITION & COSTS

Tuition: $32,540

Fees: $580

Total: $33,120

R&B: $12,150

Total: $45,270

FINANCIAL

$17,755 avg grant/scholarship amount (need)

$4,749 avg loan amount (need)

ST. JOSEPH'S COLLEGE

BROOKLYN, NEW YORK

Established in 1916, St. Joseph's College provides an affordable liberal arts education to a diverse group of students at its campuses at SJC Brooklyn, SJC Long Island, and SJC Online. Independent and coeducational, St. Joseph's prepares students for lives of integrity, intellectual and spiritual values, social responsibility, and service. These are lives that are worthy of the College's motto, Esse non videri, "To be and not to seem."

A COMPLETE EDUCATION: There are some things that just can't be learned in a classroom. At St. Joseph's College, students are encouraged to take part in fieldwork, research, internships, and study abroad prior to graduation. For instance, child study majors at St. Joseph's don't wait until senior year to become student teachers; they start logging teaching hours starting freshman year and graduate with four solid years of classroom experience. Recreation majors all complete internships at local health or recreation facilities; art students learn to analyze and appreciate art by visiting the Brooklyn Museum of Art or the Met; history students explore the architecture of hidden NYC neighborhoods; and biology students conduct research side-by-side with their professors.

STUDY ABROAD: Through the Office of Global Studies at St. Joseph's College, students are given the opportunity to travel while earning credits that enhance their education. Abroad, students can improve their foreign language skills and boost their marketability when the time comes to choose a career. Most recently, St. Joseph's students have studied in Australia, Bangkok, Budapest, Ecuador, Greece, Italy, Japan, London, Paris, Prague, Spain, and Vienna.

COMMON HOUR: Every day, St. Joseph's students take a break for Common Hour from 1-2 p.m., gathering for both planned activities and spontaneous fun. This is their time to listen to guest lecturers, debate contemporary issues, enjoy live music or dance performances, or just get to know their professors and fellow students over lunch.

THE RIGHT DIRECTION: One of the most important things students do at St. Joseph's College is bring the future into focus while making the most of the here and now. Through individual attention and interactive advisement, St. Joseph's meets students where they are academically. Its faculty guide students through the essential steps to help them grow intellectually, personally, and professionally.

THE OFFICE OF MULTICULTURAL STUDENT LIFE: The Office of Multicultural Student Life provides students with an opportunity to celebrate and embrace the diversity of the world through a variety of educational programs including off-campus trips, interactive workshops, and events. These programs can be linked to courses within academic such departments as Speech Communication, English, Modern Languages, Criminal Justice, History, Music, and Psychology. The Office has sponsored trips to diversity-related conferences, Broadway plays, and even the monumental inauguration of Barack Obama. In addition, students are encouraged to dialogue about current events and other hot topics that educate and empower them to express, question, learn and transform. All of these experiences promote and support their academic, personal, and professional growth.

CAREER SERVICES: The Office of Career Development and Engagement assists students with job searches, internship opportunities, and career assessment tools. The mission of the Office of Career Development and Engagement is to foster career development that educates, inspires confidence, and empowers students and alumni to clarify and attain their goals. The Office's vision is to assist students and alumni in discovering and exploring possibilities and develop the strategies necessary to make mindful career decisions. The counselors in the Office of Career Development and Engagement provide students and alumni with a strong foundation upon which to learn about their skills and interests. Counselors help students with résumés, cover letters, interviews, and personal statements. Students are also given assistance in identifying and exploring career options of interest.

http://www.sjcny.edu/

P: (718) 940-5800

PRIVATE - CATHOLIC

STUDENT PROFILE

3,878 undergraduate students

81% of undergrad students are full time

34% male – 66% female

2% of students are from out of state

86% freshman retention rate

68% graduated in 6 years

FACULTY PROFILE

169 full-time faculty

11 to 1 student/faculty ratio

ADMISSIONS

3,220 Total Applicants

2,187 Total Admissions

516 Total Freshman Enrollment

67.92% of applicants admitted

SAT Ranges: CR 450-550, M 460-560, W 440-540

ACT Ranges: C 19-24

TUITION & COSTS

Tuition: $23,500

Fees: $623

Total: $24,123

FINANCIAL

$11,383 avg grant/scholarship amount (need)

$4,375 avg loan amount (need)

ST. THOMAS AQUINAS COLLEGE

SPARKILL, NEW YORK

From the day students first arrive, St. Thomas Aquinas College celebrates their strengths, talents, and individuality. The College encourages students to push past their limits and strive for great things, providing the opportunities for them to learn and grow in mind, body, and soul. With a choice of leading-edge academic programs, exciting field experiences, NCAA Division II athletics, and an array of student clubs, students can explore their creativity and meet new friends. Anyone can be who they are in a place where everyone knows their name.

INSIDE THE CLASSROOM: St. Thomas Aquinas College students are presenting scholarly research at international conferences; forensic science majors are interning with the local sheriff's department to investigate crimes; biology students are conducting hypothesis-driven research in state-of-the-art labs; and future educators are working with faculty to enrich science education through digital literacy and 3D gaming. These opportunities prepare students to land jobs and/or pursue graduate study after graduation.

BEYOND THE CLASSROOM: STAC students study abroad and expand their global breadth and understanding, traveling to France, Spain, Italy, and other countries all over the world. Honors students can also look forward to a study abroad experience at Oxford University in England.

IN THE COMMUNITY: The largest organization on campus, the Spartan Volunteers, hosts fundraisers for local nonprofits, collects books for underprivileged inner-city schools, and gives food and clothing to New York City's homeless population during the popular monthly Midnight Run. These are just a few examples of how St. Thomas Aquinas students are reaching out to those in need and educating students to be responsible citizens.

INVOLVED PROFESSORS: At St. Thomas Aquinas College, a personalized education builds upon each student's strengths and talents. This is possible through STAC's small class sizes and extraordinary educators who are deeply committed to getting to know their students' unique needs. The faculty work side-by-side with students to help them grow intellectually, applying their knowledge to solve problems in the real world. Professors get to know their students personally and provide helpful advice to guide them through fulfilling years at STAC.

ACCESS TO ALUMNI: The St. Thomas Aquinas College Career Network provides students and alumni various opportunities to develop their skills through internships, virtual career fairs, etiquette seminars, résumé-building workshops, and mock interviews. The College pairs students with alumni from around the nation and world, creating a collegial and relaxed setting for an exchange of real-world perspectives. Oftentimes, these relationships lead to internship and employment opportunities, channels for sound professional advice, and everlasting friendships.

PREPARATION THAT LEADS TO RESULTS: St. Thomas Aquinas College puts tools at students' fingertips for them to build their confidence and become polished job candidates. Whatever career students choose, STAC prepares them to enter tomorrow's workforce with the knowledge and skills they need to succeed.

SUCCESSFUL ALUMNI: STAC alumni show the value of their education by achieving success in careers across a wide range of industries and by pursuing advanced degrees in medicine, law, and education. St. Thomas Aquinas College alumni include CEOs of international corporations, financial analysts at leading investment firms, social media experts, and award-winning journalists. They are teachers educating new generations, doctors who heal the sick, lawyers and politicians working to ensure justice, and performers who are entertaining audiences across the nation. In so many diverse professional paths, graduates of St. Thomas Aquinas College are applying their education to achieve their personal best, reach out to others, and make the world a better place.

http://www.stac.edu/

P: (845) 398-4100

PRIVATE

STUDENT PROFILE

1,696 undergraduate students

66% of undergrad students are full time

44% male – 56% female

18% of students are from out of state

82% freshman retention rate

55% graduated in 6 years

FACULTY PROFILE

60 full-time faculty

104 part-time faculty

15 to 1 student/faculty ratio

ADMISSIONS

1,918 Total Applicants

1,513 Total Admissions

276 Total Freshman Enrollment

78.88% of applicants admitted

SAT Ranges: CR 410-520, M 420-530, W 410-510

ACT Ranges: C 18-22

TUITION & COSTS

Tuition: $28,240

Fees: $500

Total: $28,740

R&B: $12,720

Room: $7,180

Board: $5,540

Total: $41,460

FINANCIAL

$19,703 avg grant/scholarship amount (total)

$7,381 avg loan amount (total)

SUNY BUFFALO STATE

BUFFALO, NEW YORK

SUNY Buffalo State is among the most diverse colleges in the SUNY system, a characteristic that's reflected in the myriad people, ideas, experiences, and program offerings found on campus. Located in the second largest city in New York state, SUNY Buffalo State offers extensive undergraduate research opportunities, internships, service-learning programs, and career development services that benefit students and the community alike.

UNDERGRADUATE RESEARCH: Undergraduate research is one of the College's most popular outlets through which to encourage student achievement and progression. Each year, hundreds of undergraduate students gain hands-on experience in their fields by partnering with faculty members on research projects. Activities include an annual student research symposium, a summer research fellowship program, a small grants program to support academic-year research, travel support for students presenting/performing at professional meetings and conferences, and faculty development opportunities related to undergraduate research.

ALL-COLLEGE HONORS PROGRAM: Available only by special admission, the All-College Honors Program offers select students exclusive honors classes as well as honors credit through a variety of disciplines. Special honors suites and lounges, as well as the luxury of priority registration, are available to participating scholars.

THE INTELLECTUAL FOUNDATIONS PROGRAM: Designed to provide the intellectual and creative foundations for all students, the Intellectual Foundations core curriculum reflects the College's commitment to the liberal arts and the empowerment to succeed in a challenging world.

INTERNATIONAL AND EXCHANGE PROGRAMS: International and Exchange Programs are dedicated to promoting the "internationalization" of the SUNY Buffalo State campus. They work to integrate of the College's international and national off-campus study opportunities, helping students prepare for careers in the fast-paced, cross-cultural global economy.

CENTER FOR THE DEVELOPMENT OF HUMAN SERVICES: The Center for the Development of Human Services offers a comprehensive menu of management, supervisory, and worker training programs that enable students to learn how to serve their future clients in a highly effective manner.

CENTER FOR HEALTH AND SOCIAL RESEARCH: Working as an integral component of Buffalo State to provide collaboration between students, faculty, and staff in intellectual development, the Center for Health and Social Research works to investigate basic and applied research topics that are among the most pressing in today's society.

WORD SWAG: Word Swag is no ordinary writing workshop; rather, it is a youth-driven space in which people gather to explore the written word while expressing themselves through various writing-based activities.

BUFFALO BEGINNINGS: The Buffalo Beginnings Program brings together recently resettled refugee youth who have yet to begin school and helps them learn more and acclimate to their new environment. This program introduces students of all ages, as well as their parents, to the American educational system, their new community, and American culture.

MONTHLY SERVICE CORPS: The monthly Service Corps initiative brings together Buffalo student volunteers with local youth who are interested in community service. Participants design and perform a monthly service project at local organizations.

BUFFALO STATE
The State University of New York

http://www.buffalostate.edu/
P: (716) 878-4017

PUBLIC

STUDENT PROFILE

9,187 undergraduate students

89% of undergrad students are full time

43% male – 57% female

1% of students are from out of state

71% freshman retention rate

49% graduated in 6 years

FACULTY PROFILE

383 full-time faculty

463 part-time faculty

16 to 1 student/faculty ratio

ADMISSIONS

13,679 Total Applicants

8,524 Total Admissions

1,859 Total Freshman Enrollment

62.31% of applicants admitted

SAT Ranges: CR 400-500, M 400-500

ACT Ranges: C 16-22

TUITION & COSTS

Tuition: (In) $6,470 (Out) $16,320

Fees: $1,199

Total: (In) $7,669 (Out) $17,519

R&B: $12,332

Room: $7,342

Board: $4,990

Total: (In) $20,001 (Out) $29,851

FINANCIAL

$7,576 avg grant/scholarship amount (total)

$6,409 avg loan amount (total)

SUNY GENESEO

GENESEO, NEW YORK

SUNY Geneseo takes intellectual minds, transforms them to see their abilities, and then shows them how to be socially responsible citizens. Students enrolled at Geneseo are part of a collaborative environment in which academics meet civic engagement.

FIRST-YEAR ADIRONDACK ADVENTURE: The First Year Adirondack Adventure is an awesome excursion available to incoming freshmen. Participants travel to Lake Placid and spend five days staying at a youth hostel and getting to know other new members of the SUNY Geneseo community. Many times, students are anxious about leaving home for college, but the Adirondack Adventure eases their transition through team-building activities and close interaction with their new friends and professors.

EDGAR FELLOWS PROGRAM: The Edgar Fellows Program is the honors sector of Geneseo. Students in the program are selected for their strong record of academic excellence and personal motivation. Edgar fellows belong to a small community of academically inclined individuals that seek a challenge in their educational experiences. Participants benefit from academic and personal support, along with research opportunities and co-curricular activities.

THE EDGAR FELLOWS CAPSTONE EXPERIENCE: The Edgar Fellows Program is a culminating capstone experience that allows students to explore their passions beyond their coursework. Students design their own research, write a critical analysis, and give an oral presentation on a subject that focuses their studies into a specific topic of interest. Projects can range from a senior thesis to community service. In any case, they demonstrate intellectual integrity, purpose, and a true sense of engaged enthusiasm.

WASHINGTON INTERNSHIP PROGRAM: The Washington Internship Program is a study away option that offers countless benefits and leadership opportunities. Participants of the program experience a near full-time internship, an academic course, and a Leadership Forum. Students build professional networks through interaction with industry leaders.

YOUBELONG: YouBelong is a program tailored to the academic and social needs of transfer students. YouBelong comfortably transitions students into the campus community through resources and opportunities to get involved and merge into their new environment. Students can receive individual guidance if they feel they are falling behind, and there are plenty of activities to address many of their needs and goals. Some of the activities include a transfer student picnic, the student organization expo fair, and a volunteer fair.

INTERNSHIPS: Internships are a great way to gain industry knowledge and hands-on experience in one's field of study. Geneseo encourages its students to seek out internship opportunities so that they are better prepared to enter into a career after graduation. The University's Internship Program offers upperclassmen the chance to engage in field work during their undergraduate experience, allowing participants to exchange part of their class time for hands-on work in a professional setting.

DEPARTMENT OF CAREER DEVELOPMENT: The Department of Career Development is the number-one resource for exploring, finding, and securing postgraduate positions. Through various programs and support, staff are able to assist students with tough decisions for their future. The office offers assistance with résumés and cover letters, postgraduate options, career exploration, jobs and internships, and interviewing.

GENESEO
THE STATE UNIVERSITY OF NEW YORK

https://www.geneseo.edu/
P: (585) 245-5211

PUBLIC

STUDENT PROFILE

5,583 undergraduate students

98% of undergrad students are full time

40% male – 60% female

2% of students are from out of state

89% freshman retention rate

82% graduated in 6 years

FACULTY PROFILE

252 full-time faculty

98 part-time faculty

20 to 1 student/faculty ratio

ADMISSIONS

9,118 Total Applicants

6,632 Total Admissions

1,330 Total Freshman Enrollment

72.74% of applicants admitted

SAT Ranges: CR 550-640, M 550-650

ACT Ranges: C 25-29

TUITION & COSTS

Tuition: (In) $6,470 (Out) $16,320

Fees: $1,643

Total: (In) $8,113 (Out) $17,963

R&B: $12,456

Room: $7,510

Board: $4,946

Total: (In) $20,569 (Out) $30,419

FINANCIAL

$6,367 avg grant/scholarship amount (total)

$6,744 avg loan amount (total)

SUNY NEW PALTZ

NEW PALTZ, NEW YORK

The State University of New York at New Paltz is an academically rigorous public university in the heart of New York State's scenic Hudson Valley, just 90 minutes north of metropolitan New York City. It's a uniquely diverse community, where people from around the world can "come as they are" and collaborate in a friendly, tolerant, and supportive environment. At New Paltz, artists work with entrepreneurs to add smart design to business plans, engineers partner with future teachers to bring technology into the k-12 classroom, and the liberal arts provide a core set of adaptable skills that make NP alumni stand out in their pursuit of post-graduation success.

STUDY ABROAD: SUNY New Paltz is a leader in helping students broaden their worldview with international study. More than 20 percent of New Paltz students study abroad (even first-years!) at programs in Paris, Cairo, Tokyo, Prague, Melbourne, Buenos Aires, London, Madrid, Jerusalem, Seoul, Rome, and dozens of other destinations. The award-winning Center for International Programs works tirelessly to make study abroad a reality for New Paltz students, helping them find and apply for competitive scholarships like the Benjamin A. Gilman International Scholarship and the Boren Scholarship.

3D PRINTING AND HVAMC: SUNY New Paltz is home to the Hudson Valley Advanced Manufacturing Center (HVAMC), where digital fabrication experts work with one of the largest and most advanced collections of 3D printers anywhere in the U.S. The HVAMC partners with businesses to provide innovative manufacturing solutions, but it's also an educational resource, offering classes in Computer-Aided Design (CAD) software and helping New Paltz students of all majors—engineers, artists, future teachers, and entrepreneurs—integrate 3D printing technologies into their education.

THE BENJAMIN CENTER FOR PUBLIC POLICY RESEARCH: The Benjamin Center for Public Policy Research at SUNY New Paltz is a one-of-a-kind organization in which students and faculty work on policy issues that move the news cycle. It serves the New York community with applied research and evaluative studies, giving students unique opportunities to work with lawmakers, businesses, educators, and media outlets on projects that truly affect people's lives. The Benjamin Center also supports The Legislative Gazette, the premier public affairs-reporting internship program that enables students to learn reporting on state government.

SUSTAINABILITY: At SUNY New Paltz, responsibility to the environment is not only a way of life, but it's also included in the curriculum. The College has a dedicated Office of Campus Sustainability, which works with students, faculty, and administrators to protect the Earth and reduce energy costs through sustainable practices. New Paltz is also a great place for students interested in green careers, with degree programs and concentrations that focus on sustainability in science and engineering, business, social sciences, and other disciplines.

LIVING-LEARNING COMMUNITIES: The Communities at New Paltz program is designed to bring together students with similar interests for shared experiences both in and out of the classroom. Students can opt in to one of these communities and gain access to a strong network of residence life staff, community mentors, and peer students, focusing on issues that can define their educations. In addition to living-learning communities that are reserved exclusively for freshmen, SUNY New Paltz welcomes all students to apply for membership in the Sustainability LLC, which promotes engagement with environmental issues; the Rivera House LGBTQA+ LLC, where students can be part of a network of change-agents working for feminist, queer, and anti-racist causes; and the East-West LLC and the Romance Languages LLC, which each fosters cultural exchange and collaboration—the former between American, Chinese, and Japanese students, and the latter between American, French, Italian, Spanish, and Latin American students.

https://www.newpaltz.edu/
P: (845) 257-3200

PUBLIC

STUDENT PROFILE

6,582 undergraduate students

94% of undergrad students are full-time

38% male – 62% female

3% of students are from out of state

87.2% freshman retention rate

72% graduated in 6 years

FACULTY PROFILE

372 full-time faculty

302 part-time faculty

15 to 1 student-to-faculty ratio

ADMISSIONS

14,042 Total Applicants

6,030 Total Admissions

1,092 Total Freshman Enrollment

42.94% of applicants admitted

SAT Ranges: CR 500-600, M 510-600

ACT Ranges: C 23-27, M 22-26, E 22-27

TUITION & COSTS

Tuition: (In) $6,470 (Out) $16,320

Fees: $1,363

Total: (In) $7,833 (Out) $17,683

R&B: $12,642

Room: $8,501

Board: $4,141

Total: (In) $20,475 (Out) $30,325

FINANCIAL

$5,016 avg grant/scholarship amount (need)

$4,293 avg loan amount (need)

SUNY ONEONTA

ONEONTA, NEW YORK

SUNY Oneonta is a mid-size, public liberal arts and sciences college with a pre-professional focus. Located in the beautiful hills of Central New York, Oneonta is part of the 64-campus State University of New York system. The University enrolls approximately 6,000 students in a wide variety of bachelor's degree programs as well as a number of graduate certificates and degrees.

FRESHMEN FIRST: Freshmen are engaged in their learning before classes even begin. Faculty and peer mentors from the Earth and Atmospheric Sciences Department lead GEOFYRST, a six-day, pre-semester field trip that explores the geology of New York and the Northeast. And, through the annual Common Read, all incoming freshmen are asked to read the same diversity-related book, which is then discussed in fall courses across several disciplines. As part of the program, the author of this book visits the campus to present the Mills Distinguished Lecture and interact with students.

STUDENT-FACULTY RESEARCH: Faculty members frequently invite students to participate in research projects. For example, students in Jacqueline Bennett's undergraduate research group helped test a green chemistry process that won a United States patent in 2014, and nine biology alumni co-authored a paper that was published in an international parasitology journal, synthesizing six years of undergraduate research with parasitology expert Florian Reyda at SUNY Oneonta's Biological Field Station. Students also do independent research on topics of their own choosing and present them at the annual Student Research & Creative Activity Day on campus. Grant awards of up to $1,500 are available for independent research and creative activity projects in any discipline. Many students also present their research at regional and national conferences, the travel for which is funded by the University.

GLOBAL CONNECTIONS: Each year, more than 500 students complete credit-bearing internships in their fields. Locations range from the Oneonta region to international destinations across 11 countries. The college also offers study abroad and exchange opportunities in 12 countries, including popular semester, year-long, or summer fashion programs at the Istituto Europeo di Design in Milan. Students can otherwise choose from more than 600 international programs offered through other SUNY institutions.

CIVIC-MINDED COMMUNITY: Community service is a big part of the Oneonta experience. Many courses incorporate service-learning activities, and more than 20 percent of students volunteer through the Center for Social Responsibility and Community (CSRC). In the spring, the CSRC hosts its signature event, "Into the Streets," a day of service that brings more than 600 students together with community volunteers to collaborate on projects at local schools, parks, and nonprofit organizations. In addition to volunteering, Oneonta students support a variety of causes through club activities. The annual American Cancer Society Relay for Life, co-hosted by the Colleges Against Cancer chapters at SUNY Oneonta and nearby Hartwick College, raised a record $67,000 in 2015. Even the Harry Potter Club is civic-minded, holding an annual Yule Ball to benefit "Oneonta Reading Is Fundamental," a nonprofit organization that distributes free books to elementary school children.

LIVING LEARNING COMMUNITIES: As of fall 2017, SUNY Oneonta offers four Living Learning Communities (LLCs) for freshmen interested in pre-health professions; leadership; sustainability and the outdoors; and teaching and social justice. Benefits of living in an LLC include mentoring, special programs, and the chance to live with other new students who have similar interests.

SUSTAINABILITY: Students are involved in a variety of activities to protect the natural environment. Several clubs have a sustainability focus, and some students work as volunteers at the Red Closet Thrift Shop on campus. Student-driven projects can even receive sustainability grants; recent awards have funded the purchase of fruit trees for the campus as well as a program to raise awareness about post-consumer food waste in the dining halls.

SUNY ONEONTA

http://suny.oneonta.edu/
P: (607) 436-3500

PUBLIC

STUDENT PROFILE

5,825 undergraduate students

99% of undergrad students are full time

40% male – 60% female

1.4% of students are from out of state

86% freshman retention rate

72% graduated in 6 years

FACULTY PROFILE

280 full-time faculty

143 part-time faculty

18 to 1 student/faculty ratio

ADMISSIONS

11,427 Total Applicants

5,567 Total Admissions

1,130 Total Freshman Enrollment

48.72% of applicants admitted

SAT Ranges: CR 490-580, M 510-590

ACT Ranges: C 22-25

TUITION & COSTS

Tuition: (In) $6,170 (Out) $15,820

Fees: $1,398

Total: (In) $7,568 (Out) $17,218

R&B: $11,100

Total: (In) $18,668 (Out) $28,318

FINANCIAL

$7,000 avg grant/scholarship amount (need)

$4,189 avg loan amount (need)

SUNY OSWEGO

OSWEGO, NEW YORKA

SUNY Oswego's dynamic, interactive, and supportive environment excites students to tackle a breadth liberal arts studies alongside their career-directed majors. The possibilities are endless with an extensive choice of academic options, outstanding faculty, and challenging courses that encourage an active exchange of ideas. Oswego opens a door to the future with a large offering of internships, co-ops, service-learning, and study abroad, all of which consistently rate among the highest in the SUNY system.

BEAUTIFUL ENVIRONMENT, GREAT PEOPLE: SUNY Oswego's more than 700-acre, tree-lined campus is spread along the southern shore of majestic Lake Ontario—an awesome sight and the backdrop for some of the world's most spectacular sunsets. On one side of the Oswego campus lies the scenic Lake Ontario shoreline, and on the other side sits a tranquil town noted for its charming shops and restaurants. Students rave about their beautiful campus, a mix of historically registered buildings and newly constructed facilities that are all equipped with environmentally friendly technology. The Oswego campus, in proximity to both Syracuse and Rochester, New York, is easily reachable by car, rail, and air alike. And the town of Oswego itself is known for its welcoming attitude toward SUNY students.

CONNECTIONS FOR THE FUTURE: SUNY Oswego is small enough for anyone to make quality connections with faculty and fellow students while still being big enough to provide many avenues to unlimited horizons. The University offers more than 110 programs of study, including accounting, zoology, and a wealth of majors in between. Beyond those, SUNY Oswego continues to evolve with the changing needs in education; its newest major of electrical and computer engineering and a master's in biomedical health informatics are just two examples of pioneering programs designed to meet newer workforce demands. Highly rated experiences outside the classroom include a vibrant student involvement culture, plentiful internships, and a world of study abroad options that open doors to personal growth, career development, and the many moments that make Oswego so loved by its tens of thousands of proud alumni.

RESIDING WITH PURPOSE: SUNY Oswego offers a variety of programs for incoming first-year students. Johnson Hall houses approximately 240 students who participate in the school's nationally recognized First-Year Residential Experience program. This program aims to support students throughout their first year of college and prepare them for their future years at the University. And, after the first year, students can also take part in other community-building residence halls. Living and Learning Communities have students live in the same residence halls and take common classes with others who have similar interests, providing them a constant stream of opportunities to make connections with those around them. The Hart Hall Global Living and Learning Center, for example, focuses on programs that emphasize community service and global-themed courses.

BEYOND THE BOOKS: SUNY Oswego enrolls over 7,000 full-time undergraduate students in an encouraging, challenging, and open-minded environment. Notable for its high level of student participation in international study, SUNY Oswego has been ranked in the top 10 nationally among colleges of its size for study abroad programs. Study abroad options for Oswego students include such locations as Europe (Austria, the Czech Republic, England, France, Germany, Hungary, Ireland, Spain, and Italy), Ecuador, Peru, China, Japan, Australia, New Zealand, Mexico, Benin, and Cuba. Better yet, those who study abroad pay the same tuition overseas as they would on campus.

LEARN BY DOING: The Center for Experiential Learning helps students connect to numerous internship opportunities. Recently, students have prepared for careers in nearly every profession through internships with various broadcast networks and stations (ABC, CBS, NBC, FOX, MTV); the Federal Aviation Administration; PwC; the New York Yankees; Walt Disney World; and many others. Although SUNY Oswego has received many awards and recognitions for its high standard of education, the real testament to the quality of education are the 83,000 successful alumni who span the globe. For example, an Oswego broadcasting degree launched the careers of NBC's Al Roker and ESPN's Linda Cohn and Steve Levy.

Sidebar

http://www.oswego.edu/

P: (315) 312-2250

PUBLIC

STUDENT PROFILE

7,155 undergraduate students

96% of undergrad students are full time

49% male – 51% female

3.5% of students are from out of state

80% freshman retention rate

66% graduated in 6 years

FACULTY PROFILE

359 full-time faculty

214 part-time faculty

17 to 1 student/faculty ratio

ADMISSIONS

10,715 Total Applicants

5,824 Total Admissions

1,440 Total Freshman Enrollment

54% of applicants admitted

SAT Ranges: CR 500-590, M 510-600

ACT Ranges: C 22-27

TUITION & COSTS)

Tuition: (In) $6,670 (Out) $16,320

Fees: $1,521

Total: (In) $8,191 (Out) $17,841

R&B: $13,740

Room: $8,590

Board: $5,150

Total: (In) $21,931 (Out) $31,581

FINANCIAL

$7,538 avg grant/scholarship amount (need)

$4602 avg loan amount (need)

THE KING'S COLLEGE

NEW YORK, NEW YORKT

THE KING'S COLLEGE
NEW YORK CITY

The King's College is a Christian liberal arts college in New York City. It seeks students who desire to engage the world and transform society through principled leadership grounded in biblical truth. King's students become men and women of integrity and competence, well prepared for rewarding careers.

FIRST-YEAR SEMINARS AND EXPERIENCES: First-year students are offered an optional accelerated course called "Touchstone: Design Your Life at King's." This course introduces students to the principles of "design thinking," a process of creative discovery and problem solving, equipping them with tips to use their strengths in both coursework and community life as well as tools for self-awareness, self-management, and thriving in college and beyond. Additionally, the House System provides an immediate community for all students with wide range of activities that connect them to their Housemates and the broader King's community.

COMMON INTELLECTUAL EXPERIENCES: All King's students complete a core curriculum in addition to the courses in their chosen major. This core curriculum was inspired by Oxford University's program in Politics, Philosophy, and Economics. It is designed to familiarize all students with history, Christianity, Western philosophy, and the economic and political theories generated by these forces. The addition of the core to a student's chosen field of study helps develop the critical thinking and communications skills they need to succeed whether they are writing scripts, arguing court cases, or working on Wall Street.

WRITING-INTENSIVE COURSES: In accordance with the College's mission, King's students must be able to write well. They must meet deadlines; command a variety of tones, genres, and formats; and discern the right approach for their audiences. Writing courses are capped at seventeen students so that each one can receive individual feedback and guidance on their writing skills. Knowing that a few writing courses are not enough to develop excellent writers, the College also incorporates writing assignments into the majority of its courses. Within the core alone, 84% of the courses require significant writing assignments. And, when it's appropriate for course content, faculty members assign frequent writing exercises and grade written assignments with as much emphasis on the quality of the students' writing as on the substance of their papers.

INTERREGNUM: One of King's most unique traditions is Interregnum, a three-day event in April. The entire school gathers for competitions in speech and debate, performing arts, visual arts, academic and creative writing, and more. These three days are the culmination of a yearlong study of a theme that is established the preceding summer. Previous themes have included Compassion, Mortality, and Ambition. The entire school participates, giving students the opportunity to use their unique talents and help their House win.

UNDERGRADUATE RESEARCH: Seniors who achieve academic distinction may choose to complete a research-writing or creative project with a professor of their choice. Students serving as Faculty Assistants frequently contribute collaborative research to the scholarly pursuits of their faculty supervisors. A number of students have also, under the mentorship of faculty in and out of classes, published reviews and op-ed pieces in such national media as Christianity Today, National Review, and Forbes.com.

DIVERSITY AND GLOBAL LEARNING: The International Ventures program at King's offers students a series of short-term, summer, and semester-long experiences, some with academic credit and others for enrichment and service. Destinations typically include key European cities like Paris, Florence, and Berlin; Indonesia; Israel (in partnership with Passages Israel); Australia, Latin America, the Middle East, and Uganda (in partnership with the Council for Christian Colleges and Universities); the Caribbean; and, for academically qualified students, a semester at Oxford (in partnership with Summit Oxford).

https://www.tkc.edu/
P: (888) 969-7200

PRIVATE - CHRISTIAN

STUDENT PROFILE
513 undergraduate students
95% of undergrad students are full time
38% male – 62% female
66% freshman retention rate
45% graduated in 6 years

FACULTY PROFILE
27 full-time faculty
17 part-time faculty
15 to 1 student/faculty ratio

ADMISSIONS
2,529 Total Applicants
1,001 Total Admissions
150 Total Freshman Enrollment
39.58% of applicants admitted

SAT Ranges: CR 550-660, M 520-590, W 530-640

ACT Ranges: C 24-29, M 21-26, E 24-31

TUITION & COSTS
Tuition: $32,870
Fees: $400
Total: $3,270
R&B: $13,000
Total: $46,270

FINANCIAL
$21,783 avg grant/scholarship amount (need)
$3,235 avg loan amount (need)

THE SAGE COLLEGES

ALBANY, NEW YORK

Sage is a community of scholars committed to empowering its students. Interdisciplinary academics, community engagement, international exposure, and artistic and athletic endeavors are among the pillars of the educational experience at The Sage Colleges. Altogether, Sage enrolls more than 3,000 students in bachelor's, master's, and doctoral programs.

INDIVIDUALIZED EDUCATION EXPERIENCE: Sage students and faculty comment again and again on the centrality of close working relationships throughout the educational experience. From introductory courses to advanced, individually tailored study projects, this personalization and flexibility is apparent. Just one example is an anthropology course that is team taught by the College's president and another professor. Its theme intertwines with the school's fall theater production, so students from the class and the production interact, as will all members of the community who attend a performance.

DEGREE OPTIONS: On the Troy campus, Sage has introduced the Discovery Degree, a three-year BA program that allows students to earn their degree a year sooner or to advance to a Sage graduate program if they chose. Many Sage students enter College expecting to continue for a master's degree. Through the Discovery Degree, they can plan their courses in order to facilitate a "fast track" into a wide variety of advanced degree programs.

MANAGEMENT SIMULATION: Sage offers the only management program in the Northeast to offer a certain new finance simulation to give students practice before they work for banks, brokerage firms, or traders. And recently, Sage has been offering a cutting-edge strategy simulation class to give students experience in managing a firm from all aspects of business—marketing, finance, and operations. Students get a macro, birds-eye view of running a business, differing greatly from the pigeonholed view of most business schools in the country.

SERVICE-LEARNING: Sage has partnered with the Greater Capital Region Teacher Center and three other universities to create Project SLATE (Service-Learning and Teacher Education) to teach future professors how to utilize community service as a vehicle for teaching and learning. As Sage President Susan Scrimshaw said, "Service-learning is one of the best ways for students to learn; it provides them with experience and preparation for lives as engaged citizens. It also provides our Colleges with concrete ways to give back to our communities and to model good citizenship. At Sage, we urge our students to be engaged in our local and global communities; to be excellent in academics; and to hone skills relevant to the 21st century." For service-learning projects and activities, Project SLATE draws on the resources of existing partnerships with diverse youth and family, early childhood, social service, and community-based educational enrichment and advocacy organizations in the region.

TROY AND ALBANY: In both Troy and Albany, a vast array of opportunities exist to network, learn, play, and work. The area is home to a number of major museums, teaching hospitals, the New York State capital, community service organizations, and some of the largest international corporations.

THE CAREER PLANNING OFFICE: Sage takes advantage of all the networking resources of the region, whether they be in finance, manufacturing, research, consulting, or other fields. The Career Planning Office works with students as early as their first year to help them think about the skills they'll need in order to succeed in their chosen career. The office also helps students develop ways to present themselves to graduate schools and employers. This careful preparation, along with the inherent value of Sage graduates, reflects in Sage's consistent 97% placement rate.

http://www.sage.edu/
P: (518) 292-1730

PRIVATE

STUDENT PROFILE

1,634 undergraduate students

87% of undergrad students are full time

20% male – 80% female

10% of students are from out of state

78% freshman retention rate

60% graduated in 6 years

FACULTY PROFILE

140 full-time faculty

13 part-time faculty

12 to 1 student/faculty ratio

ADMISSIONS

2,495 Total Applicants

1,345 Total Admissions

263 Total Freshman Enrollment

53.91% of applicants admitted

TUITION & COSTS

Tuition: $27,000

Fees: $1,400

Total: $28,400

R&B: $12,220

Room: $6,330

Board: $5,890

Total: $40,620

FINANCIAL

$24,155 avg grant/scholarship amount (total)

$7,469 avg loan amount (total)

UNIVERSITY AT ALBANY, SUNY

ALBANY, NEW YORK

The University at Albany, founded in 1844, is an agent of positive change in terms of academic success, professional development, and global good. With nine schools and colleges, the University offers innovative programs paired with hands-on learning, enabling students to gain impressive skills for their careers.

STUDY ABROAD: Students have access to 1,000+ programs across the globe in such places as China, Costa Rica, and Great Britain. Any UAlbany student can explore culture, tradition, and language through the trip of a lifetime! They can volunteer at an orphanage, research a dying language, shadow in a hospital, study from another perspective, and more. Regardless of which academic path they choose, students have many options to study with a wide selection of summer, winter, spring break, semester, and full academic year programs.

LIVING-LEARNING COMMUNITIES: Students can opt to live in one of 25 small communities based on a common interest or academic path. They live together, take two classes together, and enjoy a weekly lunch with their faculty mentor. Choices vary from the World of Wellbeing and Fitness to the World of Politics to the World of Zombies. Leadership opportunities also exist for students through this program, as they can apply to be World Representatives or World Ambassadors who assist in the community-building process.

INTERNSHIPS: Students looking for job, internship, and fellowship opportunities use UAlbany's online database, Handshake, to find the perfect experience for them. From part-time jobs during the semester to post-graduation, full-time positions, Handshake provides a way for students and recent alumni to connect directly with recruiters.

HONORS COLLEGE: The Honors College provides a home for students who seek an academic challenge through a small community of dedicated scholars. Small, innovative classes with discussions, field experiences, debates, simulations, and group projects allow students to develop critical thinking skills. Honors Courses range in topic, covering such subjects as Weather and Climate Issues for the 21st Century, Genomics and Biotechnology, and Writing About Love and Loss.

HEAR FROM WORLD LEADERS: From Bill Nye the Science Guy to Supreme Court Justice Sonia Sotomayor, students experience the highest level of excellence and achievement through UAlbany's Speaker Series. World leaders and thinkers are brought to campus each year to inspire students to reach higher and dream bigger.

MAKE A DIFFERENCE: New York's capital city is a diverse landscape where urban and rural meet, filled with a range of outlets for volunteer work. Local nonprofits and campus groups provide opportunities to volunteer across all areas, including teaching, health care, policy, and environmental work. Over 7,000 students participate in volunteer endeavors each year.

LISTEN TO FAMOUS AUTHORS: To enhance and celebrate writing and the arts, the NYS Writers Institute hosts approximately 40 writers each year at UAlbany, all of whom collaborate to conduct seminars, writing workshops, and readings. The University also partners with Fence Magazine, which is recognized as one of the top literary journals in the nation.

RECEIVE FREE BUSINESS HELP: Students can receive free business help from the Blackstone LaunchPad center on campus, where an expert venture coach helps to turn ideas for businesses into a reality. UAlbany is one of only 25 LaunchPad-university partnerships in the nation.

GET INVOLVED: With 300+ clubs and organizations, students can choose from cultural, political, religious, academic, pre-professional, and recreational options. Competitions, fundraisers, fashion shows, cultural events and performances, dinners, and more happen each day on campus.

CONNECT WITH ALUMS: UAlbany's 176,000+ alumni network offers students a lifelong connection to a worldwide community. The UAlbany Career Advisory Network is an online database that enables students to connect with alumni professionals and ask for career advice.

UNIVERSITY AT ALBANY
State University of New York

http://www.albany.edu/

P: (518) 442-3300

PUBLIC

STUDENT PROFILE

12,955 undergraduate students

96% of undergrad students are full time

51% male – 49% female

68% of students are from out of state

84% freshman retention rate

65.7% graduated in 6 years

FACULTY PROFILE

684 full-time faculty

504 part-time faculty

18 to 1 student/faculty ratio

ADMISSIONS

23,799 Total Applicants

12,944 Total Admissions

2,725 Total Freshman Enrollment

54.39% of applicants admitted

SAT Ranges: CR 500-580, M 510-590

ACT Ranges: C 22-26

TUITION & COSTS

Tuition: (In) $6,470 (Out) $21,550

Fees: $2,753

Total: (In) $9,223 (Out) $24,303

R&B: $12,942

Room: $8,042

Board: $4,900

Total: (In) $22,165 (Out) $37,245

FINANCIAL

$7,679 avg grant/scholarship amount (need)

$4,585 avg loan amount (need)

ALLEGHENY COLLEGE

MEADVILLE, PENNSYLVANIA

Allegheny College treats the undergraduate period as a holistic experience in which students are developed to be more than just intellectual beings; they are molded into thoughtful leaders and contributors.

FIRST-YEAR/SOPHOMORE REQUIREMENT: The First-Year/Sophomore requirement is fulfilled by three specific courses that are taken during the first two years of college. These courses emphasize critical thinking, engaged and thoughtful reflection, and improved writing skills. Students will also learn how to conduct research, a skill that will prove to be helpful all throughout their undergraduate experience.

STUDENT-DESIGNED MAJORS: Students have the opportunity to design their own majors so that they may cater their education specifically to their own goals. With the help of advisors, students draft a plan that outlines the objectives and purposes of their program. They receive the guidance they need to organize their curriculum and ensure that they continue to get the strong, comprehensive education that Allegheny has to offer.

STUDENT-FACULTY COLLABORATION: Students have the opportunity to collaborate with faculty on research projects. In some cases, faculty even lead specific projects that require student aid! This common, incredibly rewarding experience is what has placed Allegheny within the top 10 percent of schools for faculty and student collaboration.

LIVING-LEARNING COMMUNITIES: Allegheny's Living-Learning Communities are offered to freshmen in order to surround them with academic support and opportunities for community bonding. The majority of students who have been involved in an LLC say it dramatically changed their college lifestyle; they mention their increased engagement with course material as well as the strong friendships that came from their shared experiences.

SPECIAL INTEREST HOUSING: Special Interest Housing is a unique sector of Allegheny's residential life. Students have the option to design a program that explores a specific interest with the help of residence life staff and a house advisor. Special Interest Housing is a great way for students to leave their mark on Allegheny. Some of the houses available include the Meditation House, Green Living, and Animal Welfare.

CLUBS & ORGANIZATIONS: There are plenty of ways for Allegheny students to get involved outside of class. The College offers over 100 clubs and organizations, the interests of which range from service groups to honor societies. Students looking to have a direct influence on campus events and social life can also join the Allegheny Student Government or Gator Activities Programming. Aside from these organizations, Allegheny also offers a bustling Greek Life, leadership societies, interest clubs, media organizations, performance groups, and religious clubs.

MEADVILLE, PENNSYLVANIA: Students are encouraged to explore nearby Meadville and catch a flick, see an art exhibit, or even just walk around. Meadville boasts one of the oldest outing clubs in the nation, which provides plenty of recreation opportunities to students and the community.

COMMUNITY SERVICE AND OUTREACH: Community service is an extremely important, valued part of the Allegheny undergraduate experience. Not only does it allow students to give back to the community, but it teaches humility and an appreciation for one's own privileges. Allegheny students rack up over 25,000 hours of service a year, pursuing projects on their own as well as through their coursework. Faculty love to enrich their classes with service-learning to integrate academic theory and real-world situations. Students take what they learn and turn their ideas into compassion action.

ALLEGHENY COLLEGE

http://allegheny.edu/
P: (814) 332-3100

PRIVATE

STUDENT PROFILE

1,931 undergraduate students

98% of undergrad students are full time

46% male – 54% female

52% of students are from out of state

83% freshman retention rate

75% graduated in 6 years

FACULTY PROFILE

190 full-time faculty

10 to 1 student/faculty ratio

ADMISSIONS

4,324 Total Applicants

2,955 Total Admissions

492 Total Freshman Enrollment

68.34% of applicants admitted

TUITION & COSTS

Tuition: $41,970

Fees: $500

Total: $42,470

R&B: $10,740

Room: $5,650

Board: $5,090

Total: $53,210

FINANCIAL

$27,624 avg grant/scholarship amount (total)

$8,852 avg loan amount (total)

CABRINI UNIVERSITY

RADNOR, PENNSYLVANIA

Cabrini University is a nonprofit, co-educational school that offers more than 35 majors, five master's degrees, and two doctoral degrees. Founded by the Missionary Sisters of the Sacred Heart of Jesus and named for St. Frances Cabrini, the patron saint of immigrants, the university embraces learners of all faiths and fosters a supportive academic community.

FIRST-YEAR EXPERIENCE: Before students start their first semester at Cabrini, their transition to college is guided by the award-winning First-Year Experience (FYE) program. It all begins at the Summer Orientation and New Student Orientation, both of which connect students to peer mentors and future classmates, additionally giving families access to faculty and staff. New students continue their transition to college in the credit-bearing College Success Seminar, which helps with academic preparation throughout the entire first year. All of the FYE activities create a sense of community for the incoming class while working closely with students so that they may understand all the ways to get involved and seek help on campus.

JUSTICE MATTERS CORE CURRICULUM: From the beginning of their college experience, students start Cabrini's "Justice Matters" core curriculum, which builds writing and analytical skills with a focus on issues of human rights, inclusivity, and other social issues. Justice Matters classes are writing-intensive and are taken from the first year through to the third year, finishing with a capstone in the fourth year. Engagements with the Common Good (ECG) classes sit at the heart of the curriculum, leading students on a journey of self-discovery and greater awareness of the world. First-year ECGs range from Mental Health & Society to Hip Hop: Language of Social Justice. Second-year ECGs include subjects such as Race, Gender, Youth Empowerment; Rethinking Addiction; and Democracy & Diversity. In ECG third-year courses, students can explore everything from Working for Global Justice to Food Insecurity.

COMMUNITY SERVICE AND THE CORE: Community service is integrated within the Justice Matters core curriculum, and Cabrini faculty, students, and staff provide more than 25,000 hours of service a year in nine different countries. For students who wish to continue their exploration of justice or service, Cabrini offers service trips every year to places such as Argentina, Guatemala, Swaziland, and Nicaragua.

STUDY ABROAD & STUDENT RESEARCH: As students hit their stride, they can explore Cabrini's study abroad trips or participate in undergraduate research opportunities. Cabrini offers students 7- or 10-day Immersion Trips to places like London and Guatemala as well as semester and summer programs abroad in Australia, England, Ireland, Italy, and Semester at Sea. Students work closely with faculty to study everything from the immunology of earthworms to the impact of Citizens United on corporate culture. Students present their research findings at the annual Academic Symposium with poster presentations, short talks, and informal dialogue with faculty, staff, and other students.

LEARNING COMMUNITIES: Though all of the above activities help to build new friendships and mentorships, Cabrini also offers students an opportunity to join Learning Communities (LCs). LCs allow students with similar interests the opportunity to take classes and exploration trips together throughout the first year. Students can also choose to take part in a Living and Learning Community (LLC), living with a small group of classmates in one of Cabrini's 12 residence halls. These Learning Communities are available to both freshmen and sophomores and range in themes, including The Art of Persuasion, Body Language, and Voices of Justice.

NEAR PHILADELPHIA, NEW YORK CITY, AND WASHINGTON, DC: Cabrini is ideally situated only 30 minutes from the center of Philadelphia, PA, offering a shuttle to the train station for easier access to the city's thriving art and food scene. From Philadelphia, students can hop on an Amtrak train and be in New York within 1.5 hours or DC in under 2 hours. Cabrini classes and clubs also schedule trips to these key northeast cities, giving students access to cosmopolitan areas while offering a quieter suburban home base on campus.

---

https://www.cabrini.edu/

P: (610) 902-8100

PRIVATE - CATHOLIC

STUDENT PROFILE

1,501 undergraduate students

92% of undergrad students are full time

38% male – 62% female

30.1% of students are from out of state

70% freshman retention rate

FACULTY PROFILE

83 full-time faculty

229 part-time faculty

ADMISSIONS

3,187 Total Applicants

2,264 Total Admissions

481 Total Freshman Enrollment

71.04% of applicants admitted

TUITION & COSTS

Tuition: $30,400

Fees: $950

Total: $31,350

R&B: $12,140

Total: $43,490

FINANCIAL

$7,627 avg grant/scholarship amount (need)

$3,257 avg loan amount (need)

CARLOW UNIVERSITY

PITTSBURGH, PENNSYLVANIA

Carlow emphasizes a well-rounded liberal arts education with a solid foundation in ethics and social justice. Its students carry with them the values that have defined Carlow University for nearly a hundred years. They go on to do good—and do well—in their chosen professions. According to a recent career outcomes report, 94 percent of Carlow alumni were employed or continuing their studies at Carlow or other universities within six months of graduation.

FIRST-YEAR SEMINARS: Carlow University's First-Year Seminar (FYS) orients students to the University community and builds a foundation for their academic success. Within a small group setting, FYS connects students with Carlow's history and mission, familiarizing them with key support services and departments. Most importantly, FYS connects students with other students as well as with faculty. Students explore their new University together as they delve further into their own academic and professional goals. Students also take either College Writing and Research or Presentations and Argumentation with the same group of FYS classmates.

THE CARLOW COMPASS: The Carlow Compass, Carlow's core curriculum, is rooted in liberal arts and the Catholic intellectual tradition. It is designed to navigate and explore a student's educational pathway within a course of study, emphasizing career-readiness and ethical leadership.

STUDY ABROAD: Undergraduates at Carlow can take advantage of many study abroad opportunities, from a semester in Italy to an entire year in Northern Ireland. Some of Carlow's unique offerings include the service-oriented Carlow Cares spring break trips to places like Nicaragua. Carlow's MFA in Creative Writing includes two intensive residencies per year, which consist of a two weeks' stay in Pittsburgh and another two weeks at Trinity College in Ireland.

UNDERGRADUATE RESEARCH: Thanks to the size of Carlow University, undergraduate research has always been an important dimension of its biology and chemistry programs. Unlike research universities, which often hold undergraduate classes that are taught by graduate students, students at Carlow have opportunities to work directly alongside faculty. Together, they pursue meaningful research projects that can lead to publications in journals and presentations at professional conferences.

WRITING-INTENSIVE COURSES: As students move through the core curriculum, they take course-level writing assessments to measure the progress of their writing skills at the initial stages of the curriculum. These assessments are useful tools that help determine clear steps for improvement throughout the continuation of their coursework. In their third year, all students (including transfers) complete an "anchor" experience in which they undergo a formative writing assessment, receiving recommendations for additional writing support and improvement before they move on to their disciplinary capstone experiences in their final year.

CAPSTONE: In their junior and senior capstone experiences, students pursue their own independent research under the direct oversight of a faculty member. They then present this information to the Carlow community—including their peers—through Carlow's Scholarship Day, an annual event that highlights undergraduate research in all disciplines through poster presentations, panels, demonstrations, and readings.

CAREER SERVICES: Carlow's Office of Career Development provides career-planning services that prepare students and alumni for successful transitions from college to their careers. They provide career advising sessions, career-related programming, internship/job search support, and employer engagement both on and off campus.

http://www.carlow.edu/
P: (800) 333-2275

PRIVATE - CATHOLIC

STUDENT PROFILE

1,280 undergraduate students

77% of undergrad students are full time

16% male – 96% female

5% of students are from out of state

77% freshman retention rate

57% graduated in 6 years

FACULTY PROFILE

97 full-time faculty

167 part-time faculty

12 to 1 student/faculty ratio

ADMISSIONS

806 Total Applicants

696 Total Admissions

218 Total Freshman Enrollment

86.35% of applicants admitted

SAT Ranges: CR 440-540, M 430-530

ACT Ranges: C 19-24, M 17-24, E 18-24

TUITION & COSTS

Tuition: $27,136

Fees: $628

Total: $27,764

R&B: $10,784

Total: $38,548

FINANCIAL

$3,739 avg grant/scholarship amount (need)

$3,442 avg loan amount (need)

CEDAR CREST COLLEGE

ALLENTOWN, PENNSYLVANIA

For over 150 years, Cedar Crest College has taken a bold approach to education by creating a college and curriculum designed for women who want to achieve at the highest levels. Recognizing the multidimensional nature of students, Cedar Crest College is dedicated to the education of the next generation of leaders by preparing the whole student for life in the global community.

EXPERIENCE: Students instead learn through experience in every major. From internships to service projects, Cedar Crest students graduate with skills that employers find valuable as well as the wherewithal to contribute immediately to their career fields and communities.

EXPEDITION: Cedar Crest makes it a priority to provide each and every student with a high-impact global experience. Starting in the spring of 2018, Cedar Crest College will officially launch the Sophomore Expedition—a program that will take the entire sophomore class to an off-campus destination for service and learning. The cost of transportation and lodging will be covered by the College, making sure to prevent finances from inhibiting such an amazing experience.

EXPOSURE: It's said that success is "all about who you know," but Cedar Crest College knows that it's far more than that. Highly credentialed faculty members develop close-knit relationships with their students as they help to build a solid platform for a successful career. Students are also connected to professionals through their professors' networks, getting to know industry experts on first-name bases. Not only are they acquainted with experts, but they are friends and colleagues with them. This ultimately provides in-depth exposure to opportunities that perfectly communicate the value of a Cedar Crest education.

EXCEL: Leaders innovate, inspire, and—most of all—take action! And in the Cedar Crest community, students do just that. With growth opportunities around every corner, they develop critical thinking skills, communication abilities, and confidence. Whether they organize a fundraiser, start their own club, or drive their own research projects, Cedar Crest students develop the skills necessary to excel upon entering the workforce.

EXEMPLIFY: Cedar Crest provides all the resources students need to develop the essential skills for living balanced and healthy lifestyles. No matter what major students choose, they can always incorporate their passions into hands-on experiences. Whether through athletics, dance, theatre, or even a second major, Cedar Crest offers a range of academic experiences, each customized to individual student. Not only does the College provide students with an outstanding education grounded in the liberal arts, but it also ensures that they graduate in four years through its Four-Year Guarantee program.

DUAL DEGREES: Students can save both time and money through one of Cedar Crest's dual degree programs. Usually requiring only one extra year of coursework, these programs allow students to pursue both their bachelor's and master's degrees simultaneously. Undergraduate accounting, art, business administration, chemistry, performing arts, psychology, and writing students are able to obtain a Master of Business Administration or Master of Education quickly so that they may get a kick-start to their careers without years and years of study.

FIRST-YEAR FRIDAYS: First-Year Fridays are a unique feature of Cedar Crest's first-year experience program. In addition to taking small, close-knit seminars together, freshmen have the opportunity to bond outside of the classroom with weekly events catered specifically to them. Every Friday, the College hosts an event that gives these students the opportunity to stay social and integrate into their community with such activities as guest speakers, film screenings, and excursions off campus.

http://www.cedarcrest.edu/
P: (800) 360-1222

PRIVATE

STUDENT PROFILE

1,342 undergraduate students

54% of undergrad students are full time

7% male – 93% female

35% of students are from out of state

69% freshman retention rate

69% graduated in 6 years

FACULTY PROFILE

72 full-time faculty

110 part-time faculty

10 to 1 student/faculty ratio

ADMISSIONS

1,246 Total Applicants

652 Total Admissions

170 Total Freshman Enrollment

52.33% of applicants admitted

SAT Ranges: CR 438-570, M 450-550, W 440-550

ACT Ranges: C 20-23, M 19-22, E 19-24

TUITION & COSTS

Tuition: $33,904

Fees: $600

Total: $34,504

R&B: $10,549

Room: $5,160

Board: $5,389

Total: $45,053

FINANCIAL

$24,140 avg grant/scholarship amount (total)

$8,286 avg loan amount (total)

CHATHAM UNIVERSITY

PITTSBURGH, PENNSYLVANIA

Chatham University students experience a dynamic academic community that empowers them to explore and define their abilities. Chatham has been developing sought-after leaders who leave an impact on the world for over 140 years.

INTERNSHIPS FOR ALL: All undergraduate students are required to participate in an internship in order to gain hands-on experience within their field. Career Advisors work one-on-one with students to provide easy, helpful guidance through every stage of the internship process. With such a great focus on professional success, Career Development is driven to set students up with positions that are relevant and applicable to their prospective careers.

INTEGRATED DEGREE PROGRAM: Students already looking ahead to graduate school can enroll in Chatham's Integrated Degree Program (IDP). Because graduate schools are already competitive enough, Chatham makes sure that its students are secure in their pursuits for further education. Those who declare an IDP interest are guaranteed admission to a Chatham graduate program and can begin taking graduate classes during their time as undergrads. IDP can save both time and money by awarding both a bachelor's and master's degree in as little as five years total.

BACHELOR OF SUSTAINABILITY: In 2010, Chatham established the Falk School of Sustainability & Environment in order to produce leaders in the ever-developing field of environmental studies. Its unique sustainability program for undergraduates allows students to pursue such important concentrations as sustainable technology, natural resource management, sustainable business & management, and sustainable policy & communications. No longer a niche field, sustainability requires focus from excellent scholars who are passionate about the environment's future. This program takes an interdisciplinary approach in order to analyze the policies, patterns, and social and economical issues related to the plant.

GLOBAL FOCUS PROGRAM: Every year, Chatham's Global Focus program chooses a theme around which to shape the general education curriculum and direct acts of service and exploration. First-year seminars, as well as various common-core courses, are specifically redesigned each year to fit this Global Focus, providing students a common, shared experience that is nevertheless unique to each University class. Students can also attend guest lectures and participate in research, writing, and film contests to immerse themselves in the issues that the Global Focus brings to to Chatham's attention. These school-wide efforts have ranged all the way from global climate change to the economies of specific countries.

AWARENESS MONTHS: Diversity Awareness and Celebratory months are taken seriously on Chatham's campus. Each month, students and faculty bring their attention to marginalized cultures through acts of service and inclusion. Planning committees comprised of both community members and those within the Chatham family organize events that broaden knowledge and challenge stereotypes, celebrating the world's variety of races, genders, religions, and more.

SELF-DESIGNED MAJOR: Understanding that some topics cannot be explored fully through a single lens of thought, Chatham allows students to design their own major through an interdisciplinary combination of courses. Students who create their own major work with an advisor to set their desired learning outcomes and prepare an academic structure that best represents their focus. The self-designed major allows students to delve deeply into topics that may not be common but are nevertheless vital and best understood through a complex combination of lessons.

chatham
UNIVERSITY

http://www.chatham.edu/
P: (412) 365-1825

PRIVATE

STUDENT PROFILE

930 undergraduate students

60% of undergrad students are full time

10% male – 90% female

38% of students are from out of state

77% freshman retention rate

56% graduated in 6 years

FACULTY PROFILE

110 full-time faculty

209 part-time faculty

9 to 1 student/faculty ratio

ADMISSIONS

627 Total Applicants

328 Total Admissions

104 Total Freshman Enrollment

52.31% of applicants admitted

TUITION & COSTS

Tuition: $32,234

Fees: $1,195

Total: $33,429

R&B: $10,368

Room: $5,258

Board: $5,110

Total: $43,797

FINANCIAL

$29,006 avg grant/scholarship amount (total)

$5,875 avg loan amount (total)

DICKINSON COLLEGE

CARLISLE, PENNSYLVANIA

Dickinson students take control of their academic journeys. They are active, engaged, smart, and bold. Dickinson College teaches its students how to positively enact change through thoughtful analysis and informed decision making.

SERVICE LEARNING: Dickinson embraces service-learning as a valuable experience that is a truly integral part of education. Service-learning allows faculty to connect their classes to the community by pushing students to apply academic theory to real-world issues, thereby perpetuating Dickinson's mission to graduate students who are thoughtful and impactful citizens. Service-learning gives students the chance to connect their studies to society and work to understand how they can impact the world.

GLOBAL STUDIES AND ENGAGEMENT: Dickinson supports several global studies programs and research centers. Most of these programs are located in provincial towns, enhancing opportunities for both students and faculty alike. In smaller cities, participants have better access to local government leaders, community members, and internship opportunities. Faculty are often directly involved in abroad experiences, as they often teach or mentor while working alongside their students. Dickinson puts a strong amount of focus on its global studies programs so as to ensure that the College's mission and values are upheld no matter where students go.

STUDENT-FACULTY COLLABORATIVE RESEARCH: While there is an opportunity to conduct independent research, Dickinson also offers student-faculty collaborative research that exposes them to guided apprenticeship. In this relationship, a student and faculty member work together on the same project as equals. This collaborative effort involves varying degrees of supervision, giving students both structure as well as the wiggle room for their own curiosities.

FIRST-YEAR SEMINAR: Dickinson's First-Year Seminar is a foundational experience in which students develop the critical writing and communication skills they need to succeed during college. Students also learn proper study habits, which are sure to come in handy as their workload increases. The First-Year Seminar encourages students to develop their own ideas and defend their arguments with critical analysis. They can choose from 40 different seminars, all of which provide the opportunity for students to explore new topics outside of their major. The goal of this program is to prepare individuals for successful careers as inquisitive, ambitious undergraduates, and while the general outcomes are consistent among all seminars, the topics vary by discipline.

LIVING-LEARNING COMMUNITIES: Dickinson's learning communities are part of the First-Year Seminar. Through this great residence structure, students are separated into clusters that live and learn together so as to foster a true sense of friendship early on in their college career. The goals of these learning communities are to enhance student and faculty interactions, increase comprehension of course material, and form a bond among peers.

INTERNSHIP NOTATION PROGRAM: The Internship Notation Program (INP) is Dickinson's way of identifying and tracking internship experiences. Students involved in the program complete a series of tasks, including actual internship experience, reflective assignments, and online submissions. Several of Dickinson's programs require students to complete an internship through INP. There are many benefits to the program: internships are recognized by the college, students gain hands-on experience, and the work is considered valuable to employers.

GENERAL DEGREE REQUIREMENTS: In order to arm themselves with a strong academic skill set, every Dickinson student enrolls in a set of courses that strengthen their writing proficiency, quantitative reasoning, and global awareness. They also provide texture to their specific majors by bringing in the perspectives of foreign languages, the humanities, and the social and natural sciences.

Dickinson

https://www.dickinson.edu/
P: (717) 243-5121

PRIVATE

STUDENT PROFILE

2,420 undergraduate students

99% of undergrad students are full time

42% male – 58% female

71% of students are from out of state

92% freshman retention rate

85% graduated in 6 years

FACULTY PROFILE

234 full-time faculty

55 part-time faculty

10 to 1 student/faculty ratio

ADMISSIONS

6,031 Total Applicants

2,841 Total Admissions

731 Total Freshman Enrollment

47.11% of applicants admitted

TUITION & COSTS

Tuition: $49,014

Fees: $450

Total: $49,464

R&B: $12,362

Room: $6,376

Board: $5,986

Total: $61,826

FINANCIAL

$28,127 avg grant/scholarship amount (total)

$6,561 avg loan amount (total)

DREXEL UNIVERSITY

PHILADELPHIA, PENNSYLVANIA

As one of the largest private schools in the U.S., Drexel is constantly making strides in both the realms of research and personal achievements. Students are exposed to new technologies, are taught to be strong leaders, and are prepared to make positive changes within the global community.

WELCOME TO DREXEL: The first week of college can be difficult for some students. For most, it's the first time they are living away from their parents. Drexel recognizes this as a sensitive time but nevertheless wants all new students to remain optimistic and excited. College is an amazing time in any young person's life; it's a period of major growth, both academic and personal. With that in mind, Drexel has established a Welcome Week to ease the transition into college. Welcome Week starts with move-in day and is followed by a week full of activities. Students are introduced to campus and learn about upcoming events. There are also several activities to promote interaction between peers.

FIRST-YEAR LEARNING COMMUNITIES: As part of the First-Year Program, students participate in a learning community in which they gather weekly to discuss course work with their peers and study as a group. Learning communities promote conversation outside of the classroom, which enhances the learning experience and increases comprehension of course material. The Dragon Scholars Program (DSP) is one of such learning communities available to all first-year students. The program begins the summer before freshman year and continues as a first-year experience. DSP is a learning community that promotes academic excellence alongside many personal, academic, and social benefits to participating in the program. Not only do students gain a better understanding of their new academic standards, but they also bond with the other members of the program.

STAR SCHOLARS: STAR stands for Students Tackling Advanced Research. The program is open to first-year students the summer after their freshman year. STAR allows students to collaborate with faculty on research projects—a valuable experience most often given to master's students. STAR awards each participant with a $4,000 dollar stipend and on-campus housing. Students work a total of 400 hours over the course of the summer. There are many benefits to participation including one-on-one interaction with faculty and experience with research processes. At the end of each summer, Drexel hosts a showcase to celebrate all of the research completed by the STAR scholars. Community members, faculty, and family are invited to attend the event and learn more about each student's body of work. ISTAR, the international sector of the STAR program, invites students of academic prowess to pursue research in a location that best supports research in a specific field.

COOPERATIVE EDUCATION: Drexel's cooperative education has a longstanding history of success and opportunity. Students have the option to participate in up to three co-op experiences as undergraduates. Each experience is incredibly valuable to the student, who gains industry knowledge and builds professional networks. Co-op students tend to graduate with higher honors and greater starting salaries. Co-ops demonstrate that a student has gained hands on experience—a valuable skill to employers. There are three different co-op tracks that students can choose from. The Three Co-op track takes five years to complete, and involves three six-month stretches of employment. The second track, One- Co-op option, takes four years to finish and includes just one period of employment. The last option has no co-op. Some majors do not require a co-op in order to graduate and, for these students, a diploma can be obtained within four years.

http://www.drexel.edu/
P: (215) 895-2000

PRIVATE

STUDENT PROFILE
16,464 undergraduate students
86% of undergrad students are full time
53% male – 47% female
84% freshman retention rate
68% graduated in 6 years

FACULTY PROFILE
1,572 full-time faculty
1,050 part-time faculty
10 to 1 student/faculty ratio

ADMISSIONS
28,757 Total Applicants
21,494 Total Admissions
2,730 Total Freshman Enrollment
74.74% of applicants admitted
SAT Ranges: CR 530-630, M 565-680
ACT Ranges: C 25-30

TUITION & COSTS
Tuition: $41,744
Fees: $2,370
Total: $44,114
R&B: $14,367
Room: $8,682
Board: $5,685
Total: $58,481

FINANCIAL
$25,661 avg grant/scholarship amount (total)
$10,168 avg loan amount (total)

EASTERN UNIVERSITY

WAYNE, PENNSYLVANIA

Located in Wayne, Pennsylvania, Eastern University is a top Christian College that offers 90+ areas of study including B.A., B.S., B.S.N., B.S.W., Minors, and Pre-professional options. Eastern also hosts prestigious programs like the Templeton Honors College, Leadership Fellows Program, and W. Goode Scholars. Eastern Athletics boast of regionally and nationally competitive athletics in 20 sports.

WHY BIBLICAL JUSTICE?: Since 1925, Eastern has been a champion of biblical justice—It's what Eastern is known for around the globe. Eastern's first-year and transfer students contributed approximately 6,600 service hours to the greater Philadelphia region. Coupled with 32+ study abroad/away programs, students' capacities are expanded to see a world much bigger than they imagined.

TEMPLETON HONORS COLLEGE: The Templeton Honors College at Eastern University is designed to challenge and prepare academically gifted undergraduate students for leadership and service as individuals of influence in culture, society, and their professions. The program takes a holistic approach to the life of the mind, character formation, and skill development.

IDEAL LOCATION, CLOSE-KNIT COMMUNITY: Eastern is nestled in affluent Wayne, PA; has been named the 5th Most Beautiful Christian Campus in the World ;and is listed among the 100 Safest College Campuses in the U.S. This gorgeous suburban location, along with its close proximity to Philadelphia, affords students many opportunities to get involved on and off campus. By walking to the train station, students are just a 25-minute train ride to downtown Philadelphia, which has been lauded as one of America's top 10 best college communities.

GETTING INVOLVED: At Eastern, students get a sense of closeness within their community. From faculty to staff to students, it seems that the pillars of Faith, Reason, and Justice resonate with and unite the campus. Students often put their faith in action with over 40 different student organizations, ensembles, productions that serve the diverse community, and beyond. Regionally and nationally competitive sports teams are complemented by a robust intramural program. Many students enjoy the fine and performing arts in dance, music, and theatre. Others can be found making an impact in one of the many multicultural clubs. Eastern facilitates Christian growth through dynamic, voluntary chapels, student-led worship, weekly dorm "floor" discipleship groups, and partnerships with Young Life and FCA. At Eastern, students can expect to fill their days with great speakers and fun concerts, enjoying college and creating a lifetime of memories.

ACADEMICS WITH INTEGRITY: A 10:1 student-to-professor ratio ensures personal attention all throughout the college experience. And with such highly, nationally recognized faculty, students know that they learn from and connect with the best. Notable faculty include recent bestselling author, Dr. Phil Cary; global expert of astronomy, Dr. David Bradstreet; international performer-composer-conductor, Dr. Ron Matthews; and fulbright scholar, Dr. Julia Stewart. Eastern embraces a Christian worldview and endeavors to integrate Faith, Reason, and Justice within each graduate's understanding of the world that surrounds them.

INTERNSHIPS & OPPORTUNITIES: Eastern University maintains a robust network locally and abroad, connecting students to internships that often result in their first firm foot set into a career. 81% of students complete an internship by graduation, and 95% of those students report that their experiences helped secure their next step after graduation.

http://www.eastern.edu/
P: (800) 452-0996

PRIVATE - CHRISTIAN

STUDENT PROFILE

2,082 undergraduate students

85% of undergrad students are full time

32% male – 68% female

32.5% of students are from out of state

78% freshman retention rate

65% graduated in 6 years

FACULTY PROFILE

127 full-time faculty

359 part-time faculty

10 to 1 student/faculty ratio

ADMISSIONS

1,992 Total Applicants

1,219 Total Admissions

442 Total Freshman Enrollment

61.19% of applicants admitted

SAT Ranges: CR 470-570, M 460-570

ACT Ranges: C 19-23, M 17-25, E 18-24

TUITION & COSTS

Tuition: $31,700

Fees: $615

Total: $32,315

R&B: $10,980

Total: $43,295

FINANCIAL

$7,241 avg grant/scholarship amount (need)

$3,941 avg loan amount (need)

ELIZABETHTOWN COLLEGE

ELIZABETHTOWN, PENNSYLVANIA

Elizabethtown College is an independent, residential, coeducational college located on 203 acres in south central Pennsylvania. Its approximately 1,800 undergraduates hail from nearly 30 states and 40 countries.

FIRST-YEAR SEMINARS: First-Year Seminars are topical in nature. Each has a unique focus that allows students to broaden their understanding of the world and what it means to learn. Seminars are especially helpful for developing skills in critical thinking and writing. No seminar is grounded in a particular major, as Elizabethtown College wants its students to become well-rounded scholars. Each seminar includes out-of-class learning experiences, including plays, lectures, art exhibits, film screenings, and field trips to museums in Philadelphia and Washington or hiking destinations along the Appalachian Trail.

SOPHOMORE-YEAR EXPERIENCE: Elizabethtown College created the Sophomore-Year Experience (SYE) to tackle the sense of drift–or "sophomore slump"–that is reported by sophomores nationwide. The SYE is designed to ease the transition from the structured programs of the first year to the more independent programs, such as internships and research experiences, associated with the junior and senior years. During the Sophomore-Year Experience, students explore traditional and communal experiences while integrating the College's CORE majors and minors. With this in mind, they look more closely at vocation and life purpose while attending retreats, social events specific to sophomores, and a majors and minors fair.

SCHOLARSHIP AND CREATIVE ARTS DAY: Scholarship and Creative Arts Day (SCAD) is an annual conference in which select students present academic research in their respective disciplines; some showcase talents through recitals and a juried art exhibit. All Elizabethtown College students are encouraged to share their ideas and show their creativity during SCAD. Those interested in participating in SCAD find a faculty mentor who will sponsor the project and who will review a 250-word proposal that describes and summarizes the student's research.

WARE LECTURE ON PEACEMAKING: The Ware Lecture on Peacemaking, which takes place in the spring, has brought Nobel Peace Prize recipients, influential journalists, and political leaders from around the world to Elizabethtown College. Past speakers include Kim Phuc, the Vietnam War "Napalm Girl;" Nicholas Kristof, a Pulitzer Prize-Winning New York Times Columnist; Mary Robinson, former president of Ireland and chair of Realizing Rights: The Ethical Global Initiative; and Shirin Ebadi, Nobel Peace Prize recipient and founder of the Association for Support of Children's Rights in Iran. The fall Leffler Lecture also features speakers of national and international renown, including Michele Norris, former NPR host of All Things Considered and founder of the Race Card Project, and John Hunter, educator and inventor of the World Peace Game.

LIVING-LEARNING COMMUNITIES: The College offers Living-Learning Communities (LLC), which mix the curricular, co-curricular, and residential components of a student's college life. The LLCs focus on academics and activities that related to specific courses, programs of study, or themes. Past LLCs have centered on eating disorder awareness, service and mentorship through jazz, developing activities for older citizens, simple living, and hunger and homelessness awareness. LLCs have a positive impact on academic performance and intellectual development, as they offer a sense of belonging and civic engagement.

COMMUNITY AND CIVIC ENGAGEMENT CERTIFICATE PROGRAM: E-town offers the Community and Civic Engagement Certificate Program to students interested in integrating curricular and co-curricular learning that is focused on social justice in local, national, and international communities. The program is designed as an experiential, community-based service-learning opportunity as students investigate social inequities such as poverty and homelessness throughout their academic program of study. Service and community-based learning is considered a high-impact educational practice, which includes civic knowledge, intercultural knowledge and competence, ethical reasoning and action, and foundations and skills for lifelong learning.

http://www.etown.edu/
P: (717) 361-1000

PRIVATE

STUDENT PROFILE

1,762 undergraduate students

99% of undergrad students are full time

38% male – 62% female

36% of students are from out of state

82% freshman retention rate

78% graduated in 6 years

FACULTY PROFILE

129 full-time faculty

50 part-time faculty

12 to 1 student/faculty ratio

ADMISSIONS

3,453 Total Applicants

2,442 Total Admissions

504 Total Freshman Enrollment

70.72% of applicants admitted

SAT Ranges: CR 500-610, M 500-620

ACT Ranges: C 23-28, M 21-27, E 21-28

TUITION & COSTS

Tuition: $43,490

R&B: $10,560

Total: $54,050

FINANCIAL

$25,140 avg grant/scholarship amount (need)

$4,537 avg loan amount (need)

GANNON UNIVERSITY

ERIE, PENNSYLVANIA

Gannon University is training graduates for the world of the 21st century through expert faculty, innovative academic programs, and exceptional learning environments. A university rich in history and tradition and committed to the future, Gannon prepares its students to be leaders in their fields.

GLOBAL LEARNING: Preparing students to be global citizens is part of the University's Mission and is experienced through an array of programs and opportunities. Gannon University offers study abroad, semester exchange, and faculty-led travel courses opportunities in over 15 countries across the world. In addition to academic-based experiences, Gannon offers service trips and travel opportunities with residence hall-based learning communities as well.

UNDERGRADUATE RESEARCH: Gannon University integrates teaching with research and service-learning, enabling students to enhance their academic experience with hands-on opportunities outside the classroom. Gannon offers research options through such grant-funded opportunities as NASA's Undergraduate Student Instrument Program (USIP) and onboard the University's 53-foot research vessel, the Environaut, while studying freshwater and marine biology on Lake Erie. Students in the Dahlkemper School of Business work alongside entrepreneurs and business professionals by conducting research on markets, technologies, and opportunities for real-world companies in the University's Small Business Development Center and Erie Technology Incubator (ETI).

HONORS PROGRAM: For academically talented and highly motivated students, Gannon's Honors program offers a rigorous curriculum that prepares them to be ethical, thoughtful, and effective leaders with a global worldview. Selected from the top ten percent of Gannon's incoming class, honors students excel not only academically, but also in leadership.

SERVICE IN THE COMMUNITY: Service to community is a concept embedded in the University's Mission and inspired by Catholic Social Teaching. Through annual such activities as the United Way's Day of Caring and Gannon's Invitation to Volunteer Everywhere (GIVE) Day, students, faculty, staff, alumni, and friends gather to volunteer in the neighborhoods surrounding campus, the city of Erie, and other cities across the country. This gives Gannon students the opportunity to be present in their community and support community partners. Alternative Break Service Trips are also held domestically and internationally to engage concepts of service, simplicity, community, and reflection.

HOUSING COMMUNITIES: To immerse students in learning that extends beyond the classroom, Gannon is home to several learning communities that are arranged by professional and academic interests. Students enrolled in the health sciences can learn and study demanding coursework in a learning community in North Hall, Gannon's newest residence hall. The Bishop Donald W. Trautman House is a home for Gannon students who want to be part of a special living and learning community focused on holistic development in the Catholic faith. Juniors and seniors in the Transforming Residents Abroad Via Engaged Learning (T.R.A.V.E.L.) program can live on-campus in learning communities that meet regularly to study a variety of topics. These communities range all across disciplines and enrich any participating student's overall college experience.

INTERNSHIP OPPORTUNITIES: Abundant hands-on learning opportunities are directly next to Gannon's campus in the heart of Erie's central business, administrative, and cultural districts. With several businesses, minor-league sport teams, hospitals, and schools located within blocks of campus, students are easily in touch with a variety of internship opportunities.

http://www.gannon.edu/

P: (814) 871-7000

PRIVATE - CATHOLIC

STUDENT PROFILE

631 undergraduate students

99% of undergrad students are full time

40% male – 60% female

33.9% of students are from out of state

77.52% freshman retention rate

63.59% graduated in 6 years

FACULTY PROFILE

238 full-time faculty

165 part-time faculty

12.3 to 1 student/faculty ratio

ADMISSIONS

4,710 Total Applicants

3,662 Total Admissions

631 Total Freshman Enrollment

77.75% of applicants admitted

SAT Ranges: CR 450-560, M 470-570

ACT Ranges: C 20-26, M 20-26, E 19-25

TUITION & COSTS

Tuition: $30,180

Fees: $752

Total: $30,932

R&B: $12,320

Total: $43,252

FINANCIAL

$19,725 avg grant/scholarship amount (need)

$4,483 avg loan amount (need)

GENEVA COLLEGE

BEAVER FALLS, PENNSYLVANIA

Geneva's evangelical Christian faculty challenge students with a curriculum grounded in the inerrant truth of the Bible. The school's top-notch academics are accompanied by a full integration of faith in every aspect of student life.

WELL-ROUNDED STUDENTS: With intellectually demanding courses and a strong biblical foundation, Geneva College prepares students to accept the challenge of serving Christ as leaders in their homes, communities, and fields of study. The school's liberal arts core curriculum produces graduates that are well rounded, adaptable critical thinkers—qualities that employers highly value.

CROSSROADS: Geneva's Center for Off-Campus Study features over 40 study abroad choices to help students stretch their horizons. From Geneva's own Semester in Scotland program to integrated courses in China and Israel, students have numerous opportunities to discover their unique places in the world.

THE CENTER FOR STUDENT ENGAGEMENT: The Center for Student Engagement helps students grow deeper in their relationship with Christ through a variety of ministries. Each year during Spring Break, interested students participate in Quest Trips to serve others both domestically and internationally. Locally, Geneva students work with community service organizations such as Habitat for Humanity, Tiger Pause Youth Ministries, Big Brothers Big Sisters, and others. Campus ministries include Bible studies, discipleship, and a number of student-led groups.

PROFESSIONAL CLUBS: Professional development clubs, like the Geneva College Business Club and Geneva's chapter of the Public Relations Student Society of America (PRSSA), are very active. These clubs bring speakers to campus, take participants on educational trips, and provide valuable networking opportunities.

PINKERTON CENTER FOR TECHNOLOGY DEVELOPMENT: The Pinkerton Center for Technology Development (PCTD) is a project-based learning environment through which Geneva students are able to use engineering and technical resources to support local companies. Engineering students also obtain hands-on experience by participating in national contests like the SAE Baja, Steel Bridge Building, and Solar Splash Boating Competitions.

HONORS PROGRAMS: The Geneva College Honors Programs—First-Year, Young Scholars, and Academic Partners—provide opportunities for students to challenge themselves by digging deeper into the college experience. Students explore what it means to be a Christian scholar while discovering the lordship of Christ in every aspect of academic life. First-Year Honors students receive a $2,000 Travel & Research Honorarium that may be used for exciting opportunities like off-campus study, academic research, and conference attendance.

GUESTS@GENEVA: Distinguished lecturers, well-known musicians and performers, best-selling authors, accomplished scholars, and leading religious figures are invited to campus each semester to enrich the educational experience with their wisdom. Past guests have included American political commentator Fred Barnes, Academy Award-winning filmmaker Gregg Helvey, philosopher Dr. Alvin Plantinga, author Mosab Yousef, Civil Rights activist Rutha Harris, and Nobel Prize-winning chemist Dr. Roald Hoffmann.

CHAPEL: Weekly chapel is a time for the campus to gather and praise God, hear His word, and seek His favor and direction. Attendance is mandatory for students and the entire campus community is encouraged to participate actively in their faith.

ARTS AND ENTERTAINMENT: Geneva offers a group for every interest, including student publications like The Geneva Cabinet student newspaper; music ensembles like the Genevans choir and marching and symphonic bands; and the theatre program, which produces a show every semester.

GENEVA COLLEGE

http://www.geneva.edu/
P: (800) 847-8255

PRIVATE - CHRISTIAN

STUDENT PROFILE

1,464 undergraduate students

94% of undergrad students are full time

49% male – 51% female

26% of students are from out of state

83% freshman retention rate

64% graduated in 6 years

FACULTY PROFILE

91 full-time faculty

15 to 1 student/faculty ratio

ADMISSIONS

1,678 Total Applicants

1,230 Total Admissions

335 Total Freshman Enrollment

73.30% of applicants admitted

SAT Ranges: CR 450-590, M 450-590, W 430-560

ACT Ranges: C 21-27, M 20-27, E 20-26, W 6-8

TUITION & COSTS

Tuition: $25,450

R&B: $9,630

Total: $35,080

FINANCIAL

$14,961 avg grant/scholarship amount (total)

$8,413 avg loan amount (total)

GETTYSBURG COLLEGE

GETTYSBURG, PENNSYLVANIA

Gettysburg College is committed to a liberal education that prepares students to be active leader and participants in a changing world. The college encourages a free and open marketplace of ideas to help students learn and grow.

UNDERGRADUATE RESEARCH AND CREATIVE ACTIVITY: Undergraduate research is an incredible responsibility that involves creative inquiry and student discovery as it pushes students to think critically and draw their own conclusions. Instead of professors leading the way, students are expected to take a role of leadership while professors simply oversee their work. There are several ways to get involved with research at Gettysburg, and the college offers a number of internal research opportunities. Mellon Summer Scholars is one of the notable internal research programs available at Gettysburg. Students enrolled in this program engage in faculty-mentored research over the course of the summer, allowing them the time and resources to delve deeply into their own area of study.

LEADERSHIP OPPORTUNITIES: In order to prepare students for the demands of their future careers, Gettysburg has established a host of leadership-building opportunities that involve students with increased responsibility. The Garthwait Leadership Center is responsible for creating intellectual experiences that give students and alumni the chance to act as leaders. Students of sophomore, junior, and senior status are invited to become Leadership Mentors, individuals dedicated to leading others and developing as confident individuals. Each LM is expected to work an average of ten hours a week, maintain a GPA of 3.0 or higher, attend weekly meetings, and engage in one-on-one appointments with professional staff. They have several different responsibilities across campus, working with everyone from students to alumni to help the College thrive.

THE RESIDENTIAL COLLEGE PROGRAM: The Residential College program at Gettysburg connects academics to residential life. Students enrolled in the same seminar and writing courses are housed together, extending class discussion into a more comfortable, less formal setting. By combining residence life with academics, students are given a support system in which they can openly exchange their ideas. This program serves as great practice for the kind of participation and class discussion that continues to be expected of each student throughout college. Aside from the academic benefits, students are also given social opportunities like field trips, community service projects, and themed dinners.

COMMUNITY SERVICE: Community service will always be an integral part of the undergraduate experience. Service is stepping back from the educational demands of college and addressing the needs of the community. Active and engaged graduates are more well-rounded individuals who harbor valuable traits of humility and responsibility. Gettysburg is highly committed to the service of others and works to provide students with numerous ways to get involved. Immersion projects, for example, are a great way for students to get involved over school breaks. During winter break, spring break, and the month of May, students can travel to domestic and international sites to perform acts of service. With social justice at the core of each mission, students collaborate with their host community to address the needs of the people. Immersion projects are highly educational, allowing students to apply their knowledge to a specific issue at hand. Some of the past sites have included: Washington D.C., Haiti, Nicaragua, and Pennsylvania.

---

http://www.gettysburg.edu/
P: (717) 337-6000

PRIVATE

STUDENT PROFILE
2,447 undergraduate students
99% of undergrad students are full time
47% male – 53% female
69% of students are from out of state
91% freshman retention rate
83% graduated in 6 years

FACULTY PROFILE
222 full-time faculty
86 part-time faculty
10 to 1 student/faculty ratio

ADMISSIONS
6,386 Total Applicants
2,540 Total Admissions
699 Total Freshman Enrollment
39.77% of applicants admitted

TUITION & COSTS
Tuition: $49,140
R&B: $11,730
Room: $6,290
Board: $5,440
Total: $60,870

FINANCIAL
$28,594 avg grant/scholarship amount (total)
$4,754 avg loan amount (total)

GROVE CITY COLLEGE

GROVE CITY, PENNSYLVANIA

GROVE CITY COLLEGE
ESTABLISHED 1876 PENNSYLVANIA

Faith and freedom are the pillars upon which Grove City College is built, standing as the fundamental elements in everything the College does and hopes to accomplish. Since 1876, Grove City College has been bringing the best of these worlds together to create an experience that is academically rigorous, authentically Christian, and an amazing value.

EDUCATION ABROAD: Grove City College believes that learning occurs everywhere, whether that be in a campus classroom or halfway around the world. It places value on students' willingness to leave their comfort zones through travel, learning, service, and outreach in order to become well informed and well rounded. The College's Office of International Education assists students as they enroll in study abroad programs at international universities, faculty-led travel courses, summer excursions, individual mission trips, and international internships. The College's International Study Center in France welcomes juniors in any major to enjoy its semester-long program experience. The Chile Study Program allows students to become immersed in Latin American culture. In these programs and more, around half of all students have an experience abroad before graduation.

DIVERSITY ON CAMPUS: Grove City College is actively focused on fostering a diverse learning environment by promoting a climate of respect, unity, and service. The college celebrates different ethnic and denominational backgrounds as a reflection of the community's oneness in Christ. This commitment takes shape in the diversity of Grove City's students, faculty, and administration and can be seen in campus organizations, athletics, the arts, and other extracurricular activities. Students not only emerge from the College with a true appreciation and respect for all people, but also with the skills to be successful in today's complex and varied world.

THE EXERCISE SCIENCE PROGRAM: One of the newest additions to an already extensive list of majors is the Exercise Science program, which prepares students for such fields of work as physical therapy, rehabilitation counseling, exercise physiology, personal training, strength and conditioning coaching, and many other health-related professions. In addition to the program's in-depth coursework, its students complete an internship that gives them over 300 hours of professional experience.

LIFE OUTSIDE THE CLASSROOM: Grove City College believes in taking a holistic approach to learning, opening the environment up for students to take part in a wide range of social, recreational, professional, spiritual, and leadership opportunities. The college newspaper, yearbook, literary magazine, and radio station are joined by many different Christian groups as well as fraternities and sororities. Over 17% of students annually participate in 19 varsity sports (ten for women, nine for men) and/or club intercollegiate sports, and 60% of students participate in intramural or recreational sports.

CAREER SERVICES: Many people think that the reason to go to college is to get a good job. Grove City College thinks that such an idea is much too limited; it believes that the purpose of an education is to discover how God has uniquely designed everyone for their individual vocation. The College's approach to Career Services is anything but a last-minute writing and interviewing class wedged into senior year. Rather, Career Services personnel invest in students, guiding them through a four-year process of development for lifelong success. The effectiveness of such an approach is proven by the more than 25,000 Grove City College alumni who are performing remarkable work in a vast array of successful careers.

http://www.gcc.edu/
P: (724) 458-2100

PRIVATE - CHRISTIAN

STUDENT PROFILE

2,444 undergraduate students

98% of undergrad students are full time

50% male – 50% female

46% of students are from out of state

89% freshman retention rate

85% graduated in 6 years

FACULTY PROFILE

13 to 1 student/faculty ratio

ADMISSIONS

1,541 Total Applicants

1,248 Total Admissions

547 Total Freshman Enrollment

80.99% of applicants admitted

SAT Ranges: CR 536-655, M 540-654

ACT Ranges: C 24-29, M 24-28, E 23-30

TUITION & COSTS

Tuition: $16,154

R&B: $8,802

Room: $5,222

Board: $3,580

Total: $24,956

FINANCIAL

$5,845 avg grant/scholarship amount (total)

$11,650 avg loan amount (total)

GWYNEDD MERCY UNIVERSITY

GWYNEDD VALLEY, PENNSYLVANIA

As one of 16 Sisters of Mercy colleges and universities in the United States, GMercyU is shaped by its Catholic identity and Mercy heritage. It's a place where values are valued, open dialogue is encouraged, and service is expected.

FIRST-YEAR EXPERIENCE: To help students make a successful transition to college, Gwynedd Mercy University's First-Year Experience program focuses on helping students successfully manage the academic and social aspects of college life as well the importance of giving back through community service. Through two courses and myriad planned activities, students join together to explore and develop academic integrity, time management, communication skills, research skills, information literacy, and social responsibility. Students also participate in a common reading program, complete an AlcoholEdu program, and spend time learning about the University's Mercy history and heritage as well as the high-impact practices that support students in becoming a Distinctive Mercy Graduates.

GLOBAL LEARNING AND SERVICE: Beginning as early as students' first week on campus, Gwynedd Mercy University places a tremendous emphasis on service. In keeping with the University's Mercy history and heritage, students are encouraged to step outside their immediate worlds and take part in weekly service projects across the greater Philadelphia area. They're also invited to participate in annual Alternative Spring Break service trips that are designed to make differences in communities and the lives of individuals around the country and the world. In 2015, for example, one group of students traveled to an Apache Reservation in Arizona to join Stephen Rufe, Education '12 by working with his elementary school students.

E-STEM PROGRAM: Supported by a grant from the National Science Foundation, Gwynedd Mercy University's Ethics in Science, Technology, Engineering, and Mathematics (E-STEM) Program is designed to help grow the STEM workforce in the United States. E-STEM students build the ethical framework needed to make a positive difference in STEM fields as they benefit from an E-STEM Living Learning Community; faculty and peer-to-peer mentoring; E-STEM study skill modules; training in ethics, decision making, and leadership; and internship and networking opportunities within the STEM disciplines. Eligible students also may receive a $3,000 or $8,000 annual scholarship.

LEARNING COMMUNITIES: In addition to Living-Learning Communities, such as those offered as part of the E-STEM and Honors Program, Gwynedd Mercy University offers a wide array of co-curricular opportunities for students to join their peers as they develop their leadership skills, support those in need, gain real-world experience, and further explore the world and their role in it.

SERVICE-LEARNING: Service-learning is an integral part of the GMercyU experience. In keeping with the University's history and heritage of helping those most in need, all students engage in service-learning programs. In addition to those included in the First-Year Experience and offered throughout the year, students are encouraged to make service a regular part of their lives. Each year, Gwynedd Mercy University takes students across the country and around the world as part of its Alternative Spring Break service-learning experiences.

CAPSTONE COURSES: All students complete a capstone course designed to synthesize the knowledge and skills that they gained throughout their studies. They provide a means for their demonstration of advanced research, critical thinking, communication, and other essential skills within their disciplines.

INTERNSHIPS, CLINICALS, PRACTICALS: All of Gwynedd Mercy University's education and nursing & health professions students gain hands-on experience as part of their clinical and student teaching requirements. The University also encourages students in other majors to take advantage of many internship opportunities as well as join professional associations, participate in student research projects, and attend/present at industry conferences.

Gwynedd Mercy University

https://www.gmercyu.edu/
P: (800) 342-5462

PRIVATE - CATHOLIC

STUDENT PROFILE

1,935 undergraduate students

93% of undergrad students are full time

25% male – 75% female

20% of students are from out of state

80.2% freshman retention rate

57% graduated in 6 years

FACULTY PROFILE

75 full-time faculty

224 part-time faculty

10 to 1 student/faculty ratio

ADMISSIONS

850 Total Applicants

785 Total Admissions

241 Total Freshman Enrollment

92.35% of applicants admitted

SAT Ranges: CR 410-500, M 420-510

ACT Ranges: C 18-22

TUITION & COSTS

Tuition: $31,780

Fees: $700

Total: $32,480

R&B: $11,300

Total: $43,780

FINANCIAL

$17,810 avg grant/scholarship amount (need)

$4,097 avg loan amount (need)

IMMACULATA UNIVERSITY

IMMACULATA, PENNSYLVANIA

Immaculata University is a Catholic, coeducational institution of higher education sponsored by the Sisters, Servants of the Immaculate Heart of Mary. Its programs are rooted in academic rigor, ethical integrity, and Christian core values—encouraging students to pursue lives full of learning and professional excellence. With a belief in the dignity and potential of all, Immaculata integrates its students into a community of service that empowers them to assume meaningful roles in this diverse and changing world. Contributing to the development of the whole self, Immaculata affirms a liberal education as an integrative process in the formation of a truly educated person. Immaculata University is located in Chester County, Pennsylvania, 20 miles west of Philadelphia, between Paoli and Exton. It is an active campus of curious and insightful minds.

LEARNING COMMUNITIES: Students can participate in Special Interest Learning Communities, groups of students who connect with like-minded peers to assess a topic of their choosing. Members enjoy guests speakers, off-campus trips, and community events. The Campus Ministry Office also offers several extremely popular volunteer service trips each year.

GUIDANCE AND TUTORING: Many Immaculata professors begin their career in-industry. The school's small class sizes help teachers provide individual attention to each of their students. The "Pathways to Success" program also get students in touch with the most qualified sources of support, ensuring that help and guidance are provided throughout the entire college experience. Math and Writing centers are available for students who need extra help with assignments, and professors are often available to work individually with their students in order to help them understand and conquer course material.

STUDENT ACTIVITIES: With over 50 clubs and organizations to choose from, Immaculata students are always active and engaged. Students are constantly forming new groups, expanding options for activities on a yearly basis. They can also get involved in 19 NCAA Division III sports and intramurals/club sports, or they can view or participate in one of the spectacular performing arts ensembles. The Immaculata Symphony, a university-community organization, offers six concerts each year. Performances are also given by special ensembles and the Music Department's faculty/student groups.

GUEST SPEAKERS: The campus community benefits from several guest speakers who are happy to impart their wisdom onto those willing to listen. Events include the Edith Stein Lecture Series, the Spirituality Under the Dome, and Spirituality Days, each of which is offered each year. Additionally, Immaculata has invited keynote speakers to present a wide-array of topics, including cyber security, social media and businesses, and Black History Month.

PROUD STUDENTS: Students' hard work is recognized by several annual poster presentations that are open to the entire campus community. Internships are a huge component of the educational experience, and many students have the opportunity to present what they learned to their classmates and the campus community.

CAREER SERVICES: Students can utilize the services of the Career and Professional Development staff to get access to résumé-building assistance, interview tips, and job-search resources. The Career Services Department ensures that students have the opportunity to shadow professionals in their chosen career fields. They also conduct mock interviews and host the annual "Etiquette Dinner," a unique opportunity for seniors to prepare for the business world.

http://www.immaculata.edu/
P: (610) 647-4400

PRIVATE - CATHOLIC

STUDENT PROFILE

1,694 undergraduate students

60% of undergrad students are full time

31% male – 69% female

34% of students are from out of state

83% freshman retention rate

70.4% graduated in 6 years

FACULTY PROFILE

71 full-time faculty

218 part-time faculty

8.9 to 1 student/faculty ratio

ADMISSIONS

1,586 Total Applicants

1,250 Total Admissions

187 Total Freshman Enrollment

78.81% of applicants admitted

SAT Ranges: CR 440-530, M 420-550

ACT Ranges: C 20-23

TUITION & COSTS

Tuition: $34,410

Fees: $800

Total: $35,210

R&B: $12,500

Total: $47,710

FINANCIAL

$3,645 avg grant/scholarship amount (need)

$4,244 avg loan amount (need)

LA ROCHE COLLEGE

PITTSBURGH, PENNSYLVANIA

A small, private institution in Western Pennsylvania, La Roche College provides a skills-driven education to prepare students for success in today's global economy. With more than 50 undergraduate majors, La Roche offers competitive programs in both high-demand fields and creative industries, with particular strengths in business, criminal justice, design, education, psychology, and health and medical sciences. Located just 15 minutes north of downtown Pittsburgh, this residential college provides a vibrant campus community for more than 1,500 men and women who enjoy over 30 student organizations and an exciting NCAA Div. III athletics program. Founded by the Sisters of Divine Providence in 1963, La Roche educates students to be lifelong learners and achievers in an increasingly diverse and global society.

STUDY ABROAD OPPORTUNITIES INCLUDED WITH TUITION: La Roche's Study Abroad + Study USA program, already included in the cost of tuition, allows students to travel the U.S. or study abroad. The program covers the cost of travel, lodging, and most meals. From Alaska and California to Cuba, Europe, and South America, students have experienced new places and other cultures at no additional cost.

THE LA ROCHE EXPERIENCE: One highlight of the College's core curriculum is The La Roche Experience, a required sequence of courses for all traditional freshmen, sophomores, and juniors. This program introduces students to the principles of peace and justice, giving them the skills and perspective to make a positive impact in today's society. Coursework includes service learning, value-based simulations, spiritual self-exploration, reflective journal exercises, and college-wide seminars that focus on global issues.

SERVICE: In addition to clubs and organizations, La Roche offers a variety of service-learning opportunities for students to do more for the outside community and examine social issues. La Roche students, faculty, and staff provide service in a variety of ways, including working with at-risk children and their families, visiting the elderly, participating in neighborhood cleanup and rehabilitation, and taking food, blankets, and other essentials to the homeless.

HANDS-ON LEARNING: Although professors reserve class time for discussion, experimentation, and interaction, learning at La Roche happens both inside and outside of the classroom. La Roche students hone their career skills by gaining real-life experience through internships, hands-on projects, and industry-connected faculty. For example, Criminal Justice students intern for professionals in criminal justice, gaining practical experience in La Roche's onsite crime scene investigation laboratory.

STUDENT LIFE: An active student-life allows students to explore new interests, meet new people, and develop leadership skills. Activities serve many interests, with everything from intramural sports, fishing, and skiing, to special events such as the GLOBE International Fashion Show and Spring Carnival. More than 30 student clubs and organizations include academic and professional organizations, multicultural clubs, and campus media.

ALUMNI CIRCLE: La Roche prepares students to become responsible citizens as well as confident, compassionate leaders in an ever-changing world. Ninety-two percent of graduates find employment, go onto graduate school, perform military service, or participate in volunteer initiatives such as AmeriCorps and the Peace Corps within one year of graduating. Members of La Roche's Distinguished Alumni Circle include graduates who have achieved outstanding career success. These alumni include company directors, vice presidents, accomplished doctors, teachers, and award-winning writers. One Distinguished Alumna has served as a management consultant, lawyer, board advisor, and an entrepreneur since graduating from La Roche.

http://www.laroche.edu/
P: (412) 536-1272

PRIVATE - CATHOLIC

STUDENT PROFILE

1,398 undergraduate students

83% of undergrad students are full time

44% male – 56% female

12% of students are from out of state

78% freshman retention rate

45% graduated in 6 years

FACULTY PROFILE

62 full-time faculty

122 part-time faculty

12 to 1 student/faculty ratio

ADMISSIONS

1,167 Total Applicants

1,114 Total Admissions

291 Total Freshman Enrollment

95.46% of applicants admitted

SAT Ranges: CR 420-520, M 410-520, W 400-510

ACT Ranges: C 17-23, M 17-23, E 16-23, W 6-8

TUITION & COSTS

Tuition: $25,500

Fees: $750

Total: $26,250

R&B: $10,630

Room: $6,730

Board: $3,900

Total: $36,880

FINANCIAL

$16,743 avg grant/scholarship amount (total)

$6,183 avg loan amount (total)

LAFAYETTE COLLEGE

EASTON, PENNSYLVANIA

Lafayette provides university-sized resources in an small college environment exclusive to undergraduates. With such great opportunity, anything is possible at Lafayette College.

FIRST-YEAR SEMINAR (FYS): First-year seminar courses are limited to 16 students per class. These courses may each cover specific topics, but they all have the same vital components aimed at improving writing and communication skills. Students are taught to participate and engage actively with other peers as they learn the basic skills needed for research and college-level scholarship.

AN EDUCATIONAL EXPERIENCE OUTSIDE OF THE CLASSROOM: Lafayette gives its students several opportunities to learn outside of the traditional classroom setting. The College embraces study abroad as an integral part of the undergraduate experience, teaching the values that come cross-cultural communication and exploration. Other nontraditional opportunities include undergraduate research, first-year seminars, and community outreach.

THE COLLEGE WRITING PROGRAM (CWP): The College Writing Program has been a part of Lafayette's curriculum since 1987. The program incorporates writing into several different courses across all disciplines, helping to increase students' understanding and practice with the writing process in multiple fields of study. The ability to communicate through writing is an incredibly useful tool, and Lafayette works hard to ensure that each graduate has had the proper training. CWP also offers select undergraduates to train as writing associates, practicing their own skills while tutoring their peers.

ATTIC: The Academic Tutoring and Training Information Center (ATTIC) is designed to provide students with the necessary tools to succeed in the face of any challenge they face in school. It works to give clear direction to students, helping them maximize their educational experience by offering a selection of programs, including tutoring and academic advising.

COMMUNITY SERVICE: Lafayette students are regularly involved in community service initiatives, which are organized weekly and also include trips to places in need. In addition to voluntary service, students can also take credit-granting classes that include supplementary service projects. This gives them the opportunity to see their classroom theories applied to real-life situations.

A DIVERSE COMMUNITY: Lafayette is committed to fostering a diverse community that is accepting of all backgrounds and beliefs. The College environment encourages inclusivity for all members of the campus community, calling students to learn from one another and embrace each other's differences.

ATHLETICS, HEALTH, AND WELLNESS: Lafayette has 23 NCAA Division I athletic programs—11 men's, 11 women's, and 1 co-ed. Lafayette also offers several recreational sport options, including club and intramural sports. And for students who just want to exercise, fitness classes are available to everyone. On top of the recreational activities offered, the College also provides health and counseling services to ensure the mental and physical well-being of each individual.

GIVING STUDENTS THE RIGHT TOOLS: Lafayette students humbly demonstrate their intellectual capabilities in such an ever-changing and demanding society. Such real-world skills include innovation, critical thinking, problem solving, communication, and applied knowledge. Students gain such a strong capacity for growth through a variety of disciplines and activities, ensuring that, upon graduation, they are well equipped to handle any challenges that their careers or future schooling might present.

FACULTY ADVISER: Every incoming student is assigned a faculty advisor to assist with their academic- and career-related questions. Once they declare their major, they are then redirected to a specified advisor within their chosen department. Students are encouraged to maintain contact with faculty advisors, as they act as highly beneficial, knowledgeable guides for their students' academic and personal opportunities.

http://www.lafayette.edu/
P: (610) 330-5000

PRIVATE

STUDENT PROFILE

2,533 undergraduate students

98% of undergrad students are full time

51% male – 49% female

71% of students are from out of state

95% freshman retention rate

90% graduated in 6 years

FACULTY PROFILE

238 full-time faculty

48 part-time faculty

10 to 1 student/faculty ratio

ADMISSIONS

7,465 Total Applicants

2,258 Total Admissions

672 Total Freshman Enrollment

30.25% of applicants admitted

SAT Ranges: CR 580-670, M 620-710, W 590-690

ACT Ranges: C 27-31, M 27-31, E 27-33, W 8-9

TUITION & COSTS

Tuition: $46,590

Fees: $420

Total: $47,010

R&B: $13,920

Room: $8,610

Board: $5,310

Total: $60,930

FINANCIAL

$36,912 avg grant/scholarship amount (total)

$6,753 avg loan amount (total)

LEBANON VALLEY COLLEGE

ANNVILLE, PENNSYLVANIA

Lebanon Valley College offers degrees in health sciences, actuarial science, analytical finance, physical and natural sciences, computer & data science, mathematics, arts, music education and production, digital communications, design and technology, criminal justice, business, English, environmental and global studies, and more.

SUMMER ENRICHMENT PROGRAM: The Summer Enrichment Program (SEP) is a seven-day program geared to provide incoming first-year, transfer ALANA (African/African American), Latina, Asian, and Native American), and multiracial students a jumpstart for college life. The program combines peer mentoring, residential living, academic success, and leadership development to assist them in making a successful transition to collegiate academics and the LVC community.

FIRST-YEAR EXPERIENCE: The First-Year Experience (FYE) introduces LVC students to the unique value of their school's education both during the summer before school and throughout their freshman year. Through participation in small, seminar-style courses, the FYE promotes intellectual questions, developing the core skills that are essential to meet LVC's rigorous curricular demands. Students reside together in learning communities and receive support from dedicated faculty, staff, and peer and writing mentors.

INTERNATIONAL FACULTY-LED EXPERIENCES: Students have numerous opportunities to study abroad, conduct research, or perform community service internationally with their professors. Recent faculty-led student experiences occurred in Canada, England, Germany, Hungary, Italy, Mexico, the Netherlands, Paraguay, Peru, and elsewhere.

ANNUAL COLLOQUIUM: The mission of the annual LVC Colloquium is to provide students with the opportunity for a unifying intellectual experience that cuts across disciplinary and departmental boundaries. The Colloquium devotes programming to a sustained treatment of a subject, theme, or problem through conversations, lectures, roundtables, films, and integrated course materials. It even hosts presentations given by leading thinkers, authors, scientists, and policy-makers from around the world.

INQUIRY: Inquiry is a two-week celebration of student research, scholarship, and creative achievements that happens to coincide with the Council for Undergraduate Research's week-long celebration of student accomplishments. Inquiry includes induction ceremonies into national and international academic honor societies, poetry readings, music recitals, and oral research presentations. At the concluding Inquiry Symposium, nearly 200 undergraduates from every academic department display their work to an audience of faculty, peers, trustees, administrators, and friends of the College.

LEADERSHIP DEVELOPMENT: Leadership development is an important part of the College's co-curriculum. Student representatives are voting members of every primary campus committee, including the College's Board of Trustees, and students serve on all upper-level administrative search committees. They also attend leadership symposia and events, including the NCAA National Convention, trips to the Gettysburg battlefields, and more.

SOCIAL JUSTICE INSTITUTE: Each January, the Office of Intercultural Affairs & Inclusive Programs sponsors a leadership-driven Social Justice Institute enable students to explore oppression's impact on true equality. A true highlight of this Institute is its trip to an urban center, which engages students to participate in service alongside social justice-based agencies. Recent Institutes have served in New York City, Philadelphia, and Washington, D.C.

CENTER FOR CAREER DEVELOPMENT: LVC's Center for Career Development engages students to become active participants in the development and implementation of their career plans and graduate/professional school pursuits. It plays a unique and complementary role in the overall educational experience, helping students acquire the knowledge and skills they need to perform effectively in the world of work.

http://www.lvc.edu/

P: (717) 867-6161

PRIVATE

STUDENT PROFILE

1,651 undergraduate students

97% of undergrad students are full time

46% male – 54% female

20.8% of students are from out of state

85% freshman retention rate

74.3% graduated in 6 years

FACULTY PROFILE

108 full-time faculty

135 part-time faculty

11 to 1 student/faculty ratio

ADMISSIONS

3,329 Total Applicants

2,413 Total Admissions

456 Total Freshman Enrollment

72.48% of applicants admitted

SAT Ranges: CR 490-590, M 510-620

ACT Ranges: C 19-25, M 21-27, E 19-26

TUITION & COSTS

Tuition: $39,410

Fees: $1,140

Total: $40,550

R&B: $10,980

Total: $51,530

FINANCIAL

$24,641 avg grant/scholarship amount (need)

$4,405 avg loan amount (need)

LYCOMING COLLEGE

WILLIAMSPORT, PENNSYLVANIA

Lycoming College is a residential, four-year college in Williamsport, PA, USA. This institution emphasizes exceptional student achievement with a comprehensive yet supportive educational program. A small student-to-faculty ratio, interactive classroom environments, and a dedication to accessible human resources all foster close mentoring relationships between students and faculty.

FIRST-YEAR SEMINARS: In support of its liberal arts mission, Lycoming's First-Year Seminar program offers first-year students the opportunity to explore a topic that may be totally new to them. The First-Year Seminar provides a unique opportunity for science majors to explore civil rights, criminal justice majors to explore nutrition, history majors to discover the mathematics behind games and gambling, or art majors to study how groundbreaking technologies impact social relationships. Freshmen are stretched to broaden their minds and discover a new interest by selecting a First-Year Seminar outside of their immediate areas of interest.

UNDERGRADUATE RESEARCH: Lycoming has been working to create funded research opportunities for students having recently earned a $100,000 grant from The Andrew W. Mellon Foundation (the first from the Mellon Foundation in the College's history). The grant supports faculty members and students as they collaborate in research projects within the arts, humanities, and humanities-focused social sciences. The outcomes of these student-faculty collaborative projects often include regional and national conference presentations as well as co-authored publications in scholarly journals. Such experiences and credentials are sure to place Lycoming College students in strong, competitive positions for top-tier employment and graduate school admission.

GLOBAL LEARNING: Lycoming College encourages students to take part in a study abroad program during their undergraduate career, offering a range of opportunities that vary in length and location. Students can travel during the May Term, summer session, or even for a full semester or year. New exchange agreements at international universities in Grenoble, France, and Puebla, Mexico, host outstanding opportunities for Lycoming students to study all around the world.

WRITING-INTENSIVE COURSES: The Lycoming College Writing Program was established in recognition that writing skills promote intellectual growth as a distinguishing factor of an education. This program aims to support students through both general and subject-specific writing, strengthening their ability to communicate effectively across media. In the program's designated courses, students are encouraged to write in a variety of contexts in which they receive faculty guidance and reinforcement. All writing-intensive classes include formal writing instruction in the classroom, student writing, instructor feedback, and student revision.

LEARNING OUTSIDE THE CLASSROOM: Lycoming has recently invested in the distinctive Outdoor Leadership & Education initiative in an effort to improve life outside the classroom and develop students' abilities in leadership. Learning while doing is one of the most effective ways to gain and apply new knowledge and skills, and so the Outdoor Leadership & Education program is committed to providing students with opportunities to grow through intentionally designed outdoor experiences in an adventurous fun-filled environment. In its first full year of operation, the Outdoor Leadership & Education program cultivated a growing student interest and now continues to offer an exploration Pennsylvania Wilds and the chance to "learn without boundaries."

CAPSTONE COURSES & PROJECTS: Every major at the College includes a capstone experience that challenges students to showcase their learning outcomes from their specific majors. The capstone serves as a culminating academic experience for students, typically at the end of their college career, to demonstrate all facets of major curriculum in one comprehensive project.

http://www.lycoming.edu/
P: (570) 321-4000

PRIVATE

STUDENT PROFILE
1,246 undergraduate students
99% of undergrad students are full time
48% male – 52% female
48% of students are from out of state
79% freshman retention rate
71.68% graduated in 6 years

FACULTY PROFILE
89 full-time faculty
33 part-time faculty
12.5 to 1 student/faculty ratio

ADMISSIONS
1,876 Total Applicants
1,305 Total Admissions
343 Total Freshman Enrollment
69.56% of applicants admitted

SAT Ranges: CR 470-550, M 470-570

ACT Ranges: C 20-25

TUITION & COSTS
Tuition: $36,432
Fees: $955
Total: $37,387
R&B: $11,418
Total: $48,805

FINANCIAL
$29,394 avg grant/scholarship amount (need)
$4,630 avg loan amount (need)

MANSFIELD UNIVERSITY OF PENNSYLVANIA

MANSFIELD, PENNSYLVANIA

At Mansfield University, students are afforded incredible opportunities from the moment they first enroll at MU right up to the time they graduate. A Mansfield University experience develops the student holistically by combining rigorous academics with a broad range of extracurricular opportunities at an affordable cost. Student success is the primary focus of the Mansfield faculty and staff, all of whom strive to develop and maintain a premier learning environment with premier opportunities for the entire student body.

FIRST-YEAR MODULES: There are 7 modules within the first-year experience, each of which creates a guideline for the abilities students should gain throughout their college career. With the support of faculty and staff, students are taught to hone their skills in Resiliency, Stress Management, Time Management, Debt Management, Note Taking, Test Taking, and Improving Study Time. Students proficient in these modules are prepared for any academic challenge presented to them, and it is through the Mansfield curriculum that they become truly amazing scholars.

INTRODUCTORY SEMINARS: Mansfield's first-year seminars are part of an introductory program called the First-Year Experience. They act as an academic component that allows students to explore new and exciting topics in a small-group setting. Some examples of previous first-year seminars have included Animal Allies, Mates, and Rivals; Public issues in a Global Economy; Debates in Current Affairs; Our Lives through Music; Art & History of the Book; Grimm Variations; Discovering France; and Zombie Apocalypse.

SPECIAL INTEREST HOUSING: First-year students have the option to live in Themed Housing Communities, which are designed to bring students in touch with others who shared similar interests, passions, and goals. Able to live in residential spaces that foster out-of-classroom learning and community, participating freshmen find their niche and melt into the Mansfield University culture right away! The Creative Artist community gathers students who have a drive to create art and seek the encouragement and inspiration of other talented students. Explorer community residents push each other to try new things, meet new people, and attend a variety of activities, and the Outdoor Enthusiast residents join each other in exciting trips around the Pennsylvania landscape. Students can also join a Healthy Living community to promote wellness, or they can let their imaginations run wild in the Sci-Fi, Fantasy, & Horror community.

IMPACT MENTORING PROGRAM: The IMPACT Mentoring Program is an initiative headed by the Office of Retention to address the common challenges that face first-year students. Through the support of compassionate mentors, the Office of Student Life, and the Office of Retention, freshmen are given the tools they'll need to succeed. This program has helped students overcome such challenges as finding friends, selecting courses, and interacting with professors. IMPACT may be a resource directed at freshmen, but mentors are always available to help anyone throughout their entire time at college. It is with the guidance of such dedicated staff that Mansfield students truly feel at home.

INTERNATIONAL EXCHANGES AND STUDY ABROAD: Students who participate in international exchange and study abroad gain valuable skills in cross-cultural communication and education. Mansfield knows that study abroad is an incredible opportunity and thus works hard to provide plenty of options to students. Currently, the University has exchange agreements with 150 institutions across the world through a membership with the International Student Exchange Programs (ISEP). Mansfield's specific agreements include partnerships in such countries as Australia, Canada, France Germany, and Spain.

http://www.mansfield.edu/

P: (800) 577-6826

PUBLIC

STUDENT PROFILE

2,249 undergraduate students

91% of undergrad students are full time

40% male – 60% female

15% of students are from out of state

76% freshman retention rate

50% graduated in 6 years

FACULTY PROFILE

135 full-time faculty

108 part-time faculty

15 to 1 student/faculty ratio

ADMISSIONS

1,918 Total Applicants

1,698 Total Admissions

401 Total Freshman Enrollment

88.53% of applicants admitted

SAT Ranges: CR 420-540, M 430-530, W 390-510

ACT Ranges: C 17-22, M 17-23, E 16-22

TUITION & COSTS

Tuition: (In) $7,060 (Out) $17,650

Fees: $2,974

Total: (In) $9,806 (Out) $20,624

R&B: $11,340

Room: $7,904

Board: $3,436

Total: (In) $21,146 (Out) $31,964

FINANCIAL

$5,763 avg grant/scholarship amount (total)

$8,907 avg loan amount (total)

MERCYHURST UNIVERSITY

ERIE, PENNSYLVANIA

Mercyhurst's motto–Carpe Diem, Latin for "Seize the Day"–is at the heart of everything the University does. At Mercyhurst, students find a community that celebrates experiences both inside and outside the classroom, experiences that challenge them to write more, practice harder, dig deeper, and see the world from an unconventional perspective. College isn't about reveling in what one has done in the past; it's about uncovering who one is and who they want to become.

THE FRESHMAN EXPERIENCE: Mercyhurst primes its students with an introduction to academic writing and thought as it integrates them into the college lifestyle. COMP120 (Writing and Research), along with two one-credit courses (iMU10: Introduction to Mercyhurst and iMU102: Involvement at Mercyhurst), help ease the transition from high school to college. These courses sharpen students' skills while introducing them to their new peers.

INVESTED PROFESSORS: Students have access to more than 165 faculty members who are eager to share years of invaluable training and field experience. In many cases, they even work side-by-side with students on exciting research projects. Not only does Mercyhurst employ some of the nation's brightest academic minds, but such professors are also approachable and dependable. Even as freshmen, students take advantage of unique opportunities to collaborate with notable faculty who act as mentors and advocates on the path to knowledge, growth, and success. At Mercyhurst, a liberal arts education is about studying what one loves and applying it to real-world circumstances. Ultimately, what really unites Mercyhurst graduates is their shared ability to ask questions, spark discussion, engage in critical and creative thinking, research complex issues, and write effectively. These are essential skills that are prized by employers in today's idea- and service-driven economy.

STUDY ABROAD: Consistently, 75% of students annually choose to take either a single intensive course or embark on a study abroad excursion thanks to Mercyhurst's flexible scheduling. Among the most popular study abroad programs are the Faculty-Student Academic Travel (FSAT) opportunities, which have taken students and professors to study narrative and film in Spain; aquatic ecology in Belize; video storytelling in Peru; and dance appreciation in France and Israel. Students have also studied in Ireland, Portugal, Germany, Italy, Switzerland, England, Vietnam, Japan, Costa Rica, Guyana, Haiti, Mexico, South Africa, Nigeria, and China. The options for international travel are endless, as students can even pursue external study through such recognized programs as Academic Programs International and Semester at Sea.

LAKER FOR LIFE: Students' four years at Mercyhurst shape who they become personally, professionally, and socially. Generation after generation of Lakers, students graduate carrying a deepened self-awareness, a wealth of knowledge and experience, and an abundance of friendships. Through everything that the Mercyhurst community does to help its students preserve and evolve their individuality, students and alumni are bonded together by the University's Mercy values and the lifelong search for what is true, good, and beautiful. The Laker community extends beyond the University's iconic iron gates to every corner of the world–it is a thriving community of individuals pursuing their passions for the common good. Mercyhurst students are not simply Lakers for their four years as undergrads; they're Lakers for the rest of their lives.

LEADERS IN SERVICE: Mercyhurst has been honored with distinction for its University-wide commitment to community service, providing a platform that enables students to log more than 40,000 hours of community service each year. The Freshman Day of Service introduces new students to the Mercy tradition and values of service, having them set aside time in order to make a phenomenal impact to the surrounding community.

ON-TIME GRADUATION: Graduating on time is the best way to avoid any unnecessary tuition costs in one's college education, so Mercyhurst makes earning a degree within four years a priority. In fact, the University's four-year graduation rate is the highest in Erie County and one of the highest in the region. Mercyhurst's 15-to-Finish program encourages students to take 15 credits every semester, helping them make wise decisions with their academic advisors as they schedule their courses.

http://www.mercyhurst.edu/

P: (814) 824-2000

PRIVATE - CATHOLIC

STUDENT PROFILE

3,100 undergraduate students

98% of undergrad students are full time

44% male – 56% female

56% of students are from out of state

78% freshman retention rate

67% graduated in 6 years

FACULTY PROFILE

165 full-time faculty

48 part-time faculty

13 to 1 student/faculty ratio

ADMISSIONS

3,254 Total Applicants

2,448 Total Admissions

724 Total Freshman Enrollment

75% of applicants admitted

TUITION & COSTS

Tuition: $34,050

Fees: $2,270

Total: $36,320

R&B: $14,690

Room: $8,260

Board: $6,430

Total: $51,010

FINANCIAL

$22,411 avg grant/scholarship amount (total)

$7,868 avg loan amount (total)

MESSIAH COLLEGE

MECHANICSBURG, PENNSYLVANIA

Messiah College is nationally recognized for bringing together top-tier academics and Messiah College is nationally recognized for bringing together top-tier academics and Christian faith. The College's motto, "Christ Preeminent," shapes every experience its students have at school. Lifelong friendships, support from faculty mentors, outstanding preparation for successful lives and careers, and transformational service and ministry—at Messiah, one's life, faith, world, and possibilities open up. Students come to see anew.

FIRST-YEAR SEMINARS AND EXPERIENCES: When students arrive on Messiah's campus, they find themselves among a lot of new people from a variety of different schools, cultures, and backgrounds. To help ease the transition to college life, Messiah has created a "First-Year Experience" through which students can immediately build community with students who are going through the exact same transitions. Living in the same residence halls, sharing similar classroom experiences, and attending special chapels and social events together helps each freshman get to know people quickly and naturally. Special first-year courses foster the ability to think, read, write, and speak effectively so that students can be flexible and adaptable to the changes of the world across the spectrum of different fields and life experiences. These courses provide students with the basis upon which to enhance their skills in thinking, reading, listening, writing, and speaking.

STUDY ABROAD: Messiah College's off-campus programs provide students with transformative, safe, and quality semester-long and short-term cultural learning experiences that assist them in navigating the complexities the world and understanding their place in it. Students may choose from more than 30 semester-long off-campus programs in more than 40 countries. Students may also take a short-term trip during J-Term or May-Term.

UNDERGRADUATE RESEARCH: Each summer, 8-12 Messiah College students earn competitive internal Steinbrecher research fellowships, which allow them to live on campus and work one-on-one with faculty in laboratory research for 10 weeks over the summer. On the national stage, Messiah students are also selected for competitive research experiences for undergraduates (REUs) in universities across the country, and in some cases, internationally.

WRITING-INTENSIVE COURSES: The writing program at Messiah includes four components: a College Writing Workshop; a First-Year Seminar; Created and Called for Community; and a writing-enriched course developed for one's specific major. Messiah's writing courses build on the intellectual and writing skills developed during First-Year Seminar but hone in on major-specific writing skills within students' chosen disciplines. These courses vary considerably across disciplines, as they address the specific needs of each fields with different writing emphases and topics.

LEARNING COMMUNITIES: In "Created and Called for Community," one of the four components of Messiah's writing program, students consider a central question: "What is my vocation as a faithful steward of God's creation?" They seek answers by engaging biblical themes of creation, forgiveness, compassion, peacemaking, and reconciliation through an examination of literary, historical, artistic, philosophical, and theological works. They use the lens of Messiah College's distinctive foundational values, focusing on the importance of community and hospitality. Students develop the ability to be theologically reflective; to develop an appreciation for their own identity and Christian vocation; and to cultivate their intellect and character in preparation for lives of leadership through service in the world. Thus, in addition to developing intellectual skills of the liberal arts, "Created and Called for Community" also lays a foundation in the outcome of Social Responsibility.

http://www.messiah.edu/

P: (717-- 691-6000

PRIVATE - CHRISTIAN

STUDENT PROFILE

2,723 undergraduate students

98% of undergrad students are full time

39% male – 61% female

38% of students are from out of state

88.1% freshman retention rate

77% graduated in 6 years

FACULTY PROFILE

192 full-time faculty

149 part-time faculty

12 to 1 student/faculty ratio

ADMISSIONS

2,469 Total Applicants

1,950 Total Admissions

691 Total Freshman Enrollment

78.98% of applicants admitted

SAT Ranges: CR 500-620, M 510-630, W 490-600, E 7-8

ACT Ranges: C 21-28, M 21-28, E 21-29, W 21-30

TUITION & COSTS

Tuition: $32,350

Fees: $830

Total: $33,180

R&B: $9,920

Room: $5,250

Board: $4,670

Total: $43,930

FINANCIAL

$17,299 avg grant/scholarship amount (need)

$4,867 avg loan amount (need)

MILLERSVILLE UNIVERSITY OF PENNSYLVANIA

MILLERSVILLE, PENNSYLVANIA

Millersville University is one of the highest-ranked public universities in Pennsylvania. It has focused its program initiatives to enhance student learning and engagement, each centered on its commitment to the liberal arts and science tradition. More than 60 programs of study are offered with hands-on learning opportunities and experiential experiences with public, private, regional and global organizations.

GLOBAL STUDENTS: Millersville provides its students with global studies opportunities in the form of study abroad, international internships, student teaching abroad, research collaboration, and professional training. Through many partnerships, students are afforded the ability to study around the globe in places like Australia and China. The Office of Global Education & Partnerships works with students and parents to ensure that each effort to study or work abroad is met with the most sincere and valued assistance. Millersville recognizes study abroad, in any capacity, as an integral part of a college experience. Students who have experienced another country's culture have gained a repertoire of valuable skills.

EXPERIENTIAL LEARNING AND CAREER MANAGEMENT: The Experiential Learning and Career Management service is designed to guide students' academic and career goals through advising and counseling. Within this service, there are concentrations, all working toward the advancement of student success. The Career Services Office is also dedicated to helping students identify and fulfil their career goals. Students explore their various career desires and learn how they can get to where they want to be. Job and Internship fairs are also available to students, introducing them to prospects for work or practice within their chosen field.

INTERNSHIPS: Through internships, students can apply the theories they learn at the academic level to professional contexts. Campus resources at Millersville are prepared to help students locate and secure positions as interns. Millersville also gives students the opportunity to practice within their field on a global scale. They can travel abroad and complete internships with international companies, regardless of their chosen field of study.

STUDENT ACTIVITIES: Millersville provides a friendly and supportive community to its students— the kind of environment that encourages academic and personal growth. There are plenty of opportunities to succeed and have fun on Millersville's campus. Outside of class, students can get involved in such extracurricular activities as: experiential learning programs, athletic teams, and clubs and organizations. Some have the option to get involved in departmental honors programs and societies or academic clubs within their majors, such as the Collegiate Entrepreneurs' Organization, a group within the Business major. There are also 50 clubs at Millersville that are dedicated to art and culture. Interested students can join groups like the Creative Writers Guild or the Jewelry and Metal Arts Guild, or they can take the Greek route and join a sorority or fraternity. Greek students gain experience working with faculty and alumni, and they help their community through service initiatives. Overall, involvement in Greek Life is bonding experience where students can grow and learn from one another.

INVESTED PROFESSORS: Millersville faculty are respected scholars in their fields. They work closely with students, helping them to discover their individual talents and potential. Professors act as mentors, inspiring students to explore their abilities both in and outside of academia. Staff and faculty work together to groom students into strong, intelligent leaders. The goal is to teach students how to discover their individual, academic potential, which they eventually take into their own hands to mold and develop. Millersville asks for the best from its students.

Millersville University
LANCASTER

http://www.millersville.edu/
P: (717) 871-4636

PUBLIC

STUDENT PROFILE

7,055 undergraduate students

87% of undergrad students are full time

44% male – 56% female

9% of students are from out of state

76% freshman retention rate

62% graduated in 6 years

FACULTY PROFILE

315 full-time faculty

164 part-time faculty

20 to 1 student/faculty ratio

ADMISSIONS

6,053 Total Applicants

4,422 Total Admissions

1,336 Total Freshman Enrollment

73.05% of applicants admitted

SAT Ranges: CR 450-550, M 450-550, W 430-530

ACT Ranges: C 19-24

TUITION & COSTS

Tuition: (In) $8,460 (Out) $17,650

Fees: (In) $2,458 (Out) $2,686

Total: (In) $10,918 (Out) $20,336

R&B: $12,188

Room: $8,034

Board: $4,154

Total: (In) $23,106 (Out) $32,524

FINANCIAL

$5,298 avg grant/scholarship amount (total)

$8,407 avg loan amount (total)

MOUNT ALOYSIUS COLLEGE

CRESSON, PENNSYLVANIA

Established in 1853, Mount Aloysius is a liberal arts and science-based institution with a commitment to career-directed study. Rooted in Catholic tradition, Mount Aloysius is one of the nation's 18 Mercy-sponsored colleges. MAC began as an Academy and has evolved into a comprehensive college which provides undergraduate and graduate education. At Mount Aloysius, students enjoy the company of a nationally known, experienced faculty. With most professors holding terminal or doctorate degrees, faculty bring to the classroom both academic and real-world experience.

MERCY SERVICE: The spirit of service is alive at Mount Aloysius. Many student organizations use the Mercy heritage as a steppingstone to helping others. In the past, for example, students have traveled to Honduras to build an orphanage and volunteered at a school for deaf children in Jamaica. Along with faculty and staff, MAC students have also made annual trips to Camp Coast Care in Mississippi to help rebuild the gulf coast after hurricane Katrina. They have collected food donations for regional food banks, involved themselves in Earth Day, practiced the UN Day of Peace, contributed to Coaches vs. Cancer, and so much more.

WELL-ESTABLISHED, MARKET-DRIVEN EDUCATION: Mount Aloysius College continually researches employment trends and market demands, adding or changing programs to address the world's emerging needs. Its core curriculum is designed to help students become analytical and reflective in the face of these changes. Students learn to approach their work within the context of the larger world beyond MAC's borders, receiving a "classic" college curriculum that is reinvented for today's career-centric students.

INTERNSHIPS: MAC student interns build practical experience in a wide range of professional settings. Some have served as clinical interns in a physical therapy practice, while others have been assistants to the Watershed Manager in the Pennsylvania Department of Environmental Protection. For those who are more competitive, Mount Aloysius offers students the opportunity to compete for highly coveted internship positions. For example, the College has had a pre-med student attend a 10-week internship with the Pittsburgh Tissue Engineering Initiative at McGowan Institute for Regenerative medicine.

TALENTED, ACTIVE STUDENTS: Recreational opportunities include cross-country skiing, mountain biking, and intramural sports. On campus, a traditional, multi-day competition called the "Mini-Olympics" involves seasoned athletes and bookworms alike. One particularly notable organization is the Vox Nova Choral Ensemble, which is comprised of non-music majors and renowned for its Baroque and Renaissance selections. Under the direction of Nancy Rosenteel Way, Vox Nova made a live recording at the invitation of Pittsburgh radio station WQED, which aired the performance.

CAREER SERVICES: The practical career assistance at Mount Aloysius prepares students for real-world careers in their fields of study. MAC goes beyond the classroom to help students gain practical experience. The career services department offers résumé-building assistance, mock interview opportunities, career workshops, job fairs, and referrals to prospective employers.

CONTINUING LIVES OF LEARNING: Many Mount Aloysius alumni have continued their educations at such graduate or law schools as: Berklee College of Music, Boston College, Bucknell University, Catholic University, Dickinson School of Law, Drexel University, Duquesne School of Law, Georgetown University, Notre Dame University, Princeton University, Temple University, The University of Pennsylvania, Thomas Cooley School of Law, Villanova University, and Xavier University.

http://www.mtaloy.edu/
P: (814) 886-6383

PRIVATE - CATHOLIC

STUDENT PROFILE

1,477 undergraduate students

79% of undergrad students are full time

30% male – 70% female

92% of students are from out of state

80% freshman retention rate

FACULTY PROFILE

72 full-time faculty

131 part-time faculty

13 to 1 student/faculty ratio

ADMISSIONS

1,246 Total Applicants

829 Total Admissions

278 Total Freshman Enrollment

66.53% of applicants admitted

SAT Ranges: CR 425-525, M 425-525

ACT Ranges: C 18-20

TUITION & COSTS

Tuition: $19,790

Fees: $1,000

Total: $20,790

R&B: $9,186

Room: $4,620

Board: $4,566

Total: $29,976

FINANCIAL

$4,600 avg grant/scholarship amount (need)

$4,000 avg loan amount (need)

MUHLENBERG COLLEGE

ALLENTOWN, PENNSYLVANIA

Muhlenberg College

Muhlenberg College provides challenging academics and passionate teaching within a warm and caring community environment. The College has a strong heritage of developing students who think independently, live ethically, and contribute to society wholeheartedly. Students forge strong bonds with the College, their professors, and each other, leading to lifelong friendships.

FIRST-YEAR SEMINAR: The First-Year Seminar program is designed for freshmen to question, discuss, and think critically about their own basic beliefs and values. Covering a broad range of topics, these seminars stress writing and speaking skills. Previous course offerings have included: "Reflections of Pop Culture," "Exploring Cultural Identity," and "Sprawl and Life in Suburbia."

STUDY ABROAD: Muhlenberg sends over 100 students abroad each year, ensuring that their financial aid follows them beyond the school's borders. The College has agreements with 33 universities around the world, guaranteeing that courses taken abroad transfer back to their Muhlenberg transcripts. Two of the most popular programs are the London Theatre semester and an international business program at the University of Maastricht, Netherlands. Students can also choose programs in Argentina, Australia, China, Czech Republic, Denmark, Ecuador, France, Germany, Ireland, Israel, Italy, Japan, Scotland, and Spain.

THE INSTITUTE OF ENTREPRENEURSHIP: The Institute of Entrepreneurship prepares Muhlenberg students for the innovation and self-reliance appropriate for a variety of life and career pursuits. Students receive support in the creation and development of business ventures. For example, Muhlenberg students have started a magazine for Lehigh-area college students and established a weekly laundry service for students. The Institute also offers coursework in entrepreneurial studies.

INTERDISCIPLINARY STUDY AND SERVICE PROJECTS: The Interdisciplinary Study Program in Central America allows Muhlenberg students to pursue research and service projects while improving their Spanish language skills. Guided by faculty who are experts in conservation biology and environmental sociology, students the delicate problem of environmental and cultural conservation in developing Latin American countries. Previous research projects have included comparative studies of public education, water quality studies and ecotourism, and other forms of conservation. Prior service projects have focused on such issues as medical care, education, housing, and sustainable development.

A STEP AHEAD: Muhlenberg students have the opportunity to jumpstart their graduate education during their undergraduate career. The 3-2 program with Duke University allows students to spend three years at Muhlenberg and two years at Duke while earning a B.S. and M.S. in forestry and environmental studies. There is also a similar program for engineering students at Columbia University or Washington University—St. Louis.

SPIRITUAL LIFE: Spirituality is an important component of the Muhlenberg experience. The Institute for Jewish-Christian Understanding serves as an expression of Muhlenberg's commitment to interfaith relations. It uses the resources of the academic community to foster research and dialogue as well as to build bridges of understanding between the faith traditions. The Lutheran Student Movement holds weekly Bible study and other activities, and students can also participate in activities sponsored by Catholic Newman Center and the Jewish Hillel House, both of which have recently received new facilities. Students from all backgrounds and beliefs find a welcoming place in which they can practice their faith and fellowship at Muhlenberg.

MULTICULTURALISM: Through lectures, workshops, exhibits, and other events, the Office of Multicultural Life is committed to making a difference in the lives of all students. Recent lectures have included: "Cultural Heritage: Myths and Stereotypes" and an Alternative Medicine seminar. The Office also serves as a base of support to Asian, Latino, Native American, and African-American students. The diverse community at Muhlenberg is sure to enhance the learning experience for all students.

http://www.muhlenberg.edu/
P: (484) 664-3200

PRIVATE

STUDENT PROFILE

2,397 undergraduate students

96% of undergrad students are full time

40% male – 60% female

73% of students are from out of state

93% freshman retention rate

85% graduated in 6 years

FACULTY PROFILE

182 full-time faculty

125 part-time faculty

11 to 1 student/faculty ratio

ADMISSIONS

5,015 Total Applicants

2,426 Total Admissions

582 Total Freshman Enrollment

48.37% of applicants admitted

TUITION & COSTS

Tuition: $45,590

Fees: $285

Total: $45,875

R&B: $10,770

Room: $5,850

Board: $4,920

Total: $56,645

FINANCIAL

$22,475 avg grant/scholarship amount (total)

$8,392 avg loan amount (total)

NEUMANN UNIVERSITY

ASTON, PENNSYLVANIA

Neumann University offers a uniquely personal and affordable experience for students, in a campus culture that emphasizes respect for individuals, concern for the environment, and social responsibility. Located just a half hour outside Philadelphia, PA, Neumann is committed to first-rate academic instruction and real-world career preparation. This promise reflects Neumann's core philosophy, which is that knowledge is a gift to be shared in the service of others and that learning is a lifelong process. The University offers degrees in a broad range of subjects and there are internships or clinical experiences in every field. More than 650 students live on campus in residence halls that are air conditioned and provide wireless Internet access. Campus life is active and welcoming, offering opportunities to form lifelong friendships, participate in the arts, and play sports.

FRANCISCAN CULTURE: Neumann enriches and challenges each person intellectually, spiritually and socially. The Franciscan culture fosters personal growth and service to society. The academic focus is to provide a base of instruction in the liberal arts and then offer a variety of career-oriented programs to prepare students for post-graduation success.

CAMPUS MINISTRY: Campus Ministry organizes dozens of community service projects every year, giving students the chance to volunteer at Wind River Indian Reservation in Wyoming, the St. Francis Inn soup kitchen in Philadelphia, the Sandwiches for Survival program in Chester, PA, and many other worthy causes.

DEDICATED FACULTY: Neumann University professors care about student success. They discuss assignments after class, extend office hours to accommodate committed students, discuss career options and internship opportunities, and involve students in research. Except for a few large nursing lectures, classes will have fewer than 30 students. Faculty members at Neumann know the names of their students, say hello to them in hallways, and chat with them over coffee in the café. Many faculty members at Neumann bring real-world experience to the classroom. A management professor worked for 20 years on Wall Street. A political science professor is a former political candidate. Faculty members in nursing have worked in hospitals and other healthcare settings.

AMAZING EDUCATIONAL OPPORTUNITIES: Exciting academic features include newly renovated nursing labs; a sport and entertainment management program with a 4+1 option for a bachelor's and master's degree in five years; an education major that includes certification in elementary, secondary or special education, a pre-pharmacy program in conjunction with Duquesne University, and a pre-law 3+3 program with Widener University.

THE INSTITUTE: The Institute promotes Gospel values through many programs, including evenings of reflection, training workshops and inspirational speakers. The evenings of reflection provide opportunities for each team, its chaplain and coaches to pause, pray and come together outside the athletic arena. Training workshops help team captains learn leadership, communication and team building.

GRADUATES READY TO SUCCEED: Graduates of Neumann University are confident young women and men, who are prepared for success in the post-graduation world. They can express themselves clearly in writing, speak in front of large audiences, access a thorough body of knowledge gained in the classroom, and apply that theory to practical situations. They are able to think and reason, analyzing situations with principles that they developed at Neumann. Those principles (based on the core values of reverence, integrity, service, excellence, and stewardship) were encouraged, stretched, tested and, finally, adopted in the process of Neumann's uniquely personal experience.

---

http://www.neumann.edu/

P: (610) 558-5616

PRIVATE - CATHOLIC

STUDENT PROFILE

2,403 undergraduate students

75% of undergrad students are full time

36% male – 64% female

70% freshman retention rate

50% graduated in 6 years

FACULTY PROFILE

97 full-time faculty

201 part-time faculty

13 to 1 student/faculty ratio

ADMISSIONS

2,253 Total Applicants

2,046 Total Admissions

401 Total Freshman Enrollment

90.81% of applicants admitted

SAT Ranges: CR 410-490, M 410-500, W 390-480

ACT Ranges: C 17-21

TUITION & COSTS

Tuition: $25,792

Fees: $1,126

Total: $26,918

R&B: $11,754

Room: $7,114

Board: $4,640

Total: $38,672

FINANCIAL

$14,751 avg grant/scholarship amount (total)

$9,021 avg loan amount (total)

POINT PARK UNIVERSITY

PITTSBURGH, PENNSYLVANIA

Point Park University is a private university with a strong liberal arts tradition. Point Park's Downtown Pittsburgh location, experienced faculty, and career-focused approach to education provide endless internship and job opportunities for its thousands of students.

UNIVERSITY 101: Every new Point Park student is immediately welcomed into the University and its surrounding city through the fully immersive UNIV 101 Course. This course, aptly titled "City-University Life," equips those who are new to the urban college lifestyle with everything they need to thrive in Pittsburgh. Not only does UNIV 101 teach students how to read, think, and organize like the advanced scholars they are, but it also provides them a tightly knit group of friends who are going through the same college transition. They bond as they go on class excursions throughout the city of Pittsburgh, familiarizing themselves with the city and making a home for themselves among their peers. Through off-campus field trips around Pittsburgh, on-campus projects and events, and guest lectures from local speakers, UNIV 101 constructs a comfortable college environment with a display of all the best that Point Park has to offer.

STUDY ABROAD: There's no better way to become a socially aware, global citizen than by experiencing different cultures firsthand. Point Park partners with Regent's University London and the American University of Rome in order to guarantee students inspiring European experiences. For the same tuition cost of attending school in Pittsburgh, students who enroll in University-sponsored study abroad programs can fulfill their degree requirements within the rich cultural environments of England and Italy's bustling capital cities.

HONORS PROGRAM: Students in the Honors Program take leadership development to the next level. For their excellence in academics, they have the opportunity to enhance their leadership skills by serving their fellow Point Park peers and the urban community around them. Not only do they get to act as mentors and leaders in other organizations, but they also arrange multiple community service projects throughout the year. These projects are life changing for both the volunteers and the people they serve, as they contribute to a great cause all while building experience that looks great on résumés.

ACADEMIC VILLAGE: The Academic Village Initiative is an ongoing project that is constantly transforming the experience of Point Park University students and enriching the lives of Pittsburgh residents. Throughout several blocks of the city, the Academic Village is a spirited, environmentally conscious addition to downtown Pittsburgh that includes projects for an urban park, a multipurpose Student and Convocation Center, a new performance space for the Pittsburgh Playhouse, and more. These developments form a collective hub for fun and intellectually stimulating life in the city.

CAREER DEVELOPMENT: Thanks to its location in the heart of Pittsburgh, Point Park University is able to connect its students directly to neighboring companies for extraordinary internship and job opportunities. The hands-on experiences that internships provide help students build their résumés and excel early on in their postgraduate careers. Living in the middle of the city already gives Point Park students a professional edge, but the staff at the Career Development Center take their access to success a step further by aiding in the job search, reviewing and editing résumés and cover letters, and training for job interviews. Students are guaranteed to find career experience that complements their academic and professional pursuits.

CENTER FOR STUDENT SUCCESS: The Center for Student Success assigns each student a success coordinator and faculty advisor in order to ensure a smooth four-year graduation process. With a commitment to the "Pathways to Success," the Center helps guide students to finish their course requirements in a timely manner and utilize the school's resources for future, postgraduate achievements. Advisors want everyone to succeed, and so they are always available to help students find a successful, healthy work-life balance.

---

http://www.pointpark.edu/

P: (412) 391-4100

PRIVATE

STUDENT PROFILE

3,140 undergraduate students

84% of undergrad students are full time

43% male – 57% female

24% of students are from out of state

73% freshman retention rate

58% graduated in 6 years

FACULTY PROFILE

139 full-time faculty

316 part-time faculty

13 to 1 student/faculty ratio

ADMISSIONS

4,021 Total Applicants

2,836 Total Admissions

595 Total Freshman Enrollment

70.53% of applicants admitted

SAT Ranges: CR 450-560, M 430-530

ACT Ranges: C 19-25, M 17-24, E 18-27

TUITION & COSTS

Tuition: $13,890

Fees: $1,250

Total: $15,140

R&B: $10,840

Total: $25,980

FINANCIAL

$16,708 avg grant/scholarship amount (need)

$5,454 avg loan amount (need)

ROSEMONT COLLEGE

BRYN MAWR, PENNSYLVANIA

Rosemont College, founded by the Society of the Holy Child Jesus, is a co-educational liberal arts institution in the Catholic tradition. It has 25 academic areas of study and offers honors, three-year, and dual degree options. The College also offers collaborative programs, such as Fast Track and Early Assurance medical programs with Drexel University College of Medicine, Philadelphia College of Osteopathic Medicine, and Temple University School of Dentistry. Rosemont is well known for its innovative General Education Curriculum, which combines a carefully chosen selection of classes with 21st-century educational practices. Rosemont doesn't just train students for the workplace; it cultivates students' cultural, religious, and artistic sensibilities in order to improve the quality of their lives. Students develop a sense of social responsibility, strong intellectual and practical skills that span all areas of study, and a demonstrated ability to apply everything they've learned in real-world settings.

THE ROSEMONT DIFFERENCE: Each Rosemont student participates in a special assessment program at the beginning of their first year to evaluate their individual academic skills, personality traits, and learning styles. Their findings are then reviewed and applied to a personalized learning plan that gives them a better understanding of their abilities. This plan serves as a touchstone to chart academic growth and progress, helping foster success both at Rosemont and beyond.

LEARNING WITHOUT LIMITS: With a student body composed of 53% minority students, Rosemont encourages a community that embraces diversity, change, and inclusion. The College's core values are trust in and reverence for the dignity of each person; diversity in human culture and experience; and persistence and courage in promoting justice with compassion.

THEORY AND PRACTICE: Traditional undergraduate students can choose from twenty-seven academic majors. Regardless of their area of study, their education comes in two crucial components: academic curriculum and experiential learning. All students complete the curriculum for their respective major as well as at least one experiential component, which can take the form of service learning, an internship, or study abroad.

EXPLORATIVE PROFESSORS: With small classes, Rosemont professors often teach "on location." Their classrooms can span across a plethora of cultural and educational sites in Philadelphia or even in a foreign country, studying everything from policy to languages. The student body is comprised of more than 400 undergraduate students, with a student-to-faculty ratio of 10:1 and an average class size of 12. This allows for more personal classroom attention. Approximately 75 percent of full-time faculty members hold a Ph.D. or the highest degree in their field.

ON-CAMPUS ACTIVITIES: Rosemont offers many opportunities to grow, ranging from involvement in student organizations and clubs to athletics and service to the community. Having fun is easy through the Residence Life staff, as they easily get the word out to the 70% of students who live on campus. With at least one campus event per weekend, Rosemont students always have something to do!

CAREER SERVICES AND ALUMNI: Through coursework, internships, service, and study abroad, Rosemont students learn to apply classroom concepts to real-life situations. The Office of Career Services helps students prepare to search for jobs and enter the professional world, hosting events throughout the year including an annual Career Bootcamp. Approximately 8,000 living Rosemont alumni can be found in high-ranking positions in science and medicine, publishing, politics, business, education, law, and the arts.

ROSEMONT COLLEGE

http://www.rosemont.edu/
P: (610) 527-0200

PRIVATE - CATHOLIC

STUDENT PROFILE

529 undergraduate students

86% of undergrad students are full time

35% male – 65% female

29% of students are from out of state

65% freshman retention rate

47% graduated in 6 years

FACULTY PROFILE

29 full-time faculty

97 part-time faculty

10 to 1 student/faculty ratio

ADMISSIONS

875 Total Applicants

618 Total Admissions

135 Total Freshman Enrollment

70.63% of applicants admitted

SAT Ranges: CR 400-520, M 380-505, W 390-505

ACT Ranges: C 15-20, M 16-21, E 15-20

TUITION & COSTS

Tuition: $31,520

Fees: $980

Total: $32,500

R&B: $13,400

Total: $45,900

FINANCIAL

$28,745 avg grant/scholarship amount (total)

$7,079 avg loan amount (total)

SAINT FRANCIS UNIVERSITY

LORETTO, PENNSYLVANIA

Saint Francis University offers academic study within the Franciscan tradition of using one's talents to serve others. The more than 60 offerings include highly targeted, career-focused majors grounded in the liberal arts tradition of inquiry and self-discovery. Highly regarded programs in health science, education, business, and science attract a diverse student body to the beautiful campus setting. The values of respect, drive, generosity, and joy run deep in the University culture and help to prepare ethical, knowledgeable professionals with a passion to shape the world. This holistic approach to career preparation is supported by respected faculty who work closely with students in small settings to meet individual goals. Saint Francis University is located in Loretto, a quaint town in Cambria County, Pennsylvania, about two hours east of Pittsburgh. The residential 600-acre campus is located in a scenic portion of the Allegheny Mountains centrally located between New York and Washington, D.C.

ETHICAL CITIZENSHIP FOR THE 21ST CENTURY: Through the General Education program, Ethical Citizenship for the 21st Century, students build a solid academic base while establishing critical-thinking skills, a love for learning, and a strong moral foundation. The program extends beyond the classroom to include lectures, presentations, performances, service projects, and other educational activities. Such an educational experience is diverse and practical while also being highly integrated and focused. Core components of this program include the community enrichment series, a writing competency exam, wellness initiatives, the summer reading program, study abroad, and service learning.

COMMUNITY ENRICHMENT SERIES: The University sponsors a wide range of cultural events that are integrated into the curriculum as "CES" credits. By attending a lecture, concert, theatrical performance, or other select events on campus, students can receive community enrichment credits toward the completion of their degree. Outside groups such as the American Shakespeare Center are invited to host a variety of activities, while the University's staff collaborate to host events like the "International Coffee House" sessions.

DIVERSITY/GLOBAL EXPERIENCES: "A Global Vision" is one of the key tenets of the University's "Goals of Franciscan Education." To foster understanding of other cultures, the university encourages study abroad through semester-long study at the university-operated facility in Ambialet, France, as well as shorter excursions such as Engineering in Bolivia and Sign Language Immersion in Jamaica. On campus, students participate in diversity programming throughout the year, with one of the larger events being "Multicultural Week."

TRANSFORMATIONAL EXPERIENCES: Saint Francis University highly values the extra steps students take to become professionally engaged in the world beyond college. Because of that, the University now issues two separate transcripts to its graduates in order to highlight every effort. In addition to a standard academic transcript, students receive a transcript that acknowledges accomplishments within six categories of Transformational Experiences: internship, study abroad, community service, leadership experiences, and campus ministry. This is known as a student's L.I.S.T (Leadership, Involvement, & Service Transcript).

UNDERGRADUATE RESEARCH AND SERVICE: Saint Francis students enhance the theoretical knowledge gained through classroom experiences with faculty-guided research and service projects. As a core element of the University's Franciscan mission, every student is required to participate in some form of research and service, and many start as early as their freshman year. As part of their class curricula, undergraduate and graduate students can work alongside Ph.D. faculty members in research and service projects. They can also enjoy unique experiences through such specialized outreach centers as the Center for Watershed Research and Service, The Keirn Family World War II Museum, the Center for the Study of Occupational Regulation, and the Center for Rural Cancer Survivorship..

---

http://www.francis.edu/

P: (814) 472-3100

PRIVATE PUBLIC

STUDENT PROFILE

2,045 undergraduate students

78% of undergrad students are full time

39% male – 61% female

87% freshman retention rate

72% graduated in 6 years

FACULTY PROFILE

130 full-time faculty

14 to 1 student/faculty ratio

ADMISSIONS

1,932 Total Applicants

1,432 Total Admissions

417 Total Freshman Enrollment

74.12% of applicants admitted

SAT Ranges: CR 460-570, M 470-590, W 450-560

ACT Ranges: C 21-26, M 20-26, E 20-25

TUITION & COSTS

Tuition: $31,078

Fees: $1,100

Total: $32,178

R&B: $11,190

Room: $5,622

Board: $5,568

Total: $43,368

FINANCIAL

$20,587 avg grant/scholarship amount (total)

$10,885 avg loan amount (total)

SAINT JOSEPH'S UNIVERSITY

PHILADELPHIA, PENNSYLVANIA

Saint Joseph's University is a nationally recognized, Catholic, Jesuit university that has advanced the professional and personal ambitions of men and women by providing a rigorous education. Located in the historic city of Philadelphia, Saint Joseph's students get a high-quality education in a thriving urban atmosphere. They can enjoy the outdoors or take a stroll around the various shopping streets in town, enjoying their lives throughout their formative college years.

EXPERIENTIAL LEARNING: Experiential learning is the integration and application of academic theory into real-world experience. It takes many forms, some of which include study abroad, service learning, and internships. The university recognizes that these learning opportunities lead to more successful undergraduate careers and thus provides students with ample resources to get involved. In fact, the university works so hard that 95% of students graduate with at least one incredible experiential learning experience.

PHILADELPHIA: In addition to Saint Joseph's vast amount of on-campus activities, there are also great opportunities available throughout the city of Philadelphia. Philly is the fifth largest city in the U.S., which means that it has a ton to offer. Students are invited to explore the city and take advantage of all the cultural attractions, recreational activities, restaurants, and venues for all kinds of shopping. On top of that, Philadelphia offers incredible access to internships, jobs, and networking.

STUDY ABROAD: Saint Joseph's offers 37 programs in 23 countries! With so many possibilities, each students is bound to find a program that suits their needs and academic goals. Recent additions to Saint Joseph's study abroad program are Mary's University in London and a Russian Studies immersion in St. Petersburg. While study abroad is an incredible experience, not every student can adjust their course plan and commit to an entire semester of travel. For these students, there are short-term, faculty-led study abroad programs held during the winter and summer intersessions. During the summer and winter abroad excursions, students have the opportunity to immerse themselves in new culture, all while learning from experienced faculty in intensive, deeply focused courses. These programs have taken students to such destinations as China, Greece, Chile, and Rome.

COMMUNITY SERVICE: Community service is just as fulfilling and impactful for one's college career as academics and extracurricular activities. Saint Joseph's considers service to be both a personal mission and an integral part of the undergraduate experience, as it allows students to enact positive change through hands-on work and an application of academic theory. Students can get involved through Alternative Spring Break, weekly volunteer opportunities, and service learning courses. Service learning courses involve three components: lecture, service, and reflection. Through coursework and class discussion, students are given the tools they need in order to make a difference in others' lives while supporting their own academic growth.

RESIDENTIAL LEARNING COMMUNITIES: Residential Learning Communities (RLCs) allow students to live among peers who share similar interests and aspirations. RLCs offer great benefits like an intimate learning environment, a supportive network, focused programming, and close interaction with faculty. In general, students who participate in a RLC have a higher level of satisfaction with their educational experience. Examples of Saint Joseph's RLCs include the First-Year Business Community, Arts Community, Science Community, Emerging Leaders Program, and the Romero Learning Community, which focuses on service and advocacy work.

---

http://www.sju.edu/

P: (610) 660-1000

PRIVATE - CATHOLIC

STUDENT PROFILE

5,391 undergraduate students

86% of undergrad students are full time

45% male – 55% female

90% freshman retention rate

79% graduated in 6 years

FACULTY PROFILE

297 full-time faculty

13 to 1 student/faculty ratio

ADMISSIONS

8,325 Total Applicants

6,814 Total Admissions

1,175 Total Freshman Enrollment

81.85% of applicants admitted

TUITION & COSTS

Tuition: $42,000

Fees: $180

Total: $42,180

R&B: $14,928

Room: $9,748

Board: $5,180

Total: $57,108

FINANCIAL

$19,339 avg grant/scholarship amount (total)

$10,364 avg loan amount (total)

SLIPPERY ROCK UNIVERSITY

SLIPPERY ROCK, PENNSYLVANIA

Slippery Rock University is a four-year, public, coeducational, comprehensive university offering a broad array of undergraduate and select graduate programs to more than 8,600 students. The University, a member of the Pennsylvania State System of Higher Education, is a recognized leader in evidence-based planning and decision-making. SRU provides students with a superior learning experience that intentionally combines academic instruction with applied learning opportunities that will help them succeed in an increasingly complex world.

FIRST-YEAR COMMUNITY: Community building and student leadership development are hallmarks of a Slippery Rock University experience. The University is recognized for several first-year initiatives. The FYRST program kicks off student engagement by placing freshmen into close-knit peer groups and pairing them with faculty mentors who work one-on-one to provide individualized introductions to the school. First-year courses also help to integrate students into Slippery Rock, helping them develop community-building skills while finding their own individual strengths.

CREDENTIALED FACULTY: Great teaching may start in the classroom at Slippery Rock University, but it extends across campus and around the world. In fact, while attending SRU, students' classrooms are just as likely to be the Roman ruins or a jungle in Peru as they are to be a room on campus. One thing is certain, though: no matter where they learn, they are sure to study with faculty members who have a strong, inspired passion for teaching. Only fully credentialed faculty teach at SRU. The University does not allow graduate assistants or research fellows to teach classes, as Slippery Rock's faculty members already place their first priority on instructing students. Nowhere is this rarity more evident than in the tremendous opportunities the faculty provide for undergraduate students to collaborate with them on high-quality research. These practical, cutting-edge research projects provide a pathway for students to make intellectual or creative contributions to their discipline, build self-confidence, gain experience to enhance their career opportunities, and improve their communication and presentation skills.

STUDY ABROAD: SRU students are encouraged to participate in international study, research, and travel programs. SRU has been ranked 10th nationally among master's-degree granting institutions for the number of students participating in short-term study abroad programs by the Institute for International Education. Recent study opportunities have taken students to Poland, China, the Bahamas, Ireland, Greece, Egypt, Ghana, the Netherlands, Russia, England, and elsewhere.

CO-CURRICULAR EXPERIENCE PROGRAM: The Co-Curricular Experience Program is an official record of leadership accomplishments and involvement in student organizations, community service activities, and professional development programs. This program acts as a valuable resource for students when they apply for internships, graduate or professional schools, or their first career positions, highlighting all the hard work they do outside of their coursework. Compass Leadership is a signature program within the University's Center for Student Involvement and Leadership. It provides a sequence of workshops through which students can earn certification for acquiring basic, intermediate, or advanced leadership competencies. Participation in Compass Leadership workshops is recorded and posted on the student's Co-Curricular Experiences Transcript.

STUDENT LEADERSHIP: Through the Center for Student Involvement and Leadership, SRU students participate in programs that give them the chance to make a difference in the lives of people both at home and around the world, practicing academic skills and earning certifications for their competence in leadership. Results from the National Survey of Student Engagement show that SRU students consistently rate their experience at SRU higher than those attending peer institutions.

---

http://www.sru.edu/

P: (800) 929-4778

PUBLIC

STUDENT PROFILE

7,566 undergraduate students

93% of undergrad students are full time

43% male – 57% female

14% of students are from out of state

83% freshman retention rate

68% graduated in 6 years

FACULTY PROFILE

371 full-time faculty

69 part-time faculty

22 to 1 student/faculty ratio

ADMISSIONS

5,781 Total Applicants

3,952 Total Admissions

1,523 Total Freshman Enrollment

68.36% of applicants admitted

SAT Ranges: CR 450-540, M 460-540, W 420-520

ACT Ranges: C 19-24, M 18-24, E 18-24

TUITION & COSTS

Tuition: (In) $7,060 (Out) $10,590

Fees: $2,813

Total: (In) $9,645 (Out) $13,403

R&B: $10,022

Room: $6,620

Board: $3,402

Total: (In) $19,667 (Out) $23,425

FINANCIAL

$6,039 avg grant/scholarship amount (total)

$8,135 avg loan amount (total)

SUSQUEHANNA UNIVERSITY

SELINSGROVE, PENNSYLVANIA

Susquehanna University educates enterprising, independent thinkers who gather from 34 states and 22 countries. Students graduate with the broad-based academic foundation and essential 21st-century job skills—critical thinking, writing, teamwork, and communication—which are highly sought after by employers and graduate schools alike. Its challenging academics, alongside opportunities for internships and research, result in a 96.5 percent placement rate within six months of graduation.

A GLOBAL PERSPECTIVE: Nine out of ten employers cite intercultural skills as a desirable trait for new employees, and Susquehanna's nationally recognized Global Opportunities (GO) program prepares students for the cultural competencies needed in today's global marketplace. Susquehanna is one of only a handful of universities to require a domestic or overseas study-away experience. The GO experience allows students to become more culturally aware and better prepared to be leaders in a diverse, dynamic, and interdependent world. As a result, Susquehanna students see firsthand how different social and cultural forces shape the world and discover how to make a difference.

HONORS PROGRAM: Intensely curious, active learners excel in the challenging and individualized Honors Program for academically talented students. About 10 percent of incoming students are invited to join and embrace leadership, performance, music, and athletics. The students follow a sequence of special courses and projects that are complemented by discussion groups, lectures, off-campus visits, and residential programs throughout their four years at Susquehanna. First-year Honors students can even elect to live together in a living-learning community designed specifically for them.

THE COMMON READING: Each year, Susquehanna's students, faculty, and staff select a new theme for the coming year. Incoming first-year students are given a common reading assignment related to this theme, creating a shared academic experience and point of discussion to bind them in their first semester. Faculty and staff also read the common reading and find ways to use it in the classroom, in the residence halls, in administrative offices, over lunch, and more. This introduction to a life of discussion and reflection leads to engaged interaction that pushes students to grow and develop.

LIVING-LEARNING COMMUNITIES: Residence life is a big part of the student experience at Susquehanna. Housing options range from traditional residence halls to suites and houses, and students can also elect to reside in a living and learning community (LLC). LLCs are groups of peers who live together and share a passion for a particular topic, academic program, or class. Interested first-year students can choose to join an LLC centered on global business, the Honors program, civic engagement and service, diversity, identity, or inclusion.

SCENIC, SAFE, AND CENTRALLY LOCATED CAMPUS: Nestled on the banks of the Susquehanna River, Selinsgrove, Pennsylvania, is a picturesque and safe community whose shops and restaurants are located within walking distance of Susquehanna's beautiful 325-acre campus. Only one hour from the state capital, Harrisburg, and within three hours of New York City, Philadelphia, Baltimore, and Washington, D.C., students have easy access to bustling metropolitan areas in which to network with alumni, pursue internships, and explore professional opportunities.

CAREER SERVICES: Career development is a campus-wide effort at Susquehanna. Many professors make a personal commitment to help students find internships, apply to graduate schools, or just understand their options. This intentional career planning starts from the moment that students arrive on campus, and very spring semester, Susquehanna hosts an annual student-alumni networking conference. This multi-day event includes career-specific panel discussions, money-management advice sessions, and résumé tips.

http://www.susqu.edu/
P: (800) 326-9672

PRIVATE

STUDENT PROFILE

2,126 undergraduate students

99% of undergrad students are full time

45% male — 55% female

49.6% of students are from out of state

86.1% freshman retention rate

71.3% graduated in 6 years

FACULTY PROFILE

133 full-time faculty

127 part-time faculty

12 to 1 student/faculty ratio

ADMISSIONS

5,304 Total Applicants

4,033 Total Admissions

668 Total Freshman Enrollment

76.04% of applicants admitted

SAT Ranges: CR 500-610, M 510-610

ACT Ranges: C 23-27

TUITION & COSTS

Tuition: $43,160

Fees: $560

Total: $43,720

R&B: $11,620

Total: $55,340

FINANCIAL

$28,023 avg grant/scholarship amount (need)

$4,166 avg loan amount (need)

THIEL COLLEGE

GREENVILLE, PENNSYLVANIA

Thiel College is a private liberal arts institution founded in the Lutheran tradition. Located in Greenville, Pennsylvania, the College offers 60 majors and minors, 25 varsity sports, and a 10:1 student-faculty ratio to more than 900 students. A dedicated faculty paired with dynamic research and internship opportunities produce students who achieve numerous graduate school admissions and job placements. Coeducational from its beginnings, Thiel College remains committed to combining tradition with innovation as it celebrates 150 years. Its educational investment returns value all throughout its graduates' lifetimes, as every faculty and staff member is passionate about helping their students succeed.

STUDY ABROAD: One of the most transformational and exciting experiences at Thiel is the chance to study abroad. As part of a commitment to educational excellence and global awareness, the College offers resources for students to become world-ready leaders through many study abroad programs. Thiel is one of only 15 schools in western Pennsylvania to offer funds through the Vira I. Heinz Program to female first-time international travelers. For all Thiel students, there are several other scholarships also available, in addition to many outside sources. Students can go abroad for full semesters or through shorter experiences like the service trip to Nicaragua during spring break.

FACULTY AS MENTORS: Thiel professors get to know students as individuals, not just by their names. Faculty members are excellent mentors, recognized scholars, and experienced professionals in their fields. The low student-faculty ratio provides students the opportunity to develop close relationships with their professors, providing them a strong sense of belonging in the College community. The school's Honors Institute makes these connections easy by offering a unique core curriculum that is specially designed to train thinkers to become leaders and is best taught through one-on-one interaction. This personal, rigorous teaching even extends beyond the classroom; the Greenville Neuromodulation Center Faculty/Student Research Institute at Thiel, for example, pairs students with faculty mentors to conduct original research.

STUDENT ACTIVITIES: Campus life at Thiel offers students dynamic community service experiences and vibrant co-curricular activities. With more than 50 student clubs and organizations and eight fraternities and sororities, students can find venues for deep connection, leadership, and service. The student body engages the community by participating in the annual Spring into Action service event as well as by hosting several successful fundraising campaigns.

IMPRESSIVE PLACEMENT: Thiel consistently produces successful outcomes for students. In a recent survey, 94.3 percent of graduates reported that they were employed or in graduate school within six months. Many students participate in internships—some as early as the second semester of their first year! Thiel boasts a network of 10,000+ active alumni and was recently named to Forbes' Grateful Graduates Index—a testament to consistent student success.

NON-BUSINESS MAJORS CERTIFICATE: Thiel offers a Fundamentals of Business for Non-Majors concentration that allows students in every field to understand the foundational skills they need to succeed in any professional industry. Supplying students a breadth of education regarding budgeting, legal systems, and management, this concentration aims to build essential skills in areas of study far beyond business itself.

CAREER SERVICES: The Career Development Center works one-on-one with students in order to map out their plans both for their four-year journey at Thiel as well as their lifelong journey beyond college. It offers a range of assessments and guidance tools to help students decide what they might want to do with their degree and how they can achieve their goals. The staff are also prepared to lead a range of seminar series, presenting upon request on such topics as job searching, professional etiquette, and obtaining internships.

---

http://www.thiel.edu/
P: (724) 589-2345

PRIVATE

STUDENT PROFILE

926 undergraduate students

96% of undergrad students are full time

54% male – 45% female

36% of students are from out of state

67% freshman retention rate

41% graduated in 6 years

FACULTY PROFILE

60 full-time faculty

36 part-time faculty

10 to 1 student/faculty ratio

ADMISSIONS

2,275 Total Applicants

2,275 Total Admissions

206 Total Freshman Enrollment

100.00% of applicants admitted

SAT Ranges: CR 410-510, M 420-520

ACT Ranges: C 17-21, M 17-23, E 15-21

TUITION & COSTS

Tuition: $27,038

Fees: $2,130

Total: $29,168

R&B: $11,336

Total: $40,504

FINANCIAL

$20,044 avg grant/scholarship amount (need)

$4,346 avg loan amount (need)

UNIVERSITY OF PITTSBURGH AT BRADFORD

BRADFORD, PENNSYLVANIA

University of Pittsburgh
Bradford

The University of Pittsburgh at Bradford is a supportive, friendly institution for students who want to earn a world-renowned degree in a personalized environment. Pitt-Bradford's 1,500 students enjoy the close-knit campus community, which means that they receive personalized attention from their professors as well as the administrators and staff on campus. Since Pitt-Bradford is a regional campus of the University of Pittsburgh, students receive the globally respected and recognized University of Pittsburgh degree.

VIBRANT LIFE: Pitt-Bradford offers more than 40 majors and more than 50 minors and pre-professional programs, from biology, criminal justice, and psychology to nursing, accounting, and energy science and technology. Most classes are small (the average class size is 19!), which enables professors to get to know their students individually. Students also have ample opportunities to take part in the robust campus life: Division III athletics, intramurals and recreational activities; more than 60 student clubs and organizations; and arts and cultural events.

RESEARCH: Pitt-Bradford transforms students' lives by offering them an array of experiences that help them to develop critical-thinking skills, build their confidence, and prepare them for life after graduation. Many students have the opportunity to conduct research and present their findings during the annual Honors Day event, and some undergraduate researchers have even co-written and published papers with their professors. Other students take on internships to experience the world of work, or study abroad to immerse themselves in a different culture and its people.

REAL-WORLD LEARNING: Many professors take advantage of the University's location to lead exciting, hands-on projects for their students. In the Aquatic Biomonitoring class, for example, students monitored the health of streams in the neighboring Allegheny National Forest. Other students are collaborating with the U.S. Forest Service to perform an environmental assessment in the forest, the first step before the construction of mountain biking trails on the federal lands.

GROUNDBREAKING FACILITIES: There are several exciting areas on campus at which students can get cutting-edge, hands-on experience. Students who major in computer information systems and technology work on projects in their own dedicated lab. Criminal justice majors investigate simulated crime scenes and collect evidence like the pros in the Crime Scene Investigation (CSI) House. Nursing students practice their techniques on computerized mannequins in a simulation lab, and psychology students practice their counseling techniques and observe other sessions in the psychology lab suite.

STUDENT LEADERSHIP: Since Pitt-Bradford is a smaller campus, many students can take on leadership roles, even as underclassmen. They can serve in a leadership role in Student Government Association, Student Activities Council, or Greek life. After their training, they can work as peer tutors in the Academic Coaching and Tutoring Center, interact with prospective students and their parents as Student Ambassadors, or work closely with donors and others as a member of the Blue and Gold Society.

OUTSIDE THE CLASSROOM: Besides offering students more than 60 clubs and organizations, Pitt-Bradford provides an array of cultural activities each academic year. For example, authors can come to read from their work and answer questions about their craft, student theatre productions give students a chance to perform on stage, musicians from nearly every genre perform, and artists who create work in all media display their pieces on campus. Students can also take part in vocal ensembles and art exhibitions or even write and publish original work to the University's own literary magazine.

http://www.upb.pitt.edu/
P: (814) 362-7500

PUBLIC

STUDENT PROFILE

1,499 undergraduate students

92% of undergrad students are full time

46% male — 54% female

17% of students are from out of state

72% freshman retention rate

53% graduated in 6 years

FACULTY PROFILE

30 full-time faculty

24 part-time faculty

18 to 1 student/faculty ratio

ADMISSIONS

2,244 Total Applicants

1,468 Total Admissions

392 Total Freshman Enrollment

65.42% of applicants admitted

SAT Ranges: CR 430-530, M 450-550, W 400-500

ACT Ranges: C 19-24, M 20-25, E 20-24, W 6-8

TUITION & COSTS

Tuition: (In) $12,452 (Out) $23,268

Fees: $870

Total: (In) $13,322 (Out) $24,138

R&B: $8,480

Room: $5,160

Board: $3,320

Total: (In) $21,802 (Out) $32,618

FINANCIAL

$9,217 avg grant/scholarship amount (need)

$7,578 avg loan amount (need)

UNIVERSITY OF PITTSBURGH AT GREENSBURG

GREENSBURG, PENNSYLVANIA

University of Pittsburgh Greensburg

Founded in 1963, the University of Pittsburgh at Greensburg is a public liberal arts college located in Southwestern Pennsylvania. As a regional campus of the world-renowned University of Pittsburgh system, Pitt-Greensburg students earn the accreditation of a Pitt education in small, intimate class settings. Students' close, personal interaction with award-winning instructors enables opportunities for student-faculty partnership in experiential learning projects that have real-world impacts. Additionally, students are able to collaborate with faculty in original research, which both empowers undergraduate students with vital disciplinary skills and provides them with professional experience typically only accessible at the graduate level.

NEW-AGE LEARNING: Pitt-Greensburg's 'liberal arts education for the 21st century' model emphasizes the role of communicative and critical thinking skills across the disciplines—a foundation ensuring that, regardless of their field of study, graduates are equipped for lifelong learning. Cutting-edge, digital-age programs and support services bolster students' digital literacy to keep pace with rapid technological advancement in the workplace.

THE GREEN SCHOLAR PROGRAM: The Green Scholar program affords a graduate-level experience at the undergraduate level by placing a student under the individual guidance of an instructor in his or her field for the purpose of original, collaborative research. Along with the profound experiential value of such a relationship, students receive monetary compensation for their collaborative effort as well as any professional publication credit/accolades resulting from their research partnership with their professor.

THE GEM PROGRAM: The Greensburg Experience More (GEM) co-curricular program was designed to empower students with a skillset applicable to work and academic situations and marketable to future employers. This program is built around such learning outcomes as leadership development, service to others, career planning and development, cultural awareness and appreciation, and Pitt-Greensburg pride. These initiatives sculpt students to be well-rounded scholars who have a passion for learning and a broader sense of pride and compassion for their community.

THE ACADEMIC VILLAGE: Established near the turn of the millennium, the Academic Village is a campus learning community open to both resident and commuter students of any major. Students in the Academic Village work intimately with faculty from all disciplines on academic and cultural event planning, debates and discussions, and small group workshops. Students are equipped and encouraged to explore their interests in a community setting. Village members are held to high academic standards and are expected to be active members of the Village community.

COMMUNICATION PROFICIENCY: Pitt-Greensburg holds a high standard for proficiency in written communication. Based on their level of proficiency as incoming freshmen, students are required to complete up to two courses in general written composition before proceeding to a research-intensive writing course tailored toward analysis of a theme in their specific discipline. Students are encouraged to become immersed in emerging forms of communication that are specific to their discipline. Digital Humanities at Pitt-Greensburg, for example, involves an integration of coursework and research collaboration between faculty and students, resulting in sustainable, lasting humanities research and a greater understanding of how to present their ideas.

CAREER SERVICES/INTERNSHIPS: The Pitt-Greensburg Office of Career Services provides essential resources for students and alumni to present themselves professionally to potential employers, to network and make useful connections, to research and pursue potential career/internship/volunteer options, and so much more. It also works with the Center for Applied Research (CFAR) to get students in touch with opportunities to innovate and work on projects that build their professional experience. CFAR draws together the intuition and insight of staff, faculty, and students from across disciplines to conduct research in partnership with community organizations.

http://www.greensburg.pitt.edu/

P: (724) 837-7040

PUBLIC

STUDENT PROFILE

1,517 undergraduate students

95% of undergrad students are full time

48% male – 52% female

42% of students are from out of state

79% freshman retention rate

58% graduated in 6 years

FACULTY PROFILE

76 full-time faculty

12 part-time faculty

18 to 1 student/faculty ratio

ADMISSIONS

2,505 Total Applicants

1,877 Total Admissions

467 Total Freshman Enrollment

74.93% of applicants admitted

SAT Ranges: CR 460-560, M 460-555

ACT Ranges: C 20-25, M 19-25, E 18-24

TUITION & COSTS

Tuition: (In) $12,688 (Out) $23,710

Fees: $930

Total: (In) $13,618 (Out) $24,640

R&B: $9,220

Room: $6,110

Board: $3,110

Total: (In) $22,838 (Out) $33,86

FINANCIAL

$8,221 avg grant/scholarship amount (need)

$4,315 avg loan amount (need)

VILLANOVA UNIVERSITY

VILLANOVA, PENNSYLVANIA

Villanova University was founded in 1842 by the Order of St. Augustine. To this day, Villanova's Augustinian Catholic intellectual tradition is the cornerstone of its academic community in which students learn to think critically, act compassionately, and succeed while serving others.

UNDERGRADUATE RESEARCH: Undergraduate research is alive and well at Villanova. For many years now, the University has excelled in research, providing the resources for its students to create works that are often presented and published. Many like to believe that research is limited to the laboratory, but this is simply not true; each and every discipline has opportunities to engage in research throughout many media. There are so many incredible benefits to research that Villanova actively encourages all of its students to take part. Those who participate gain valuable skills in inquiry, citation, critical thinking, and higher-level conceptualization. Externally, undergraduate research looks impressive to both graduate schools and prospective employers.

FALVEY SCHOLARS: The Falvey Scholars program awards superior work in undergraduate research. Each year, select students are nominated and judged by a committee in recognition for their exceptional projects. Awards are given in five areas: Arts, Sciences, Engineering, Nursing, and Business. Selected students are given the opportunity to share their findings with the campus community, inspiring the community with the groundbreaking work made possible by the University.

VILLANOVA SEMESTER ABROAD: Villanova currently has five abroad programs established through the Office of Education Abroad. These programs range from a semester to a year in length and are offered to all Villanova students. The standout, unique component of these programs is the exclusive opportunity to take related courses that are only offered to Villanova students. This allows the Villanova experience to extend beyond the campus and into destinations around the world.

HONORS PROGRAM: Villanova's honors program is designed to challenge and meet the needs of academically talented students. Its small seminar courses promote class discussion, and foster personal attention, and open up the chances for students to be leaders around campus. Villanova's honors program Taking a holistic approach to its students, this program addresses academic development in consideration of students' spirits, bodies, and minds as they grow as strong individuals.

LEVEL: LEVEL is a unique campus initiative aimed at closing the gap between the able-bodied students and those with disabilities. With inclusivity as the focal point of its mission, Villanova strives to bring light to a situation that is often misunderstood. People with disabilities are often regarded in a negative way and are thus given less opportunity to succeed in life. LEVEL, therefore, works very hard to disband these myths and provides the disabled community with chances to get involved. Its name comes from the idea of leveling the playing field among populations with varying amounts of privilege.

PHILADELPHIA: Villanova is just a stone's throw away from Philadelphia, the fifth largest city in the U.S. With over 90 colleges and universities, Philadelphia is a hub for higher education that also offers an array of cultural events and recreational activities. Villanova students are highly encouraged to explore the city and take advantage of all its amenities and resources.

THE CAREER CENTER: The Career Center is the go-to resource for all things related to postgraduate success. Students are welcome to stop by and utilize the many services offered at the center, meeting with career counselors to clarify their life trajectories. Villanova also hosts a series of workshops and career fairs, allowing students to network with industry professionals and gain valuable skills for the workplace.

VILLANOVA
UNIVERSITY

http://www1.villanova.edu/main.html

P: (610) 519-4500

PRIVATE - CATHOLIC

STUDENT PROFILE

6,977 undergraduate students

92% of undergrad students are full time

47% male – 53% female

82% of students are from out of state

96% freshman retention rate

90% graduated in 6 years

FACULTY PROFILE

698 full-time faculty

401 part-time faculty

12 to 1 student/faculty ratio

ADMISSIONS

16,206 Total Applicants

7,761 Total Admissions

1,700 Total Freshman Enrollment

47.89% of applicants admitted

SAT Ranges: CR 590-690, M 610-710, W 590-690

ACT Ranges: C 29-32, M 27-32, E 29-34

TUITION & COSTS

Tuition: $46,966

Fees: $650

Total: $47,616

R&B: $12,707

Room: $6,737

Board: $5,970

Total: $60,323

FINANCIAL

$28,855 avg grant/scholarship amount (total)

$7,837 avg loan amount (total)

WAYNESBURG UNIVERSITY

WAYNESBURG, PENNSYLVANIA

As a Christian liberal arts University, Waynesburg provides students with opportunities to pursue truth in God's world through rigorous scholarship, academic excellence, and creative expressions. At Waynesburg University, students are called to create their own legacy and are charged with the task to impact their campus, their community, and the world.

FIRST-YEAR SEMINARS AND EXPERIENCES: Every Waynesburg University freshman is enrolled in WBE 108 – Fiat Lux, named for the University's motto (Latin for "Let there be Light" from Genesis 1:3). This introductory course serves to familiarize new students with Waynesburg's mission of faith, learning, and service. As a part of the curriculum, students are required to take part in a community service project.

COMMON INTELLECTUAL EXPERIENCE: One of the ways in which Waynesburg University fosters common intellectual experiences is through the "Common Read Program," a first-year reading experience for incoming freshmen. Students are expected to read a carefully selected book and participate in a variety of classroom activities, discussions, and University events that enhance their understanding of the text, the book's themes, and one another.

UNDERGRADUATE RESEARCH: Waynesburg University hosts an annual Undergraduate Research and Scholarly Work Symposium that is open to the public. This event features student presentations in such fields as biology, chemistry, forensic science, history, and nursing.

DIVERSITY/GLOBAL LEARNING: Waynesburg University offers a unique International Studies minor option, employing many opportunities for students to gain a global education. One such example is the Vira I. Heinz Program for Women in Global Leadership, which provides scholarships to students who have never left the United States so that they may study abroad for a summer. Waynesburg is one of only 13 higher education institutions in the country to participate in this life-changing program. Students can also partake in Faith Learning and Service Immersion Trips, which extend beyond domestic borders to places like Nassau, Bonaire, Montego Bay, Patzun, Juana Diaz, Taipei, Belize, and the Dominican Republic.

SERVICE LEARNING: Consistent with the WU mission, the Center for Service Leadership challenges students to pursue lives of purpose, growing as servant leaders who make connections between the head, hands, and heart. The Center for Service Leadership at Waynesburg University has developed partnerships with over 40 local, regional, and international service agencies, and its staff plan a number of mission trips to take students all over the world during holiday breaks.

INTERNSHIPS: Several of Waynesburg University's academic programs and majors require students to complete a relevant internship prior to graduation. Waynesburg students have interned at ABC, the Bayer Corporation, CONSOL, the LA County Probation Department, Mary Kay, Mylan, the Pittsburgh Zoo and PPG Aquarium, Ruby Memorial Hospital, Sea World, Special Olympics, UPMC Sports Medicine, Walt Disney World, and Yale University, just to name a few.

CAPSTONE COURSE AND PROJECTS: A broad variety of Waynesburg University majors incorporate a capstone project to wrap up students' studies in their field. While the work involved can be intensive, it's a truly satisfying and appropriate way to complete a college career. Waynesburg faculty advisors encourage their students to begin thinking about these capstone projects as early as their freshman year, ensuring that their portfolios and collections of work can be robust and compelling when the time comes to bring everything together.

WAYNESBURG UNIVERSITY

http://www.waynesburg.edu/
P: (800) 225-7393

PRIVATE - CHRISTIAN

STUDENT PROFILE

1,422 undergraduate students

93% of undergrad students are full time

42% male – 58% female

80% freshman retention rate

62% graduated in 6 years

20% of students are from out of state

FACULTY PROFILE

80 full-time faculty

150 part-time faculty

12 to 1 student/faculty ratio

ADMISSIONS

1,418 Total Applicants

1,214 Total Admissions

347 Total Freshman Enrollment

85.61% of applicants admitted

SAT Ranges: CR 450-550, M 455-550

ACT Ranges: C 20-26, E 19-26

TUITION & COSTS

Tuition: $21,620

Fees: $410

Total: $22,030

R&B: $9,170

Total: $31,200

FINANCIAL

$13,312 avg grant/scholarship amount (need)

$4,834 avg loan amount (need)

WEST CHESTER UNIVERSITY

WEST CHESTER, PENNSYLVANIA

Located just 25 miles from Philadelphia, WCUPA is a public, regional, comprehensive institution committed to providing high-quality undergraduate education as well as a vibrant on-campus community.

CO-CURRICULAR PORTFOLIO: The Co-Curricular Portfolio is WCUPA's way to make a meaningful record of a student's involvement outside of the classroom. The point of the portfolio is to demonstrate that students have impactful experiences outside of their schoolwork. Résumés can only fit so much information, and so extracurricular experiences must often be excluded or abbreviated. The portfolio allows students to showcase their experiences in clubs, sports, service, leadership, and more. This detailed scope says much more about students' overall abilities and skillsets.

UNDERGRADUATE RESEARCH: Undergraduate research is both a huge responsibility and a major achievement. Students who conduct research gain experience with inquiry, methodology, technical writing, discovery, and presentation, all of which are highly valuable to both employers and graduate schools. There a few different opportunities to engage in research, one of which includes a summer research experience. Students selected for the summer program become research fellows, conducting scholarly/creative work over a five-week period.

LEARNING ASSISTANCE & RESOURCE CENTER: When it's all said and done, a college education is about each student's individual and personal pursuit. That means students need to be self-motivated and self-reliant—qualities that can take time to develop. The Learning Assistance & Resource Center (LARC) recognizes the practice needed for healthy academic habits, thereby providing services aimed to increase educational responsibility among students. LARC's tutors work one-on-one with students to develop skills in critical thinking, problem solving, participation, and leadership. LARC's goal is to prepare all students to become successful, independent thinkers.

PRE-MAJOR ADVISING: Deciding a major isn't always easy, and many students may even need a guiding hand to see all their possible choices. Faculty members are happy to act as pre-major advisors in order to help their students select the appropriate major for them. Undecided students are given a wealth of resources in order to let them explore their choices before coming to a conclusion. Through pre-major advising, students can discover passions they never knew they had.

WCUPA STUDY ABROAD: Study abroad is an incredible opportunity to see and experience another part of the world. Through the Center for International Programs, West Chester is able to connect students with various programs across the world. Examples of the life-changing adventures offered to West Chester students include foodway tours of France and Italy throughout Spring Break; a full semester or year at the Hosei University in Tokyo; a summer of cultural and political study in Costa Rica; and winter-break participation at the Rafiki Africa Foundation in Kenya.

LEADERSHIP OPPORTUNITIES: Leadership experience, especially at the collegiate level, is a valuable asset to employers and grad schools. Students who can demonstrate experience as leaders show that they are capable handling advanced roles in challenging situations. Considering that leadership is a powerful skill, West Chester provides it students numerous opportunities to gain experience. For example, students have the chance to gain certificate recognition for their leadership work in areas of civic and social need, demonstrating their commitment to communication, leadership, service, global awareness, and recognition of diversity. Additionally, Women Leading Up helps the community learn from great women leaders in the Philadelphia area, studying what it takes to make a great female leader.

http://www.wcupa.edu/
P: (610) 436-1000

PUBLIC

STUDENT PROFILE

14,212 undergraduate students

90% of undergrad students are full time

41% male — 59% female

16% of students are from out of state

88% freshman retention rate

71% graduated in 6 years

FACULTY PROFILE

727 full-time faculty

271 part-time faculty

19 to 1 student/faculty ratio

ADMISSIONS

12,624 Total Applicants

7,408 Total Admissions

2,396 Total Freshman Enrollment

58.68% of applicants admitted

SAT Ranges: CR 490-580, M 490-580, W 470-570

ACT Ranges: C 21-26, M 19-25, E 20-26

TUITION & COSTS

Tuition: (In) $7,060 (Out) $17,650

Fees: (In) $2,402 (Out) $2,630

Total: (In) $9,462 (Out) $20,280

R&B: $8,127

Room: $4,848

Board: $3,279

Total: (In) $17,589 (Out) $28,407

FINANCIAL

$5,627 avg grant/scholarship amount (total)

$8,578 avg loan amount (total)

YORK COLLEGE OF PENNSYLVANIA

YORK, PENNSYLVANIA

Students come to York College of Pennsylvania because they want to take action. They want internships and paid, cooperative learning. They want to conduct research with faculty and meet with their professors one-on-one. They want to get engaged right away, joining the school's award-winning radio station or entering in the Elevator Pitch Competition. And, most of all, they want to pay half of what other top private colleges are asking without sacrificing a solid education. From day one, York College does all that and more.

FROM DAY ONE: Students find that it doesn't take long to get hands-on at York College, where "From Day One" is both a motto and the school's approach to learning. Students get instruction from their professors—not graduate students—100% of the time, and they don't have to wait long to start using state-of-the-art equipment in the labs or to get involved in such department activities as an on-campus radio show and the "YCP Hacks" coding and creation event. For students wanting to enhance and broaden their worldview, they can also set up a trip to study abroad anywhere in the world, whether they spend a full semester or a minimester embracing new cultures.

FIRST-YEAR SEMINAR: York College believes that the best way to maximize an education is to get off to the strongest start possible. Therefore, its First-Year Seminar program works to ensure incoming students an incredible experience, using specialized, sometimes off-beat topics that promote a comfortable and interesting transition into college academics. Peer fellows also volunteer to offer mentoring and guidance to help new students navigate the first year. Such a supportive experience can extend even further, as several FYS courses are also part of learning communities in which students can live with others in the same course and create an ongoing cycle of academic and personal development.

COMMUNITY ENGAGEMENT: York College embraces the surrounding area through the Center for Community Engagement. Located in a renovated building in downtown York, the Center draws students into the community through events like a special night at the York Revolution ballpark and various volunteer efforts. The Center is also home to the Graham Scholars program, which enables entrepreneurial and innovative students to discuss and debate ideas to improve the world.

LEADERSHIP DEVELOPMENT CENTER: Each year, the Leadership Development Center brings industry leaders and experts—such as Mia Hamm and Piper Kerman—to campus to present inspiring lectures. It also hosts an array of activities with students, faculty, and the community at-large. The goal of these events is to garner appreciation for the critical role that leadership and professionalism play in students' future careers. The Student Life and Global Programming office adds to York College's cultural enrichment in order to celebrate diversity. Among its organized events is the Kente Service for seniors during which each student wears traditional Kente cloth from Ghana.

SERVICE-LEARNING: If students are interested in volunteering beyond the annual Spartan Service Day, they can be involved in the service-based Eisenhart Scholars or join one of many clubs that make service a main focus. Greek life at York also has a service component. Through Greek life and other student organizations, York students show how committed they are to giving back to the community with empathy and compassion.

CAREER DEVELOPMENT: Nine in ten recent graduates are employed or are in graduate school, shining as a testament to York College's effectiveness. This success is due in part to the efforts of the Career Development Center, which holds a massive career fair, résumé clinics, job-search advice, and more. The Spartan Career Path also makes it easy for employers to find potential employees and for students to find potential internships.

https://www.ycp.edu/
P: (717) 849-1600

PRIVATE

STUDENT PROFILE

4,154 undergraduate students

93% of undergrad students are full time

45% male – 55% female

78% freshman retention rate

60% graduated in 6 years

FACULTY PROFILE

181 full-time faculty

280 part-time faculty

15 to 1 student/faculty ratio

ADMISSIONS

5,799 Total Applicants

3,535 Total Admissions

894 Total Freshman Enrollment

60.96% of applicants admitted

SAT Ranges: CR 470-560, M 470-580

ACT Ranges: C 20-25, M 18-26, E 18-24

TUITION & COSTS

Tuition: $17,560

Fees: $1,870

Total: $19,430

R&B: $10,830

Total: $30,260

FINANCIAL

$5,424 avg grant/scholarship amount (need)

$4,107 avg loan amount (need)

PROVIDENCE COLLEGE

PROVIDENCE, RHODE ISLAND

Providence College offers over 4,000 undergraduate students a compelling promise to challenge and engage them in life-changing educational experiences. A Catholic, liberal arts college–the only one in the United States to be administered by the Dominican Friars–Providence has earned a national reputation for providing a distinctive education in a stimulating intellectual, spiritual, and social environment.

SERVICE-LEARNING AND COMMUNITY INVOLVEMENT: Providence College provides both curricular and cocurricular service-learning outreach to the community. Through the Feinstein Institute for Public Service, Providence College students currently provide outreach to many different community organizations. Service-learning has also been incorporated into academic disciplines, including education, military science, social work, and political science. In 1996, Providence College even became the first institution to offer an undergraduate degree in public and community service studies, displaying a perfect example of its commitment to service. Over two thousand students annually engage in a vast array of voluntary service activities through campus ministry and a number of other campus groups. Examples of Providence College's impactful service has included work with Habitat for Humanity and the Special Olympics, visits to the elderly and hospitalized children, and tutoring in Providence public schools.

STUDY ABROAD: The College's study abroad options are designed to augment its liberal arts perspective as an integral component of the undergraduate academic experience. 197 various year-long, semester-long, and short-term study abroad programs are offered across the Middle East, Africa, Asia, Australia and New Zealand, Central and South America, and Europe. One noted program is the new Center for Theology & Religious Studies' trip to Rome, which includes a Providence College faculty resident director. Additionally the Washington, D.C. Semester Program combines academic study and experiential learning in a one-semester program spent at American University in Washington, D.C.

STUDENT-TEACHER RESEARCH AND SCHOLARSHIP PROJECTS: Teaching is the primary focus of Providence College faculty. In fact, the school does offer any courses that are taught by teaching assistants or graduate students. Providence College students engage in original research and scholarship projects with the faculty in fields that range from political science to bioinformatics. Their results are often published in academic journals or presented at national conferences.

THE CIV: The Development of Western Civilization Program, or Civ, is the cornerstone of the Providence College core curriculum. Students take this two-year interdisciplinary program throughout their freshman and sophomore years, covering the areas of history, philosophy, literature, theology, and the fine arts from ancient Mesopotamia to modern times. Civ is team-taught by four faculty members from each of these disciplines, altogether sharing their thoughts and perspective on the events, art, literature, philosophy, and religious ideals of the time. The program provides a strong foundation for the rigor of undergraduate study, complementing each student's pursuits regardless of major.

PROVIDENCE, RHODE ISLAND: Providence College's 105-acre campus is located within two miles of Rhode Island's capital city. The intimacy of the campus–with everything and everyone just a short walk away–enables students to enjoy a private, tranquil oasis for living and learning, and its location puts them in touch with a vibrant city just minutes away. Providence has been nationally recognized for its urban renaissance, hosting a blend of arts, culture, entertainment, and shopping. As one of America's first cities, Providence is rich in history, culture, and tradition–and today, it still enjoys a reputation as one of America's most desirable cities.

CAREER SERVICES: The College's Career Services office actively helps students prepare for the workforce while they are still pursuing their undergraduate degrees. The office's staff maintains a database of about seven hundred internships, coordinates career shadowing and networking programs, and conducts numerous workshops to prepare students for employment or graduate school.

---

http://www.providence.edu/

P: (800) 721-6444

PRIVATE - CATHOLIC

STUDENT PROFILE

4,028 undergraduate students

93% of undergrad students are full time

45% male – 55% female

88% of students are from out of state

90% freshman retention rate

85% graduated in 6 years

FACULTY PROFILE

305 full-time faculty

170 part-time faculty

12 to 1 student/faculty ratio

ADMISSIONS

10,215 Total Applicants

5,800 Total Admissions

1,034 Total Freshman Enrollment

56.78% of applicants admitted

TUITION & COSTS

Tuition: $44,520

Fees: $880

Total: $45,400

R&B: $13,390

Room: $7,720

Board: $5,670

Total: $58,790

FINANCIAL

$24,063 avg grant/scholarship amount (total)

$10,240 avg loan amount (total)

BENNINGTON COLLEGE

NORTH BENNINGTON, VERMONT

Bennington College is a private, nonsectarian liberal arts college located in Bennington, Vermont. Bennington is the only college to require that students spend a term every year at work in the world, creating well-rounded, well-prepared graduates. Bennington is located in the beautiful southwestern tip of Vermont, bordering New York's capital district.

NEVER-ENDING DISCOVERY: Bennington prides itself on the thriving individuality that each of its students brings to the table. The College encourages students to explore their intellectual potential through service terms and interactive learning. A Bennington education reminds students never to stop moving; they should be in a constant state of discovery and renewal, seeking out ways to make sure that their learning never stops.

FIELD WORK TERM: A unique field work requirement is included in every Bennington student's curriculum. Throughout a designated, seven-week period in January and February, all students participate in field experiences, implementing academic theory into professional settings. This frequent, skill-building guarantee builds each student's professional networks and prepares them with a repertoire of marketable experiences.

THE PLAN PROCESS: Students are given responsibility over their education through a structure called the "Plan Process." This model gives them the ability to evaluate their educational experience through in-depth meetings and writing assignments, checking in on their progress and passions as they pursue their degree. Ultimately, the goal of the Plan Process is to get students to articulate why they have chosen their respective fields of study so that they may understand their goals for the future.

STUDY ABROAD: Bennington offers its students the option to study abroad for a semester or a full year. Students have the choice to study through one of Bennington's own programs or to pursue third-party trips that better suit their interests. This gives everyone the chance to customize their international travel and find the best opportunities to support their individual goals.

DETAILED EVALUATION: Faculty members are actively involved in the lives of their students, especially throughout the Bennington Plan Process. Professors work in close collaboration with students and help them decide which area of study to pursue. They do their best to inform students of their departments' programs and gauge each student's specific needs through one-on-one advising. This highlights an especially unique aspect of a Bennington education: the friendly dynamic between its professors and students. Students are not just given grades, but also written evaluations of their performances in each course. These evaluations give students detailed feedback that encourages their development and praises their performance. This hands-on approach to teaching allows professors to form meaningful relationships with their students as they invest in their educational experiences.

ACTIVITIES AND LEADERSHIP: Bennington students have access to 40 clubs and organizations, the interests of which span from academic to extracurricular. Students may choose to participate in these clubs as members, but they can also involve themselves further as leaders. Serving as committee members, student government representatives, and more, student leaders have several opportunities to step up and take change. Students seeking extra responsibility can also work as admissions interns to give tours to prospective students or work for The Bennington Free Press, the student newspaper.

COMMUNITY OUTREACH: The Community Outreach and Action Program gives students the tools to excel and learn in areas of leadership, service, and global education. Students work to give back to the community and promote civic engagement. The Bennington community is actively involved in such organizations as Habitat for Humanity and Four Winds Nature Institute.

BENNINGTON COLLEGE

http://www.bennington.edu/
P: (802) 442-5401

PRIVATE

STUDENT PROFILE

704 undergraduate students

97% of undergrad students are full time

35% male – 65% female

84% of students are from out of state

82% freshman retention rate

68% graduated in 6 years

FACULTY PROFILE

55 full-time faculty

58 part-time faculty

10 to 1 student/faculty ratio

ADMISSIONS

1,099 Total Applicants

693 Total Admissions

215 Total Freshman Enrollment

63.06% of applicants admitted

TUITION & COSTS

Tuition: $47,590

Fees: $630

Total: $48,220

R&B: $14,200

Room: $7,680

Board: $6,520

Total: $62,420

FINANCIAL

$34,989 avg grant/scholarship amount (total)

$6,384 avg loan amount (total)

CASTLETON UNIVERSITY

CASTLETON, VERMONT

Established in 1787, Castleton University is small enough to be a community in which every student matters, yet it offers more than 75 diverse and challenging programs of study for undergraduate and graduate students, 29 varsity sports, and over 40 clubs and organizations. The university strives to provide a high-quality liberal arts education while stressing the importance of community service and civic engagement.

FIRST-YEAR SEMINAR: Castleton's First-Year Seminar Program helps students make a successful transition into college life. The program introduces students to campus resources and promotes the academic skills that students need to be prosperous in their new environment.

DEDICATED FACULTY: Castleton faculty members are a dedicated community of professionals comprised of scholar-teachers whose academic and artistic endeavors enlarge and enrich the lives of their students, their colleagues, and the university. Ninety-four percent of faculty hold doctoral or appropriate terminal degrees in their field of academic specialty, and all full-time faculty in the Graduate Programs hold doctoral degrees.

COMMUNITY ENGAGEMENT: Castleton has a rich history of community engagement, serving the town of Castleton and its surrounding communities since it's founding year of 1787. From their first day on campus, students are taught to make a difference at Castleton before going out to make a difference in the world. Community engagement is an important aspect of the Castleton experience, from classroom curriculums to residence life and student activities. Ultimately, students are provided with rich, real-world experiences that truly prepare them for lives of work and service.

RESEARCH OPPORTUNITIES: Through experiential learning, Castleton students have the opportunity to engage in collaborative research and creative endeavors with faculty from a variety of academic programs. Learning opportunities include independent study, honors theses, and capstone projects. Many faculty-student collaborative research projects are supported by funds from the Academic Dean's' Office throughout the academic year.

STUDY ABROAD: The Castleton Study Abroad Office works hard to provide students with rewarding abroad opportunities. Throughout the years, Castleton students have had the opportunity to explore the international culture and landscapes of such locations as Costa Rica, Iceland, Peru, Greece, New Zealand, London, Cambodia, and China.

EDUCATIONAL AND CULTURAL EVENTS: Castleton hosts a wide variety of educational and cultural events that are open to the campus and greater community, including lectures, musical concerts, performing arts, multicultural celebrations, films, live performances, and conferences. These events enrich the cultural and academic experiences for Castleton students while also providing an opportunity to enhance their understanding of the world.

CAREER SERVICES: With the mission of preparing students to transition successfully from a college life to a professional career, Castleton's Office of Career Services helps current students and recent graduates achieve their professional career goals. Members of the Career Services team assist students with all aspects of career planning, including choosing a major, exploring career-related interests, developing effective internship and job searching strategies, applying to graduate schools, and changing careers.

INTERNSHIPS: Castleton helps to provide on- and off-campus internships for all students, consistently finding local, national, and international opportunities. Opportunities through the Castleton Internship Program provide positions of responsibility for students in a professional environment under the supervision of an on-site professional and faculty advisor. Past internships have included positions with such business as NBC, Fox News, Edgewood Entertainment, PUMA International, WCAX, Kate Spade, Rutland Regional Medical Center, Vermont Country Store, and Green Mountain Power.

http://www.castleton.edu/
P: (800) 639-8521

PUBLIC

STUDENT PROFILE

1,968 undergraduate students

91% of undergrad students are full time

49% male – 51% female

27% of students are from out of state

75% freshman retention rate

47% graduated in 6 years

FACULTY PROFILE

97 full-time faculty

118 part-time faculty

9 to 1 student/faculty ratio

ADMISSIONS

2,505 Total Applicants

1,983 Total Admissions

482 Total Freshman Enrollment

79.16% of applicants admitted

SAT Ranges: CR 430-530, M 430-540

ACT Ranges: C 17-23, M 17-23, E 15-22

TUITION & COSTS

Tuition: (In) $10,872 (Out) $26,424

Fees: (In) $1,328 (Out) $1,328

Total: (In) $12,200 (Out) $27,752

R&B: $10,290

Room: $6,128

Board: $4,162

Total: (In) $22,490 (Out) $38,042

CHAMPLAIN COLLEGE

BURLINGTON, VERMONT

http://www.champlain.edu/

P: (800) 570-5858

PRIVATE

Founded in 1878, Champlain College is a small, not-for-profit, private college situated in the heart of Burlington, Vermont, and overlooking scenic Lake Champlain. In addition to its main campus in Burlington, Champlain College has two international campuses: one in Montreal, Canada, and one in Dublin, Ireland. Many of the College's residence halls are restored Victorian-era mansions, giving students a unique atmosphere in which to learn and live. Champlain's distinctive, career-focused approach to education also prepares students to become skilled practitioners, effective professionals, and engaged global citizens from their very first semester.

UPSIDE-DOWN CURRICULUM: The Upside-Down Curriculum is a unique educational approach that allows students to take essential courses and begin experiencing their major starting in their first semester. Not only does its format allow students to get into internships earlier, but it also makes it possible to take as many as six classes in one's major during their first year at Champlain. With this approach, students have four full years to develop the skills essential for success in their defined career.

A WORLD OF OPPORTUNITY: One of Champlain's goals is to ensure that all students graduate prepared to be global citizens and leaders. It all starts inside the classroom. The faculty at Champlain incorporate international experiences into their course curricula—from traveling to Nicaragua for service work with a class on human rights to pen-palling with students in South Africa to discuss Nelson Mandela's legacy. During junior year, all students are encouraged to engage in a study abroad experience at one of Champlain's international campuses in Montreal, Canada, and Dublin, Ireland, or nearly anywhere in the world, including New Zealand, China, Italy, Argentina, South Africa, and Scotland.

SERVICE-LEARNING: Students in Champlain College's Education and Human Studies Division benefit from service-learning, which is used as an instructional strategy that blends community service with academic learning. Emphasis is placed on reflection, active student participation, and connecting the curriculum to the real world. With a focus on social justice and pressing social issues that impact all EHS professionals, students are well prepared for life beyond college.

REAL-WORLD ADVANTAGE: Thanks to Champlain's Upside-Down Curriculum, many students become internship-ready early in their college careers. Nearly 90% of Champlain's students complete one or more internships by graduation. Multiple internships give students a depth and breadth of professional experience, a tremendous competitive advantage when starting out in the job market or applying to top-tier graduate schools.

CAREER FLAGSHIP PROGRAM: Champlain's distinctive Career Flagship Program equips students with the career readiness and personal financial skills to ensure their successful transition from college to career. The four-year, curriculum-embedded program works alongside students' major and the Core curriculum in order to enable practical, hands-on learning through professional workshops (Career SMARTalks), seminars, lectures, company visits, and employer information sessions. Students also participate in internships, field experiences, and career-building opportunities early on, taking advantage of cutting-edge recruiting technologies to focus their job search. They can also learn how to manage their money in the future and create a plan to pay back their student loans.

THE CHAMPLAIN COLLEGE CAREER COLLABORATIVE: Champlain has been in the business of providing a career-focused education since 1878. Champlain's comprehensive approach to professional readiness is systematically orchestrated and passionately administered through Champlain College's Career Collaborative. These career partners are among the most forward-thinking emerging consulting teams in higher education. They all work to make continual improvements to the College's strategy and programs for career development.

STUDENT PROFILE

2,263 undergraduate students

98% of undergrad students are full-time

62% male – 38% female

78% of students are from out of state

82% freshman retention rate

62% graduated in 6 years

FACULTY PROFILE

110 full-time faculty

169 part-time faculty

14 to 1 student-to-faculty ratio

ADMISSIONS

4,576 Total Applicants

3,201 Total Admissions

650 Total Freshman Enrollment

69.95% of applicants admitted

SAT Ranges: CR 520-630, M 500-610

ACT Ranges: C 22-28, M 22-27, E 22-28

TUITION & COSTS

Tuition: $39,718

Fees: $200

Total: $39,918

R&B: $14,906

Total: $54,824

FINANCIAL

$20,423 avg grant/scholarship amount (need)

$4,266 avg loan amount (need)

GREEN MOUNTAIN COLLEGE

POULTNEY, VERMONT

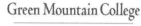

Green Mountain College (GMC), rated #1 in sustainability in the nation, dynamically ties environmental awareness and activism into its curriculum. With the help of its top-notch faculty, all of whom are leader in their fields, GMC successfully instills the drive for meaningful change in the hearts of each of its students.

FIRST-YEAR EXPERIENCE: Students new to Green Mountain College are welcomed quickly and comfortably into the dynamic college lifestyle with the help of relationship-building first-year programs. Through a series of commonly shared experiences, first-year students are given all the tools they need to succeed in college as well as an engaging insight into GMC's mission of environmental conservation. Leading up to freshman orientation, new students participate in the Wilderness Challenge, an adventurous series of outdoor activities within the beautiful Vermont ecosystem. Hiking, kayaking, and more, they bond and form lifelong friendships before their classes even begin. All GMC students enroll in "Images of Nature and Culture" and "Voices of Community," two preparatory classes that develop upper-level writing skills through engaging course topics. These common learning experiences deepen students' understanding of their place in this ecologically and culturally rich world. Supplemented with frequent field trips, these courses excite students to become strong, knowledgeable writers.

ENVIRONMENTAL LIBERAL ARTS CORE SEQUENCE: A college education is most valuable when it educates students not only to be masters in their concentrated fields, but also to be well-rounded citizens who are knowledgeable of a variety of issues and perspectives. Through the Environmental Liberal Arts (ELA) core curriculum, Green Mountain College stretches students' limits with courses that teach valuable subjects beyond their majors.

BROADENED HORIZONS: Environmental conservation requires an astute awareness of a variety of international cultures, as today's economic and ecological challenges are global in scale. Because GMC highly values this internationally conscious outlook, it offers a breadth of programs that make travel abroad possible for any student who is interested. Among the options for faculty-led courses abroad include such places as Brazil, China, Italy, New Zealand, and Nepal. Additionally, GMC has created student-exchange programs in partnership with the University of Wales-Aberystwyth, Nagoya University in Japan, and South Korea's Hannam University.

GREENMAP: It's no secret that Green Mountain College prides itself in its respect for the world's ecosystems. Though the College takes its mission of sustainability very seriously, its students and faculty are just as committed to having fun with what Earth's natural resources have to offer. The Green Mountain Adventure Programming, or GreenMAP, makes outdoor recreation easy for anyone to enjoy. GMC students have the opportunity to become Trip Leaders, inspiring individuals who bring the heart of GreenMAP to anyone looking for an adventure. In charge of thrilling excursions among the beautiful Vermont wilderness, Trip Leaders get to serve as safe, life-changing, and fun volunteers.

LIVING-LEARNING COMMUNITIES: A school founded on principles of community engagement and global wellness, Green Mountain College prides itself in fostering an inclusive environment for every incoming student and visitor. It offers nine specialty residence floors to house students with similar interests as part of an initiative to strengthen the GMC community. Themed around subjects related to sustainability, creative arts, activism, and more, these specialty floors bring students together into an environment that anyone would love to call home.

A DELICATE BALANCE: Rounding off the Environmental Liberal Arts curriculum, every GMC student enrolls in a seminar-based capstone course that challenges them to determine the responsibilities of a truly engaged citizen. Each semester, a new capstone course is created to tackle a contemporary issue, asking students to think creatively about new movements and policies. Through their capstone courses, students refine their skills as researchers, writers, and environmentally conscious change-makers. By the end of the course, each student completes a project that reflects both their academic aptitudes as well as their global values.

---

http://www.greenmtn.edu/

P: (800) 776-6675

PRIVATE

STUDENT PROFILE

582 undergraduate students

97% of undergrad students are full time

49% male – 51% female

90% of students are from out of state

66% freshman retention rate

38% graduated in 6 years

FACULTY PROFILE

40 full-time faculty

42 part-time faculty

14 to 1 student/faculty ratio

ADMISSIONS

825 Total Applicants

544 Total Admissions

132 Total Freshman Enrollment

65.94% of applicants admitted

SAT Ranges: CR 480-590, M 460-530

ACT Ranges: C 18-24

TUITION & COSTS

Tuition: $33,898

Fees: $1,962

Total: $35,860

R&B: $11,492

Total: $47,352

FINANCIAL

$25,928 avg grant/scholarship amount (need)

$4,006 avg loan amount (need)

UNIVERSITY OF VERMONT

BURLINGTON, VERMONT

The University of Vermont provides a mixture of big-school opportunities and small-school benefits. Students enjoy collaborating with their professors while growing into successful leaders of tomorrow.

UVM BILATERAL EXCHANGE: UVM takes part in various exchange programs all around the world, allowing students to study abroad at partner institutions while an international student from those schools come to study at UVM. This program is a balance of domestic and international education, altogether giving students the opportunity to continue their studies within their discipline at world-class institutions. Such partner institutions include Aoyama Gakuin University in Japan, Stockholm University in Sweden, and Universidad Panamericana in Spain.

FIGS: First-year interest groups, or FIGs, allow students to live among peers who share similar interests and academic schedules. A FIG takes the learning experience outside of the classroom and integrates it into residence life, allowing students to get the most out of their majors from the very beginning of their college lives. For example, UVM offers BioFIG for first-year biology, biological science, zoology, and plant biology students. BioFIG allows students to take classes with one another and participate in a weekly seminar, which is incredibly important for developing peer collaboration and supplementary course discussion.

SERVICE LEARNING: The Office of Community-University Partnerships & Service Learning (CUPS) is responsible for community-based learning initiatives. Service learning is considered a high-impact practice that involves students directly with the community. Students are given the chance to integrate academic theories into real-world situations, allowing for higher-level conceptualization and application of subject matter. There are plenty of different options available. UVM supports direct and indirect service, consulting, and community-based research. There are 91 service learning courses offered at UVM, so there are plenty of ways to get involved. The university collaborates with 200 community partners, 90% of which have reported satisfaction with the UVM's service. Examples of courses available include: Sustainable Development in Small Island States; Critical Perspectives on Service Learning and Communication; Intro to Early Childhood Education; Sustainable Food Purchasing; and Community and International Economy Transformation

FIRST-YEAR EXPERIENCE: In their first year, students are introduced to university life through various learning communities and social activities. The First-Year Experience is a combination of Teacher-Advisor Program (TAP) seminars as well as larger courses. TAP is an elective course with a strong focus on writing. In small group seminars students discuss topics of interests and explore multiple viewpoints. Aside from the semester-long TAP seminars, UVM offers 4 full-year residential programs. Students enrolled in a year-long program take 4-6 connected courses that are taught by faculty from different departments. Participation in a full-year course is highly beneficial, as students get to explore topics highly in depth as they discover their talents and interests.

FIRST-YEAR SUMMER READ: UVM requires all incoming freshmen to complete a summer reading assignment prior to arriving on campus. The book's themes are integrated into the first-year experience, and students from all disciplines are expected to contribute. In the fall, the author visits campus to give a free lecture and book signing.

http://www.uvm.edu/

P: (802) 656-3131

PUBLIC

STUDENT PROFILE

10,973 undergraduate students

91% of undergrad students are full time

44% male – 56% female

78% of students are from out of state

86% freshman retention rate

77% graduated in 6 years

FACULTY PROFILE

1,289 full-time faculty

374 part-time faculty

15 to 1 student/faculty ratio

ADMISSIONS

25,274 Total Applicants

17,907 Total Admissions

2,400 Total Freshman Enrollment

70.85% of applicants admitted

SAT Ranges: CR 550-650, M 550-640, W 540-650

ACT Ranges: C 25-30, M 24-28, E 24-31, W 8-9

TUITION & COSTS

Tuition: (In) $14,664 (Out) $37,056

Fees: $2,104

Total: (In) $16,768 (Out) $39,160

R&B: $11,150

Room: $7,376

Board: $3,774

Total: (In) $27,918 (Out) $50,310

FINANCIAL

$14,525 avg grant/scholarship amount (total)

$7,983 avg loan amount (total)

AVERETT UNIVERSITY

DANVILLE, VIRGINIA

Averett's culture of personal attention prepares students for success. With a 14:1 student-faculty ratio, passionate professors, and strong academic support, graduates are confident thinkers and capable doers who are ready to serve and lead.

AN INDIVIDUALIZED EDUCATION: Averett's size is its greatest strength! Students aren't lost in the crowd. Instead, they're nurtured and supported by caring, experienced faculty and staff in a vibrant and active campus environment. Engaging faculty in turn engage their students in experiential, hands-on learning that is interactive, meaningful, and relevant to careers. Averett students complete general education requirements and fulfill their graduation requirements in part through out-of-the-classroom activities such as undergraduate research, service-learning, internships at area organizations, and clinicals/practica.

STUDY ABROAD: Averett offers both long- and short-term study abroad programs. There is no experience like that of living and learning in another country, immersed in a different language, and culture and familiarizing oneself with delicious food and new friends. Employers are always on the lookout for "risk takers" who have demonstrated their self-reliance, leadership, and critical thinking skills, and what better way to gain such experience than by studying abroad? Averett, through its company affiliations, exchange programs, articulation agreements, and faculty-led study courses, offers a great variety of opportunity for summer study or semester- and year-length abroad programs in many countries.

LEADERS ON CAMPUS: Averett students take an active role in shaping their both college experience as well as the future of the University itself. Student representatives on Averett boards and committees have an equal voice in matters of programs, issues, and policy. In this way and others, Averett develops students into thoughtful leaders for the future.

HEALTH SCIENCES INITIATIVE: Averett created its expanded health sciences initiative due to an increased rate of biology and physical sciences students' interest in healthcare-related training. This initiative includes investigating possible new academic programs in nursing and sports medicine. Community support is very high for the initiative, with more than $2.4 Million donated in less than a year. Such generosity is making possible the new, cutting-edge simulation labs that are being built at Averett's Riverview Campus in Danville's Historic Tobacco Warehouse District. Health Sciences students are able to practice and learn on simulative mannequins before facing real patients. Although it might be hard to tell the difference at times, the simulators are designed to react like humans; for example, they sweat!

TECHNOLOGY IN THE CLASSROOM: Averett knows that learning-based technology plays an important role for students in all majors! A new full-motion flight simulator allows Aeronautics students to gain experience in conditions and locales they might not experience in thousands of hours of real flying. For example, they can practice take-offs and landing in the high-altitude and low-humidity around Denver, all without leaving the ground in Danville. This and many other innovations are giving many Averett students the best education possible.

RANDOM ACTS OF KINDNESS: At a small, vibrant school like Averett, individual students can make a big impact in a short amount of time. Recently, for example, Averett RAs started performing Random Acts of Kindness, spreading the idea of compassion across the entire campus. Before long, the local ABC station had a camera team interviewing Averett students and following them around town to film their Random Acts of Kindness! In just a few months, the idea went from an RA meeting to being on the six o'clock news. And that's just one example of how "Cougars Can!"

---

http://www.averett.edu/
P: 800-AVERETT

PRIVATE

STUDENT PROFILE

852 undergraduate students

96% of undergrad students are full time

48% male – 52% female

39% of students are from out of state

55% freshman retention rate

33% graduated in 6 years

FACULTY PROFILE

56 full-time faculty

33 part-time faculty

13 to 1 student/faculty ratio

ADMISSIONS

1,878 Total Applicants

1,120 Total Admissions

210 Total Freshman Enrollment

59.64% of applicants admitted

SAT Ranges: CR 410-510, M 420-518

ACT Ranges: C 16-22

TUITION & COSTS

Tuition: $29,150

R&B: $8,600

Room: $5,810

Board: $2,790

Total: $37,750

FINANCIAL

$14,499 avg grant/scholarship amount (total)

$12,044 avg loan amount (total)

CHRISTOPHER NEWPORT UNIVERSITY

NEWPORT NEWS, VIRGINIA

CHRISTOPHER NEWPORT UNIVERSITY

A four-year public university in Newport News, Virginia, Christopher Newport University enrolls 5,000 students in rigorous academic programs in the liberal arts and sciences. CNU offers great teaching and small class sizes with an emphasis on leadership, civic engagement, and honor. The University's success at creating an incomparable environment for academic and student life alike has received top recognition being named one of America's schools to watch for having made "the most promising and innovative changes in academics, faculty, student life, campus, and facilities." As a public liberal arts institution, Christopher Newport University prides itself in its commitment to student development. CNU aims to broaden perspectives, fostering a welcome heart for diversity in each and every student.

PRESIDENT'S LEADERSHIP PROGRAM: Christopher Newport prepares students for a lifetime of success, helping them reach their full potential as they develop the skills essential for making a difference in the world. Beginning with the nationally recognized President's Leadership Program (PLP), high-ability students are selected to engage in a combination of academic study, experiential learning, and personal development that prepares them for a life of leadership, service, and civic responsibility.

LEARNING COMMUNITIES: All freshmen enroll in a learning community (LC) of 15-30 students, taking two to four classes together. Based on an area of academic interest, these courses—necessary for degree completion—set students on the path to graduating in four years. And by living in close proximity and forming natural study groups, LC members support each other through the college transition.

EXPERIENTIAL LEARNING: Beyond the classroom, CNU students engage in activities that enhance and support classroom learning, including internships with top employers, study abroad, and undergraduate research—all of which foster independent learning. The University recently launched Research LENS, an initiative that enhances basic research literacy by helping students translate literacy skills into discipline-specific research.

ACADEMIC SUCCESS: Hands-on assistance can be found in the Center for Academic Success, which offers one-on-one tutoring and facilitated study groups, supplemental instruction, and a Writing Center. Additional services include academic coaching, an anonymous Captains Care referral system to identify students struggling in a particular area, student success workshops and online modules, and a two-credit course for those who need help adjusting to college life and academics. In addition, as they strive to excel both on and off the field of play, Christopher Newport's student-athletes receive focused support through the Center for Academic Success' Student-Athlete Academic Support Program. This includes mandatory study sessions, focused workshops, academic support mentors, and other helpful services.

CORE ADVISORS: First- and second-year students receive essential support through a faculty core advisor who helps them become committed scholars, excel in extracurricular activities, and explore major and career options. Core advisors meet with students at least four times in their first semester, providing advice and insight regarding service learning, undergraduate research, study abroad, internships, and other campus opportunities. Once students officially declare their major, they begin working with a major advisor.

---

http://www.cnu.edu/
P: (757) 594-7000

PUBLIC

STUDENT PROFILE

4,921 undergraduate students

99% of undergrad students are full time

43% male – 57% female

8% of students are from out of state

86% freshman retention rate

75% graduated in 6 years

FACULTY PROFILE

276 full-time faculty

179 part-time faculty

15 to 1 student/faculty ratio

ADMISSIONS

7,532 Total Applicants

4,682 Total Admissions

1,228 Total Freshman Enrollment

62.16% of applicants admitted

SAT Ranges: CR 530-630, M 530-620

ACT Ranges: C 23-28

TUITION & COSTS

Tuition: (In) $8,236 (Out) $20,032

Fees: (In) $5,418 (Out) $5,418

Total: (In) $13,654 (Out) $25,450

R&B: $11,224

Room: $6,904

Board: $4,320

Total: (In) $24,878 (Out) $36,674

FINANCIAL

$6,731 avg grant/scholarship amount (need)

$4,279 avg loan amount (need)

COLLEGE OF WILLIAM & MARY

WILLIAMSBURG, VIRGINIA

William & Mary, the second oldest college in the nation, attracts attention for its research initiatives and talented student body. Students at William & Mary are well-rounded individuals who are wholly committed to both academic achievement as well as service to others.

FIRST-YEAR EXPERIENCE INITIATIVES: The First-Year Experience (FYE) at William & Mary is made up of four components called "Essential Initiatives." Each of the Essential Initiatives is considered an integral part of both the FYE and the undergraduate experience as a whole. The "Making a Tribe Choice—Be Upstanding!" initiative teaches student how to intervene if they notice a student faced with an unhealthy situation. By observing this step of the FYE, students come together as a community of learners and supporters. The "Community Values and Responsibilities" program is an extension of the first year experience. After orientation, members of the Honor and Student Conduct Council put on a series of sketches that outline some of the social challenges that freshmen commonly face. The "Tribe Unity" initiative invites students from diverse backgrounds share their experiences and perspective with incoming freshmen. And, finally, "Healthful Relationships" shares tips on how to maintain healthy relationships and give support to survivors of abuse.

COLL 400 - THE CAPSTONE: The last step of the Arts & Sciences undergraduate program is the capstone experience, which allows every student to turn independent inquiry into original work. Individuals typically complete their capstone during their senior year to culminate the experiences they have had within their major. By the end of a capstone experience, W&M wants students to be able to identify the true value of a liberal arts education as well as their identities as scholars.

EDUCATORS AS VOLUNTEERS: Future educators are making a difference even while enrolled at William & Mary. College Partnership for Kids (CPK) is a volunteer effort that connects W&M students to local public schools, allowing these education majors to work with local students both one-on-one and in a group. This exchange is meant to improve confidence and self-esteem among children. Students may also take part in Project Phoenix, also known as ProPho. This is a tutoring and mentoring service that allows students to work with students from the Berkeley and Toano middle schools. Volunteers lead mentoring activities to focus on one of five areas: community engagement, career exploration, culture education, health/fitness, and life skills.

COHEN CAREER CENTER AND INTERNSHIPS: The Cohen Career Center is the go-to resource for all things career- and internship-related. Students are invited to stop by and take advantage of all the center has to offer, including interview and résumé tips, help finding internships, and advice about career decisions. The Center connects students to local internships that allow them to gain hands-on experience while still attending school. Students involved in the Local Internship Program connect with several different organizations throughout the Williamsburg area and can access positions across multiple fields and disciplines.

STUDY ABROAD: Study abroad is the experience of a lifetime; students who go abroad assuredly gain cross-cultural communication skills as well as an appreciation for new customs and languages. William & Mary has several great abroad programs, a handful of which are directed by or connected to faculty members within the Department of Modern Languages. Standout programs include the exchange program with L'Institut d'Etudes Politiques in Lille, France, in which students take courses in French politics and sociology as well as a summer trip to Beijing in which students discover Chinese language, literature, and culture. These experiences, among so many others, show W&M students the life-changing effects of cultural immersion.

WILLIAM & MARY
CHARTERED 1693

https://www.wm.edu/
P: (757) 221-4000

PUBLIC

STUDENT PROFILE

6,301 undergraduate students

99% of undergrad students are full time

44% male – 56% female

30% of students are from out of state

95% freshman retention rate

90% graduated in 6 years

FACULTY PROFILE

838 full-time faculty

154 part-time faculty

12 to 1 student/faculty ratio

ADMISSIONS

14,952 Total Applicants

5,153 Total Admissions

1,518 Total Freshman Enrollment

34.46% of applicants admitted

SAT Ranges: CR 630-730, M 630-730, W 620-720

ACT Ranges: C 28-32, M 27-32, E 29-34

TUITION & COSTS

Tuition: (In) $11,525 (Out) $35,122

Fees: (In) $5,394 (Out) $5,950

Total: (In) $16,919 (Out) $41,072

R&B: $10,978

Room: $6,792

Board: $4,186

Total: (In) $27,897 (Out) $52,050

FINANCIAL

$18,179 avg grant/scholarship amount (total)

$7,134 avg loan amount (total)

EMORY & HENRY COLLEGE

EMORY, VIRGINIA

Noted for its exceptional beauty, Emory & Henry remains firmly grounded in its 175-year commitment to excellence in liberal arts education. Dedicated to creating informed minds and global citizens, Emory & Henry translates an emphasis on civic virtues to active service-learning. Emory & Henry students take learning beyond the classroom. By reaching out to local communities, they gain a deeper understanding of themselves and the world around them.

PARTICIPATE, LEARN, AND GROW: Emory & Henry students are not just engaged in the realm of academia; they are engaged with the world. The Appalachian Center for Community Service establishes partnerships between local rural community organizations and the campus community. The Center coordinates and administers many volunteer opportunities such as the Big Brothers and Big Sisters program, the Make a Wish Foundation, and the Migrant Health Network clinic. Students are encouraged to extend their service learning beyond typical volunteerism and to further examine the root causes of social inequities.

GLOBAL ENGAGEMENT: The Study Abroad program at Emory & Henry encourages students to expand their horizons by studying internationally. While students can choose to study throughout the world, Emory & Henry hosts international study centers in China, the Middle East, and Europe. Each year, Emory & Henry features close to 100 concerts, lectures, arts performances, films, exhibits, and poetry readings. In addition, the college hosts a literary festival and, in January, students present the Winter Forum, a campus-wide, social-issue conference that features an internationally renowned speaker.

A GENUINELY COMPASSIONATE FACULTY: The E&H campus is located in the village of Emory, which is home to students and E&H professors alike. Emory is a learning community that strongly supports students' enlightenment and success. Emory & Henry professors are nationally renowned for excellence in teaching. During the past 24 years, 12 E&H professors have received the highest teaching honors in the state of Virginia, and one was named U.S. Professor of the Year.

UNDERGRADUATE RESEARCH: Some biology students collect microbes 150 feet underwater. Some physics students photograph binary stars. Some political science students present their work to major professional conferences. Across the curriculum, E&H professors prepare students by encouraging research and providing them with research opportunities that most college students do not receive until graduate school.

OUTDOOR ADVENTURE PROGRAM: Any E&H student has the chance to enroll in the Outdoor Adventure program, an exploration of the nearby natural landscape and such beautiful attractions as the Appalachian and Iron Mountain trails, the Virginia Creeper Trail, the Mount Rogers National Recreation Area, and the Jefferson and George Washington national forests. The College provides a wide array of resources that make the program shine, enabling students to go backpacking, rock climbing, paddling, cross-country skiing, and more.

SCHOOL LOCATION: The campus encompasses 331 pristine acres in the village of Emory, Virginia, in the Virginia Highlands. The campus is within view of Virginia's two highest peaks, Mount Rogers and Whitetop Mountain, and is near the historic town of Abingdon, Virginia, home of the renowned Barter Theatre. Also within easy driving distance is the metropolitan Tri-Cities region of Bristol, Johnson City, and Kingsport.

NEW PROGRAM: E&H has recently implemented a new undergraduate Exercise Science program. This study of exercise and the human body allows students to understand clinical health and general wellness, preparing them for amazing professions in such fields as dietetics, kinesiology, and public health. This program equips students with the prerequisites for further graduate studies in the field and gets them a great head-start in pursuit of their honorable professional fields.

http://www.ehc.edu/

P: (800) 848-5493

PRIVATE

STUDENT PROFILE

1,024 undergraduate students

98% of undergrad students are full time

52% male — 48% female

70% freshman retention rate

54% graduated in 6 years

FACULTY PROFILE

104 full-time faculty

60 part-time faculty

11 to 1 student/faculty ratio

ADMISSIONS

1,456 Total Applicants

1,112 Total Admissions

304 Total Freshman Enrollment

76.37% of applicants admitted

SAT Ranges: CR 430-550, M 430-540, W 400-520

ACT Ranges: C 18-24, M 17-24, E 17-24

TUITION & COSTS

Tuition: $30,700

Fees: $200

Total: $30,900

R&B: $10,510

Room: $5,220

Board: $5,290

Total: $41,410

FINANCIAL

$22,878 avg grant/scholarship amount (total)

$6,778 avg loan amount (total)

HOLLINS UNIVERSITY

ROANOKE, VIRGINIA

At Hollins University, young, driven women find a supportive yet rigorous academic environment at which they are challenged to expand their intellectual horizons. The faculty is nationally recognized both for their quality and accessibility to students, and the study abroad and internship opportunities are truly outstanding. And with a national reputation for excellence, its creative writing program stands as a shining jewel of the academic programming.

OPEN THE DOOR TO A WORLD OF POSSIBILITIES: HU's 4-1-4 calendar offers students a January term that allows students to spend one month focusing exclusively on internships, special courses, or study abroad programs. During the January Short Term, students have travel and study opportunities in such countries as Italy, Spain, Germany, and Great Britain. Students can also opt to stay on campus and participate in intensive seminars, or they may complete internships at places such as ABC World News, the New York Stock Exchange, the U.S. Naval Hospital in Naples, or Betsey Johnson Designs in New York City. HU runs its own study abroad programs in Paris and London, but students can also participate in one of the school's affiliate programs in Argentina, Ghana, Ireland, Greece, Italy, Japan, Mexico, and Spain. Science majors are able to study abroad during their junior or senior years through Hollins' affiliation with the School for Field Studies. In this program, they benefit from hands-on education while completing research in ecology, environmental issues, and sustainable development.

COMMUNITY SERVICE: Hollins students realize the importance of community both on campus and off. Not only do HU women participate in local community service projects, but some also travel to Lucea, Jamaica, as part of a popular, truly impactful service-learning project.

GREAT TEACHING BY GREAT SCHOLARS: HU's 84 full-time faculty and 52 part-time faculty are all active members of both the campus community and the professional world. Teaching at Hollins is not just a job; professors are committed to being part of the community while encouraging students at both the academic and personal level.

ENCOURAGED TO EXPLORE: HU's distinguished programs in creative writing, art, and dance benefit not just those who major in them, but also the University's cultural health with art shows, readings, and dance performances.

THE BATTEN LEADERSHIP INSTITUTE: Through the Batten Leadership Institute, students can earn certificates in leadership studies by engaging in executive-level training in a range of skills that are essential for good leadership. Graduates of this program rave that their experience gave them the confidence to handle with success even the most unfamiliar situations.

SOMETHING FOR EVERYONE: Hollins' athletic teams are a source of pride within the University community. The campus riding team, for example, regularly places at or near the top in national meets. Additionally, Roanoke promotes an active arts culture, an emphasis on social equality, and a variety of community events. Students can enjoy shopping at the local farmer's market or take a day hike into the neighboring Blue Ridge Mountains. They can even get involved in HOP, which takes advantage of the surrounding scenery to combine "adventure, education, self-awareness, and leadership." HOP participants go caving, whitewater rafting, or hiking through the fully equipped outing center.

A GREAT FOUNDATION FOR AN OUTSTANDING FUTURE: In addition to the career center, which provides students with on-campus interviews, a full career-planning library, one-on-one counseling, and an extensive alumni network, Hollins also sends students to CHALLENGE, a nationally recognized career fair for graduating seniors from liberal arts colleges.

---

http://www.hollins.edu/

P: (800) 456-9595

PRIVATE

STUDENT PROFILE

639 undergraduate students

97% of undergrad students are full time

0% male – 100% female

81% freshman retention rate

57% graduated in 6 years

FACULTY PROFILE

84 full-time faculty

52 part-time faculty

9 to 1 student/faculty ratio

ADMISSIONS

2,233 Total Applicants

1,362 Total Admissions

196 Total Freshman Enrollment

60.99% of applicants admitted

SAT Ranges: CR 520-630, M 470-580, W 480-630

ACT Ranges: C 21-30

TUITION & COSTS

Tuition: $35,000

Fees: $635

Total: $35,635

R&B: $12,300

Room: $7,460

Board: $4,840

Total: $47,935

FINANCIAL

$31,150 avg grant/scholarship amount (total)

$7,750 avg loan amount (total)

JAMES MADISON UNIVERSITY

HARRISONBURG, VIRGINIA

James Madison University invites students to come forth, learn great things, and brighten the future. With plenty of global study and civic engagement opportunities, students have plenty of room to grow and succeed.

THE HUMAN COMMUNITY: Every student, no matter their major or professional program, is required to participate in the Human Community. James Madison's Human Community examines the foundations of a college education and seeks to prepare students for academic and personal success. The program is broken into five separate clusters, each with its own focus. Students take courses within these clusters and build a repertoire of marketable skills. Cluster One examines Critical Thinking, Human Communication, and Writing. Cluster Two explores the Arts and Humanities. Cluster Three focuses on scientific and mathematical investigation. Cluster Four is a study of social and cultural processes, and Cluster Five explores Individuals in the Human Community.

COMMUNITY-BASED LEARNING: James Madison regards service as an integral part of higher education. The department of Community Service-Learning partners with 75 organizations within the Shenandoah Valley community. The purpose of community-based learning is to increase student awareness of the society around them. The University also offers both international and domestic alternative spring break trips. Each service group contains approximately 12 students, 2 student co-leaders, and a faculty coordinator. Students typically volunteer for service trips during spring break, but options are available over all academic breaks. James Madison wants all its graduates to be well-rounded leaders with experience in civic engagement and service to those in need.

INTERNSHIPS: JMU students are highly encouraged to seek out internship opportunities. Not only do internships allow participants to gain industry experience, but they help establish professional networks between students and employers. Internships are different than externships, which are much shorter in duration and unpaid. An externship is perfect for students looking to get a glimpse at an industry without a long-term commitment. Internship 101 is a workshop for JMU students preparing to seek out internship and externship opportunities. Students learn about the process of selecting the right position.

STUDENT CONFERENCE: Nominated students have the opportunity to participate in the Student Conference, a celebration of undergraduate achievement. Professors select students that have demonstrated academic excellence in some presentation or body of work. The student then has the chance to demonstrate their talent at the conference. This is a great opportunity for students to practice their public communication skills.

HONORS PROGRAM: The Honors Program selects exceptional students to become members of an accelerated, academic community. Honors students enjoy several benefits like study abroad opportunities, financial support, and priority registration. Every student enrolled in the Honors Program is required to complete the Senior Honors Project. For track I and II Honors students, the final project is a capstone experience that allows students to demonstrate their intellectual abilities and talents.

RESIDENTIAL LEARNING COMMUNITIES: Residential Learning Communities (RLCs) allow students the unique opportunity to live and take classes with a small group of peers that share similar interests. There are several benefits to participation, including better interaction with faculty, academic support, and a community of peers that share common goals. James Madison offers several different community options. Just a few of the the RLCs offered at James Madison include an arts-based community, a residence for international students, a community for psychology majors, and a future educator's house.

http://www.jmu.edu/

P: (540) 568-6211

PUBLIC

STUDENT PROFILE

19,396 undergraduate students

95% of undergrad students are full time

41% male – 59% female

91% freshman retention rate

83% graduated in 6 years

FACULTY PROFILE

1531 full-time faculty

429 part-time faculty

16 to 1 student/faculty ratio

ADMISSIONS

21,439 Total Applicants

15,559 Total Admissions

4,408 Total Freshman Enrollment

72.57% of applicants admitted

SAT Ranges: CR 520-610, M 520-610

ACT Ranges: C 23-27

TUITION & COSTS

Tuition: (In) $5,724 (Out) $20,302

Fees: (In) $4,294 (Out) $4,850

Total: (In) $10,018 (Out) $25,152

R&B: $9,396

Room: $4,648

Board: $4,748

Total: (In) $19,414 (Out) $34,548

FINANCIAL

$7,597 avg grant/scholarship amount (total)

$7,103 avg loan amount (total)

LYNCHBURG COLLEGE

LYNCHBURG, VIRGINIA

Lynchburg College has been the first choice for talented scholars, leaders, and student-athletes from across Virginia and around the world. Small classes, talented and caring faculty, and liberal arts and professional programs of study all are hallmarks of the Lynchburg College experience.

FIRST-YEAR EXPERIENCE: Lynchburg College freshmen take advantage of a program built just for them. The First-Year Experience program helps them meet friends, embrace college life, and have a successful first year at Lynchburg. Connection Leaders teach them how to navigate the college experience and excel in academics even while exploring fun extra curricular programs. Meanwhile, the residence life staff provides award-winning activities that help students have fun with their neighbors.

TEAMWORK: Students work in teams all throughout their classes regardless of academic program. By working together, they develop skills that are critical to any career: leadership, negotiation, communication, holding teammates accountable, effective communication, and sharing responsibility.

RESEARCH +: Lynchburg encourages students to ask new questions and seek answers through original research. Some scholarship funds support student research, and many professors love to guide students to successful projects. Every spring, the daylong Student Scholar Showcase celebrates student research, art, literature, and other engaging academic work.

GO GLOBAL: Lynchburg students travel the globe through study abroad programs during the winter, spring, and summer breaks. In other countries, they practice foreign languages, meet people with different cultural backgrounds, and see sights in person that most people only see in pictures. There are countless other ways to get engaged at Lynchburg, all of which enrich their cultural growth. Students curate exhibitions, plan educational programs for children, make art, direct plays, complete internships, and more. Imagination is the only limit.

WESTOVER HONORS PROGRAM: Academically distinguished students are invited into the Westover Honors Program for a deeper, more challenging learning experience. Honors faculty stretch students' minds with unique courses on topics like Frankenstein and synthetic life, the world of Harry Potter, or the everyday soldiers of the American Civil War. First-year students kick off the program with a retreat that helps them build a new community among them. As seniors, they complete interdisciplinary projects that demonstrate all they have learned.

WE WRITE FOR SUCCESS: Because the pen—or the keyboard, or smartphone—is mightier than the sword, Lynchburg College offers a wide variety of Writing-Enriched courses. Students in these courses use research, writing, and revising to bring their communication skills to the next level. They become strong thinkers, communicators, and persuaders as they build their talent with the written word. In this way, students emerge as effective communicators whether they are writing academic papers, opinion articles, or even tweets.

SPEAKERS: Sit in class with a well-known poet. Meet an environmental activist and ask her about how one person can make a difference. Listen to renowned Civil War scholars give a lecture, or get performance tips from professional musicians. These are just a few things students get to do at Lynchburg College. Almost every week of the school year, lecturers and performers bring their global experiences to share at Lynchburg.

COMMUNITY SERVICE: Lynchburg College students, faculty, and staff believe in serving the people around them. Every year, they complete more than 70,000 hours of community service and raise thousands of dollars for charities. Students play a big role in Relay for Life, St. Baldrick's Day, and other big events.

http://www.lynchburg.edu/

P: (434) 544-8100

PRIVATE

STUDENT PROFILE

1,999 undergraduate students

97% of undergrad students are full time

40% male – 60% female

31% of students are from out of state

81% freshman retention rate

56% graduated in 6 years

FACULTY PROFILE

180 full-time faculty

108 part-time faculty

10 to 1 student/faculty ratio

ADMISSIONS

5,223 Total Applicants

3,331 Total Admissions

521 Total Freshman Enrollment

63.78% of applicants admitted

SAT Ranges: CR 460-560, M 460-560

ACT Ranges: C 19-25

TUITION & COSTS

Tuition: $35,650

Fees: $970

Total: $36,620

R&B: $10,120

Total: $46,740

FINANCIAL

$23,781 avg grant/scholarship amount (need)

$3,578 avg loan amount (need)

MARY BALDWIN UNIVERSITY

STAUNTON, VIRGINIA

**MARY BALDWIN
UNIVERSITY**

At Mary Baldwin University, students find the skills and the inspiration to become the architects of their lives. They are resilient, confident in their strengths, and ready to take charge. Mary Baldwin students experience the proven advantages of a close-knit women's college combined with the opportunities and access of a multifaceted, coed university, preparing them to lead both on the job and around the world.

FIRST-YEAR SEMINARS AND EXPERIENCES: All first-year residential students get to be involved in a Leadership Gateway course, which proves to be the key to unlocking the full potential of their student experience. Each gateway includes a focus in career preparation as well as the exploration of a topic of interest, whether that be leadership, healthy lifestyles, cultural identity, or academic achievement. Gateways help new students make connections with students, faculty, and staff who share their interests and passions.

UNDERGRADUATE RESEARCH: Mary Baldwin's emphasis on undergraduate research, scholarship, and creative activity represents its commitment to developing students who not only know, but more importantly, do. From field to studio, from library to laboratory, from far-away places to right next door, Mary Baldwin students know there are multiple ways to find the answer. Whether they investigate medieval frescos in an Italian cathedral or collect feather and blood samples from songbirds to quantify differences in parasite loads, excellence in research and scholarship is their goal. The University's distinctive major programs allow seniors to carry out original research or creative projects in collaboration with faculty mentors, ensuring the chance for hands-on experiences that provide real substance to their curiosity.

DIVERSITY/GLOBAL LEARNING: Mary Baldwin is committed to providing international experiences as a vital part of a personally transforming education. All students, regardless of academic major or language ability, are encouraged to travel, study, or volunteer overseas. College is the ideal time for students to gain the cross-cultural competence they need to become active participants in such an increasingly interdependent world. Short-term trips that are led by full-time Mary Baldwin faculty are open to all students throughout the May term, or students can otherwise study or volunteer abroad for a summer, semester, or full year.

A COLLEGE WITHIN A COMMUNITY: Downtown Staunton—just a short walk from campus—offers students live music, a movie theater, art galleries, coffee houses, restaurants for all budgets, and retail shopping. Staunton is also home to the world's only recreation of Shakespeare's Blackfriars Playhouse as well as the library of former U.S. President Woodrow Wilson. Five historic districts combine with modern facilities to make Staunton a destination for filmmakers, festivals, conferences, and visitors from around the world. Located between the Blue Ridge and Allegheny mountains in western Virginia, the Shenandoah Valley is filled with opportunities for camping, backpacking, hiking, skiing, whitewater kayaking, and biking (both on- and off-road). It's also a perfect setting for studying birds, wildflowers, stream biology, and ecology.

SERVICE-LEARNING, COMMUNITY-BASED LEARNING: Mary Baldwin is consistently recognized by the President's Higher Education Community Service Honor Roll as one of the top service-oriented institutions in the nation for its commitment to connecting with local and global communities. MBU students volunteer at schools, churches, food banks, homeless shelters, child care centers, and many other local nonprofits and social service organizations. Internationally, they have worked in schools, assisted underprivileged children, and helped rebuild communities in India, Nepal, El Salvador, and Belgium, just to name a few.

CAPSTONE PROJECTS: In their senior year, all undergraduate students culminate their studies by completing a capstone, which may take the form of a research project or creative work. For example, studio art majors might exhibit paintings in the campus gallery. While science majors might investigate endocrine-disrupting compounds in waterways. Students and faculty often present their capstone projects at conferences around the country and, sometimes, around the world.

http://www.marybaldwin.edu/
P: (540) 887-7019

PRIVATE

STUDENT PROFILE

1,265 undergraduate students

71% of undergrad students are full time

4% male – 96% female

51% of students are from out of state

64% freshman retention rate

37% graduated in 6 years

FACULTY PROFILE

95 full-time faculty

118 part-time faculty

11 to 1 student/faculty ratio

ADMISSIONS

5,407 Total Applicants

2,693 Total Admissions

176 Total Freshman Enrollment

49.81% of applicants admitted

SAT Ranges: CR 440-600, M 420-540

ACT Ranges: C 19-25

TUITION & COSTS

Tuition: $29,940

Fees: $391

Total: $30,331

R&B: $9,000

Total: $39,331

FINANCIAL

$17,990 avg grant/scholarship amount (need)

$4,196 avg loan amount (need)

RANDOLPH COLLEGE

LYNCHBURG, VIRGINIA

Randolph specializes in—and is committed to—providing a unique, individualized experience that supports, challenges, and inspires students to develop their best self. With its rigorous coursework and small class sizes, Randolph encourages its students to master the thought of thinking critically and innovatively. Students are actively engaged in their education with dynamic classroom discussions, integrative internship programs, and real-world experiences. In fact, 60 percent of Randolph students complete internships before graduating. Other programs give students access to summer research, visiting artists and writers programs, and unique partnerships.

FIRST-YEAR EXPERIENCES: Randolph's Passport Program is designed to introduce first-year students to the Randolph Experience. Students attend twelve Passport Events during their first year as part of their First-Year Experience. More than 35 events are offered in the program, including guest lectures, theatrical performances, cultural exhibits, and sporting events.

SUMMER RESEARCH: Randolph's Summer Research Program is an intensive 8-week, paid program that pairs students with faculty members to conduct research on a variety of topics and disciplines. The program gives them the chance to sharpen their skills in research inquiry, writing, and presentation.

GLOBAL LEARNING: A global perspective permeates the Randolph educational experience, and nearly half of all students participate in one of the College's many study abroad programs. Randolph's flagship study abroad program, Randolph@Reading, allows students to live and study in Reading, England, for a year or semester. Students can also choose from six affiliated programs in either Denmark, Mexico, Italy, Spain, France, or Greece. Professors at Randolph even lead the College's International Study Seminars, which allow students to spend their academic breaks exploring a variety of issues to prepare them for their journeys abroad.

WRITING-INTENSIVE COURSES: The College-wide Writing Program offers four full years of support and resources to students for the development of their writing skills at every ability level. Faculty in all departments formally evaluate student writing skills at the end of every semester and in every course. Each semester, the Writing Board submits to the Dean a list of students judged by two or more faculty members. These students, having proved to demonstrate excellent writing skills, are awarded annual prizes for their excellence in writing.

A GREEN CAMPUS: Sustainability is a way of life at Randolph. Students learn and teach sustainable agricultural practices in the Organic Garden, make their own laundry detergent, and engage in campus-wide recycling efforts. The Sustainability Council leads efforts to encourage the emphasis on sustainability in all aspects of campus, from the dining hall to new technology. Renovations and improvements like these keep energy efficiency at the forefront of the campus way of life.

SENIOR CAPSTONE: The senior capstone program is the culmination of a student's undergraduate studies in his or her major. The well-integrated and -unified body of intellectual work permits a worthy summarization of each student's initiative and independence in organizing, relating, and applying significant ideas within a major field.

INTERNSHIPS: Internships are an important part of the Randolph College experience that provide real-world experiences to prepare students for life after college. The College offers students numerous opportunities for such experiences through established partnerships with local employers and organizations. The College's theatre-in-residence, Endstation Theatre Company, offers Randolph students special internship opportunities, and the College's one-of-a-kind partnership with the National Gallery in London provides Randolph students with an exclusive internship program at the London museum. In addition, a new program helps students pay for expenses related to unpaid internships. Through this Jolley Mini-Grant program, students are eligible to receive up to $4,000 to offset housing and other costs.

http://www.randolphcollege.edu/

P: (800) 745-7692

PRIVATE PUBLIC

STUDENT PROFILE

665 undergraduate students

99% of undergrad students are full time

34% male — 66% female

30% of students are from out of state

77.5% freshman retention rate

65% graduated in 6 years

FACULTY PROFILE

68 full-time faculty

4 part-time faculty

10 to 1 student/faculty ratio

ADMISSIONS

1,207 Total Applicants

972 Total Admissions

184 Total Freshman Enrollment

80.53% of applicants admitted

SAT Ranges: CR 460-570, M 450-550

ACT Ranges: C 19-24

TUITION & COSTS

Tuition: $36,160

Fees: $610

Total: $36,770

R&B: $12,580

Total: $49,350

FINANCIAL

$24,925 avg grant/scholarship amount (need)

$4,595 avg loan amount (need)

SWEET BRIAR COLLEGE

SWEET BRIAR, VIRGINIA

Established in 1901, Sweet Briar has always been a proving ground for independent women who lead and achieve with fierce determination. The College's unique community and campus life foster strength and resilience in every student by surrounding her with excellent faculty, coaches, and staff who challenge her to bring her best self forward—and to own it with confidence and courage. Sweet Briar's academics are defined by its small classes, rigorous standards, and exceptional student-faculty interaction through scholarship and research. The intensive residential liberal arts environment produces graduates who are agile, creative, and unafraid of life's twists and turns. Students have a rallying cry: "There's nothing that you cannot do." And Sweet Briar women prove it every day.

COMMON INTELLECTUAL EXPERIENCES: Sweet Briar's Lectures and Events Committee sponsors regular public presentations by scholars and artists. The Writers' Series features poets and writers of both fiction and nonfiction. The Babcock Season brings artists and professional dance and theater companies to campus for performances. Noted scientists and entrepreneurs speak annually at the environmental Waxter Forum and Engineers Week Banquet. Artists in residence at the adjacent Virginia Center for the Creative Arts guest teach classes. These events provide opportunities for students to interact with professionals in master classes, social situations, and as collaborators.

FIRST-YEAR SEMINARS AND EXPERIENCES: Orientation includes activities that are aimed at helping new students get to know both the campus and rich history of Sweet Briar. Students have the opportunity to pursue one-on-one research with faculty starting their freshman year, even participating in the Honors Summer Research Program. They also have access to every piece of equipment in the chemistry and biology labs from their first semester. First-year honors seminars introduce student pursuing an honors degree to interdisciplinary methods, thought, and scholarship.

DIVERSITY/GLOBAL LEARNING: Forty percent of Sweet Briar students study abroad through the College's established JYF and JYS programs, the Virginia Program at Oxford, or another program of the student's choosing. Some students also opt for international internships, often facilitated through Sweet Briar's highly engaged, world-wide alumnae network.

LEARNING COMMUNITIES: Sweet Briar is a vibrant community focused on interactive learning both in and outside the classroom. More than 30 student-run clubs and organizations host readings, movie nights, and political watching parties. Students take on leadership roles in the Student Government Association, giving them an opportunity to practice what they have learned in the classroom. Through student government elections, a self-imposed Honor Code, and a judiciary committee that oversees violations of the Student Handbook, students learn early on how to lead with integrity and solve problems as part of a team. Student-run charitable events benefit nonprofits in the area, all while offering students the opportunity to get hands-on experience in marketing, event-planning, and business management. Additionally, the Outdoor Program partners with the environmental science and creative writing departments to offer immersive, one-of-a-kind experiences in Sweet Briar's natural environment both on and off campus.

CAPSTONE COURSES AND PROJECTS/SENIOR EXPERIENCE: All Sweet Briar students may complete a capstone experience in their major(s). This might be a yearlong engineering project, an academic essay, a portfolio of poetry or fiction, a music album, or the staging of an original play. In some cases, students continue to pursue the subject of their capstone project in graduate school.

SWEET BRIAR COLLEGE

http://sbc.edu/

P: (434) 381-6100

PRIVATE

STUDENT PROFILE

320 undergraduate students

99% of undergrad students are full time

0% male – 100% female

54% of students are from out of state

50% freshman retention rate

61% graduated in 6 years

FACULTY PROFILE

59 full-time faculty

20 part-time faculty

5 to 1 student/faculty ratio

ADMISSIONS

950 Total Applicants

884 Total Admissions

134 Total Freshman Enrollment

93.05% of applicants admitted

SAT Ranges: CR 460-620, M 420-560

ACT Ranges: C 18-27, M 17-26, E 16-28

TUITION & COSTS

Tuition: $36,520

Fees: $635

Total: $37,155

R&B: $12,900

Total: $50,055

FINANCIAL

$28,394 avg grant/scholarship amount (need)

$4,973 avg loan amount (need)

THE UNIVERSITY OF VIRGINIA'S COLLEGE AT WISE

WISE, VIRGINIA

UVa-Wise is one of the top public liberal arts colleges in the nation. A division of the University of Virginia, UVa-Wise is home to innovative majors like Virginia's only undergraduate degree program in software engineering. It is a member of the Council for Public Liberal Arts (COPLAC) and offers accredited programs in nursing, education, computer science, management information systems, and software engineering. Its 400-acre campus is located in the town of Wise amid the scenic Appalachian Mountains in southwest Virginia.

RESEARCH OPPORTUNITIES: Undergraduate research opportunities are abundant at UVa-Wise. Students work side-by-side with faculty members in laboratories or through field-based research projects. Student research at UVa-Wise has been published in The New York Times and presented at national conferences. Other opportunities for research include Healthy Appalachia, a unique partnership between the University of Virginia and UVa-Wise that looks at improving the quality of life and health care in southwest Virginia.

ENGAGED FACULTY: UVa-Wise professors love to teach; several members of the faculty have even been honored with statewide awards for outstanding classroom teaching. The UVa-Wise classes are small, averaging 17 students per class, and are taught by faculty member, not graduate students. These highly involved professors sponsor clubs, coach athletic teams, and work side-by-side with students on undergraduate research. And, at the end of four years, the faculty know students so well that they can help connect them with a valuable professional network and direct them to the graduate school opportunities that are surely the best fit.

LIFE OUTSIDE THE CLASSROOM: Southwest Virginia may be home to the State Theater of Virginia and great local music, but it's the natural beauty that truly defines the area. In these scenic foothills, students can enjoy the outdoors by bicycling, hiking, fishing, skiing, and horseback riding. There are plenty of areas to explore, including High Knob, the Guest River Gorge, the Breaks Interstate Park, and Cumberland Falls. The College's Outdoor Recreation Program takes full advantage of the area by organizing such activities throughout the year as skydiving and caving. The College also provides a number of other activities, including movies, events, and guest lectures from famous celebrities and esteemed academics.

PROFESSIONAL OPPORTUNITIES: UVa-Wise is the only school in Virginia with an undergraduate major in software engineering. Companies such as Norththrop Grumman and CGI are closely affiliated with this program, hosting a wide variety of opportunities for internships, financial assistance, and future employment opportunities. Sykes, Inc. has also partnered with UVa-Wise and the Department of Business and Economics to offer the College's students a unique opportunity for student employment within such an internationally acclaimed technical support company.

STUDY ABROAD: Students have an array of possibilities to study abroad thanks to UVa-Wise's strong relationships with sister institutions in Chile and a variety of European schools in such locations as the United Kingdom. Other partnerships open up possibilities to study at more than 400 universities in 65 countries ranging from Bulgaria to Uruguay. UVa-Wise also sponsors week-long trips to locales like India, Ecuador, China, and Belize during fall and spring break. Professors lead these trips in order to spark students' interests in travel while ensuring a high-quality education.

SERVICE: Three national fraternities and four national sororities on campus are committed to providing service both on UVa-Wise's campus and beyond. They focus on beautification projects, constructing play units for the severely handicapped, and other environmental projects.

https://www.uvawise.edu/

P: (276) 328-0102

PUBLIC

STUDENT PROFILE

2,027 undergraduate students

66% of undergrad students are full time

41% male – 59% female

5% of students are from out of state

72% freshman retention rate

41% graduated in 6 years

FACULTY PROFILE

102 full-time faculty

12 to 1 student/faculty ratio

ADMISSIONS

1,042 Total Applicants

801 Total Admissions

296 Total Freshman Enrollment

76.87% of applicants admitted

SAT Ranges: CR 420-530, M 430-510, W 410-510

ACT Ranges: C 17-22, M 16-21, E 15-22

TUITION & COSTS

Tuition: (In) $5,056 (Out) $20,658

Fees: (In) $4,164 (Out) $4,796

Total: (In) $9,220 (Out) $25,454

R&B: $10,256

Room: $6,144

Board: $4,112

Total: (In) $19,476 (Out) $35,710

FINANCIAL

$12,494 avg grant/scholarship amount (total)

$4,629 avg loan amount (total)

UNIVERSITY OF RICHMOND

RICHMOND, VIRGINIA

Students enrolled at the University of Richmond quickly become engaged and active members of the larger campus community. They benefit from close collaboration with faculty, access to several learning opportunities, and a slew of extracurricular activities.

THE RICHMOND GUARANTEE: The Richmond Guarantee says that "every undergraduate student will receive up to $4,000 for a summer internship or faculty-mentored research." University of Richmond extends this amazing opportunity for each and every student to gain hands-on experience before they graduate. This is a testament to the University's commitment to graduate intelligent, experienced individuals with valuable skill sets. Students need only to find a program that suits their academic needs, and University of Richmond will help fund their effort. The top-three industries for fellowships include: Math & Science, Social Science, and Business.

FIRST-YEAR SEMINAR 101 AND PILOT PROGRAM: The Pilot Program is an extension of University of Richmond's First-Year Seminar. Students enrolled in this program study over the course of two semesters instead of one. The classes are not connected in any way, and the topics are usually completely different from one another. The first-seminar is a foundational course that teaches students the basics of effective reading and writing skills, while the second course builds upon those skills and pushes students to fine-tune their approach.

COMMUNITY-BASED LEARNING: Community-based learning (CBL) pushes students to move beyond text to real-world applications of theories and concepts. When reality becomes part of the learning experience, students get to tackle situations that involve real people and real problems. CBL may challenge students, but such challenges push them to expand their horizons and consider issues from multiple viewpoints. It's easy to sit in a classroom and interpret text, but the real task is to put ideas into practice.

THE TOCQUEVILLE SEMINARS: The Tocqueville Seminars examine U.S. history and culture from an international viewpoint. Inspired by the work of Alexis de Tocqueville, students engage in topics like "global exchanges of peoples, cultures, and economic power" and "ethnic and religious violence." There are several courses to choose from, the topics of which range from politics to the arts.

UNDERGRADUATE HUMANITIES FELLOWS PROGRAM: The Humanities Fellows Program allows undergraduate students to pursue their own research in the humanities fields: history, culture, rhetoric, philosophy, classics, religious studies, literatures, and the arts. As a group, students talk through big concepts like love and power and, through faculty-led discussion, scholars hone their reading, writing, and critical thinking skills. Outside of class, these fellows explore museums and monuments like the Metropolitan Museum of Art and the New York Public Library. Students interested in participating must complete an application through the UR Summer Fellowships Program.

SOPHOMORE SCHOLARS IN RESIDENCE (SSIR): Sophomore Scholars in Residence (SSIR) is a unique living-learning community available exclusively to sophomores. Students in this program learn, live, and travel with one another for an entire year. Dedicated faculty transform the traditional learning experience to extend beyond the classroom and into the community, engaging students in such experiential learning as service, meeting with industry experts, and traveling as a group. Starting in the fall, SSIR scholars begin their capstone experiences, which they then present in the spring to the rest of the campus community. These SSIR capstones allow students to demonstrate their hard work and achievements outside of class, whether they be original research, performances, or group projects.

---

http://www.richmond.edu/
P: (804) 289-8000

PRIVATE

STUDENT PROFILE

3,329 undergraduate students

92% of undergrad students are full time

46% male – 54% female

93% freshman retention rate

88% graduated in 6 years

FACULTY PROFILE

408 full-time faculty

209 part-time faculty

8 to 1 student/faculty ratio

ADMISSIONS

9,977 Total Applicants

3,104 Total Admissions

807 Total Freshman Enrollment

31.11% of applicants admitted

SAT Ranges: CR 600-700, M 620-720, W 610-700

ACT Ranges: C 29-32

TUITION & COSTS

Tuition: $48,090

R&B: $11,120

Room: $5,090

Board: $6,030

Total: $59,210

FINANCIAL

$37,799 avg grant/scholarship amount (total)

$6,797 avg loan amount (total)

VIRGINIA WESLEYAN UNIVERSITY

VIRGINIA BEACH, VIRGINIA

The mission of Virginia Wesleyan University is to engage students of diverse ages, religions, ethnic origins, and backgrounds in a rigorous liberal arts education that prepares them to meet the challenges of life in a complex and rapidly changing world. In this endeavor, the University employs a wide range of approaches to teaching and learning, providing many opportunities to connect the study of the liberal arts with practical learning experiences. In accord with its United Methodist heritage, Virginia Wesleyan aspires to be a supportive community that is committed to social responsibility, ethical conduct, higher learning, and religious freedom.

THE EXTRA MILE: Students are exposed to a myriad of internship, study away, and undergraduate research experiences through The Lighthouse: Center for Exploration & Discovery. The Lighthouse is a one-stop shop to help students gain experiences that pave the way for success. Some past experiences have included taking photographs in New Zealand, visiting film studios in Hollywood, doing biology experiments in Belize, experiencing theatre in New York, studying ecotourism in Maui, and doing service-learning in Ghana.

INVOLVED FACULTY: Virginia Wesleyan professors are respected scientists. They are published authors and musicians. They are experts on environmental ethics, public relations, Buddhist philosophy, criminal behavior, supply-chain management, and Irish literature. But most of all, they are mentors and friends who develop meaningful relationships with the students whose lives they touch.

THE LIBERAL ARTS EDUCATION: As a liberal arts institution, Virginia Wesleyan embraces the values inherent in a liberal education—an education dedicated to developing the open-minded, disciplined reflection necessary not only to professional success, but also to a life of personal accomplishment and social commitment. Classes are small, and students are expected to engage their fellow students and faculty in an active learning environment. They develop intellectual confidence and independent thinking skills as well as respect for others, intellectual humility in the face of complexity, and openness to a better argument.

STUDENT ACTIVITIES: Students at Virginia Wesleyan discover just how rich and valuable the campus experience can be. There are many student clubs and organizations available to engage interests and ignite passions—everything from The Marlin Chronicle student newspaper and Habitat for Humanity to the Wesleyan Singers and Marlins Vote. There's something for everyone; the Wesleyan Activities Council brings a steady stream of musicians, comedians, speakers, and other entertainment to campus to keep students' days full of opportunities.

CAREER SERVICES: The University's Career Development & Internship Program offers counseling services to help students find the right major and gain the most benefit from their liberal arts education. This is accomplished through externships; internships and appropriate part-time/seasonal employment; assistance in preparing for an effective job search or graduate school application; and on-campus employer recruitment events.

PREPARED FOR THE WORLD: Providing the foundation for a good career is only one part of a Virginia Wesleyan education. First and foremost, Wesleyan seeks to prepare each student to be a Renaissance citizen—an honorable, caring, and culturally literate person who will lead a good and reflective life in service to their families and community. This is the transformative Wesleyan experience.

ALUMNI NETWORK: Virginia Wesleyan students are connected to a network of nearly 10,000 Marlin alumni across the country and the world. Graduates represent a wide range of professional backgrounds, gladly sharing their knowledge and experience with current students.

---

http://www.vwc.edu/

P: (757) 455-3200

PRIVATE

STUDENT PROFILE

1,402 undergraduate students

95% of undergrad students are full time

36% male – 64% female

27.2% of students are from out of state

65% freshman retention rate

47.3% graduated in 6 years

FACULTY PROFILE

92 full-time faculty

37 part-time faculty

12.8 to 1 student/faculty ratio

ADMISSIONS

1,850 Total Applicants

1,712 Total Admissions

349 Total Freshman Enrollment

92.54% of applicants admitted

SAT Ranges: CR 430-550, M 430-540

ACT Ranges: C 17-26, M 17-24, E 17-24

TUITION & COSTS

Tuition: $32,636

Fees: $650

Total: $33,286

R&B: $8,594

Total: $41,880

FINANCIAL

$22,004 avg grant/scholarship amount (need)

$7,926 avg loan amount (need)

BIRMINGHAM-SOUTHERN COLLEGE

BIRMINGHAM, ALABAMA

Birmingham-Southern College (BSC) is a four-year, private, liberal arts institution affiliated with the United Methodist Church. Committed to providing a liberal arts education of distinctive quality, BSC challenges its students to think independently, to examine the arts and sciences aesthetically and critically, and to communicate clearly.

ABOVE AND BEYOND: BSC is noted for its strong service-learning program in which 70 percent of its students participate; its study abroad (including exchange programs with international colleges and universities) and leadership studies programs; and its January Exploration term, which provides flexible options for hands-on education. Another unique aspect of a BSC education is its requirement that all students attend forty cultural events during their college career, which include lectures, art exhibits, and musical and theatrical performances. These events often connect with students' course work. In addition, seniors give public presentations of their four-year research, much like the oral requirement of doctoral programs.

STUDY ABROAD AND INTERNSHIPS: During the school's January term, many students choose to study abroad or domestically. Scholarships and other funding are available, making such worthwhile experiences accessible for many. BSC students who choose to remain on campus in January enjoy very small classes and often take advantage of internship opportunities in Birmingham, especially in the medical, legal, banking, and fine arts fields. Birmingham's medical facilities are considered among the best in the nation.

INVOLVED LEARNING: Within the general education foundations program, freshmen take two first-year seminars their first year. These courses are interdisciplinary, often include a service component, and provide an introduction to the liberal arts. One recent example includes a course in which BSC music students worked with a local elementary school to create, compose, and produce an opera. First-year courses include language studies and courses with a deep engagement in the arts.

STUDENT ACTIVITIES: Students are involved in more than eighty student organizations as well as NCAA Division III athletics. 75 percent of students stay on campus on weekends, and about 50 percent of BSC students are involved in Greek life. There are so many social activities and community-service opportunities that students around bound to have something fun to do all year long.

A CITY FOR EVERYONE: Birmingham, Alabama, known as the Magic City, is located at the foothills of the Appalachian Mountains and in the heart of the southeastern United States. It is a major urban center with more than one million people in the Birmingham metropolitan area. The city is the center for medical research, banking, music, technology, art and engineering. There are also many opportunities for local community service, such as participating in Habitat for Humanity projects, tutoring elementary students, or interning in the mayor's office.

DIRECTED TOWARD SUCCESS: BSC students who take advantage of the College's strong academic advising often graduate in four years. Students can also take advantage of career-planning services such as interest inventories, career- and job-search classes, résumé assistance, interview training, on-campus job interviews, and an alumni network. Each year, over 50 percent of graduates go on to graduate school. Nationally, the College ranks high in terms of graduates accepted to medical, dental, law, and professional schools. Within one year of graduation, 60 percent of BSC alumni enter the workforce in jobs related to their undergraduate fields of study, and many are hired by local Birmingham businesses and law firms as well as national corporations.

---

http://www.bsc.edu/
P: (800) 523-5793

PRIVATE

STUDENT PROFILE

1,346 undergraduate students

99% of undergrad students are full time

50% male — 50% female

86% freshman retention rate

61% graduated in 6 years

FACULTY PROFILE

98 full-time faculty

61 part-time faculty

13 to 1 student/faculty ratio

ADMISSIONS

3,679 Total Applicants

1,952 Total Admissions

441 Total Freshman Enrollment

53.06% of applicants admitted

SAT Ranges: CR 480-590, M 500-610

ACT Ranges: C 23-29, M 22-28, E 23-30

TUITION & COSTS

Tuition: $31,954

Fees: $1,174

Total: $33,128

R&B: $13,008

Room: $8,168

Board: $4,840

Total: $46,136

FINANCIAL

$23,694 avg grant/scholarship amount (total)

$7,147 avg loan amount (total)

SAMFORD UNIVERSITY

HOMEWOOD, ALABAMA

Samford University is a four-year, coeducational, private, residential, comprehensive liberal arts institution. Samford values its historic relationship with Alabama Baptists. Founded in 1841, Samford University is the largest independently supported university in the state of Alabama. The serene suburban campus, with its rolling hills and stately Georgian Colonial architecture, provides the ideal college environment. On top of that, Samford is only minutes away from Birmingham, a diverse metropolitan area of 1 million people that is rich in culture, history, and spirit.

A FIRE YOU CAN'T PUT OUT: Few universities offer both a rigorous liberal arts education and support for the spiritual life of their students, faculty, and staff. Samford understands that faith grows with challenge and challenges the faithful to grow. At Samford, faith grows through convocation programs, Christian student interest groups, and foreign and domestic missions. Strong faith produces humble servants, and Samford scholars are driven to pursue justice for the greater good. The Reverend Fred Shuttlesworth once described the clamor for justice as "a fire you can't put out," and he constantly challenges people to be "on fire" for justice. It provides light in the struggle for a better state, nation, and world. Some of the ways Samford is combining scholarship and faith to change the world include poverty relief partnerships, required Cultural Perspectives, courses, and more than 100 weekly opportunities for community service.

PRIME GEOGRAPHY: Thanks to a temperate climate, nature preserves, state and national parks, rivers, lakes, mountains, and exceptional scenic beauty, outdoor recreation opportunities abound in the greater Birmingham area. Samford is a partner with the Oak Mountain Interpretive Center in Oak Mountain State Park, granting its community direct access to tremendously fun and beautiful resources. And, geographically speaking, Birmingham is perfectly situated. The white-sand beaches of the Gulf of Mexico are just a few hours' drive to the south. Atlanta, Nashville, and Memphis also are only a few hours' drive away. Closer to home, Birmingham enjoys a thriving creative community. The Museum of Art, the Alabama Symphony, the Alabama Ballet, Opera Birmingham, the Sidewalk Moving Picture Festival, and many more opportunities to experience the arts are all available within the city. And, with nationally acclaimed restaurants and over 500 shopping centers, 85 antique malls, and over 70 bookstores, the Birmingham area is one of the most popular destinations in the region.

INTERNATIONAL STUDY: In any term, including the January and summer terms, Samford students study in England, Morocco, Spain, Brazil, Costa Rica, China, or a host of other countries. Samford's premiere international program is based out of a renovated Victorian home in the heart of London's famous West End. This home is within walking distance of some of the city's most famous cultural attractions.

A FLOURISHING LIFE BEYOND COLLEGE: A survey by Samford's Office of Institutional Research reported that 66% of graduates were employed and that 32% had continued their education. Famous alumni include retired Florida State Football Coach Bobby Bowden, actor Tony Hale, and opera singer Elizabeth Futral. These alumni, among so many others, supported their academic success with all the wonderful resources of their campus and surrounding city. Samford students enjoy the best of both worlds on the school's serene suburban campus, which is only minutes from one of the largest cities in the region. Birmingham is an international center for biomedical research, health care, technology, banking, and communications, meaning there are immense, endless opportunities for everyone to network and work with professionals within their field.

---

http://www.samford.edu/
P: (800) 888-7218

PRIVATE - CHRISTIAN

STUDENT PROFILE

3,168 undergraduate students

96% of undergrad students are full time

35% male – 65% female

89% freshman retention rate

74% graduated in 6 years

FACULTY PROFILE

352 full-time faculty

2 part-time faculty

12 to 1 student/faculty ratio

ADMISSIONS

3,196 Total Applicants

2,982 Total Admissions

826 Total Freshman Enrollment

93.30% of applicants admitted

SAT Ranges: CR 500-610, M 490-610, W 500-610

ACT Ranges: C 23-29, M 21-27, E 23-31

TUITION & COSTS

Tuition: $27,520

Fees: $850

Total: $28,370

R&B: $9,400

Room: $4,860

Board: $4,540

Total: $37,770

FINANCIAL

$14,804 avg grant/scholarship amount (need)

$3,715 avg loan amount (need)

SPRING HILL COLLEGE

MOBILE, ALABAMA

Spring Hill College is the first institution of higher learning in Alabama, the 3rd oldest Jesuit college, and 5th oldest Catholic college in the United States. The College's academic character is rooted in the liberal arts and sciences. Faculty and staff are committed to the Jesuit tradition of "cura personalis," a care for the spiritual, social, and intellectual growth of each person. Spring Hill offers a multidimensional education, providing students from all faiths and backgrounds a foundation for a life of continuous learning and service. The core curriculum includes studies in English literature, history, philosophy, theology, foreign language, social science, mathematics, computer science, laboratory science, and fine arts.

THE JESUIT TRADITION: Spring Hill College draws from an impressive heritage of Jesuit, Catholic education. Throughout the world, Jesuits have been inspired in excellence, teaching with a commitment to caring for the whole person—mind, body and spirit. These principles reflect the Jesuit philosophy that reason, justice, and faith are linked inextricably. And, almost five centuries after its origin, this tradition continues with every new class at Spring Hill College.

UNDERGRADUATE RESEARCH: At the culmination of the spring semester, Spring Hill hosts the Undergraduate Research Symposium. This event provides students across all disciplines with the opportunity to present their research, internship, and classroom projects to a larger audience. It also provides a space for students, faculty, and the community to examine the connection between research and education, learning the value of engaged inquiry in the pursuit of groundbreaking discovery. Student attendees who are not yet involved in research especially benefit from the symposium, as they are inspired to brainstorm their future projects and truly grasp the broad range of opportunities available at the Spring Hill College.

STUDY ABROAD: At the Spring Hill College Italy Center in Bologna, students live and study like locals in one of Europe's most vibrant cities. Academic excellence and a commitment to faith are at the core of SHC Italy Center's mission. Students are challenged to travel with purpose, enriching themselves in a globally focused set of classes. Its curriculum is a set of liberal arts and business courses, so students from all disciplines may experience a summer, semester, or year abroad. During their time abroad, students are exposed to complex global issues that impact Italy, Europe, and the world. Social justice travel programs encourage students not only to observe injustices in the world, but also to reflect on and discuss the issues to develop the skills needed to take future action.

THE LEAP PROGRAM: The LEAP Program (which stands for Leadership, Engagement and Awareness, and Personal Growth) connects academic learning with the larger world through course-related events and activities. Freshmen sign up for one three-credit introductory core course and continue to take LEAP courses that are based around a common theme. An accompanying one-hour LEAP lab helps further prepare students for academic success in areas of the Jesuit mission. With this group of fellow freshmen, faculty, and peer mentors, students experience a sense of community as they learn together and engage with the world outside the classroom.

FIRST-GENERATION AID: Established in 2008 to serve first-generation college students at Spring Hill College, the Donnelly Scholar Program provides amazing support to students unfamiliar with higher education. Second-generation college students usually have an advantage over first-generation students in that their parents have knowledge about how to maneuver through the college system. The Donnelly Scholars program, however, aims to close the gap on that advantage so that all graduates may be equipped to become successful alumni.

http://www.shc.edu/
P: (800) 742-6704

PRIVATE - CATHOLIC

STUDENT PROFILE

1,352 undergraduate students

98% of undergrad students are full time

40% male – 60% female

57% of students are from out of state

81% freshman retention rate

53% graduated in 6 years

FACULTY PROFILE

88 full-time faculty

46 part-time faculty

14 to 1 student/faculty ratio

ADMISSIONS

7,393 Total Applicants

3,055 Total Admissions

416 Total Freshman Enrollment

41.32% of applicants admitted

SAT Ranges: CR 495-600, M 490-605

ACT Ranges: C 22-27, M 20-26, E 22-29

TUITION & COSTS

Tuition: $32,032

Fees: $2,060

Total: $34,092

R&B: $12,226

Room: $6,636

Board: $5,590

Total: $46,318

FINANCIAL

$25,509 avg grant/scholarship amount (total)

$9,293 avg loan amount (total)

UNIVERSITY OF ALABAMA IN HUNTSVILLE

HUNTSVILLE, ALABAMA

THE UNIVERSITY OF
ALABAMA IN HUNTSVILLE

UAH is a public university located in Huntsville, Alabama. Its 7,500 students enjoy small class sizes, a low student-to-faculty ratio, and a challenging, engaging curriculum that incorporates theory with practical knowledge. The university's strong academic program is complemented by a vibrant campus life that features more than 130 student-run organizations, 13 fraternities and sororities, and 18 NCAA sports. And, as a tier-one research university, UAH is home to more than a dozen research centers and labs. Its close proximity to major federal and industry employers like NASA, the U.S. Army, and the HudsonAlpha Institute for Biotechnology allows students to engage in hands-on research through internship and co-op opportunities. UAH graduates' real-world experience affords them a competitive edge as they enter the workforce and prepares them for a smooth and successful transition into their chosen career field.

COOPERATIVE EDUCATION PROGRAM: The Cooperative Education Program is a balance between employment and schoolwork. Students enrolled in the program gain hands-on experience that complements the theories and concepts they learn at the academic level. There are two different schedule tracks that students can choose from: in an alternating schedule that switches on and off between work and school, and in parallel scheduling, which allows students to work and attend school, both on a part-time basis. This flexible scheduling makes it possible for students to excel both at work and in the classroom without harming their performance in one area at the expense of the other.

FACULTY-LED STUDY ABROAD: Study abroad is an amazing opportunity for students to learn about another country's culture, society, and even language. While there are options to travel for a semester or full year, UAH understands that some students cannot afford to take time away from their studies. In cases like this, faculty-led programs may be the most appropriate. In these faculty-led excursions, students are given the chance to explore foreign destinations while learning from UAH faculty members. Whether they learn about marketing in China, ancient theatre in Greece, or global health in Ireland, students know that they are receiving a first-rate education under the direction of first-rate UAH professors.

UNDERGRADUATE RESEARCH: There are plenty of experiences that students can have in order to better prepare for postgraduate success. In addition to options like internships and service, undergraduate research stands out as particularly valuable. When students engage in research, they gain skills in problem solving, communication, analysis, and inquiry. UAH recognizes that there are many benefits to research and thus provides its students with several opportunities to get involved. A common misconception is that research only happens in a lab or in the form of a thesis. This is not the case; in fact, research can take many forms like a performance, an exhibit, or a service-learning project. Because research can take so many forms, students across all disciplines are able to participate.

THEMED COMMUNITIES: Themed communities (TC) are residential learning experiences that group students based on shared interests. Participants of themed communities have the awesome opportunity to share their passions with fellow peers. Often, students in theses communities enjoy support from faculty and excel in academic performance. UAH offers 6 different themed communities for first-year students, the interests of which span across disciplines. These TCs include Engineering, Leadership, Honors, Health Professions, Health & Wellness, and General Wellness, which is aimed simply at building camaraderie among peers.

---

http://www.uah.edu/

P: (256) 824-7777

PUBLIC

STUDENT PROFILE

6,013 undergraduate students

79% of undergrad students are full time

57% male – 43% female

80% freshman retention rate

49% graduated in 6 years

FACULTY PROFILE

321 full-time faculty

199 part-time faculty

16 to 1 student/faculty ratio

ADMISSIONS

3,308 Total Applicants

2,686 Total Admissions

1,038 Total Freshman Enrollment

81.20% of applicants admitted

SAT Ranges: CR 520-650, M 550-680

ACT Ranges: C 24-30, M 24-29, E 24-32

TUITION & COSTS

Tuition: (In) $9,128 (Out) $20,622

R&B: $9,205

Room: $6,285

Board: $2,920

Total: (In) $18,333 (Out) $29,827

FINANCIAL

$10,164 avg grant/scholarship amount (total)

$6,079 avg loan amount (total)

UNIVERSITY OF MONTEVALLO

MONTEVALLO, ALABAMA

The University of Montevallo provides a unique higher educational experience in Alabama as the only public liberal arts institution in the state. With a strong emphasis on undergraduate liberal studies, a 17-to-1 student-to-faculty ratio, and professional programs supported by a broad base of arts and sciences, the cumulative experience is designed for student intellectual and personal growth.

UNDERGRADUATE RESEARCH: The mission of the Undergraduate Research program is to provide opportunities for undergraduates to foster their academic knowledge and understanding through collaborative research efforts, scholarly activity, and creative endeavor. The overarching goals of the UR program are to facilitate the undergraduate research experience between students and faculty mentors and to prepare students for graduate or professional schools. The program hosts a Run for Research in the fall and an Undergraduate Research Day in the spring. Students also have opportunities to receive travel grants to present research at both regional and national competitions and conferences, including the Southeastern Regional COPLAC Undergraduate Research Conference.

DIVERSITY/GLOBAL LEARNING: Inspired by the unique history of Montevallo, the University is dedicated to educational, cultural, and social programs designed to combat bias, bigotry, and racism. Montevallo also promotes intercultural dialogue and respect for diversity. The University offers a variety of opportunities including Korean Culture Club, Minority Student Union, and National Association for Multicultural Education, among other opportunities.

COMMON INTELLECTUAL EXPERIENCES: Students have opportunities to partake in team-taught, interdisciplinary classes, including a new Environmental Studies. Team-taught classes explore topics in multiple disciplines and are led by two professors from different fields. These courses address a combination of issues, bringing new discussion and thought angles to special topics.

LEARNING COMMUNITIES: Falcon Scholars in Action is an honors program in which 25 UM students serve clients in agencies and programs throughout Shelby County. Students selected are provided with a significant annual stipend from Shelby County in exchange for their service. Examples of services provided include GED/ACT/SAT preparation, tutoring, coordinating physical activities, and providing training in job skills, computer skills, and social skills.

CAPSTONE COURSES AND PROJECTS/SENIOR EXPERIENCE: Students at the University of Montevallo may complete a capstone course in various degree programs or through undergraduate research. Students wishing to complete their own major may apply for the Interdisciplinary Studies (IDS) Major, a self-designed course of study with faculty advisors that permits students to combine features of more than one discipline. A capstone experience is required for IDS majors.

CAREER DEVELOPMENT CENTER: The UM Career Development Center offers a variety of resources to help students prepare for their future careers and professional development. The center's services are available to all currently enrolled degree seeking students, faculty, staff, and alumni. These services range from offering help in choosing a major, finding job opportunities, applying to grad school, and offering professional development.

INTERNSHIPS/COOPS/PRACTICUMS: UM offers a variety of opportunities for students to practice in a professional setting the skills and knowledge they acquire in the classroom. In some majors, applied experiences are central to the curriculum. This is the case for clinical assignments in social work and communication science disorders and for practice teaching in education. In other majors, such as art, business, and communication studies, students may enroll in an internship for elective credit. Interns may be placed at agencies in the local community or engage in applied work outside the state through programs such as the Washington Center, a government internship in Washington, D. C.

UNIVERSITY *of* MONTEVALLO

http://www.montevallo.edu/
P: (205) 665-6000

PUBLIC

STUDENT PROFILE

2,564 undergraduate students

90% of undergrad students are full time

33% male – 67% female

77% freshman retention rate

45% graduated in 6 years

FACULTY PROFILE

151 full-time faculty

78 part-time faculty

16 to 1 student/faculty ratio

ADMISSIONS

2,024 Total Applicants

1,417 Total Admissions

505 Total Freshman Enrollment

70.01% of applicants admitted

SAT Ranges: CR 455-595, M 475-580, W 470-585

ACT Ranges: C 20-26, M 18-24, E 21-28

TUITION & COSTS

Tuition: (In) $10,740 (Out) $22,110

Fees: $670

Total: (In) $11,410 (Out) $22,780

R&B: $8,182

Room: $5,582

Board: $2,600

Total: (In) $19,592 (Out) $30,962

FINANCIAL

$8,363 avg grant/scholarship amount (total)

$6,238 avg loan amount (total)

HARDING UNIVERSITY

SEARCY, ARKANSAS

Harding University is a private, Christian, liberal arts university located in Searcy, Arkansas. Committed to the pursuit of academic excellence and the establishment of strong spiritual foundations, the University attracts students who represent all 50 states and 54 nations and territories.

FIRST-YEAR EXPERIENCE: Making key connections in the first year of college is critical to student success, so Harding's First-Year Experience engages new students during the summer and first-week orientations. The required summer orientation program, Summer Stampede, is offered in June, July, and August for students to connect with one another and begin their academic advising and scheduling. Student Impact, the orientation prior to the first week of school, is planned and conducted by upperclassmen to encourage new friendships through move-in assistance, service activities, question-and-answer sessions, and themed dinners.

DAILY CHAPEL: For 30 minutes every weekday, the entire student body assembles for chapel—a time-honored tradition of worship, community-building, and affirmation of Harding's identity as a Christian university. Led by the University president, this shared experience facilitates and strengthens the relationships within the Harding community. Times of joy, sadness, stress, and success are all felt and supported by the University's collective community.

COLLABORATIVE PROJECTS: Teamwork and interdisciplinary studies are essential tools for students' leadership and success. Throughout its various colleges and departments, Harding offers multiple opportunities for students of differing majors to engage in collaborative projects. "A Night at the Round Tables" simulates real-world collaboration for healthcare professionals by bringing together six academic departments and students for a case study. A branding exhibition groups together marketing, interior design, and graphic design students for an annual project. A seminar class in New York City and Washington D.C. offers experiential learning for mass communications, English, business, and theatre students. These projects—and many others—help connect students of various disciplines in order to achieve a well-rounded academic experience.

UNDERGRADUATE RESEARCH: Because Harding is a teaching institution, professors frequently pursue research efforts that are specifically designed to engage their students. In the College of Sciences, students can conduct a variety of annual research projects with scholarship funding from NASA. Whether they control a robotic arm using an Android phone, develop 3-D hybrid rocket fuel grains, or build robotic devices to maintain healthy plants during space missions, these students are putting their knowledge to work.

WRITING-INTENSIVE COURSES: Skills in reading, writing, speaking, and critical thinking are universally regarded as characteristics of well-educated individuals and fundamental to every academic endeavor. For this reason, the University requires classes that emphasize writing and speech in its liberal arts requirements. All students take Introduction to University Writing and Research, Critical Reading, Thinking and Writing, and Communication Principles. Writing is integrated into many courses across the University, the intensity of which vary across fields of study.

WALDRON CENTER FOR ENTREPRENEURSHIP AND FAMILY BUSINESS: The Waldron Center for Entrepreneurship and Family Business focuses on entrepreneurial academics and competitions as well as business development. The Center complements the University's entrepreneurship classes by empowering innovators and facilitating student participation in such competitions as the Donald W. Reynolds Governor's Cup (DWRGC). Three teams comprised of business and engineering majors participated in the 2017 DWRGC, all advancing to the semi-finals. One team, after creating a biometric vest, participated in the competition's final presentations and won the Innovation Award as well as a $5,000 cash prize.

---

https://www.harding.edu/

P: (501) 279-4000

PRIVATE - CHRISTIAN

STUDENT PROFILE

4,411 undergraduate students

94% of undergrad students are full time

44% male – 56% female

71% of students are from out of state

82% freshman retention rate

65% graduated in 6 years

FACULTY PROFILE

332 full-time faculty

157 part-time faculty

15 to 1 student/faculty ratio

ADMISSIONS

2,184 Total Applicants

1,663 Total Admissions

1,021 Total Freshman Enrollment

76.14% of applicants admitted

SAT Ranges: CR 500-610, M 480-610

ACT Ranges: C 22-28, M 20-27, E 22-30

TUITION & COSTS

Tuition: $17,940

Fees: $695

Total: $18,635

R&B: $6,756

Total: $25,391

FINANCIAL

$7,147 avg grant/scholarship amount (need)

$8,010 avg loan amount (need)

HENDRIX COLLEGE

CONWAY, ARKANSAS

At Hendrix, students work closely with faculty who are devoted to mentoring undergraduate students. Through the "Your Hendrix Odyssey Program," a rare combination of opportunities, resources, and research of a bigger university, is achieved while maintaining the intimate mentoring of a smaller school. Students are encouraged to pursue their passions and interest both in the classroom and beyond.

YOU LEARN MORE WHEN YOU DO MORE: "You learn more when you do more" is the educational philosophy behind The Hendrix Odyssey, an exciting component to the core curriculum. With six categories and plenty of flexibility, the Odyssey Program encourages all Hendrix students to embark on educational adventures that are personalized to their own interests and abilities. Odysseys come in all shapes and sizes—some students earn Odyssey credits through coursework or through involvement in selected campus activities and organizations. Other students venture farther afield, engaging in Odysseys that take them off campus and around the world.

THE ENGAGED CITIZEN: From the very start, students are surrounded by faculty and staff who want them to succeed. They are held to high standards, working for and with professors who become their most honest critics, biggest fans, and closest allies. The incredible Hendrix experience begins with "The Engaged Citizen" course. This class is taught as a first-year, team-taught interdisciplinary seminar that introduces freshmen to the very heart of a liberal arts education as well as what it means to be an engaged citizen. Examples of the intriguing topics within The Engaged Citizen's repertoire include "Art and Spirit" and "Aliens, Robots, and Civilization."

CONWAY, ARKANSAS: Located in the city of Conway, Hendrix students enjoy the thriving city that is home to Axiom, The Arkansas Shakespeare Theater, EcoFest, and much more. The campus includes the Hendrix Creek Preserve, which is both an environmental boon to the community and a great outdoor learning laboratory for Hendrix Students. Little Rock is just a half hour drive away from the campus, putting students in close contact with a major center of government at which one can find the Clinton Presidential Center, Heifer International, and much more. Students enjoy the annual festivals, entertainment venues, and events of Little Rock as well as the River Market District. And, for those who love the outdoors, Hendrix College is situated in a location that allows students to explore national parks, forests, lakes, rivers, caverns, and much more. Students can rent camping and canoeing equipment from campus's Wellness and Athletic center to get the most out of the natural state.

TRANSCRIPT OF EXCELLENCE: Hendrix graduates are experienced and armed with a strong degree and an impressive Odyssey transcript of experience and exploration. They have a major advantage while competing for career opportunities and graduate and professional school placements; they did not just spend four years in a classroom, but rather took their education to the next level. The liberal arts experience at Hendrix gives a student a plethora of skills outside of their major—the ability to be an articulate speaker, a clear writer, a critical thinker, and an ethical, companionate person. Hendrix graduates who immediately enter the job market report obtaining employment within six months of graduation. Career Services on campus provides career planning, résumé and cover letter assistance, on campus recruiting, a week-long CareerFest, and much more.

HENDRIX COLLEGE

http://www.hendrix.edu/
P: (501) 329-6811

PRIVATE

STUDENT PROFILE

1,327 undergraduate students

99% of undergrad students are full time

47% male – 53% female

79% freshman retention rate

68% graduated in 6 years

FACULTY PROFILE

118 full-time faculty

11 to 1 student/faculty ratio

ADMISSIONS

1,714 Total Applicants

1,412 Total Admissions

395 Total Freshman Enrollment

82.38% of applicants admitted

SAT Ranges: CR 540-680, M 580-660

ACT Ranges: C 25-32, M 29-33, E 25-34

TUITION & COSTS

Tuition: $40,520

Fees: $350

Total: $40,870

R&B: $11,244

Room: $5,790

Board: $5,454

Total: $52,114

FINANCIAL

$29,208 avg grant/scholarship amount (total)

$7,515 avg loan amount (total)

JOHN BROWN UNIVERSITY

SILOAM SPRINGS, ARKANSAS

John Brown University is committed to providing quality academics within a distinctly Christian community. It is a vibrant and growing university of the arts, sciences, and professions.

STUDY ABROAD: Study abroad is an encouraged means of satisfying the Global Studies requirement of the Core Curriculum. JBU values study abroad semesters and summers as life-changing experiences through which students can study in over twenty countries, including Ireland, Italy, Jordan, Scotland, England, China, Guatemala, Australia, New Zealand, Switzerland, South Korea, and Uganda. Wherever one goes—a JBU classroom, the Louvre in Paris, or the Bodleian Library in Oxford, England—JBU seeks to give each student every opportunity to grow and change through their academic pursuits. JBU even signed a memorandum of understanding with South Korea's Handong Global University that opened a study abroad program, research collaboration, and faculty and staff exchanges. The University provides opportunities that make its education the most pervasive and constructive it can be.

GATEWAY SEMINAR IN CHRISTIAN SCHOLARSHIP: All freshmen enroll in a gateway course that is designed to introduce students to the purpose and method of Christian higher education along with the distinctive mission of John Brown University. Through the exploration of a particular topic (which include poverty, The Chronicles of Narnia, the Holocaust, film, and more), students participate in the communal intellectual life and the application of a Christian worldview.

THE LEADER SCHOLARS INSTITUTE (LSI): As freshmen, students may apply to the selective LSI Program, a co-curricular, 4-year leadership program designed to challenge and develop students through experiential learning both in and out of the classroom. By helping individuals identify and develop their strengths, the program equips and enables students to be practical leaders.

HONORS SCHOLARS PROGRAM: As freshmen, students may apply to the Honors Scholars Program, a four-year program that combines curricular and co-curricular programs, to extend and enrich academic experiences. Classes are small and interactive and led by excellent faculty. Students also have the opportunity to co-teach with a professor, conduct research, take educational trips, study abroad, and present their research at regional and national conferences. This program is designed to attract academically motivated students, challenge Christian scholars for God's kingdom, and enrich the broader University community.

SERVE SILOAM: Soon after settling in, JBU freshmen take part in an event called Serve Siloam. Students volunteer throughout the Siloam Springs community serving individuals, local businesses and nonprofit organizations, and community centers. Through this service, students are introduced to the community and develop an internal, empathetics sense sense of obligation to care for it.

THE PARADOSIS CENTER: JBU hosts an independent research center called the Paradosis Center, named after the Greek word for "tradition." Its mission is to foster theological exchanges among Christians from Catholic, Orthodox, and evangelical backgrounds that encourage people to learn from one another and more fully understand the tradition passed down from the beginning. The Center sponsors conferences, lecture series, research projects, student activities, and publications that nourish the ability of these communities to understand, appreciate, challenge, and benefit from each other.

THE SODERQUIST CENTER FOR LEADERSHIP AND ETHICS: Soderquist Leadership is a not-for-profit organization founded in 1998 by Don Soderquist, former COO and Senior Vice-Chairman of Wal-Mart Stores, Inc. With facilities on JBU's campus, as well as through customizable training programs, individuals, teams, and organizations receive values-focused training and development that equips them to win in the marketplace. The Center also offers Soderquist Fellowships to top applicants of John Brown University's Master of Business Administration, Master of Science in Leadership and Ethics and Master of Fine Arts programs. Fellows work on a full-time basis for the Center, receive full tuition and a two-year stipend, and work alongside veteran business leaders.

http://www.jbu.edu/
P: (479) 524-9500

PRIVATE - CHRISTIAN

STUDENT PROFILE

2,126 undergraduate students

72% of undergrad students are full time

43% male – 57% female

52% of students are from out of state

81% freshman retention rate

62% graduated in 6 years

FACULTY PROFILE

119 full-time faculty

4 part-time faculty

15 to 1 student/faculty ratio

ADMISSIONS

1,166 Total Applicants

860 Total Admissions

358 Total Freshman Enrollment

73.76% of applicants admitted

SAT Ranges: CR 520-660, M 510-625, W 480-650

ACT Ranges: C 24-30, M 22-28, E 24-32, W 6-8

TUITION & COSTS

Tuition: $23,398

Fees: $1,070

Total: $24,468

R&B: $8,664

Total: $33,132

FINANCIAL

$15,763 avg grant/scholarship amount (total)

$6,785 avg loan amount (total)

BARRY UNIVERSITY

MIAMI, FLORIDA

Founded in 1940, Barry University's nine colleges and schools offers more than 100 bachelor's, master's, and doctoral degree programs. Barry University values diversity, proudly educating approximately 8,000 students from nearly all 50 states and 80 countries; 52,000 alumni worldwide; and 1,700 faculty and staff members. Barry students gain hands-on experience—both locally and internationally—as they prepare to advance their careers. The University's use of service-learning, which integrates coursework with community needs, engages students with real-world issues and encourages them to help find solutions.

A TRANSFORMATIVE EXPERIENCE THAT LEADS TO INNOVATIVE ANSWERS: Barry's service-learning programs integrate coursework with community needs, facilitating engagement at the local, national, and global levels. Barry University students collaborate with community partners to pursue systematic, self-sustaining solutions to human, social, economic, and environmental problems. This is accomplished through community service, service-learning, community-based research, internships, practicum and field placements, and advocacy projects.

PROFESSORS WHO RECOGNIZE EVERY STUDENT'S POTENTIAL: A quality education starts with faculty who possess the ability to inspire. Barry's faculty are committed to furthering the institution's mission to promote education, equality, social justice, and diversity. They are as passionate about teaching as they are their disciplines and it is with a 14:1 student-faculty ratio that faculty may interact with and mentor students on a personal level. Approximately 80 percent of Barry faculty holds a Ph.D. or terminal degree in their field. Many have also received grants and fellowships that allow them to conduct vital research, often with students working alongside them.

CENTER FOR COMMUNITY SERVICE INITIATIVES: Barry University's Center for Community Service Initiatives is the University's clearinghouse for community engagement. It functions as a catalyst for the pursuit of social justice among students, faculty, and staff. Past community service projects include farm-workers' rights advocacy, human trafficking awareness initiatives, business development in low-income areas, and photography projects for at-risk teens.

PERSONAL GROWTH IN ALL ASPECTS OF LEARNING: Barry University students enjoy a vibrant campus life in which they can organize and participate in a wide variety of academic, athletic, and social experiences. College life is not just about the classroom; at Barry, students enjoy a full range of extracurricular activities including intramural sports, student government, and more than 60 clubs and organizations. The diversity of the on-campus organizations and clubs gives Barry students the chance to incorporate their extracurricular learning to their overall educational experience. Right at the start of their first day on campus, for instance, students will find plenty to do. From its "GLO party" and "Founders' Week" in the fall to Homecoming and the "Festival of Nations" in the spring, tradition thrives at Barry. Students, faculty, staff, and alumni gather throughout the year to connect Barry's past with its present, all to create a meaningful future.

THE NEXT GENERATION OF CHANGE-AGENTS: Faithful to its traditions, the Barry University experience fosters individual and communal transformation. In this way, student learning leads to knowledge and truth, reflection leads to informed action, and a commitment to social justice leads to collaborative service. Barry graduates apply their learning and service to their constantly changing and diverse world, promoting civic engagement for the betterment of humanity. Barry graduates don't just take jobs or start careers; they become leaders and agents of change.

https://www.barry.edu/
P: (305) 899-6000

PRIVATE - CATHOLIC

STUDENT PROFILE

3,776 undergraduate students

84% of undergrad students are full time

35% male — 65% female

14% of students are from out of state

65% freshman retention rate

34% graduated in 6 years

FACULTY PROFILE

362 full-time faculty

439 part-time faculty

12 to 1 student/faculty ratio

ADMISSIONS

7,587 Total Applicants

3,498 Total Admissions

460 Total Freshman Enrollment

46.11% of applicants admitted

SAT Ranges: CR 430-510, M 410-513, W 420-500

ACT Ranges: C 18-22, M 16-21, E 16-22

TUITION & COSTS

Tuition: $43,770

R&B: $13,190

Total: $56,960

FINANCIAL

$19,316 avg grant/scholarship amount (total)

$7,492 avg loan amount (total)

FLAGLER COLLEGE

ST. AUGUSTINE, FLORIDA

Located within the beautiful, historic city of St. Augustine, Flagler College exudes all the charm and wonder that has attracted generations of explorers and entrepreneurs to the Florida coast. Its forward-thinking curriculum is inspired by Henry M. Flagler himself, a remarkable innovator known for the many hotels he built to make the Florida coast the vacation destination it is today.

FIRST-YEAR EXPERIENCE: Flagler College's first-year experience places students in relationship-building learning communities that introduce them to other first-year, transfer, and international students. New students meet their peers and settle into Flagler through the Building Your Legacy Orientation session, establishing a comfortable foundation before beginning their coursework. Flagler freshmen also enroll in a Freshman Seminar course that introduces them to liberal education and citizenship. The Seminar introduces a broad, big-picture perspective of topics that promote both worldly knowledge and ethical citizenship. This seminar serves as a bookend to the Capstone experience, which students take in their last semester as seniors.

UNDERGRADUATE RESEARCH: Priding itself in its liberal arts tradition, Flagler provides the platform to students to conduct research in any of their fields of interest. Flagler professors join research cohorts to help their students develop striking, innovative research projects that both enrich the college experience as well as contribute to the body of academic literature. Research at Flagler has been recognized both nationally and around the world, and with the help of Flagler's Internal Funding Awards, students are able to travel to conferences and access materials without needing to worry about expenses.

STUDY ABROAD: Flagler College instills in its students global leadership, and through a vast range of off-campus program options, students have opportunities to immerse themselves in the many cultures that lie far beyond the College's walls. Studying abroad pushes students to have a deeper understanding of the world as they merge firsthand cultural experiences in with their academic work. Students can study abroad independently, through an exchange with one of the College's partner universities, or through a Flagler faculty-led program. To date, there are seven approved faculty-led programs: Russia, Cuba, Vietnam, Italy, Spain, Germany, and New York City (a "study away" program). These programs offer courses with credits that transfer and fulfill degree requirements.

PASSPORT CO-CURRICULAR PROGRAM: As an incentive to encourage students to cultivate their curiosities outside of the classroom, the Passport Co-Curricular Program requires students to attend a variety of events that exhibit all the great perspectives of a liberal arts education. Typical Passport-credited events include concerts, plays, and debates, all of which support and deepen students' academics across all disciplines.

LEARNING COMMUNITIES: Learning Communities, intrinsic to the First-Year Experience at Flagler, are groups of courses that exemplify the value of a well-rounded, interdisciplinary education. Students choose and take courses that provide different academic perspectives, often taught by professors in different disciplines, around one central topic of interest. The courses fulfill general education requirements and teach students to observe cultural themes and issues with a combination of scientific, artistic, sociological, and political lenses.

INTERNSHIPS: Internships are offered with the help of Career Development Center. Every Flagler student has all the resources they need to find the experience that is best suited for their career paths. Many internships qualify for academic credit, fulfilling both students' present and future needs with the same life-changing opportunity.

CAREER SERVICES: Flagler's Career Development Center provides students with the necessary resources to pursue graduate school educations and fulfilling careers through an offering of services for every step of the job application process.

---

http://www.flagler.edu/
P: (800) 304-4208

PRIVATE

STUDENT PROFILE

2,701 undergraduate students

96% of undergrad students are full time

39% male – 61% female

44% of students are from out of state

72% freshman retention rate

61% graduated in 6 years

FACULTY PROFILE

112 full-time faculty

126 part-time faculty

16 to 1 student/faculty ratio

ADMISSIONS

5,260 Total Applicants

2,655 Total Admissions

620 Total Freshman Enrollment

50.48% of applicants admitted

SAT Ranges: CR 490-588, M 470-560, W 480-570

ACT Ranges: C 21-26, M 20-25, E 21-27

TUITION & COSTS

Tuition: $16,830

R&B: $9,630

Room: $4,720

Board: $4,910

Total: $26,460

FINANCIAL

$7,428 avg grant/scholarship amount (total)

$7,596 avg loan amount (total)

FLORIDA SOUTHERN COLLEGE

LAKELAND, FLORIDA

Florida Southern College is a rapidly rising star among the nation's best private colleges. Located along Central Florida's high-tech corridor, the College enrolls undergraduate students from 43 states and 39 countries on its scenic, 113-acre campus.

STUDENTS WHO EXCEL: Students conduct real-world research alongside their professors in all disciplines; take master classes and perform on stage with internationally recognized musicians; and showcase their artistic talents in art galleries. Those seeking an added dimension to their studies enroll in the popular and prestigious Honors Program, which includes field studies in a variety of artistic, business, and scientific enterprises.

INDIVIDUAL ATTENTION: Florida Southern's dynamic professors are not only noted experts in their fields, they are also dedicated—first and foremost—to their students' success. FSC's student-to-faculty ratio is 13:1, and there are no teaching assistants. Students find that the small classes enable them to get to know their professors well and allow time for personal attention. Professors are dynamic and creative, and they constantly introduce innovative concepts both in and out of the classroom. With fewer students in each class, it is that much easier to access the tools, technology, and resources that foster learning.

JUNIOR JOURNEY PROGRAM: Through an innovative Junior Journey program, all incoming first-year students are guaranteed an international travel experience in their junior or senior year, which is included in their tuition. Florida Southern students pursue their interests around the world in such exciting locations as Australia, China, Costa Rica, Ireland, Italy, New Zealand, Spain, and the United Kingdom.

SERVICE TO THE COMMUNITY: FSC students have a passion for public service, building leadership skills while logging 30,000 hours annually in support of such organizations as Big Brothers/Big Sisters, Habitat for Humanity, and the Salvation Army, to name a few. FSC has been named to the President's Community Service Honor Roll for the past five years.

ADVISORS AND ACADEMIC RESOURCES: All first-year students adjust quickly to academic life through a unique program that pairs each student with a faculty advisor for regular meetings during the first semester. Better yet, Florida Southern is one of the few colleges in the country to have a dedicated Dean of Student Success who helps students make the most of the College's many academic resources.

GET IN THE WATER!: With sunshine 330 days per year and beautiful Lake Hollingsworth just steps away, water sports are extremely popular at FSC. Students enjoy water skiing, kayaking, and sailing, and the College sponsors getaways to nearby beaches, canoe trips on local rivers, and hiking and horseback riding trips. With such great resources, Florida Southern makes it easy to live a healthy lifestyle. The Nina B. Hollis Wellness Center also offers fitness classes from aerobics to yoga, and the 8-lane competition pool is great for laps, water polo, and parties.

INTERNSHIPS: Every FSC student is guaranteed an internship thanks to the College's location in the heart of Central Florida's high-tech corridor as well as to FSC's established partnerships with nationally and internationally recognized corporations. AAA, Chevrolet, Coca-Cola, Disney, ESPN, Fox News, GEICO, Lakeland Regional Medical Center, Merrill Lynch, NASA, National Institutes of Health, Publix Super Markets, and SeaWorld all rave about FSC students' impressive educational preparation during their internships.

READY FOR SUCCESS: Because FSC students have leadership experience, complete meaningful internships, study abroad, and participate in real-world research and professional performances, they are ready to experience career success right away. In fact, most recent graduates report landing great jobs in their fields or enrolling in prestigious professional and graduate schools.

---

http://www.flsouthern.edu/

P: (800) 274-4131

PRIVATE

STUDENT PROFILE

2,559 undergraduate students

89% of undergrad students are full time

36% male — 64% female

39% of students are from out of state

80% freshman retention rate

57% graduated in 6 years

FACULTY PROFILE

149 full-time faculty

13 to 1 student/faculty ratio

ADMISSIONS

6,190 Total Applicants

2,806 Total Admissions

698 Total Freshman Enrollment

45.33% of applicants admitted

SAT Ranges: CR 520-620, M 530-610, W 500-600

ACT Ranges: C 24-29, M 23-30, E 22-27

TUITION & COSTS

Tuition: $30,810

Fees: $650

Total: $31,460

R&B: $10,210

Room: $6,030

Board: $4,180

Total: $41,670

FINANCIAL

$18,221 avg grant/scholarship amount (total)

$6,188 avg loan amount (total)

LYNN UNIVERSITY

BOCA RATON, FLORIDA

An independent institution, Lynn is known for its innovative learning programs and diverse student body, educating students from over 100 countries. Lynn embraces new ideas and technologies that empower its faculty to deliver its nationally praised core curriculum in creative ways.

ACCELERATED BACHELOR'S DEGREE: Lynn's accelerated bachelor's degree is an incredibly unique program that offers students the chance to complete a 4-year degree in just 3 years. Students who participate work closely with academic advisors to create a degree program that is unique to their individual needs. There are countless benefits to participation in this program: students in the accelerated bachelor's degree can take extra courses at no cost and enjoy the advantage of an early graduation, decreased tuition, the opportunity to design their own path of study, and the ability to jumpstart their careers to get ahead in the workplace.

JANUARY (J)-TERM: The January Term is a unique learning experience in which students can apply academic theories to projects, social initiatives, and internships. The goal of a J-Term is to allow students to explore their disciplines more deeply through real-life application. Each January Term, students are expected to complete one course that explores specialized and application-based subjects.

STUDY ABROAD: Lynn's study abroad programs allow students to visit more than 30 cities around the world at no additional cost to their normal tuition. And, unlike other schools, Lynn students don't have to wait until their sophomore year to study; they can go abroad as early as their second semester. Trips range from three weeks to a year in length, and new cities are continually added to the possible repertoire. The Center for Learning Abroad is a great resource for students interested in finding a program. It helps students coordinate the logistics of going abroad, all while making sure the program is contributing to the completion of their degree.

CLOSE-KNIT CLASSROOMS: The average class size at Lynn is 20 students, lending a hand to a learning style that is both individualized and unique. With small class sizes, students have the opportunity to thrive in an environment in which their individual skills are valued and respected. Faculty don't lead large lectures in front of a sea of students whom they treat as mere numbers. Instead, they are actively engaging small groups of students to push their academic potentials and find educational success.

iPAD®-POWERED LEARNING: Lynn is known around the nation for its iPad®-powered learning initiative, which provides undergraduate day students with their own iPad Pro, Smart Keyboard, and Apple Pencil to keep and use in their classes. Lynn is also known for its innovative coursework that applies traditional subjects like science and math to everyday situations, building students' theoretical understanding and applying it to practical approaches.

THE INSTITUTE OF ACHIEVEMENT AND LEARNING: Since 1991, Lynn's Institute of Achievement and Learning has helped students achieve academic success, teaching them how to capitalize on their individual strengths. Whether students need help with planning, organization, studying, writing, or testing, the IAL has certified coaches and tutors readily available for assistance. Undergraduates can opt for full-program participation or choose a la carte services as needed.

INTERNSHIPS AND WORK EXPERIENCE: Most Lynn students take internships as part of their graduation requirements. South Florida is a center of commerce, culture, finance, international trade, and start-ups, which means that students have numerous opportunities to put their studies to practical use.

---

http://www.lynn.edu/

P: (800) 888-5966

PRIVATE

STUDENT PROFILE

2,053 undergraduate students

95% of undergrad students are full-time

50% male — 50% female

58% of students are from out of state

68% freshman retention rate

45% graduated in 6 years

FACULTY PROFILE

106 full-time faculty

70 part-time faculty

20 to 1 student-to-faculty ratio

ADMISSIONS

3,514 Total Applicants

2,872 Total Admissions

566 Total Freshman Enrollment

81.73% of applicants admitted

SAT Ranges: CR 440-530, M 430-530

ACT Ranges: C 19-24, M 17-22.5, E 18-24

TUITION & COSTS

Tuition: $35,260

Fees: $2,250

Total: $37,510

R&B: $11,970

Total: $49,480

FINANCIAL

$9,991 avg grant/scholarship amount (need)

$4,572 avg loan amount (need)

NEW COLLEGE OF FLORIDA

SARASOTA, FLORIDA

Founded in 1960 as a private college for academically talented students, New College became a public college in 1975 through a merger with the State of Florida System, thereby resulting in its affiliation with the University of South Florida. Today, as the state's independent honors college, New College of Florida retains its distinctive academic programming and all the high standards that make it a college of choice for students who can manage the freedom and responsibility of designing their own education.

GREAT STUDENT-FACULTY RELATIONSHIPS: With its low student-to-faculty ratio of 10:1, its unique series of seven academic contracts, and its independent study requirements, New College ensures that students and faculty work together toward a real mastery of specific subjects. Faculty get to know students well as they assist them in achieving their learning goals from course to course and project to project, and they often tailor class assignments to individual interests and abilities. Instead of letter grades, faculty give narrative evaluations for each student. All NCF faculty are full-time, and 99 percent hold the Ph.D. or terminal degree in their fields. They are happy to give their students one-on-one tutorials that are otherwise only found at the graduate level. Filled with passion, these professors define the personalized educational experience of NCF.

MODERN FACILITIES: Modern facilities support many individual research options, including the R.V. Heiser Natural Sciences Complex, which features an on-site Raman spectroscopy lab; the Pritzker Marine Biological Research Center, which includes more than ninety saltwater and freshwater research aquariums; a two-thousand-volume library dedicated to Mesoamerican archaeology that includes an oral history archive; and the Caples Fine Arts Complex, which houses a performing arts center, practice rooms for musicians, sculpture and painting studios, and a welding shop and kiln for ceramics.

SOCIAL TOLERANCE: NCF students say that freedom and tolerance define the social tone of the college. Respect for sexual orientation, political affiliation, freedom of speech, ethnic heritage, and cultural associations are paramount. The idiosyncratic garb of individual students expresses these attitudes, and New College is proud to see the thriving friendships that form across typical social lines.

COMMUNITY INVOLVEMENT: Off campus, NCF students volunteer or intern at more than one hundred community organizations, including tutoring at public schools, participating in Habitat for Humanity projects, and working other programs sponsored by the United Way and the Boys & Girls Clubs of America. Fifty-five NCF students have received the Sarasota Environmental Award, honoring their involvement in community activities.

RESIDENTIAL LIFE: NCF students are actively involved in campus life and the local community as a whole. On average, over 75 percent of all students live on campus in a variety of housing options, including five residence halls that opened in fall 2007 and a historic residence hall complex designed by and named for renowned architect I. M. Pei. Residential life at NCF underscores the symbiotic relationship between academics and social life on campus, and it is typical on weekends for many of the students to gather either formally or informally for student "walls," or parties, during which discussions of Hegel intertwine seamlessly with dancing and socializing.

SARASOTA, FLORIDA: Sarasota, located fifty-five miles south of Tampa on Florida's west coast, is known as the Circus City, offering a vibrant cultural life in addition to its world-renowned natural beauty and wildlife. Sarasota is home to the John and Mable Ringling Museum of Art, which sits adjacent to the New College campus. NCF's College Hall was the former home of circus magnates Charles and Edith Ringling. The Marie Selby Botanical Gardens and the famous Lido and Siesta Key beaches on the Gulf of Mexico are also nearby.

http://www.ncf.edu/
P: (941) 487-5000

PUBLIC

STUDENT PROFILE

861 undergraduate students

100% of undergrad students are full time

39% male – 61% female

17% of students are from out of state

81% freshman retention rate

71% graduated in 6 years

FACULTY PROFILE

87 full-time faculty

20 part-time faculty

10 to 1 student/faculty ratio

ADMISSIONS

1,655 Total Applicants

1,009 Total Admissions

261 Total Freshman Enrollment

60.97% of applicants admitted

SAT Ranges: CR 610-720, M 560-660, W 570-670

ACT Ranges: C 27-31, M 24-28, E 27-33, W 8-9

TUITION & COSTS

Tuition: (In) $5,227 (Out) $27,159

Fees: (In) $1,689 (Out) $2,785

Total: (In) $6,916 (Out) $29,944

R&B: $8,932

Room: $6,348

Board: $2,584

Total: (In) $15,848 (Out) $38,876

FINANCIAL

$9,976 avg grant/scholarship amount (total)

$5,255 avg loan amount (total)

ROLLINS COLLEGE

WINTER PARK, FLORIDA

Rollins is one of the nation's best institutions of higher education. Its top-ranked undergraduate and graduate degree programs feature small classes that are taught by renowned faculty. The academic experience is further enhanced by study abroad and internship opportunities as well as ways to participate in student organizations and the local community. Bordering Lake Virginia, Rollins is a lush, 70-acre campus located in Winter Park in the heart of Central Florida.

STUDY ABROAD: More than 60 percent of Rollins students study abroad before they graduate, and many choose to repeat their experiences to explore more and more new lands in which to learn. Ranked among the top 10 master's degree-granting institutions in the country for the number of students who study abroad, Rollins is committed to providing the community with a broad international perspective. Students can choose from off-campus field studies and Rollins-approved study abroad programs offered in such places as Australia, China, Costa Rica, Greece, Morocco, Nepal, Peru, Spain, Turkey, and the United Kingdom.

A SCHOOL OF SERVICE: Rollins has consistently won awards that recognize its commitment to community service and engagement. For six consecutive years, Rollins has been named to the President's Higher Education Community Service Honor Roll, the highest federal recognition a college or university can receive for its commitment to community service. Rollins provides students opportunities to bring their academic curriculum to life through service projects that benefit local community members and beyond. These real-world engagement experiences include community engagement-designated courses, alternative spring breaks, immersion programs, and nonprofit internships.

ACHIEVED SCHOLARS: Rollins boasts an economically, ethnically, and geographically diverse learning community with a student body that represents 43 states and 50 countries across the world. The College also has a long history of producing students who are awarded a wide variety of prestigious scholarships. In 2013, Rollins was named a top producer of Fulbright scholars, with eight students awarded Fulbright scholarships and two faculty members awarded Fulbright grants in the 2013/2014 academic year. Since receiving its first Fulbright award in 1951, Rollins has produced a total of 49 Fulbright scholars, 24 of whom have been awarded since 2006.

SUSTAINABILITY: Rollins has been a leader in environmental education and sustainable business practices for more than 20 years. Sustainability-focused academics, initiatives, and student-led programs have become ingrained in nearly every facet of life at Rollins. Rollins' dedication to environmental stewardship and social responsibility has been recognized as one of the most environmentally responsible colleges in the U.S. and Canada.

INTERNSHIPS: Internships play an important role in a student's education at Rollins. The College's location near Orlando provides access to a bustling metropolitan area and international airport, resulting in exceptional opportunities for undergrad and graduate internship positions with a variety of companies and organizations.

BEAUTIFUL CAMPUS IN A BEAUTIFUL CITY: The Rollins College campus is awe-inspiring. The tree-lined, 70-acre lakefront campus is located two blocks from historic downtown Winter Park and just minutes from downtown Orlando and Central Florida. The cities allow students to enjoy Florida's natural beauty and take courses in buildings that are known for their magnificent Spanish-Mediterranean style.

http://www.rollins.edu/
P: (407) 646-2161

PRIVATE

STUDENT PROFILE

2,687 undergraduate students

92% of undergrad students are full time

41% male – 59% female

44% of students are from out of state

89% freshman retention rate

71% graduated in 6 years

FACULTY PROFILE

232 full-time faculty

10 to 1 student/faculty ratio

ADMISSIONS

4,922 Total Applicants

2,972 Total Admissions

493 Total Freshman Enrollment

60.38% of applicants admitted

TUITION & COSTS

Tuition: $44,760

R&B: $13,910

Room: $8,230

Board: $5,680

Total: $58,670

FINANCIAL

$27,137 avg grant/scholarship amount (total)

$8,588 avg loan amount (total)

UNIVERSITY OF MIAMI

CORAL GABLES, FLORIDA

University of Miami grooms its students to become strong individuals with excellent leadership skills. Students are taught to recognize their duty to both the local community as well as the global society. UMis known for its major research initiatives. The University is involved in nearly $330 million in research a year—a vast majority of which is put to good use at the Miller School of Medicine.

UNDERGRADUATE RESEARCH: The College of Arts and Sciences is the #1 authority on undergraduate research at UM. Research is an amazing opportunity for students to demonstrate both their knowledge and curiosity within a specific area of study. Research can vary from collaborating with a professor to creating original work abroad. There are multiple opportunities for UM students to get their projects funded, including the Lois Pope Neuroscience Summer Scholarship, which sends students on intensive efforts for advanced research. The "Beyond the Book" Scholarships for Research-Based Learning also gives students the chance to explore learning opportunities beyond the classroom. Research in this program can range from fieldwork to summer lab research, exploring interesting topics with the assistance of a $2,500 stipend.

THE COLLEGE OF ENGINEERING RESIDENCE: The College of Engineering has an established residence in University Village. Students living in the apartment are involved in a residential research experience in collaboration with the National Science Foundation. The focus of the project is develop habits of sustainability in conjunction with new technology.

THE OFFICE OF CIVIC AND COMMUNITY ENGAGEMENT: The Office of Civic and Community Engagement facilitates and promotes relationships between students, faculty, and community partners. University of Miami regards service as an integral part of the undergraduate experience and pushes students to recognize their duty to the community. By participating in service, students have the amazing opportunity to shape the city around them and enact positive change. University of Miami takes on several different initiatives and projects and offers service learning courses and community-based research. Examples include the Urban and Environmental Sustainability program, which maintains that issues of sustainability are complex and need to be examined from many different perspectives, as well as the Affordable Housing Initiative, which brings students and faculty across several disciplines to work with community partners in the promotion of affordable housing throughout Southern Florida.

FIRST-YEAR SEMINAR: First-year seminars are available to students enrolled in the College of Arts & Sciences. In small groups, these students collaborate with one another and learn the foundations of a liberal arts education, all while exploring fascinating topics that push students to ponder challenging questions. The "Religious Liberty from Socrates to Hobby Lobby" seminar explores the true definition of religious liberty, challenging current issues that face freedom, and "Encountering the Holocaust—History, Literature, and Film" is a deep exploration of the historical texts, film, monuments, and literature during the devastating 20th-century period of genocide.

RESIDENTIAL FIRST-YEAR EXPERIENCE: As an extension of the first-year experience, students live among one another in learning communities that foster their academic and personal growth. There are four desired outcomes for the residential first-year experience: academic success, community, transition, and safety/wellness. Students live and learn together as they adjust to the lifestyle and demands of their new college environment.

UNIVERSITY OF MIAMI

http://www.miami.edu/

P: (305) 284-2211

PRIVATE

STUDENT PROFILE

11,100 undergraduate students

94% of undergrad students are full time

49% male – 51% female

53% of students are from out of state

92% freshman retention rate

82% graduated in 6 years

FACULTY PROFILE

2,635 full-time faculty

337 part-time faculty

12 to 1 student/faculty ratio

ADMISSIONS

33,419 Total Applicants

12,628 Total Admissions

2,084 Total Freshman Enrollment

37.79% of applicants admitted

SAT Ranges: CR 590-690, M 610-700, W 580-680

ACT Ranges: C 28-32, M 27-32, E 28-34, W 8-9

TUITION & COSTS

Tuition: $44,400

Fees: $1,324

Total: $45,724

R&B: $12,908

Room: $7,556

Board: $5,352

Total: $58,632

FINANCIAL

$26,256 avg grant/scholarship amount (total)

$8,635 avg loan amount (total)

AGNES SCOTT COLLEGE

DECATUR, GEORGIA

Located in metropolitan Atlanta, Agnes Scott College offers the comfort of a small town with the conveniences of a modern city. The combination of beautiful Collegiate Gothic architecture and modern renovations on the 100-acre campus makes Agnes Scott the perfect place to live and study.

ENTHUSIASTIC WOMEN WITH A COMMITMENT TO EDUCATIONAL EXCELLENCE: Agnes Scott students appreciate not only the value of education in the traditional setting, but also the vast opportunities for learning outside the classroom. Their dedication to pursuing knowledge in all forms is evidenced by the College's extensive options for experiential learning.

FIRST-YEAR SEMINARS: The first-year seminars engage students through intensive small-group study on a particular topic. The small class size fosters group discussion and a sense of community.

STUDY ABROAD: Agnes Scott offers several different opportunities to study abroad. In addition to independent study abroad options in more than thirty countries, students may opt to participate in the faculty-led Global Awareness Program. This program allows students to focus on one non-Western European country and includes two successive courses with a three-week international travel and study portion. Students examine the region through a variety of lenses, including language, culture, geography, history, politics, and economics. About 40 percent of Agnes Scott students study internationally compared to a national average of only 7 percent.

THE CENTER FOR WRITING AND SPEAKING: The Center for Writing and Speaking offers opportunities for students to enhance their communication skills in formal settings. Individual peer tutors guide students by collaborating on ideas, offering course-specific assistance, and encouraging the intellectual progress of each individual.

HISTORY AND COMMUNITY: Founded in 1889 as the Decatur Female Seminary, Agnes Scott College adopted its present name in 1906 and remains affiliated with the Presbyterian Church. Agnes Scott College is located on a one hundred-acre campus in Decatur, Georgia, that combines traditional Gothic architecture and modern renovations. The College recently completed a one hundred and twenty-million dollar renovation and expansion project that includes the state-of-the-art Bullock Science Center. Agnes Scott's location in the town of Decatur, a vibrant community of about twenty thousand, provides students with a comfortable home, while nearby Atlanta offers the combination of conveniences and advantages of a major metropolitan area.

HOUSING: All traditional-aged students not commuting from their permanent residences are required to live in campus housing. In addition to traditional residence halls, upper-level women have the option to live in a more independent setting: the Avery Glen apartment complex. Additionally, three restored Victorian homes adjacent to the campus serve as theme houses, each of which focuses on a particular language or discipline. Recent theme-housing options have included a Spanish language house, an environmental studies house, and an international house.

TRADITIONS: Agnes Scott College boasts several distinctive campus traditions. Every year, for example, graduating seniors ring the bell in the Main Tower when they have secured a job or a placement in graduate school. For nearly one hundred years, October's Black Cat has marked the unofficial end of new student orientation, comprising of a weeklong celebration with a spirit competition, a bonfire, and a formal dance.

CAREER PLANNING: The career planning office works to fully understand the needs and goals of every student while helping them find employment opportunities. Its career resource library and career observation days provide students with the necessary information to make informed decisions about their future. And, in order to ensure that the women of Agnes Scott will be able to apply their college experiences in meaningful careers, the career assessment and counseling program offers an open ear to listen to concerns, doubts, and overall goals.

http://www.agnesscott.edu/

P: (800) 868-8602

PRIVATE

STUDENT PROFILE

902 undergraduate students

97% of undergrad students are full time

1% male – 99% female

87% freshman retention rate

68% graduated in 6 years

FACULTY PROFILE

88 full-time faculty

43 part-time faculty

9 to 1 student/faculty ratio

ADMISSIONS

1,461 Total Applicants

902 Total Admissions

272 Total Freshman Enrollment

61.74% of applicants admitted

TUITION & COSTS

Tuition: $36,996

Fees: $240

Total: $37,236

R&B: $11,150

Room: $5,310

Board: $5,840

Total: $48,386

FINANCIAL

$27,310 avg grant/scholarship amount (total)

$7,086 avg loan amount (total)

BERRY COLLEGE

MT. BERRY, GEORGIA

With the largest contiguous campus in the world, Berry College is known nationally for its premier Work Experience Program where students compete for jobs of increasing responsibility. Every office and program on campus employs students, truly creating one living-learning community.

SOAR: Student Orientation, Advising, and Registration (SOAR) is a two-part introductory program for all incoming freshmen and transfer students. The goal of SOAR is to transition students into college life as seamlessly and successfully as possible. There are a number of activities that take place during the June orientation, and all are designed to answer students' and parents' questions about the school and campus life. During SOAR, students meet with academic advisors, meet new students, receive housing information, and much more. Students return to campus in August to take part in Viking Venture, an extension of orientation. At Viking Venture, students get to know their peers and learn about academic and campus resources before the semester starts

EMERGING LEADERS PROGRAM: The Emerging Leaders Program identifies freshmen who have promising leadership potential and gives them opportunities to develop their leadership skills in and around the campus. Participation in the program is highly beneficial, as these students are given the chance to network with faculty and upperclassmen leaders. Those enrolled in the program take part in an overnight retreat, followed by bi-monthly meetings that explore different topics. After the spring semester, participants become honored alumni of the program and continue to act as leaders on campus.

BERRY COLLEGE SHORT-TERM INTERNATIONAL PROGRAM (SIP): The short-term international programs, or SIPs, are led by Berry faculty. Study abroad in itself is a dynamic and beneficial experience that pushes students out of their comfort zones. Oftentimes, abroad experiences serve as developmental periods, in which students learn a great deal about themselves and their position in the world. SIPs offer the added component of Berry instruction, allowing students to continue learning from Berry faculty as they navigate their new surroundings. Berry's education mission is preserved all over the world as students explore such life-changing experiences as a crash course on Coral Reef Ecology in Honduras or an International Multimedia Reporting Practicum in Austria.

COMMUNITY-BASED LEARNING: Berry's commitment to service extends beyond volunteerism and into hands-on learning. Faculty are increasingly finding ways to connect their studies to the needs of the community, creating an equal balance of discussion/reflection and active, compassionate work. Service-learning is an incredible opportunity to put academic theory into practice, all while making a positive change in the community. Berry offers several different courses across multiple disciplines, such as Anthropology of Food, Public Relations Writing , and Social Science Research Methods.

LIVING-LEARNING COMMUNITIES: A living learning community (LLC) integrates academics into residence life. There are many benefits to participation, including a greater sense of community and academic support. Currently, Berry offers three different LLC options, each of which is set up in cottage-style housing. These include the Year of Service LLC, a foreign language-intensive house, and the Cultural House, which explores topics like diversity, inclusion, and social justice.

ACADEMIC INTERNSHIPS: Berry offers students the opportunity to complete an internship for academic credit. Students who choose to pursue such an must demonstrate clear goals as well as a commitment to reflect and build upon their work experience. And, in addition to the many abroad opportunities available at Berry, students may also choose to pursue an international internship. In partnership with outside providers, Berry students can select a program that aligns with their career and personal goals. There are opportunities available in science, engineering, and service—to name a few.

http://www.berry.edu/

P: (706) 232-5374

PRIVATE

STUDENT PROFILE

2,123 undergraduate students

98% of undergrad students are full time

38% male – 62% female

37% of students are from out of state

83% freshman retention rate

64% graduated in 6 years

FACULTY PROFILE

174 full-time faculty

35 part-time faculty

12 to 1 student/faculty ratio

ADMISSIONS

4,347 Total Applicants

2,407 Total Admissions

575 Total Freshman Enrollment

55.37% of applicants admitted

SAT Ranges: CR 530-630, M 520-610, W 510-610

ACT Ranges: C 24-29, M 23-27, E 24-31

TUITION & COSTS

Tuition: $31,770

Fees: $226

Total: $31,996

R&B: $11,190

Room: $6,320

Board: $4,870

Total: $43,186

FINANCIAL

$20,553 avg grant/scholarship amount (total)

$7,588 avg loan amount (total)

GEORGIA GWINNETT COLLEGE

LAWRENCEVILLE, GEORGIA

Georgia Gwinnett College doesn't believe in preserving the status quo. It believes that every student should have every opportunity to succeed. No other college is blazing trails, raising standards, and revolutionizing the college experience like Georgia Gwinnett, where education is a journey that challenges, supports, and connects students. In only 11 years, GGC has grown from 118 students to nearly 12,000. What was once 260 acres of rolling terrain has become a bustling metropolitan college campus, located only 35 miles northeast of Atlanta.

HANDS-ON LEARNING: At GGC, students are actively encouraged by faculty mentors to take full advantage of the many opportunities offered during their college career. Loaded with study abroad programs, internships, community service projects, athletics, and student organizations, GGC offers a rich variety of activities that develop the whole person. The faculty also seek ways to engage students in applying their course work to the world beyond campus, organizing things like group projects for charities and student-driven undergraduate research projects. At Georgia Gwinnett, each individual student enjoys a tailored college experience that is guided by personal attention and mentorship. They enjoy a private-school experience for a public-school investment.

A STEP ABOVE THE REST: At GGC, students and faculty engage in collaborative group activities and active, hands-on learning experiences. Every classroom is wired with "smart" capabilities, providing modern instructional technologies to support active learning and keep students connected. Whether by laptop or tablet, students can study organic chemistry, text questions or quiz answers to their professors, or even download a lecture the same day they heard it in person. GGC's style is not all about lectures and tests; rather, it's about giving students the tools to succeed in the real world.

LIFE AT GGC: Residential life is a cut above the rest. Instead of typical community bathrooms and bunk beds, GGC affords its students private rooms with bathrooms that are only shared between two students. Additionally, students have the luxury of living rooms with 46-in flat-screens, well-equipped kitchenettes, study rooms, and on-site laundry with email notifications. Students yearning for an urban adventure can enjoy the exciting nightlife, entertainment, and major league sports of downtown Atlanta. Closer to campus, however, is the small-town atmosphere of Lawrenceville, which is made up of bustling commercial districts that blend the past with the present. The Mall of Georgia is practically next door, and the mountains are a short drive away.

MEANINGFUL FACULTY RELATIONSHIPS: The student/faculty relationships at GGC are truly special. GGC faculty are specifically hired for their teaching skills and dedication to student mentorship. Students have nominated their professors for the highest teaching award within the University System of Georgia, which has been granted to GGC faculty five times in the past seven years. This is a truly remarkable distinction for such a young institution, indicative of the quality of its faculty. It is not an exaggeration to say that Georgia Gwinnett's faculty care about students. One can see faculty enjoying lunch with students in the dining hall or involved in impromptu study groups in one of the college's many spacious gathering areas. They willingly provide their cell phone numbers so that students may reach them after hours for questions and advice.

ACADEMIC SUPPORT: Georgia Gwinnett arms students with an unstoppable support system. While no college can guarantee student success, GGC is specifically designed to help students succeed. Personal faculty mentorship keeps students on track, and professors contact students who miss class to see if they need help. Many programs, including free tutoring, have been developed to support students regardless of their academic level.

http://www.ggc.edu/
P: (678) 407-5000

PUBLIC

STUDENT PROFILE

11,468 undergraduate students

68% of undergrad students are full time

44% male – 56% female

1% of students are from out of state

66% freshman retention rate

21% graduated in 6 years

FACULTY PROFILE

460 full-time faculty

213 part-time faculty

18 to 1 student/faculty ratio

TUITION & COSTS

Tuition: (In) $3,920 (Out) $14,634

Fees: $1,704

Total: (In) $5,624 (Out) $16,338

R&B: $11,450

Room: $8,320

Board: $3,130

Total: (In) $17,074 (Out) $27,788

FINANCIAL

$4,772 avg grant/scholarship amount (total)

$6,044 avg loan amount (total)

OGLETHORPE UNIVERSITY

ATLANTA, GEORGIA

OGLETHORPE
UNIVERSITY

Founded in 1835, Oglethorpe is Atlanta's leading liberal arts and sciences university, renowned for its groundbreaking Core program. Oglethorpe holds a unique position as a traditional liberal arts college in a vibrant international city, offering an academically rigorous undergraduate education that is combined with opportunities to apply knowledge through unparalleled experiences.

CIVIC ENGAGEMENT: Each year, Oglethorpe hosts four annual Days of Service, two alternative breaks, and various daily volunteer opportunities within four key focus areas: education, environmental stewardship, health & wellness, and homeless & hunger. Students, staff, and faculty members collaborate at various nonprofits during Orientation Day of Service (August), Atlanta Day of Service (October), MLK Day of Service (January), and Oglethorpe University Day of Service (April). Through Alternative Winter and Spring Breaks, Oglethorpe has traveled to New Orleans, Savannah, Tuscaloosa, and even Guatemala. Some ongoing service opportunities include tutoring middle school students at PATH Academy, sorting food items at the Atlanta Community Food Bank, providing guidance to 8th graders through the service-learning initiative at Drew Charter School, and helping to weed, harvest, and water the OU-Brookhaven Community Garden.

GLOBAL EDUCATION: Students engage on an international level through the Center for Global Education, which offers study through partner institutions in twelve countries along with independent study abroad at an institution of a student's choosing. There are also short-term, for-credit trips throughout the year and unique associate programs with Oxford University (England) and the Umbria Institute (Italy). In 2012, Oglethorpe launched a strategic partnership with study abroad provider Global LEAD. Within this partnership, Oglethorpe also introduced GO: Rome, a study abroad center in Italy, as part of the "Global Oglethorpe" program.

UNDERGRADUATE RESEARCH: Oglethorpe's 13:1 student-to-faculty ratio guarantees personal attention for each student on his or her academic journey. Through coursework and opportunities through the Honors Program, students can even publish papers or present research at academic conferences with faculty support. For years Oglethorpe's students have been actively engaged in the Atlanta community through internships at some of the country's largest businesses or through the Rich Foundation Urban Leadership Program. The Oglethorpe Journal of Undergraduate Research (OJUR) is a scholarly journal that promotes undergraduate research as it seeks to preserve and make available the creative and academic invention of Oglethorpe's campus constituency. The journal serves as both a digital repository of scholarly output and a platform for publishing original works. Additionally, since it took part in launching a Service-Learning Program in 2006, Oglethorpe has been helping students integrate classroom theories and curriculum with hands-on service-learning opportunities in the real world.

PROFESSIONAL DEVELOPMENT: It's rare for a liberal arts college to be so interconnected—both geographically and relationally—to an international city like Atlanta. The A_LAB provides Oglethorpe students the opportunity to gain the kind of practical experience that both complements their academic program as well as solidifies their career decisions. Over 40% of upperclassmen at Oglethorpe have completed internships with such companies as The Carter Center, CNN, Georgia Pacific, Atlanta Magazine, Zoo Atlanta, the Atlanta History Center, and the Georgia State Legislature. In addition to these Atlanta-based internships, Oglethorpe maintains resources and affiliations for nationwide opportunities.

---

http://www.oglethorpe.edu/
P: (404) 261-1441

PRIVATE

STUDENT PROFILE

1,155 undergraduate students

92% of undergrad students are full time

41% male – 59% female

73% freshman retention rate

53% graduated in 6 years

FACULTY PROFILE

63 full-time faculty

15 to 1 student/faculty ratio

ADMISSIONS

2,768 Total Applicants

2,172 Total Admissions

326 Total Freshman Enrollment

78.47% of applicants admitted

SAT Ranges: CR 530-630, M 510-600, W 500-600

ACT Ranges: C 22-28, M 17-25, E 19-29

TUITION & COSTS

Tuition: $33,520

Fees: $280

Total: $33,800

R&B: $12,180

Total: $45,980

FINANCIAL

$25,699 avg grant/scholarship amount (total)

$7,757 avg loan amount (total)

PIEDMONT COLLEGE

DEMOREST, GEORGIA

PIEDMONT COLLEGE

Piedmont College was founded in 1897 to do one thing: provide a rock-solid academic experience for students who want to enrich their lives with the best foundation in the liberal arts. Today, students who come to Piedmont from across Georgia, as well as from around the world, continue to find an educational opportunity that is second to none in the Arts & Sciences, Business, Education, and Nursing & Health Sciences.

EXPERIENTIAL LEARNING: The Compass program is a distinctive graduation requirement at Piedmont. This model encourages students to step out of the classroom and engage with the wider community by designing their own projects to promote six "Compass Points," including Creativity & Innovation, Social Ethics, Leadership, Vocation, Cultural Awareness, and Service-Learning. The experiences gained through Compass projects are included in each student's official transcript, making it easier for future graduate programs or employers to judge the value of their co-curricular efforts.

TRAVEL THE WORLD: Travel Study is a valuable way for Piedmont students to learn about life in different parts of the world. Classes for Travel Study are conducted during the summer to take students to such magnificent places as Italy, England, France, Japan, Germany, and Chile. For a longer study experience, students can enroll for a full semester overseas, paying the same tuition, room, and board as if they were attending the Demorest campus. Currently, full-semester studies are available at the University of Nottingham in England and at the University of Paderborn in Germany.

NETWORKING FOR THE FUTURE: Internships play an important role in higher education, and Piedmont works with students to help them secure work experiences with businesses and organizations at the state, national, and international level. Piedmont students have recently completed internships in Europe with such international companies as Marriott, Avon, and Pfizer. Student research is also an important part of the Piedmont liberal arts program and, each year, students join faculty members in collaborative research that is eventually presented at state and national conferences. With the benefit of their small classes, professors are able to mentor students in research and take active roles in assisting them with presentations. These independent research projects provide undergraduates opportunities that are otherwise found exclusively in master-level programs.

STUDENT ORGANIZATIONS: More than 40 clubs and organizations help bring students from different academic areas together to investigate common interests. Such groups as the Outdoor Club explore northeast Georgia's many hiking and camping areas, while many academic honor societies involve students from every school and department in a variety of projects with area community service organizations.

EVOLVING WITH THE CHANGING WORLD: Students are at the heart of everything at Piedmont College. Piedmont's focus on the liberal arts began with its founding in 1897 and, since that time, the College has expanded its mission so that it may now include schools of Arts & Sciences, Business, Education, and Nursing & Health Sciences. Within the more than 50 undergraduate majors, the College continues to provide students with a strong foundation in the liberal arts tradition. Teaching students to think for themselves, with special emphasis on developing critical thinking skills, is key to each student's success.

STUDENT SUCCESS CENTER: Recognizing that success is defined in many ways, Piedmont recently opened a new Student Success Center to localize career and personal counseling to one central location on campus. The Success Center also provides tutoring services for academic support in all areas. Its tutors are selected by department chairs, trained in the art of tutoring, and monitored to provide the individualized attention students need in order to achieve their personal best.

https://www.piedmont.edu/
P: (800) 277-7020

PRIVATE

STUDENT PROFILE

1,148 undergraduate students

88% of undergrad students are full time

34% male – 66% female

9% of students are from out of state

63% freshman retention rate

46% graduated in 6 years

FACULTY PROFILE

128 full-time faculty

110 part-time faculty

11 to 1 student/faculty ratio

ADMISSIONS

1,135 Total Applicants

647 Total Admissions

281 Total Freshman Enrollment

57% of applicants admitted

SAT Ranges: CR 430-550, M 440-550

ACT Ranges: C 19-24

TUITION & COSTS

Tuition: $23,112

R&B: $9,400

Total: $32,512

FINANCIAL

$14,708 avg grant/scholarship amount (need)

$3,017 avg loan amount (need)

REINHARDT UNIVERSITY

WALESKA, GEORGIA

Since 1883, Reinhardt has focused on meeting student needs one person at a time. Reinhardt's emphasis is on personalized education, which is best provided in small classes by talented professors who challenge and care about their students. Students find Reinhardt's academic programs engaging, challenging, and rewarding—an investment that yields positive returns to both their personal and professional lives. Graduates take full advantage of Reinhardt's opportunities and enter their professions with the richness of a broad liberal arts education. They are well prepared, having gained specific professional skills through their participation in engaged classroom experiences, co-curricular enrichments, challenging research projects, rewarding service initiatives, exciting internships, and life-transforming studies abroad.

FIRST-YEAR EXPERIENCE: From the beginning of students' college careers, Reinhardt plugs them into courses that set them on paths for success at college, in careers, and for life. First-year students enroll in Critical Thinking Seminar, individually themed by the professor who teaches the course. Some past course examples include The Curiosity Cabinet, Film and Environmental Studies, and Blazing the Trails: The Role College Students Played in the Civil Rights Movement.

LEARNING WHILE SERVING: Reinhardt professors value the experience of learning while serving others. Whether teaching art or business, Reinhardt faculty help students apply the skills they learn in class to help others. For instance, Digital Art students produced videos for local nonprofit organizations. Business technology students partnered with SERV International, raising money for children living in an orphanage in Kenya. Marketing majors, along with other United Methodist-affiliated colleges, led a campus-wide awareness and fundraising campaign for "Imagine No Malaria." Students in Sociology spent their spring break in Ixmiquilpan, Mexico, working to provide education, food, and clean water to underserved families of the region.

STUDY ABROAD: Reinhardt faculty instruct study abroad courses each summer. To support students financially, the University applies a portion of the student's tuition payment for the course to the expense of the trip. Recent trips include a combined study of ancient art and theatre in Athens, Greece, and the island of Crete; studies of the Cold War for sociology and communication majors in Germany and Czech Republic; and biological and psychological studies in Ecuador and the Galapagos Islands. Every other summer, students who major in World Languages and Culture can study abroad in Spain.

CONVOCATION OF ARTISTS AND SCHOLARS: The Robert L. Driscoll Convocation of Artists and Scholars is an annual student performance, exhibition, and research conference. Juniors and seniors from across campus read research papers, share internship experiences, show art work, and perform music and theatrical productions for faculty, staff, and students. For nearly a week in the beauty of a North Georgia spring, Reinhardt celebrates student learning among the blooms.

MULTICULTURALISM: Celebrating global diversity, students of Reinhardt University organize an International Festival each year, featuring poster sessions, performances, and culinary delights. Reinhardt's diverse student body has facilitated an opportunity for students to learn from each other; it also allowed them to work together in a culturally diverse atmosphere.

LEADERSHIP ACADEMY: The Student Leadership Academy convenes, each October, the Annual Student Leadership Conference, featuring a keynote address from a regional leader alongside themed workshops and seminars that are specifically designed for Reinhardt students. The Academy also hosts Leadership and Lemonade, a series of monthly symposia that focus on such leadership skills as conflict mediation, financial management, and personality inventories.

Reinhardt University
Shaping Lives - Building Futures

http://www.reinhardt.edu/
P: (770) 720-5600

PRIVATE - CHRISTIAN

STUDENT PROFILE

1,238 undergraduate students

91% of undergrad students are full time

54% male – 46% female

4% of students are from out of state

58% freshman retention rate

35% graduated in 6 years

FACULTY PROFILE

68 full-time faculty

104 part-time faculty

12 to 1 student/faculty ratio

ADMISSIONS

1,158 Total Applicants

1,051 Total Admissions

293 Total Freshman Enrollment

90.76% of applicants admitted

SAT Ranges: CR 430-530, M 430-520

ACT Ranges: C 18-22, M 16-22, E 16-22

TUITION & COSTS

Tuition: $20,744

Fees: $900

Total: $21,644

R&B: $7,948

Total: $29,592

FINANCIAL

$10,439 avg grant/scholarship amount (need)

$3,933 avg loan amount (need)

TOCCOA FALLS COLLEGE

TOCCOA FALLS, GEORGIA

Toccoa Falls is the perfect academic community for students who are looking for an institution that will positively impact both their academic and spiritual lives. Following the motto, "where character is developed with intellect," Toccoa Falls College is serious about providing solid academics that build skills for a lifetime, and equally serious about promoting a solid Christian worldview that provides a stable foundation for a meaningful life. TFC deliberately integrates scripture, truth, wisdom, and service into all that it does. Whether they are sitting in class, taking online courses, hiking beautiful trails, relaxing by the falls, swimming in the pond, studying in the library, or just spending time with friends, students are bound to experience the power of Toccoa Falls College's mission.

FAITH IN THE CLASSROOM: In the classroom, students encounter faculty who integrate their faith into the subject matter. TFC understands that amassing facts can be pointless without the integration of knowledge and Biblical understanding. Its faculty ultimately stress the importance of God's wisdom over that of humans, as true understanding comes from God Himself. As the inerrant, authoritative word of God, the Bible provides all the direction anyone needs to develop Godly character. Faculty teach that, in spite of competing worldviews in our culture today, God's absolute truths will always withstand the test of time.

FIELDS OF STUDY: All TFC students are challenged to integrate scripture, truth, wisdom, and service into the major of their choice. The College currently offers thirty-three majors in a wide range of fields, including Pre-Med, Nursing, Outdoor Leader and Education, Sport Management, Counseling Psychology, Music, Ministry, Business Administration, and Cross-Cultural Studies.

SERVICE AND OUTREACH: Service and outreach are an integral part of the educational experience at TFC. The College clearly understands that the Bible urges everyone to serve others both locally and globally. While enrolled at TFC, students are required to complete a student ministry assignment during four separate semesters of enrollment. In addition to student ministry assignments, TFC students in a variety of majors also have the opportunity to participate in an internship or capstone course. This is a unique opportunity for students to demonstrate what they have learned through a culminating project that showcases their knowledge.

CROSS-CULTURAL STUDIES AND GLOBAL EDUCATION: The Cross-Cultural Studies major offers students the opportunity to study abroad their senior year. Students may select one of the various centers located outside the United States to complete this experience, allowing them to walk away with a better understanding of cross-cultural principles. Other TFC students are also able to take advantage of the Best Semester abroad by partnering with the Council for Christian Colleges and Universities.

LIFE OUTSIDE THE CLASSROOM: There is more to the college experience than just classrooms and the library. With so many student clubs and organizations on campus, there is always something happening at TFC! Toccoa Falls provides many opportunities to foster Christian community and enrich Christian personality. In addition to the customary associations of residence hall life, there are special events such as class socials, banquets, intercollegiate athletic games, class outings, and special services in which the entire school participates. These social events provide an opportunity for the students to mature in relation to oneself, others, and their Lord. It is through this maturing the college seeks to develop the whole student in areas of social, physical, mental, and emotional development.

http://www.tfc.edu/
P: (888) 785-5624

PRIVATE - CHRISTIAN

STUDENT PROFILE
937 undergraduate students
78% of undergrad students are full time
46% male — 54% female
66% freshman retention rate
46% graduated in 6 years

FACULTY PROFILE
48 full-time faculty
59 part-time faculty
13 to 1 student/faculty ratio

ADMISSIONS
759 Total Applicants
345 Total Admissions
150 Total Freshman Enrollment
45.45% of applicants admitted

SAT Ranges: CR 440-570, M 420-520

ACT Ranges: C 18-26, M 17-23, E 16-26

TUITION & COSTS
Tuition: $20,110
Fees: $600
Total: $20,710
R&B: $7,260
Total: $27,970

FINANCIAL
$13,759 avg grant/scholarship amount (total)
$6,604 avg loan amount (total)

UNIVERSITY OF WEST GEORGIA

CARROLLTON, GEORGIA

A t the University of West Georgia, students and faculty alike transform lives and change perceptions, constantly challenging themselves to ask "what if" and refusing to accept that their possibilities are limited. The University embraces diversity, values community, and drives growth. It engages and works collectively to be the best comprehensive university in America, sought after as the best place to work, learn, and succeed.

IGNITE PROGRAM: The UWG Ignite Program is a summer bridge program designed for students who have demonstrated the ability to be successful in college but have not yet met the University's admissions requirements. These students begin classes in the summer and gain access to the campus resources and services that serve as support for their transition to college-level work. The Ignite program runs over the course of five weeks from late June to late July. As part of the Ignite program, students live on campus, take two courses, and participate in engaging activities that promote student success. With this extra help, they are more likely to succeed all throughout their studies.

FIRST-YEAR SEMINARS: With 28 FYS sections in Fall 2017 (and a plan to expand the number of sections in Fall 2018), UWG's first-year seminars involve a dynamic collaboration between faculty and professional staff from the Student Affairs and Enrollment Management Division. The seminars each have a unique academic focus, but the broader goals of the seminar are consistent across each section: 1) Introduce first-year students to the importance of lifelong, active learning and the value of intellectual inquiry; and 2) Provide first-year students with an opportunity for meaningful dialogue with faculty as a way to develop mentoring relationships and foster positive faculty-student interactions throughout their college careers.

UNDERGRADUATE RESEARCH: The University of West Georgia's Office of Undergraduate Research was established to facilitate collaboration between faculty mentors and student researchers; coordinate University-wide research events, such as Research Day and Big Night; assist students in their preparation and travel to research conferences; and encourage new initiatives to create, enhance, and expand undergraduate research opportunities for all West Georgia students. Faculty-directed undergraduate research complements classroom learning through learning by doing, providing an additional educational opportunity that transforms students into scholars. Undergraduate research experience is invaluable and provides UWG scholars a multitude of opportunities both during and beyond their undergraduate career.

WRITING-INTENSIVE COURSES: Writing-intensive courses have been an institutional focus at UWG for many years. Students can elect to receive a writing-intensive DSW (Discipline Specific Writing) certificate as part of their major, indicating their intention to grow as communicators. As required in multiple core areas, students fulfill UWG's Quality Enhancement Plan (QEP) through courses that focus on improving student writing.

LIVING-LEARNING COMMUNITIES: Living-Learning Communities (LLCs) are a great example of UWG's commitment to scholarly achievement, creative expression, and service to humanity. These communities also help students make their mark in their own way. LLCs at UWG are specialized living environments for small groups of residential students. LLCs center on a specific theme while integrating related academic courses, custom programming, and staff mentoring.

CAREER SERVICES: The mission of Career Services at the University of West Georgia is to provide students with the comprehensive resources needed to attain their professional career goals. Through collaboration with campus, employer, and community partnerships, they help students and alumni by facilitating career development through career counseling, student employment, experiential learning, and the job search process. The staff aim to educate and empower students to be proactive in their lifetime academic and career success.

---

https://www.westga.edu/

P: (678) 839-5000

PUBLIC

STUDENT PROFILE

11,155 undergraduate students

81% of undergrad students are full time

36% male – 64% female

27% of students are from out of state

72% freshman retention rate

41.21% graduated in 6 years

FACULTY PROFILE

424 full-time faculty

289 part-time faculty

21 to 1 student/faculty ratio

ADMISSIONS

7,974 Total Applicants

4,712 Total Admissions

2,434 Total Freshman Enrollment

59.09% of applicants admitted

SAT Ranges: CR 440-520, M 430-500

ACT Ranges: C 18-22, M 17-21, E 18-22

TUITION & COSTS

Tuition: (In) $5,226 (Out) $18,444

Fees: $1,962

Total: (In) $7,188 (Out) $20,406

R&B: $9,652

Room: $5,300

Board: $4,352

Total: (In) $16,840 (Out) $30,058

FINANCIAL

$4,965 avg grant/scholarship amount (need)

$4,058 avg loan amount (need)

YOUNG HARRIS COLLEGE

YOUNG HARRIS, GEORGIA

Founded more than 130 years ago by The United Methodist Church, Young Harris College has been transformed into a progressive model of liberal arts education that features innovative academic programs, state-of-the-art facilities, and competitive NCAA Division II athletics. Young Harris College has an intimate environment that invites students and faculty to foster strong relationships that last long after graduation.

FIRST-YEAR EXPERIENCE: YHC's First-Year Foundations course is designed to provide support and encouragement to new students, helping to ensure their personal and academic success. The course provides an opportunity for students to work with a YHC faculty or staff member and an upper-class student peer mentor. They receive help to work through adjusting to college, learning to manage time and stress, setting priorities, and understanding academics and campus life.

STUDY ABROAD AND GLOBAL LEARNING: Living and studying abroad gives students perspective and an understanding of other cultures. YHC offers multiple international and scholarship programs each year so that students can study at prestigious schools overseas, including Universitat Pompeu Fabra in Spain and Harlaxton College in England. Students can spend a semester, summer, or full academic year abroad in Asia, Latin America, Africa, or Europe. YHC also provides opportunities for students to travel and study abroad under the direct supervision of YHC faculty.

SERVICE AND COMMUNITY-BASED LEARNING: True to its culture of service and mission to engage the community, Young Harris College offers numerous programs for passionate students to put their energy, time, and talent to good use within the YHC community and beyond. Through the Center for Appalachian Studies and Community Engagement, S.E.R.V.E., and YHC LEAD, students are challenged to become ethical and effective leaders who work to better their communities through positive change and service. The Center for Appalachian Studies and Community Engagement is committed to the celebration of Appalachian culture and to service that engages students with communities in the region. The center leads initiatives centered on service learning, Appalachian studies, community engagement, social justice, and sustainability.

INTERDISCIPLINARY RESEARCH: Stepping outside the familiar four walls of the classroom to present original ideas and research is an enriching element of the YHC student experience. The annual Undergraduate Research Day empowers students from across the academic disciplines to work alongside faculty and peers to enhance their learning experience

OUTDOOR LEADERSHIP: What started as a student interest group on campus has grown into an extraordinary bachelor's degree program in Outdoor Leadership. The National Forest Service permits YHC to program in the Chattahoochee, Cherokee, and Nantahala National Forests. Students study land and water pursuits management, environmental ethics, primitive survival, and much more. YHC's outdoor leadership majors learn from highly qualified instructors who lead by example in a classroom unlike any other: the great outdoors.

INTERNSHIP OPPORTUNITIES: Outside of the classroom, YHC students are given ample opportunities to hone their skills in a variety of on- and off-campus environments. Internships with local businesses and organizations are extensive. YHC's close proximity to businesses in Atlanta and the surrounding area also contribute to the College's pool of internships and provide fertile ground to exercise the work of the classroom. YHC's Student Success Center helps connect students with potential internship opportunities.

STUDENT SUCCESS CENTER: The Student Success Center provides tutoring, personal academic counseling, assistance with English as a second language, study skills seminars, disability services, and quiet study space for students. Students work one-on-one with an advisor in the Center to choose classes, learn about internship opportunities, and receive interview and résumé prep.

http://www.yhc.edu/

P: (800) 241-3754

PRIVATE

STUDENT PROFILE

1,115 undergraduate students

99% of undergrad students are full time

44% male — 56% female

61% retention rate

43.76% graduated in 6 years

FACULTY PROFILE

74 full-time faculty

80 part-time faculty

12 to 1 student/faculty ratio

ADMISSIONS

2,333 Total Applicants

1,284 Total Admissions

338 Total Freshman Enrollment

55.04% of applicants admitted

SAT Ranges: CR 440-570, M 440-550

ACT Ranges: C 18-25

TUITION & COSTS

Tuition: $28,012

Fees: $1,005

Total: $29,017

FINANCIAL

$20,420 avg grant/scholarship amount (need)

$4,165 avg loan amount (need)

BRESCIA UNIVERSITY

OWENSBORO, KENTUCKY

Brescia University is a Catholic liberal arts institution founded in the Ursuline tradition of personal and social transformation through education. Directed to foster academic and moral excellence in a student-centered environment, Brescia offers undergraduate and graduate programs that produce value-driven graduates. Students leave Brescia with the talents and skills to build successful careers; to nourish strong families; and to make a difference in the lives of others, the life of the Church, and the life of the community.

BECOMING WE: Brescia University believes that "I become me, by becoming we." Brescia believes that students become fully alive by putting others first. Students become the best versions of themselves when they live for and serve others. Whether students do that on their own, with their teams, or as part of a club or organization, they will find opportunities to become part of something larger than themselves: a community. Numerous service-related clubs and organizations are established, and the athletic teams all participate in service-learning opportunities.

THE URSULINE VALUES: Brescia University was founded by the Ursuline Sisters of Mount Saint Joseph. Founded in 1535 by St. Angela Merici as a community of women devoted to loving God and doing good works, the Ursuline Sisters soon devoted themselves almost exclusively to education, especially that of girls and young women. Across Europe and the United States (and, eventually, all over the world), "Ursuline" became synonymous with the highest quality of education. Ursuline education is a unique educational pedagogy that thrives on the idea of providing personalized attention and opportunities to those who might otherwise have none. And, proudly, Brescia University educates students in that same manner.

INTELLECTUALLY STIMULATING EVENTS: Numerous opportunities for an engaging exposure to new ideas are available at Brescia University. The Young Lecture Series fosters a faculty-driven effort to bring a variety of speakers of notoriety to campus. Furthermore, the Owensboro World Affairs Council hosts its monthly lecture series at Brescia, offering students front seats to renowned speakers and topics of global impact. The Anna Eaton Stout Art Gallery also proudly displays works of art with national, regional, and local reputation.

THE URSULINE PROMISE FOR SUCCESS: St. Angela Merici, founder of the Ursuline Order, embraced individual differences and promoted the development of the whole person. To maintain both her vision and the Brescia mission, all courses in the curriculum prepare graduates to: demonstrate the ability to think critically, analyze information, and communicate effectively; attain the competence and readiness necessary for graduate school or careers in each individual's appropriate field; possess the capacity to adapt to diverse environments; and to understand and apply ethical standards in promoting justice and service to others.

STUDENT ACTIVITIES: The best way for students to reach their full potential at Brescia University is to get involved. Not only do students who become engaged with the community feel accepted and possess a sense of belonging, but involved students do better academically. Residence life, intramurals, student activities, campus ministry events, athletics, and the arts are among the many opportunities to become involved. Students are encouraged to find their passion and pursue it.

BRESCIA UNIVERSITY

https://www.brescia.edu/
P: 1-877-BRESCIA

PRIVATE - CATHOLIC

STUDENT PROFILE

1,043 undergraduate students

74% of undergrad students are full time

26% male – 74% female

20% of students are from out of state

61% freshman retention rate

30% graduated in 6 years

FACULTY PROFILE

49 full-time faculty

116 part-time faculty

8 to 1 student/faculty ratio

ADMISSIONS

4,153 Total Applicants

1,991 Total Admissions

159 Total Freshman Enrollment

47.94% of applicants admitted

SAT Ranges: CR 420-502, M 457-480

ACT Ranges: C 19-24, M 19-26, E 18-24

TUITION & COSTS

Tuition: $19,950

Fees: $200

Total: $20,150

R&B: $8,750

Total: $29,100

FINANCIAL

$5,721 avg grant/scholarship amount (need)

$4,129 avg loan amount (need)

CENTRE COLLEGE

DANVILLE, KENTUCKY

Centre College challenges students both in and out of the classroom with rigorous academics and extracurricular opportunities. Students are bound to enjoy a personalized education that's second to none while engaging themselves in an active, vibrant community. Students also enjoy Centre's "Southern twist," a warm and pleasant atmosphere that makes it easy to build friendships and make meaningful connections.

CENTRE COMMITMENT: As part of the Centre Commitment, all Centre students are guaranteed an internship, study abroad, and graduation within four years, or Centre will provide up to a year of additional study, tuition-free. Centre is ranked among the nation's top ten in study abroad percentage, with 85% enrollment across the campus. Semester-long study is offered at campuses in England (London or Reading), France, and Mexico, with exchange programs in Japan, Northern Ireland, and England. A variety of three-week study opportunities are available at other locations around the world, including Italy, Vietnam, Barbados, Spain, and Turkey.

CENTRETERM: The first year at Centre includes a small, non-lecture-format seminar during the three-week CentreTerm in January. This seminar gives students an opportunity to share and experience special interests with professors and classmates. Freshman seminars often include field trips, dinner discussions, and other interesting learning activities.

A WELCOME ENVIRONMENT: Centre College is located in historic Danville, Kentucky, on a 115-acre campus with sixty buildings, thirteen of which are included in the National Register of Historic Places. The College features athletic, academic, and library facilities that enable amazing collegiate experiences. Nationally recognized for its high quality of life, Danville is progressive, safe, friendly, and perfectly placed as a gateway to the region and the world. It's called the City of Firsts for its many historical milestones, including the first courthouse in Kentucky as well as the first post office west of the Alleghenies. In 2000, the city helped Centre host the year's only vice presidential debate.

A PERSONALIZED EDUCATION: Not only are Centre's teachers among America's best educated, but they're also among America's most involved. Centre professors teach all classes, not teaching assistants who are not yet experts in their fields. They also hold classes in their homes or host academic opportunities in the residence halls, allowing them to get to know students both in and out of class. Centre's average class size of eighteen allows students one-on-one time with their professors. These friendly, dedicated instructors give students their home phone numbers, stop by and chat in the dining commons, and show up at students' recitals or soccer matches. Because professors know students personally, they help them stretch to achieve their very best.

UNDERGRADUATE RESEARCH: Centre students work closely with professors on collaborative research, allowing them not only to form close working relationships with experts in their fields, but also to play an intrinsic part in the innovative projects that are happening on campus. Participating in joint research projects and publishing their research gives students valuable experience as well as impressive résumé credits.

ACTIVE STUDENTS: Centre students, 98% of whom live on campus, are bright and friendly people who bring life to their campus community. Centre students are diverse both geographically as well as socioeconomically. They enjoy having fun but are equally serious about their education. Centre students regularly win the nation's most prestigious fellowships and scholarships, including Rhodes, Rotary, Fulbright, Goldwater, and Truman. And, thanks to the College's vast offerings of ways to be deeply involved in their educations, students can grow as confident leaders. They can also enjoy Centre's twenty-one varsity teams, about one hundred campus organizations, and more than two thousand events each year.

http://www.centre.edu/
P: (800) 423-6236

PRIVATE

STUDENT PROFILE

1,367 undergraduate students

100% of undergrad students are full time

50% male – 50% female

89% freshman retention rate

86% graduated in 6 years

FACULTY PROFILE

125 full-time faculty

13 part-time faculty

11 to 1 student/faculty ratio

ADMISSIONS

2,716 Total Applicants

1,933 Total Admissions

374 Total Freshman Enrollment

71.17% of applicants admitted

SAT Ranges: CR 540-660, M 570-740

ACT Ranges: C 26-31, M 25-30, E 27-33

TUITION & COSTS

Tuition: $38,200

R&B: $9,620

Total: $47,820

FINANCIAL

$24,010 avg grant/scholarship amount (total)

$6,562 avg loan amount (total)

GEORGETOWN COLLEGE

GEORGETOWN, KENTUCKY

GEORGETOWN
C O L L E G E

Georgetown College is committed to inspiring excellence in its students, supporting its community with caring Christian values. Despite its small size, Georgetown offers a strong, rigorous array of liberal arts and pre-professional programs that otherwise would be expected only from a large university.

FRESHMAN SEMINAR: The Freshman Seminar is a course that has been designed by students to help make the transition from high school to college easier. During the course, students gain tools for college navigation, life management, class management, and the art of listening. Participants also study such topics as diversity, understanding the self, relationships, and teamwork.

STUDY ABROAD: Georgetown College offers academic programs in Asia, Australia, and Europe as well as North, South, and Central America. Regardless of major or academic concentration, these programs add an important cross-cultural dimension to the liberal arts education. Not limited to language study, these provide opportunities for students in many disciplines, including the natural sciences, pre-professional fields, and the humanities.

REGENT'S PARK COLLEGE–OXFORD UNIVERSITY: Georgetown's unique agreement with Regent's Park College of Oxford University allows Georgetown students, faculty, and associates to participate in an academic partnership with the Baptist College at Oxford. This enhances Georgetown's reputation as a center for innovative Christian thought, producing numerous benefits for both institutions. GC students learn under the Oxford system's rigorous tutorial method and, while there, work side-by-side with other students from all over the world.

ACS-APPROVED: The Chemistry Department at Georgetown College has received American Chemical Society-Approval, recognized for hosting a broad and rigorous chemistry education that gives students the intellectual, experimental, and communication skills needed to become effective scientific professionals. A recent study of GC alumni found that more than 70% of Chemistry graduates go on to graduate or professional school (often medical, dental, or veterinary), and a high percentage enter directly into chemically related jobs in industry or government.

PHI KAPPA PHI HONOR SOCIETY: Georgetown's Phi Kappa Phi Honor Society—the nation's oldest and most selective collegiate honor society for all academic disciplines—has been recognized as a Chapter of Merit. Since its founding in 2003, Georgetown College's chapter has inducted more than 400 members, including current students, alumni, faculty, staff, and administration.

GEORGETOWN AND THE HORSE CAPITAL OF THE WORLD: The City of Georgetown's focal point is its historic Main Street area, which is lined with charming older homes and commercial buildings, more than 100 of which are listed on the National Register of Historic Places. Known as the "Antique Capital of Kentucky," Scott County and other counties in the Bluegrass are often also called the "Horse Capital of the World" for containing the world's highest concentration of thoroughbred horse farms.

ALPINE COLLEGE CHALLENGE COURSE: An Alpine Challenge Course, built in 1998, benefits Georgetown College students as well as the surrounding community. Located on the East Campus Complex, the Alpine Challenge Course is a series of ropes, logs, and cables constructed to create a unique series of obstacles. The course is often used by Freshman Seminar classes, among others, to help build cooperation, trust, and individual leadership skills.

THE GRAVES CENTER FOR CALLING & CAREER: The Graves Center for Calling & Career assists students in discerning their calling to lead happy, productive lives. To promote student success after college, the center creates a "vocational team" that encourages students, parents, teachers, and staff to work together toward the same goals. The center also provides a range of programs and opportunities that build and strengthen this team.

http://www.georgetowncollege.edu/

P: (800) 788-9985

PRIVATE - CHRISTIAN

STUDENT PROFILE

978 undergraduate students

93% of undergrad students are full time

48% male – 52% female

23% of students are from out of state

72% freshman retention rate

57% graduated in 6 years

FACULTY PROFILE

84 full-time faculty

65 part-time faculty

10 to 1 student/faculty ratio

ADMISSIONS

2,145 Total Applicants

1,452 Total Admissions

282 Total Freshman Enrollment

67.69% of applicants admitted

SAT Ranges: CR 443-533, M 460-560

ACT Ranges: C 20-25, M 19-25, E 20-27

TUITION & COSTS

Tuition: $34,280

R&B: $8,710

Room: $4,190

Board: $4,520

Total: $42,990

FINANCIAL

$14,998 avg grant/scholarship amount (need)

$3,018 avg loan amount (need)

TRANSYLVANIA UNIVERSITY

LEXINGTON, KENTUCKY

Throughout its nearly 240-year history, Transylvania University has remained steadfastly committed to outstanding undergraduate education. Transylvania, taken from the Latin word meaning "across the woods," is located in Kentucky's beautiful Bluegrass Region and stands proudly as the nation's 16th oldest college. At Transylvania, students find a personal approach to learning, characterized by small classes and caring faculty who put their impressive academic credentials to use for students' benefit.

REAL-WORLD LEARNING: Transylvania's location is just two blocks from the financial district of the dynamic city of Lexington, meaning that internships and part-time job opportunities are plentiful at banks, financial services companies, and accounting firms. As the legal and healthcare center for eastern and central Kentucky, Lexington also offers internship opportunities for students interested in law and medicine. The rolling bluegrass countryside surrounding the city is home to some of the most beautiful and famous horse farms in the world, bringing students in touch with opportunities all throughout the the thoroughbred industry.

INTERNSHIPS AND STUDY ABROAD: While the opportunities in Kentucky are plentiful, many students also complete internships out of the state and abroad. Recent examples include positions with a member of the Scottish Parliament, at the Centers for Disease Control and Prevention in Atlanta, and with Nickelodeon TV in New York City. Transylvania's Canadian Parliamentary Internship program offers students the opportunity to work for five weeks in the office of a member of the Canadian House of Commons or Senate. Nearly 70% of Transylvania's students participate in study abroad programs, engaging in full-immersion experiences in which they learn culture and language along with their focus of study. May term classes, during which students focus on one course for four weeks, frequently include domestic or international travel components. Recent courses have found Transylvania students studying tropical ecology in Belize, working with community leaders on service projects in the Philippines, and exploring ancient cave drawings in China.

INTERDISCIPLINARY STUDY: May term classes, many of which are interdisciplinary and team-taught, foster an exceptional degree of interaction between students and faculty across fields of study. A recent course on the chemistry of ceramics was co-taught by professors from the departments of both art and chemistry, a course on contemporary Ireland was co-taught by professors in anthropology and political science, and a course on advertising was co-taught by professors in communication and music technology.

LEARNING FROM EXPERIENCED MENTORS: Transylvania's faculty members have dominated the Kentucky Professor of the Year award (from the Carnegie Foundation for the Advancement of Teaching and the Council for Advancement and Support of Education), claiming the honor four times in the past decade (more than any other Kentucky college or university).

COMMUNITY SERVICE: Transylvania students are active both in the local community and across the country through local urban outreach and alternative spring break programs. Many students arrive a week ahead of fall term to do community service in Lexington and other communities through the Jump Start and First-Year Urban programs. The Volunteer Income Tax Assistance Plan allows accounting students to provide free tax preparation help to low-income people, and Crimson Christmas is an annual campus holiday party for children of Big Brothers/Big Sisters of the Bluegrass.

STUDENT ACTIVITIES: Transylvania hosts a wide variety of lectures, art exhibitions, music performances, film screenings, and on-campus entertainment. Recent speakers have included Nobel Peace Prize winner Elie Wiesel, author Joyce Carol Oates, historians Doris Kearns Goodwin and Shelby Foote, and United Nations Human Rights Commissioner Mary Robinson. Two students recently organized a teach-in for a nonpartisan review of issues surrounding war, and there are annual celebrations of Hispanic Heritage Month and African-American History Month.

http://www.transy.edu/

P: (859) 233- 8242

PRIVATE

STUDENT PROFILE

1,053 undergraduate students

99% of undergrad students are full time

42% male – 58% female

85% freshman retention rate

73% graduated in 6 years

FACULTY PROFILE

88 full-time faculty

27 part-time faculty

11 to 1 student/faculty ratio

ADMISSIONS

1,538 Total Applicants

1,425 Total Admissions

311 Total Freshman Enrollment

92.65% of applicants admitted

SAT Ranges: CR 510-640, M 530-660

ACT Ranges: C 25-30, M 24-29, E 25-33

TUITION & COSTS

Tuition: $32,970

Fees: $1,400

Total: $34,370

R&B: $9,560

Room: $5,410

Board: $4,150

Total: $43,930

FINANCIAL

$22,238 avg grant/scholarship amount (total)

$7,188 avg loan amount (total)

UNIVERSITY OF LOUISVILLE

LOUISVILLE, KENTUCKY

University of Louisville is a premier research institution with a strong focus on the liberal arts and sciences. Students are actively involved in their individual educational experiences and have plenty of opportunities to succeed, both in the classroom and as a member of the campus community.

BOOK IN COMMON: All incoming freshmen are required to complete a reading assignment prior to arriving on campus. The point of the assignment is to create a shared, academic experience among all first-year students. The reading, known as Book in Common, eases students into college-level academics while encouraging the development of critical thinking skills. Through a series of related events and programs, students engage in conversation about the book's topic throughout the span of their freshman year. Faculty work closely with students to explore ideas and themes present within the text. Every year, Louisville also hosts an essay contest that is connected to the Book in Common reading. The essay can only be 500 words, so students must practice conveying their ideas in a concise yet compelling manner. All submissions are reviewed by faculty and staff, and one winner is chosen to receive a $350 scholarship.

STUDY ABROAD: University of Louisville provides plenty of study abroad options to its students, encouraging all of its students to take advantage of the countless benefits that come with an education abroad. Participants gain skills in areas like in cross-cultural communication, independent living, and foreign language. Programs vary in length, interest, and type. Louisville offers opportunities in exchange, third-party provider programs, short-term study abroad, and direct enroll. Most notable is the International Service Learning Program, which allows students to engage in hands-on learning and community service in areas all throughout the world. Through methods of experiential learning, students address the needs of the community and people in the city where they are working. ISLP allows students to apply academic theories to real-world issues in order to enact positive change. Locations related to this program include: Botswana, Belize, Croatia, Philippines, and Trinidad & Tobago.

CAREER SERVICES: It's important that students explore their career options before selecting a major. This can be a difficult process for students, with many not knowing how to utilize helpful resources. The Career Development Center is the number-one resource for all things internship, interview, and career-related. Students are invited to drop by and speak with a staff member in a one-on-one consultation. The Center offers services in career exploration and advising, résumés and cover letters, job and internship searches, interviewing, preparation for graduate school, work study placement, networking, and supplemental assistance for diverse student populations.

LIVING-LEARNING AND THEMED COMMUNITIES: Living-learning and themed communities are unique housing options that connect students through academics and common interests. Louisville offers several different community options that help students explore their passions and build a foundation for academic and personal success. Through living-learning communities, students can house together in order to be closely in touch with other students and peer leaders affiliated with the same academic goals and fields of study. For example, students wishing to pursue dental hygiene can live with their classmates in the Pre-Dental Hygiene LLC, while engineering students can collaborate easily with their peers in the Engineering LLC. Themed communities are also available to students so that they may focus on other topics, such as social justice and sustainability.

UNIVERSITY OF LOUISVILLE.

http://louisville.edu/
P: (502) 852-5555

PUBLIC

STUDENT PROFILE

15,768 undergraduate students

78% of undergrad students are full time

50% male – 50% female

17% of students are from out of state

79% freshman retention rate

53% graduated in 6 years

FACULTY PROFILE

1,835 full-time faculty

608 part-time faculty

13 to 1 student/faculty ratio

ADMISSIONS

9,685 Total Applicants

6,943 Total Admissions

2,797 Total Freshman Enrollment

71.69% of applicants admitted

SAT Ranges: CR 490-620, M 510-620, W 470-590

ACT Ranges: C 22-29, M 22-28, E 23-30, W 7-8

TUITION & COSTS

Tuition: (In) $10,542 (Out) $24,848

Fees: $202

Total: (In) $10,744 (Out) $25,050

R&B: $7,942

Room: $4,932

Board: $3,010

Total: (In) $18,686 (Out) $32,992

FINANCIAL

$8,705 avg grant/scholarship amount (need)

$4,074 avg loan amount (need)

CENTENARY COLLEGE OF LOUISIANA

SHREVEPORT, LOUISIANA

Centenary is a selective, private, residential liberal arts college affiliated with the United Methodist Church. The College offers 22 majors in the arts and sciences along with more than 30 minors, academic concentrations, and pre-professional programs in allied health fields, business, education, engineering, law, and museum management. Centenary students applying to medical school have a 90% acceptance rate over the past five years, while students applying to law school are accepted at a rate of 80%.

CREDO AND CHALLENGE – A FIRST-YEAR EXPERIENCE: Credo and Challenge, the first two courses in Centenary's TREK program, are designed to introduce students to liberal arts-based skills and prepare them to put their minds to practical use. Credo, Latin for "I believe," is the first course, which allows students to explore their values and beliefs in the context of their academic ambitions. In the second-semester Challenge courses, students choose from innovative, research-driven seminars examining some of the global challenges of the 21st century: rapid technological developments, economic expansion, globalization, conflict, and environmental change.

GLOBAL OPPORTUNITIES: An engaging Centenary education begins with a unique and unforgettable common global-learning experience: Centenary in Paris. All first-year students at Centenary have the opportunity to complete their first college course during this intensive learning experience that creates strong bonds among the first-year cohort and between students and their professors. Students travel to Paris for 8-10 days, live in an international student hostel, and take such rigorous courses as "Daily Bread: Sustainability in Paris," "Paris Noir: Black American in the City of Light," or "Writing Paris/Writing Home." Many Centenary students continue their international exploration through one of the College's May Module short courses in locations such as Australia, Denmark, France, Greece, and Haiti.

STUDENT LEADERS: Centenary students continue their learning outside the classroom in more than 60 student organizations, including student government, residence life, music, theatre, community service, advocacy, and Greek life. The College's Christian Leadership Center and the new Beliefs and Values Project help students identify their guiding principles and put them into practice in a diverse, pluralistic environment. Each year, Centenary students complete thousands of community service hours in the Shreveport community during campus-wide service days such as MLK Service Day and the BIG Event. Centenary also fields 15 teams in the Southern Collegiate Athletic Conference in NCAA Division III, including one of the only varsity women's triathlon teams in the country.

CAPSTONE EXPERIENCES: Centenary students have the opportunity to draw together their four years of learning both inside and outside the classroom in a variety of capstone experiences, including senior art exhibits and critiques, a senior communication portfolio, and a senior geology internship, to name just a few. Some seniors have translated internships into full-time employment after graduation, while others have built on capstone projects as the basis for further research and scholarly publications in graduate school.

MENTORS AND RESOURCES: Centenary takes an intentional, student-centered approach to personal and professional success, evolving with students' needs throughout their four years at the College. Staff in the Office of Professional Discernment use customized assessments to help entering students identify their values and talents as learn how to ascribe their attribute not only to a future career, but also to a fulfilling life. The Office of Career Services offers resources, programming, and advising for career development, internships, employment, and graduate school. The Office of the Registrar, working alongside faculty advisors, also offers individual counseling to help students fulfill their academic requirements and stay on track to graduate.

https://www.centenary.edu/
P: (318) 869-5011

PRIVATE - CHRISTIAN

STUDENT PROFILE
473 undergraduate students
99% of undergrad students are full time
43% male – 57% female
46% of students are from out of state
73% freshman retention rate
47% graduated in 6 years

FACULTY PROFILE
57 full-time faculty
29 part-time faculty
8 to 1 student/faculty ratio

ADMISSIONS
886 Total Applicants
886 Total Applicants
569 Total Admissions
130 Total Freshman Enrollment
64.22% of applicants admitted
SAT Ranges: CR 470-580, M 470-590
ACT Ranges: C 22-28, M 21-26, E 22-30

TUITION & COSTS
Tuition: $35,900
R&B: $13,150
Total: $49,050

FINANCIAL
$24,252 avg grant/scholarship amount (need)
$4,442 avg loan amount (need)

LOYOLA UNIVERSITY NEW ORLEANS

NEW ORLEANS, LOUISIANA

Loyola University New Orleans combines the academic excellence of its faculty and programs, an ideal size that fosters individual student success in a positive learning experience, and the Jesuit commitment to educating the whole person—all to provide students with a value-centered, liberal arts education. Based on a strong core curriculum, the Loyola experience provides for the intellectual, emotional, and spiritual growth of the individual.

STUDY ABROAD AND LOYOLA'S CENTER FOR INTERNATIONAL EDUCATION: Loyola offers students many exciting educational and cultural opportunities to travel and study abroad. Recent options have included summer programs in Belgium, England, France, China, India, Ireland, Spain, and Mexico, among others. Loyola's Center for International Education also coordinates semester programs in a variety of destinations throughout the world. Students receive academic credit for their participation and gain many significant experiences that they can apply to their education at Loyola, graduate work, or employment.

LOYOLA UNIVERSITY COMMUNITY ACTION PROGRAM (LUCAP): Loyola University Community Action Program (LUCAP) directs volunteers in service-oriented activities that promote community-wide involvement in the area of social justice. Students involved in LUCAP volunteer with organizations focused on environmental action, hunger relief, the death penalty moratorium movement, assisting local elderly citizens, and even in rebuilding the New Orleans community. The program aids in promoting social and spiritual growth through involvement in acts of compassion.

THE OFFICE OF SERVICE LEARNING: The Office of Service Learning at Loyola coordinates opportunities for students to combine community service with classroom instruction. The projects focus on critical, reflective thinking as well as civic and personal responsibility. Students volunteer in many capacities and at many sites, including shelters for battered women, schools, homeless shelters, hospitals, elderly care facilities, literacy centers, programs that serve the needs of the physically and/or mentally challenged, and programs that address the special needs of inner-city youth. Faculty and students collaborate to select a specific site and activities that correlate to the course content. The faculty member grants the students academic credit based on the learning that they achieve through service, not simply for completing the hours. Service-learning not only benefits the student, but also the greater New Orleans community.

COMMON CURRICULUM: The common curriculum offers a broad range of courses for students to explore multiple disciplines, regardless of their declared major. The common curriculum consists of such introductory courses as composition, literature, history, philosophy, mathematics, science, and religious studies. The advanced common curriculum courses are designed to ensure a rewarding and well-rounded education.

RESEARCH: At Loyola, there are opportunities for students in many academic disciplines to become involved in research conducted by faculty. Students are also able to conduct their own research with faculty supervision and present their findings at national conferences. Often, students are able to continue their research as they progress to graduate school.

NEW ORLEANS, LOUISIANA: Loyola's scenic uptown campus is set in the heart of one of the most prestigious neighborhoods in New Orleans. Students enjoy the numerous venues of New Orleans jazz as well as cuisine from the finest restaurants. The university is located directly across from the Audubon Zoo and Park, the city's premier recreation center. With its unique cuisine, numerous museums and historical sites, and flourishing arts community, New Orleans provides a cultural experience that few cities can match.

INTERNSHIPS: Loyola offers students various internship opportunities with both local and national companies and organizations. By participating in internships, students are able to gain relevant career-related experiences that reinforce what they have learned in the classroom and make them more marketable after graduation.

---

http://www.loyno.edu/
P: (800) 456-9652

PRIVATE - CATHOLIC

STUDENT PROFILE

2,691 undergraduate students

93% of undergrad students are full time

40% male — 60% female

77% freshman retention rate

66% graduated in 6 years

FACULTY PROFILE

324 full-time faculty

125 part-time faculty

12 to 1 student/faculty ratio

ADMISSIONS

3,591 Total Applicants

3,243 Total Admissions

667 Total Freshman Enrollment

90.31% of applicants admitted

SAT Ranges: CR 520-620, M 480-610

ACT Ranges: C 22-28, M 20-26, E 23-31

TUITION & COSTS

Tuition: $36,214

Fees: $1,366

Total: $37,580

R&B: $12,808

Room: $7,430

Board: $5,378

Total: $50,388

FINANCIAL

$23,203 avg grant/scholarship amount (total)

$5,542 avg loan amount (total)

TULANE UNIVERSITY

NEW ORLEANS, LOUISIANA

Tulane University is located in the picturesque city of New Orleans. The University is hailed for its research initiatives as well as its commitment to developing students into leaders. Tulane's motto, 'Not for one's self, but for one's own,' is an educational philosophy that drives academic and personal growth in a collegiate setting.

FIRST-YEAR EXPERIENCE: Tulane's first-year program is known as TIDES, which stands for "Tulane Interdisciplinary Experience Seminar." TIDES gathers students into small groups to promote a highly involved exchange of ideas and bonding among peers. Tulane offers 70 different seminar courses, meaning that students have countless options to select an interesting class that makes their first year as engaging and intellectually stimulating as possible. In small groups, students learn by interacting with one another, completing collaborative coursework that fosters a sense of community and teamwork.

CORE CURRICULUM: At the center of Tulane's educational structure is the Core Curriculum. Within the curriculum, there are certain requirements that each student is expected to satisfy before they can graduate. The Core Curriculum is an experience shared by the entire student body, no matter their college or discipline, ensuring that Tulane graduates all have an excellent, well-rounded foundation of knowledge. Requirements include a first-year writing component, foreign language, scientific inquiry, and cultural knowledge in the arts, humanities, or social sciences. Unique to Tulane's Core is the addition public service requirement, which teaches students how academics are utilized in order to make a positive change in the community. This requirement can take the form of a service-oriented internship or research project.

SERVICE LEARNING COURSES: Service Learning courses integrate academic concepts and theories into community service, building students' knowledge through experience while creating meaningful change within their community. Tulane offers several different courses, spanning across all disciplines in order to enable students of all interests to make a difference. For example, the Orchestra course has taken Tulane students to local elementary schools in order to share their passion for orchestral performance and instruction, and the Product and Experimental Design course enabled students to help area middle schoolers with their science fair projects. The Open Studio course has also allowed architecture majors the chance to take part in urban planning projects, and the Workshop in Creative Writing Journalism brought Tulane writers to the New Orleans Charter Science and Mathematics High School in order to help publish a biannual literary magazine.

PUBLIC SERVICE FELLOWS PROGRAM: The Public Service Fellows Program trains students to act as leaders for both on- and off-campus service initiatives. This program is worth four credit hours and counts toward the second portion of the University's graduation requirement. Public Service Fellows gain experience by leading initiatives and developing solutions to community issues. Fellows also benefit from one-on-one interaction with faculty and community partners, getting first-rate, first-hand experience from an ever-growing network of professionals.

INTERNSHIPS: There are several internship opportunities available through Tulane, enabling students the opportunity to gain professional knowledge and experience. Some of the internships available include the Africare internship, which brings students to Africa over the summer in order to assist with food security, public health, and sanitation; an internship with the County of Los Angeles Public health, which addresses specific issues that face the people of LA; and a hands-on projects within the Gulf Restoration Network, which focuses on the preservation of the Gulf of Mexico's natural environment.

http://tulane.edu/

P: (504) 865-5000

PRIVATE

STUDENT PROFILE

7,841 undergraduate students

81% of undergrad students are full time

42% male — 58% female

85% of students are from out of state

92% freshman retention rate

83% graduated in 6 years

FACULTY PROFILE

1,226 full-time faculty

586 part-time faculty

9 to 1 student/faculty ratio

ADMISSIONS

26,257 Total Applicants

8,008 Total Admissions

1,719 Total Freshman Enrollment

30.50% of applicants admitted

SAT Ranges: CR 620-710, M 620-700, W 640-720

ACT Ranges: C 29-32, M 27-32, E 30-34

TUITION & COSTS

Tuition: $45,758

Fees: $3,880

Total: $49,638

R&B: $13,184

Room: $7,566

Board: $5,618

Total: $62,822

FINANCIAL

$30,819 avg grant/scholarship amount (total)

$9,039 avg loan amount (total)

UNIVERSITY OF NEW ORLEANS

NEW ORLEANS, LOUISIANA

THE UNIVERSITY *of*
NEW ORLEANS

The University of New Orleans is the only public research university in greater New Orleans. It has educated students from all 50 states and more than 130 countries. The University grants bachelor's, master's, and doctoral degrees in four academic colleges and interdisciplinary studies.

FIRST-YEAR EXPERIENCE: The First-Year Experience (FYE) at the University of New Orleans provides a broad network of support services and programs that address the academic, personal and social needs of first-year students in order to promote their success. FYE offers outreach and interventions to students who are experiencing academic and social difficulties. All first-year students must take UNIV 1001, which helps them develop skills to manage time, well-being, and personal resources. It assists students with developing learning strategies to manage the college academic environment and gathers information on campus resources that support their academic growth and development. It offers information on career exploration, community service, wellness and involvement.

FIRST-YEAR WRITING PROGRAM: The First-Year Writing Program offers two writing-intensive courses as part of the larger process of academic inquiry: asking questions, looking for answers, engaging with different viewpoints, and reflecting on what one has learned. Instructors foster intellectual curiosity and open-mindedness, encouraging students to value writing as a necessary part of learning and communicating both in the classroom and in the world at large. Because classes are limited to 25 students, students are able to collaborate through discussion and peer review as well as receive one-on-one feedback via student-teacher conferencing.

UNDERGRADUATE RESEARCH: The University of New Orleans' Center for Undergraduate Research facilitates collaboration between undergraduate students and faculty, promotes undergraduate research to internal and external audiences, and encourages new initiatives to create undergraduate research opportunities. This research increases the interaction between students and faculty/graduate students, builds lasting bonds through group educational activities, and provides insight into future career paths. PURSUE (the Privateer Undergraduate Research and Scholarly UNO Experience) provides students with a mechanism to find faculty research mentors and take part in paid positions to work on their research projects.

INTERNATIONAL EDUCATION: The University places strong emphasis on study abroad and international education. It offers summer study abroad opportunities to 10 countries, including its flagship program in Innsbruck, Austria, which has flourished for more than four decades and educated more than 10,000 students. UNO students also study in a dozen countries as part of international student exchange programs.

JAZZ AT THE SANDBAR: Now in its 27th season, Jazz at the Sandbar is one of the University's most well-known and beloved traditions. This live music performance series, established in 1990 by faculty member Ellis Marsalis, pairs UNO jazz studies students with professional musicians to perform in front of an audience at a first-class on-campus venue.

CAREER SERVICES: The University's Office of Career Services offers resources to students with a focus on career advising, career preparation, and career events. The office helps match students with off-campus employers in sectors that are aligned with students' academic majors or career aspirations. The office also arranges job shadowing experiences, which allow them to spend time in a professional setting and gain a deeper understanding of their field. The economy of New Orleans and South Louisiana allows for internship and career opportunities in such fields as technology, financial services, energy, environmental science, transportation, hospitality, engineering, computer science, and the arts.

http://www.uno.edu/
P: (888) 514-4275

PUBLIC

STUDENT PROFILE

6,185 undergraduate students

77% of undergrad students are full time

50% male – 50% female

6% of students are from out of state

62% freshman retention rate

35% graduated in 6 years

FACULTY PROFILE

270 full-time faculty

132 part-time faculty

20 to 1 student/faculty ratio

ADMISSIONS

3,932 Total Applicants

2,267 Total Admissions

922 Total Freshman Enrollment

57.66% of applicants admitted

SAT Ranges: CR 460-600, M 480-630

ACT Ranges: C 20-24, M 19-24, E 20-26

TUITION & COSTS

Tuition: (In) $6,090 (Out) $6,090

Fees: (In) $1,914 (Out) $15,731

Total: (In) $8,004 (Out) $21,821

R&B: $9,515

Total: (In) $17,519 (Out) $31,336

FINANCIAL

$5,621 avg grant/scholarship amount (need)

$4,206 avg loan amount (need)

BELHAVEN UNIVERSITY

JACKSON, MISSISSIPPI

Belhaven University is a place where top-rated faculty and a nurturing environment merge to propel students beyond what is believed to be achievable. Belhaven leads its students to capture career and personal success, encouraging the development of a sense of spiritual maturity that can withstand the trials of life. With nationally recognized academics, a Christ-centered worldview, and the faith-affirming support to become more, Belhaven's charming and warm-weather campus is home to fabulous events and intensely fun activities.

SERVICE: Belhaven's motto is "To Serve, Not to Be Served," representing the many ways that it provides its community to get involved with mission opportunities locally, nationally, and internationally. From the annual Martin Luther King Clean-Up day to ministering students in places like Africa or Haiti, the common bond is meaningful service.

STUDENT LIFE AND THE CAMPUS COMMUNITY: Belhaven is a unique place in which lifelong friendships are formed and flourish The opportunities for meeting and getting to know fellow students are abundant, from clubs and organizations to campus-wide activities. Not only do students connect with one another, but they also get to know the faculty on a deeply personal level. The university boasts a low 12:1 student-to-faculty ratio, affording students an individualized learning experience that allows them to reach their full potential. Many of the professors live in the historic Belhaven neighborhood and invite their students into their homes for fellowship (or even just a good meal).

JACKSON, MISSISSIPPI: The university is right in the heart of a beautiful historic community that is vibrant and filled with its own world-class events and attractions. The metro Jackson area is home to the International Ballet Competition, the Mississippi Braves baseball team, first-rate museums, art galleries, and fun-filled music festivals. In fact, the Mississippi Symphony Orchestra, the Mississippi Opera, Ballet Magnificat!, and the world-renowned Singing Christmas Tree all originated at Belhaven University.

A SOLID FOUNDATION: At Belhaven, academic excellence is met with passion. Belhaven offers an unending pursuit of academic excellence with the help of personal mentoring in every degree offered. Belhaven provides a solid foundation in the comprehensive liberal arts to help students develop into well-educated individuals. Belhaven students experience one-of-a-kind academic programs, including the WorldView Curriculum, which chronologically intertwines the critical core disciplines of literature, history, art, religion, and music in a comprehensive, rigorous format.

INTERNSHIPS: Internships are available throughout many of the academic programs that Belhaven offers to its students. Ranging from Social Work to Sports Medicine and Exercise Science, there are many opportunities for students to get real-world experiences that prepare them for their future careers.

STUDY ABROAD: Belhaven offers short- and long-term opportunities for students to study abroad through the Council for Christian Colleges and Universities (CCCU) organization. Students may participate in programs in such places as China, India, Oxford, Uganda, Australia, Latin America, the Middle East, and some opportunity-laden areas throughout the United States.

ART AND SCIENCE: Belhaven has graduated many students who have pursued professions in the healthcare industry. Close to 90% of its biology and sports medicine students are accepted to healthcare-related universities to pursue studies in the medical, dental, nursing, physical therapy, and occupational therapy fields. Belhaven is steeped in arts heritage as well, having contributed to the intellectual, cultural, and spiritual growth of the city and state since 1883. Belhaven is 1 of 30 institutions in the nation that is accredited in Music, Dance, Theatre, and Visual Arts, standing as the only Christian university to have obtained all of these accreditations. There truly is something for everyone at Belhaven.

BELHAVEN UNIVERSITY

http://www.belhaven.edu/
P: (800) 960-5940

PRIVATE - CHRISTIAN

STUDENT PROFILE

1,354 undergraduate students

80% of undergrad students are full time

47% male – 53% female

59% of students are from out of state

66% freshman retention rate

48% graduated in 6 years

FACULTY PROFILE

91 full-time faculty

135 part-time faculty

12 to 1 student/faculty ratio

ADMISSIONS

3,061 Total Applicants

1,556 Total Admissions

272 Total Freshman Enrollment

50.38% of applicants admitted

TUITION & COSTS

Tuition: $22,726

Fees: $290

Total: $23,016

R&B: $8,000

Total: $31,061

FINANCIAL

$12,920 avg grant/scholarship amount (total)

$6,632 avg loan amount (total)

MILLSAPS COLLEGE

JACKSON, MISSISSIPPI

Founded in 1890, Millsaps College offers an open and exciting environment for eager minds. The dynamic and enthusiastic faculty work hand-in-hand with an engaged student body to open new doors in liberal arts education.

FIRST-YEAR SEMINAR: First-year students at Millsaps take an introduction to liberal studies seminar, a rigorous reasoning- and writing-intensive course. Topics of the seminars vary, though all seminars cover the same objectives.

CREATIVE APPLICATION OF TRADITIONAL TECHNIQUES: Millsaps' Heritage program is a wide-ranging study of the history of ideas, cultures, religions, creative works, and pivotal problems that have shaped humanity for thousands of years. This program brings together history, literature, philosophy, religion, and the arts in an integrated approach to the study of a global cultural history. The program is the equivalent of two year-long courses.

EFFECTIVE WRITERS: Unlike many colleges, Millsaps has developed a writing program independent of its English department. This program teaches students how to develop the art of communication, which is essential for any career. Millsaps embraces the philosophy that writing cannot be taught in just one semester of freshman composition; instead, it is taught continuously and within the context of every discipline. The college's required writing portfolio allows students to gather and reflect on a variety of their academic writings.

STUDY ABROAD: Millsaps boasts an exceptionally strong anthropology department, the fieldwork of which is done at the college's 4,500-acre biocultural reserve in the Yucatán province of Kiuic. Millsaps was the first school to begin excavation of this site, which was inhabited around 600 BCE. Geology, too, offers many experiential trips to Alaska, Yucatán, and Yellowstone National Park. Altogether, eight to nine courses in math, art, sociology, business, and other disciplines are offered in the college's Yucatán programs. Through its solar-powered, neo-Mayan architecture on the reserve, Millsaps creates a living and learning environment for students. There are also many other opportunities to venture off campus and abroad, including through lab research and NCUR conferences for chemistry and biology students. Millsaps offers language-immersion programs Nice, Costa Rica, and more, and students can attend summer business programs in London, Munich, and the Netherlands.

COMMUNITY SERVICE: There are many opportunities for service at Millsaps. Students are active in tutoring programs, Habitat for Humanity, local soup kitchens, and other organizations. The college's "One Campus, One Community" program focuses on community service projects in North Midtown (an area near Millsaps) and Jackson's K-12 schools.

PRE-PROFESSIONAL PROGRAMS: Millsaps has a long tradition of offering one of the best and strongest pre-med programs in the state. Every year, graduates claim a significant number of the one hundred open slots at University of Mississippi Medical School. About 15 percent of each year's graduates major in biology or chemistry, while political science and biology majors have access to a strong pre-law program.

A FUTURE IN BUSINESS: Millsaps' business program is fully accredited by AACSB and accounts for 15 to 20 percent of total graduate and undergraduate enrollment every year. Accounting, economics, and business administration are the main focuses in the business division.

INTERNSHIPS: The college's location just one mile from downtown Jackson, the state's capital and financial center, affords students the opportunity to intern with high-level executives. Mentorship programs are in place for medicine, business, law, and all other areas of study.

http://www.millsaps.edu/
P: (800) 352-1050

PRIVATE

STUDENT PROFILE

760 undergraduate students

99% of undergrad students are full time

50% male – 50% female

55% of students are from out of state

78% freshman retention rate

66% graduated in 6 years

FACULTY PROFILE

97 full-time faculty

17 part-time faculty

9 to 1 student/faculty ratio

ADMISSIONS

3,657 Total Applicants

1,925 Total Admissions

223 Total Freshman Enrollment

52.64% of applicants admitted

SAT Ranges: CR 520-630, M 525-630

ACT Ranges: C 23-28, M 20-26, E 22-31

TUITION & COSTS

Tuition: $33,306

Fees: $2,204

Total: $35,510

R&B: $12,412

Room: $7,006

Board: $5,406

Total: $47,922

FINANCIAL

$26,041 avg grant/scholarship amount (total)

$6,941 avg loan amount (total)

CULVER-STOCKTON COLLEGE

CANTON, MISSOURI

Culver-Stockton College is a four-year residential, co-educational community in affiliation with the Christian Church (Disciples of Christ), located in Canton, Missouri. C-SC offers more than two dozen majors and four pre-professional programs that are designed to help students succeed in the classroom and beyond. At C-SC, education revolves around doing, seeing, traveling, interning, and practicing. C-SC takes a traditional 15-week semester and splits it into two terms: a 12-week term and a 3-week term. During the 12-week term, students take 3-4 classes instead of the traditional 5-6. Then, in the 3-week term, they apply their focus to one single class. This 3-week term is an exceptional opportunity for trips abroad and internship experiences.

ACADEMIC AND CULTURAL EDUCATION: Culver-Stockton offers dozens of active and vibrant Academic and Cultural Education (ACE) events each semester. ACE programming includes lectures from nationally known speakers, authors, and business owners; intellectual conversations regarding current events; fine arts events; and more. Students get credit for attending ACE events, and alumni often speak about the impact that their ACE experiences made on their lives.

OFF-CAMPUS EDUCATION: C-SC students have outstanding academic opportunities available to them for out-of-the-classroom learning experiences. Culver-Stockton has more than 700 corporate internship partners as well as many course options for Travel Study all around the world. C-SC focuses on experiential education, executing its stellar education through simulations, research, service-learning, and more.

EDUCATIONAL PARTNERSHIPS: C-SC partners with the American University of Antigua (AUA) College of Medicine, Kansas City University of Medicine and Biosciences (KCUMB), and Washington University to provide its eligible students easy, accelerated access to a range of graduate programs. Through a 3+4 agreement with AUA, students can complete three years of their undergraduate education and then four years in the University's medical program, earning them both a B.S. and M.D. at a faster rate than the traditional degree track. A similar agreement exists through KCUMB for students to gain an early degree in osteopathic medicine as well as through Washington University for students to tackle its occupational therapy program.

FACULTY AS MENTORS: C-SC's small community provides professors great flexibility to incorporate new ideas and disciplines into their curricula. The small student-to-faculty ratio of 15:1 allows students to form close relationships with these experts. Professors are more than just classroom instructors; they are students' academic advisors, mentors, and friends.

STUDENT ACTIVITIES: Culver-Stockton students can participate in the more than 50 student organizations on campus, including the academic honor societies, the Student Government Association, the Mock Trial Team, Greek organizations, social groups, and more. There is also a popular intramural sports program on campus that offers leagues to all students throughout the school year.

GREEK LIFE: Approximately 40% of C-SC students are affiliated with Greek life, enjoying a lively community within one of the College's five national fraternities or three national sororities. These students are part of welcoming families that work to enrich the lives of both their members and the community around them. They live with their respective group members and meet weekly for fun events and meaningful community service.

ALUMNI ACHIEVEMENTS: Over 90% of Culver-Stockton College alumni are employed or in graduate school within six months of graduation. C-SC's alumni make the most out of attending this small liberal arts institution by participating in alumni groups and mentorships that support everyone involved in their growth. C-SC alumni see high levels of success as CEOs, business owners, teachers, artists, actors, researchers, athletic trainers, and more.

---

http://www.culver.edu/

P: (573) 288-6000

PRIVATE

STUDENT PROFILE

1,049 undergraduate students

88% of undergrad students are full time

49% male – 51% female

43% of students are from out of state

68% freshman retention rate

52% graduated in 6 years

FACULTY PROFILE

56 full-time faculty

32 part-time faculty

15 to 1 student/faculty ratio

ADMISSIONS

2,913 Total Applicants

1,628 Total Admissions

260 Total Freshman Enrollment

55.89% of applicants admitted

SAT Ranges: CR 400-540, M 420-520

ACT Ranges: C 18--23, M 17-23, E 17-23

TUITION & COSTS

Tuition: $24,500

Fees: $400

Total: $24,900

R&B: $7,950

Room: $3,560

Board: $4,390

Total: $32,850

FINANCIAL

$16,562 avg grant/scholarship amount (total)

$7,826 avg loan amount (total)

FONTBONNE UNIVERSITY

ST. LOUIS, MISSOURI

Fontbonne University in St. Louis, MO, is home to a compact campus, strong values, big hearts, and plenty of passionate people, including nearly 2,000 students. The school's small size fosters meaningful relationships between friends and fellow students, as well as faculty, staff, and even alumni.

FIRST-YEAR SEMINARS AND EXPERIENCES: The foundation of Fontbonne's first-year experience is its first-year seminar, which focuses on issues of historical remembrance, social justice, and diversity. The goal is to build alliances with individuals and organizations that are bringing about positive changes in the global community. The seminar partners students with engagement opportunities in the first semester to broaden understanding and develop a foundation for future learning.

COLLABORATIVE ASSIGNMENTS AND PROJECTS: It is a common experience for Fontbonne students to be engaged in group projects inside and outside of the classroom. Fontbonne recognizes that every student brings different perspectives and experiences from which others can benefit. The idea of incorporating those differences through academic experiences challenges students to grow culturally as well as educationally. Fontbonne's rich campus culture spans across several spaces on campus and engages students in ways that are unique from traditional educational settings.

UNIQUE FALL SEMESTER EXPERIENCE: The university's annual Dedicated Semester takes place each fall and serves as a community learning experience. The entire campus focuses on a single topic of discussion like Disability; Happiness; the Immigrant Experience; and Security, Privacy, & Freedom. Specialized courses, guest speakers, experiential learning opportunities, films, and book clubs make the Dedicated Semester a chance for everyone—students, staff, and faculty alike—to come together to learn.

UNDERGRADUATE RESEARCH: Undergraduate research is a key high-impact academic experience at Fontbonne, enriching the learning experience as a cornerstone of students' education. Because faculty members lead small classes, they easily develop strong relationships with their students and act as valuable mentors throughout the research process. Some of Fontbonne's undergraduate research projects have earned patents in cybersecurity and created new "best practice" developments in communication disorders and speech pathology.

DIVERSITY/GLOBAL LEARNING: Diversity and inclusion have been a hallmark at Fontbonne University since its inception. Fontbonne incorporates diversity into its common education experience as well as outside of the classroom through several student organizations that promote understanding and tolerance for all cultures. With nearly 300 international students and the highest diversity percentage of private schools in St. Louis, Fontbonne's campus represents the real world, preparing students to lead inclusively upon graduation.

CAMPUS DIVERSITY: Fontbonne students represent 27 different countries, so the school's student population is diverse and far-reaching. A robust international department strives to integrate students from around the world into traditional campus life. One of the best examples of this, Fontbonne's annual International Bazaar, is perhaps one of the most anticipated events of the year. Students proudly represent their countries from around the world through food, dress, dance, and more as they learn from and about one another in a fun, festive environment. Additionally, Fontbonne encourages students to engage in dialogue about diversity and social justice through Peace and Justice Conversations, campus cultural events, and new traditions such as the Tunnel of Oppression.

CAPSTONE COURSES AND PROJECTS/SENIOR EXPERIENCE: A capstone experience is required in all academic programs. Consisting of a portfolio completion, research, and presentation process, the intent of the capstone experience is to create a product for future employers to see tangible evidence of the ability and knowledge of the student. Fontbonne believes these experiences are representative of the student's full body of work and help drive postgraduate success, which currently stands at a professional placement rate of 96%.

https://www.fontbonne.edu/

P: (314) 862-3456

PRIVATE - CATHOLIC

STUDENT PROFILE

1,086 undergraduate students

82% of undergrad students are full time

34% male – 66% female

20% of students are from out of state

79% freshman retention rate

53% graduated in 6 years

FACULTY PROFILE

75 full-time faculty

136 part-time faculty

11 to 1 student/faculty ratio

ADMISSIONS

494 Total Applicants

478 Total Admissions

178 Total Freshman Enrollment

96.76% of applicants admitted

ACT Ranges: C 20-25, M 18-25, E 20-26

TUITION & COSTS

Tuition: $24,475

Fees: $135

Total: $24,610

R&B: $9,191

Room: $4,994

Board: $4,197

Total: $33,801

FINANCIAL

$15,029 avg grant/scholarship amount (total)

$6,809 avg loan amount (total)

MISSOURI UNIVERSITY OF SCIENCE AND TECHNOLOGY

ROLLA, MISSOURI

Missouri University of Science and Technology is a leading research institution that brings together the collaborative efforts of both faculty and students. The University's commitment to technological and scientific discovery has led to amazing achievements, both in the realms of academia as well as return on investment.

FIRST-YEAR EXCELLENCE: Hit the Ground Running (HGR) is a summer program that allows incoming freshmen to get a sneak peek of college life. Participants come to campus for a three-week program to explore areas of math, chemistry, and English. Students are also introduced to the campus, helpful research tips, and leadership opportunities. As an added bonus, participants earn credit for their work. Even those not involved in HGR receive a helpful introduction through the First-Year Experience (FYE). FYE is the backbone of S&T's undergraduate education, exposing students to college-level academics and building upon skills in critical thinking and writing. Through FYE, students are primed to be successful scholars throughout their undergraduate careers.

EXPERIENTIAL LEARNING: Experiential learning (EL) is an educational approach that functions outside of the traditional lecture structure. EL pushes students beyond rote memorization and into the application of concepts and ideas. EL methods include: research, student design, service-learning, leadership learning, Co-Op, internships, externships, and study abroad. S&T embraces all of these methods, aiming to involve each and every student in a handful of EL practices prior to graduation.

SERVICE-LEARNING: Missouri S&T views service-learning (SL) as a valuable and integral part of the undergraduate experience, expanding its efforts to provide SL opportunities to all students. There are many fulfilling benefits to participating in SL courses; students are given the chance to apply what they have learned in the classroom, all while making positive contributions to community organizations. In SL courses, students are pushed to reflect upon their work, drawing connections between their service and academics in order to understand how they can enact change as responsible citizens.

LEARNING COMMUNITIES: Living-Learning Communities (LLCs) connect students through an integration of academics into residence life. In an LLC, students benefit from academic and personal support form their peers and professors alike. Missouri S&T encourages students to participate in an LLC in order to build their leadership skills and form community bonds with peers, all while excelling in their major field of study. Examples include the Connections Community, which focuses on a specific theme or interest to facilitate themed events and activities, and the Voyager LLC, which is exclusive to first-year students. Participants in this community live with one another and take classes structured in block scheduling. Through their shared experiences and lifestyle, freshmen are able to thrive in a safe and supportive environment in which they can explore their passions get comfortable at the University.

OURE FELLOWS PROGRAM: The OURE Fellows Program allows undergraduates to engage in interdisciplinary research projects. Students in the program conduct their research under the supervision of a faculty member after presenting their proposals at the Annual Undergraduate Research Conference. A panel of judges selects the proposals that they find promising and then provide them with the outlets through which to pursue their curiosities in research.

CO-OPS: S&T students are eligible for Co-Op experiences when they enter their second year. A Co-Op is a great way to get a leg up on the competition, immersing them in projects that grant them industry knowledge as well as hands-on experience in their field of interest.

http://www.mst.edu/

P: (573) 341-4111

PUBLIC

STUDENT PROFILE

6,839 undergraduate students

90% of undergrad students are full time

77% male – 23% female

18% of students are from out of state

87% freshman retention rate

65% graduated in 6 years

FACULTY PROFILE

404 full-time faculty

138 part-time faculty

19 to 1 student/faculty ratio

ADMISSIONS

3,592 Total Applicants

3,164 Total Admissions

1,489 Total Freshman Enrollment

88.08% of applicants admitted

SAT Ranges: CR 520-660, M 560-640, W 490-640

ACT Ranges: C 25-31, M 26-30, E 26-30, W 7-8

TUITION & COSTS

Tuition: (In) $8,286 (Out) $24,810

Fees: $1,342

Total: (In) $9,628 (Out) $26,152

R&B: $9,725

Room: $6,165

Board: $3,560

Total: (In) $19,353 (Out) $35,877

FINANCIAL

$8,805 avg grant/scholarship amount (total)

$6,873 avg loan amount (total)

ROCKHURST UNIVERSITY

KANSAS CITY, MISSOURI

ROCKHURST UNIVERSITY
Where leaders learn.

Founded in 1910, Rockhurst University is a private, coeducational Jesuit university located in Kansas City, Missouri. The University's community, as well as its academic programs, adheres to its motto: Learning, Leadership, and Service in the Jesuit Tradition. Rockhurst students are actively involved in their educations. The University embraces the Ignatian style of learning, where students' transformations span all facets of their intellectual, spiritual, and ethical lives. Students are given the challenge of taking their educations into their own hands. They must be willing to question their surroundings and actively involve themselves with subject matters.

FESTIVAL OF STUDENT ACHIEVEMENT (FOSA): The Festival of Student Achievement is an annual event that celebrates the academic successes of students, faculty, and staff. Every year, instructors or outside organizations bring to attention to some of the outstanding efforts that have been made within the Rockhurst community. Students who have completed research projects or creative pieces, put on outstanding musical or dramatic performances, or wrote compelling essays are invited to present their talents again at the Festival, showing all of their peers what they pursue beyond the walls of the classroom. They also celebrate exemplary student leadership efforts, highlighting all aspects of the extraordinary Rockhurst scholars.

HEAR IT FROM THEM: Rockhurst has a low student-to-faculty ratio of 13:1 and an average class size of 24. These impressive numbers allow students to receive a more personalized education, and professors easily and readily adopt roles as mentors who can meet the individual needs to their students. Professors at Rockhurst are passionate about the importance of student-faculty interaction. Being a professor is a rewarding experience—one that Rockhurst faculty uphold with honor. Rockhurst instructors believe that their role to influence and educate students often goes beyond the simple act of teaching. They connect with individual goals and do all they can to cater to each student's path to success both in and out of the classroom.

STUDENT ACTIVITIES: The Rockhurst community is enlivened by 70 student clubs and organizations, including the array of sororities and fraternities. The University highly encourages student involvement in extracurricular groups, as they fulfill students' lives outside of academia. Getting involved in an area that interests them allows them to meet like-minded peers and connect them with communities that honor and appreciate them. Thanks to Rockhurst's student activities, life on campus is full of fun and passion.

CAREER SERVICES: Rockhurst recognizes the importance of a college education while also acknowledging that extra work must go into making it an ultimately worthwhile investment. When students enter the workforce, their education must be accompanied by a readiness to handle the demands of society. This truth encourages Rockhurst to continue its commitment to turning out well-rounded intellectuals who are ready to tackle any challenge. Career Services is available to guide student decisions toward their desired career options and goals. Whether they know what they want to do after graduation or have no idea how their major can be effective in the workforce, the staff are available to step in at any stage of their planning process. All students are actively encouraged to utilize Career Services, even as alumni. Rockhurst students are valued both during and after their time at the University, and so they have consistent access to the resources they need to advance in their careers.

STUDY ABROAD: Rockhurst students have the option to study abroad during their undergraduate experience through numerous programs with affiliated universities as well as three programs offered by Rockhurst itself. Rockhurst's own programs take students on immersive trips to Mexico, France, and Spain.

http://www.rockhurst.edu/
P: (816) 501-4000

PRIVATE - CATHOLIC

STUDENT PROFILE

2,077 undergraduate students

69% of undergrad students are full time

40% male — 60% female

28% of students are from out of state

85% freshman retention rate

71% graduated in 6 years

FACULTY PROFILE

129 full-time faculty

110 part-time faculty

12 to 1 student/faculty ratio

ADMISSIONS

2,774 Total Applicants

2,041 Total Admissions

320 Total Freshman Enrollment

73.58% of applicants admitted

SAT Ranges: CR 490-600, M 520-610

ACT Ranges: C 23-28, M 23-30, E 22-27

TUITION & COSTS

Tuition: $34,000

Fees: $790

Total: $34,790

R&B: $9,465

Room: $5,755

Board: $3,710

Total: $44,255

FINANCIAL

$23,761 avg grant/scholarship amount (total)

$7,024 avg loan amount (total)

SAINT LOUIS UNIVERSITY

ST. LOUIS, MISSOURI

SAINT LOUIS UNIVERSITY.
— EST. 1818 —

Saint Louis University is a Catholic, Jesuit University ranked among the top research institutions in the nation. The University fosters the intellectual and character development of more than 13,000 students. Founded in 1818, it is the oldest university west of the Mississippi and the second oldest Jesuit university in the United States. Through teaching, research, health care, and community service, SLU has provided a one-of-a-kind education for nearly two centuries.

UNIVERSITY 101: Every new SLU student assimilates into the college culture with the help of University 101, a required course that introduces students to the resources they have on campus and the tools they need to set goals for their college careers. These classes usually consist of fewer than twenty students, which means that everyone has the opportunity to participate in class and form personal relationships with each of their classmates. Together, every UNIV 101 class member learns how to succeed at SLU, both academically and socially.

STUDY ABROAD: SLU collaborates with over fifty locations across the world, offering opportunities for study abroad in nearly every continent. Adventurous students immerse themselves in different cultures as they deepen their understandings of both their areas of study as well as the world around them. SLU even has its own campus in Madrid, Spain, which was the first U.S. university to be officially recognized by Madrid's Ministry of Education. Offering over 200 courses, the SLU-Madrid campus hosts an academic environment just as excellent as the campus back at home. If a full semester abroad does not fit into a student's four-year plan, they may take advantage of the Summer Program in Madrid month-long trip of classes, excursions, and beautiful Spanish culture.

UNDERGRADUATE RESEARCH: Because Saint Louis University students are among the most curious in the world, they are given the opportunity to conduct research as early as their freshman year. With the aid of invested faculty mentors, students band together to hypothesize, experiment, and discover groundbreaking new information. Research can take place during the academic year or throughout a summer session. And, because there is so much that cannot be done within the borders of a college campus, SLU makes it easy to send undergraduate researchers out into the community and beyond to different countries.

UNIVERSITY HONORS PROGRAM: The Honors Program at SLU challenges students to look at problems with a number of different perspectives and form answers that are deep and comprehensive. It admits students who commit both to intellectual growth and community service. Those in the University Honors Program get special access to their own exclusive residence hall and priority registration for their semester courses. They also get to work one-on-one with faculty mentors to help them make the most of their majors. In return, they are expected to excel as academics and serve as community leaders.

UNIVERSITY WRITING SERVICES: Writing is a critical part of nearly every area of study, and so the SLU Student Success Center offers top-notch assistance to students with any stage of the writing process. Through the Success Center, the University Writing Service (UWS) trains skilled professors, undergraduates, and graduate students to give free consultations that not only help finish individual assignments, but also develop students into strong, independent writers. Help is always available, as students can make appointments to meet both in person and online.

SAINT LOUIS, MISSOURI: St. Louis claims a number of significant cultural gems, including the famous Gateway Arch, the tallest monument in the United States; Forest Park, which is larger than New York's Central Park and contains the city's zoo, art museum, science center, and history museum; and the City Museum, which combines art and fun through recycled architecture, a huge outdoor jungle gym, and a rooftop Ferris wheel. SLU's neighborhood of Midtown is a booming performing arts district that features the historic Fox Theatre and Powell Symphony Hall, home to the second-oldest symphony orchestra in the nation. Midtown also has seen increase in development of both high-end and casual restaurants, which are packed when the Billikens host games in Chaifetz arena.

---

http://www.slu.edu/
P: (800) 758-3678

PRIVATE - CATHOLIC

STUDENT PROFILE

12,401 undergraduate students

56% of undergrad students are full time

41% male – 59% female

90% freshman retention rate

71% graduated in 6 years

FACULTY PROFILE

1,615 full-time faculty

628 part-time faculty

11 to 1 student/faculty ratio

ADMISSIONS

13,464 Total Applicants

8,527 Total Admissions

1,641 Total Freshman Enrollment

63.33% of applicants admitted

SAT Ranges: CR 530-660, M 560-680

ACT Ranges: C 25-31, M 24-29, E 25-32

TUITION & COSTS

Tuition: $38,700

Fees: $526

Total: $39,226

R&B: $10,640

Room: $5,816

Board: $4,824

Total: $49,866

FINANCIAL

$20,195 avg grant/scholarship amount (total)

$8,020 avg loan amount (total)

TRUMAN STATE UNIVERSITY

KIRKSVILLE, MISSOURI

Truman State University believes in the joy of learning. A college experience should be more than memorizing facts. Truman students enjoy small classes, participate in discussions, discover real opportunities, and learn from the people around them. They join campus groups and make friendships that last a lifetime. Most of all, they receive an education that prepares them to excel in any field.

RESEARCH: Truman students don't have to wait until graduate school to conduct groundbreaking research. Each year well over one thousand students participate in faculty-supervised research projects. Truman also typically sends the largest delegation of undergraduate students to the National Conference on Undergraduate Research, as well as to many regional and national research conferences.

DIVERSE STUDENT BODY: Truman State works hard to sustain and support a diverse culture, and around 11% of the student body is African American, Asian, Hispanic, Native Hawaiian/Pacific Islander or Native American. Truman's largest class of international students in several decades enrolled in Fall 2012 with 355 students from 52 different countries! Truman also hosts a variety of traveling scholars and international professors every year.

STUDY ABROAD: The Truman Center for International Education provides students with study abroad opportunities in approximately 500 programs situated in about 60 countries all across the globe. Semester, year-long, week-long and summer programs are available for virtually every major that Truman offers. About 25% of Truman students travel abroad during their college careers to destinations like Australia, Brazil, China, England, Fiji, France, Germany, Ghana, Italy, Japan, Malta, Morocco, New Zealand, South Africa, Thailand, and more!

DIFFERENT CULTURES AND NEW EXPERIENCES: Part of the liberal arts experience is opening one's mind to different cultures and new experiences. Truman's cultural programming facilitates this by hosting speakers and events for all students; a small sample includes musicians like Ben Folds, OneRepublic, Sara Bareilles and Regina Spektor; TV personality and scientist Bill Nye the Science Guy; and medical doctor and social activist Patch Adams.

THE PORTFOLIO PROJECT: The portfolio project at Truman is a great way for students to keep track of their achievements. Students keep an evolving record of projects in several areas, including critical thinking, interdisciplinary thinking, historical analysis, scientific analysis, aesthetic analysis, and creative work and reflection. Students can track how they have grown and developed over the course of their college experience.

THE HONORS SCHOLAR PROGRAM: All Truman students are eligible for the Honors Scholar program. The program is designed for students who are academic thrill-seekers wanting a greater challenge. By taking advanced, specialized courses in lieu of their general studies requirements, Honors Scholars can explore in-depth topics and develop an even more sophisticated viewpoint on the subject matter.

KIRKSVILLE, MISSOURI: Truman State is in Kirksville, Missouri – a town of approximately seventeen thousand located in the northeast corner of the state. The historic downtown area is within walking distance of the Truman campus and provides a connection to the Kirksville community. Kirksville offers a variety of cultures, nationalities, interests, talents, abilities, values, and experiences.

---

http://www.truman.edu/
P: (800) 892-7792

PUBLIC

STUDENT PROFILE

5,853 undergraduate students

89% of undergrad students are full time

41% male – 59% female

21% of students are from out of state

89% freshman retention rate

73% graduated in 6 years

FACULTY PROFILE

333 full-time faculty

46 part-time faculty

16 to 1 student/faculty ratio

ADMISSIONS

3,900 Total Applicants

3,080 Total Admissions

1,262 Total Freshman Enrollment

78.97% of applicants admitted

SAT Ranges: CR 580-730, M 560-680

ACT Ranges: C 25-30, M 23-28, E 24-32

TUITION & COSTS

Tuition: (In) $7,152 (Out) $13,376

Fees: $304

Total: (In) $7,456 (Out) $13,680

R&B: $8,480

Room: $5,730

Board: $2,750

Total: (In) $15,936 (Out) $22,160

FINANCIAL

$8,760 avg grant/scholarship amount (total)

$5,975 avg loan amount (total)

WILLIAM JEWELL COLLEGE

LIBERTY, MISSOURI

"Live What You Learn" is more than just a catchphrase at William Jewell—it's a way of life, a way of thinking about the college experience a little differently. Time in the classroom is not enough to prepare for the challenges and opportunities of a rapidly changing world. Jewell is where students come to "dream" and come to "do." Students emerge as better speakers, better writers, and ultimately better prepared for the wide range of personal and professional opportunities that lie ahead.

A HOST OF DISTINCTIVE PROGRAMS THAT FOSTER GROWTH AND INVOLVEMENT: Located twenty minutes north of the heart of Kansas City, Jewell students experience the best of both worlds: access to internship opportunities and cultural and entertainment venues, all with the serenity of a peaceful hillside campus. William Jewell's national and international reputation is based in part on some of the college's unique programs.

FOUR YEARS, GUARANTEED: William Jewell offers a Four-Year Graduation Guarantee, ensuring the timely completion of a great liberal arts education that positions students to transition into graduate school or their careers ahead of most peers.

CORE CURRICULUM: William Jewell College believes that, for an individual to be fully prepared to meet the challenges of today's world, he or she must be capable of placing issues within a larger context rather than isolating them within rigidly defined subject areas. Because of the multidisciplinary philosophy of the school, Jewell's distinctive core curriculum places contemporary issues against a backdrop of relevant historical, cultural, and ethical ideas. The interdisciplinary curriculum is designed for students to consider the social sciences alongside the laws that govern the natural world, to study religion in relation to the social settings from which it developed, and to measure technological advances against the ethical dilemmas they sometimes create.

OXBRIDGE HONORS PROGRAM: As the only program in the United States that offers a full curriculum of tutorial-based instruction in conjunction with a year of study in England, the writing-intensive Oxbridge Honors Program extends through all four years of college. The highly personalized approach to education, with many opportunities for personal connections with faculty members, combines the best of the British and American approaches to education. In addition, international programs allow Jewell students to study at some of the greatest universities worldwide.

ACT-IN: William Jewell was the first college in the country to acknowledge completion of the college's thirty-eight-hour liberal arts core as a recognized major in Applied Critical Thought and Inquiry (ACT-In). The ACT-In major allows all students to graduate with double (and sometimes triple) majors. The ACT-In major validates a student's learning journey beyond the classroom. Students have the opportunity to connect what they learn to what they do.

PROGRAMS OF SERVICE: Through the Center for Justice and Sustainability, every Jewell student has the opportunity to participate in projects that focus on justice and sustainability issues. The Center annually hosts a Justice Summit, bringing national and local leaders together with Jewell students to address important issues of justice and sustainability.

CAREER SERVICES: The Career Services office at William Jewell offers support to students and alumni who are seeking full- or part-time employment. In addition, emphasis is placed on career guidance and counseling, and staff work with individual students throughout their time at Jewell to explore career issues.

http://www.jewell.edu/
P: (800) 753-7009

PRIVATE

STUDENT PROFILE

1,053 undergraduate students

97% of undergrad students are full time

42% male – 58% female

82% freshman retention rate

62% graduated in 6 years

FACULTY PROFILE

88 full-time faculty

60 part-time faculty

10 to 1 student/faculty ratio

ADMISSIONS

1,456 Total Applicants

719 Total Admissions

245 Total Freshman Enrollment

49.38% of applicants admitted

SAT Ranges: CR 500-640, M 490-620

ACT Ranges: C 23-28, M 22-27, E 23-30

TUITION & COSTS

Tuition: $31,223

Fees: $600

Total: $31,823

R&B: $8,880

Room: $4,950

Board: $3,930

Total: $40,703

FINANCIAL

$22,926 avg grant/scholarship amount (total)

$7,543 avg loan amount (total)

APPALACHIAN STATE UNIVERSITY

BOONE, NORTH CAROLINA

Appalachian State University's picturesque location and lively academic environment make it the perfect place to learn and grow. The University combines the intimacy of a smaller school with the research opportunities of a larger institution to provide students with the ultimate learning experience.

FIRST-YEAR SEMINAR: Every freshman at Appalachian State is required to take a First-Year Seminar (FYS). An FYS is an introductory course that eases students into college-level academics. Seminars also help students develop their critical thinking, writing, and research skills. Class sizes are small, which allows for more one-on-one attention from faculty. Students are taught to work as a community of learners who seek similar goals. Seminars range in topic, so students are able to enjoy a unique course that best suits their interests.

THE SOPHOMORE-YEAR EXPERIENCE (SYE): The Sophomore-Year Experience is specially catered to second-year students who are still undeclared and deciding on their majors. Sophomores enrolled in the SYE receive support through Life & Career Planning, a class that offers them access to advisors and career counseling staff. SYE aims to help sophomores narrow down a career path through various resources, academic advising, and co-curricular activities.

COMMON READING PROGRAM: All first-year students are asked to read a book before they arrive on campus, starting everyone off with the same shared academic experience. By reading the selected book, students become part of a community before they even start classes. The common reading introduces students to college-level coursework, all while enriching them with thought-provoking ideas that they may contemplate together.

EDUCATION ABROAD: The Office of International Education & Development is the number-one resource for study abroad. The office staff can help with decisions regarding program selection and scheduling conflicts. Students need only make an appointment, and an advisor will sit down and answer all their questions. With such helpful information about international travel, each student is able to pick an international location and program that is best for their adventurous desires as well as their degree plans.

STUDY ABROAD 101: All students who intend to go abroad are given a preparatory introduction to international travel through Study Abroad 101. This workshop covers all the abroad opportunities that are available at Appalachian State and gives students an idea of what to expect. Topics covered in the workshop include: program types, tips on how to find a program, costs, coursework and approval, scholarships, financial aid, and the application process. After students have completed Study Abroad 101, they are invited to take Study Abroad 102, which further aids in the application process.

STUDENT RESEARCH: Undergraduate research allows students to create original bodies of work within their field of study, whether that be through a thesis or an experiment. Research demonstrates to employers that a student has gained hands-on experience working with industry-related topics, showing proof of their extended knowledge within their area of study. The Office of Student Research, established in 2005, opens up possibilities for students to engage in original inquiry and work. Appalachian State also supports faculty-mentored research among students, giving them professional guidance through highly developed projects.

RESIDENTIAL LEARNING COMMUNITIES: Appalachian State is proud to offer residential learning communities (RLCs) for the many benefits they bring to student development. Participants of RLCs often have better grades, are more involved, and enjoy academic support from faculty and peers. The University offers several RLC options that range from special interest to a First-Year Seminar residence. Most RLCs involve a course or set of courses that link the residence component of the community to academics. Students engage in an educational experience in which their peers and faculty become part of the journey.

---

http://www.appstate.edu/

P: (828) 262-2000

PUBLIC

STUDENT PROFILE

16,255 undergraduate students

94% of undergrad students are full time

46% male – 54% female

11% of students are from out of state

88% freshman retention rate

70% graduated in 6 years

FACULTY PROFILE

920 full-time faculty

351 part-time faculty

16 to 1 student/faculty ratio

ADMISSIONS

13,506 Total Applicants

8,463 Total Admissions

3,033 Total Freshman Enrollment

62.66% of applicants admitted

SAT Ranges: CR 530-620, M 530-620, W 500-600

ACT Ranges: C 23-27, M 23-27, E 23-28, W 6-8

TUITION & COSTS

Tuition: (In) $3,772 (Out) $16,939

Fees: (In) $2,781 (Out) $2,781

Total: (In) $6,553 (Out) $19,720

R&B: $7,675

Room: $4,125

Board: $3,550

Total: (In) $14,228 (Out) $27,395

FINANCIAL

$7,961 avg grant/scholarship amount (total)

$5,561 avg loan amount (total)

CATAWBA COLLEGE

SALISBURY, NORTH CAROLINA

Catawba College is a private, coeducational college in Salisbury, North Carolina that provides students a personally attentive education—one which blends the knowledge of liberal studies with career preparation. Catawba assures its students' success through adherence to four core tenets: Scholarship, Character, Culture, and Service. The College offers a robust honors program, a full complement of study abroad destinations, and an engaging First-Year Experience. Catawba boasts 20 Division II varsity athletic teams and is a member of the South Atlantic Conference.

FIRST-YEAR EXPERIENCE: The First-Year Summer Retreat and the First-Year Seminar comprise Catawba's First-Year Experience. Through the Retreat, incoming students have the opportunity to make new friends and engage with faculty and staff. During this three-day, off-campus experience, students learn about the history of Catawba and its culture. This shared experience helps provide a smooth transition into college life and assures students a social network when they arrive on campus.

LIBERAL ARTS CURRICULUM: Regardless of a student's academic interest, a Catawba education is defined by excellent professional and pre-professional programs that blend the competencies of the liberal arts, such as critical thinking, strong written and oral communications, analytical problem-solving, and working in diverse teams. The Catawba faculty are committed to infusing all classes with experiences that give students the opportunity to develop and hone these skills throughout their undergraduate career.

GLOBAL LEARNING: Catawba is committed to providing opportunities for global education, which is achieved by its partnership with University Studies Abroad Consortium (USAC). Through Catawba's membership in USAC, students have access to over 40 semester or summer abroad destinations. The College also provides opportunities for students to take course work with shorter opportunities to travel abroad with their faculty and classmates over fall or spring break.

UNDERGRADUATE RESEARCH: Students across academic disciplines look forward to the opportunity to share their research each spring during an on-campus, interdisciplinary Catawba Research and Creativity Showcase. They are also encouraged by faculty to present their scholarly research at state, regional, and national academic and professional conferences.

SALISBURY CONNECTIONS: Catawba College and the City of Salisbury enjoy a strong relationship that includes collaborations with local theatrical and musical venues, partnerships with local non-profit service organizations, and internship opportunities at local businesses and government entities. Some examples include student-organized dances and proms for local elderly and special needs populations, conducting student research to identify local strains of yeast for a microbrewery, market research for downtown businesses, and working in a partnership between the Catawba Worship Arts program and local churches of various denominations.

C2C PROGRAM: The Catawba College to Career (C2C) program is an opportunity offered to students in their sophomore year. This program allows students to take the FOCUS 2 assessment, which provides information about the student's personality, interests, and preferred work environments. This assessment provides these students with a list of potential career paths and suggests major areas of study that are best fit to prepare them for those fields. Students meet one-on-one with a Career Counselor to review their results, exploring information from the U.S. Department of Labor that provides a 10-year outlook for their recommended careers. C2C Career Counselors also work with students to develop a résumé that highlights their particular strengths and helps them develop a plan to enhance through their opportunities for growth.

CAREER SERVICES: Career Services also provides an array of offerings to Catawba students, including mock interview opportunities, etiquette dinners, résumé support, career fairs, graduate school fairs, and assistance with internship placement.

http://catawba.edu/

P: (704) 637-4402

PRIVATE - CHRISTIAN

STUDENT PROFILE

1,276 undergraduate students

97% of undergrad students are full time

47% male – 53% female

23% of students are from out of state

72% freshman retention rate

52% graduated in 6 years

FACULTY PROFILE

80 full-time faculty

65 part-time faculty

13 to 1 student/faculty ratio

ADMISSIONS

2,528 Total Applicants

1,190 Total Admissions

348 Total Freshman Enrollment

47.07% of applicants admitted

SAT Ranges: CR 420-550, M 430-540

ACT Ranges: C 18-24, M 17-24, E 16-24

TUITION & COSTS

Tuition: $29,920

R&B: $10,488

Total: $40,408

FINANCIAL

$6,855 avg grant/scholarship amount (need)

$4,520 avg loan amount (need)

ELON UNIVERSITY

ELON, NORTH CAROLINA

Elon students are fully involved. This is a university of boundless opportunity in which students have a passion to fulfill their roles as global citizens and put their knowledge into action on campus, in the community, and around the world. Elon's four-year core curriculum has a strong global focus and is organized around the themes of inquiry, knowledge, and communication.

THE ELON EXPERIENCES: Elon students connect their education to the real world through hands-on learning. The university's signature program, The Elon Experiences, provides a natural extension of the work done in the classroom and can be completed individually or combined to suit students' specific goals. Students can seek out service opportunities while they're abroad or find internships that correlate with their multi-year research project. They can even establish leadership development programs in local schools. Professors become students' mentors and guides throughout the Experiences, ensuring that, by the time students graduate, they have a wealth of real-world experiences that ease their transitions out of college.

FIRST-YEAR EXPERIENCES: Freshmen can make the most of their first years with programs and experiences that help them navigate the transition to college. A fall semester orientation course, a common reading program, and move-in help from faculty and staff make students feel welcome to the Elon community. First-Year Summer Experiences are optional programs that pair hands-on learning with such core Elon values as leadership and service. Incoming freshmen can hike the Appalachian Trail, work with Habitat for Humanity, learn how to become activists, and more.

STUDY ABROAD: Global Study at Elon includes 100+ study abroad programs and Study USA. During their time abroad, many Elon students pursue research, service, and internships. International internships can be completed for academic credit, and Elon's domestic travel programs take students not only to large cities like New York and Los Angeles, but also to rural communities in Appalachia and the Gulf Coast. Winter Term, summer, and semester-long Study USA program options are offered.

DRIVEN FACULTY: Distinguished faculty choose to teach at Elon because they love to mentor students. With small classes and a 12:1 student-to-faculty ratio, they are able to challenge individual students to reach their highest potential. Elon faculty are active and productive scholars with rich academic and professional experience. Through Elon's Center for Engaged Learning, faculty members are leading an international conversation about the most effective teaching and learning strategies.

CORE CURRICULUM: Elon's four-year core curriculum has a strong global focus and is organized around the themes of inquiry, knowledge, and communication. Students learn to see the world through many different perspectives and therefore grow to understand the complex relationships among the world's people, cultures, beliefs, and environments.

A CAMPUS OF COMFORT AND GROWTH: Elon students live and learn on a campus that has been specifically designed to encourage both personal growth and academic discovery. The high-tech campus encompasses seven distinct residential neighborhoods for students at various stages of their college careers.

PREPARED FOR THE WORLD: The Elon Core Curriculum is a set of courses and experiences that are shared by every undergraduate. The curriculum complements everyone's major, focusing on the liberal arts and sciences that are so important to Elon's mission and so vital for globally engaged citizenship in a democratic society. Students explore ideas and expand their worldview, gaining the lifelong benefits of complexity of thought, personal fulfillment, economic opportunity, and global awareness. The learning goals of the Core Curriculum reflect the same skills expected in the workplace, including critical thinking, writing, and problem-solving skills. Elon has also undertaken an extensive Writing Excellence Initiative to help students in all majors develop written communication skills that they will use throughout their lives.

ELON UNIVERSITY

http://elon.edu/
P: (336) 278-2000

PRIVATE

STUDENT PROFILE

5,903 undergraduate students

97% of undergrad students are full time

41% male – 59% female

80% of students are from out of state

90% freshman retention rate

83% graduated in 6 years

FACULTY PROFILE

441 full-time faculty

151 part-time faculty

12 to 1 student/faculty ratio

ADMISSIONS

10,256 Total Applicants

5,866 Total Admissions

1,524 Total Freshman Enrollment

57.20% of applicants admitted

SAT Ranges: CR 550-640, M 560-650, W 550-650

ACT Ranges: C 25-29, M 24-28, E 25-31

TUITION & COSTS

Tuition: $31,773

Fees: $399

Total: $32,172

R&B: $10,998

Room: $5,399

Board: $5,599

Total: $43,170

FINANCIAL

$11,735 avg grant/scholarship amount (total)

$8,297 avg loan amount (total)

GARDNER-WEBB UNIVERSITY

BOILING SPRINGS, NORTH CAROLINA

GARDNER-WEBB
UNIVERSITY

Gardner-Webb University, located just 50 miles outside of Charlotte, North Carolina, fosters an all-inclusive campus community that values its Christian roots, diversity, and academic excellence. From the on-campus bell tower that overlooks Lake Hollifield to the surrounding community of Boiling Springs, Gardner-Webb surrounds students with a rich and abundant culture, all while providing a quality education and invaluable experiences. Gardner-Webb is dedicated to higher education that engages scholarship in conjunction with Christian life, fostering intellectual development, critical reflection, and spiritual formation. Because GWU is concerned about the needs of others in order to grow in knowledge and wisdom, the University enthusiastically affirms active participation in influential and impactful initiatives.

SSTUDY ABROAD: Gardner-Webb University's study abroad program provides students with numerous opportunities to explore the world and receive class credit. With programs offered in countries like Sweden, Canada, Spain, and China, the cultural possibilities are endless! Flexible options for study abroad can range from short-term trips to entire semesters. And, with the help of faculty, they can even customize their program to take full advantage of their once-in-a-lifetime journey. A trip abroad opens up a unique medium for learning, enriching students' minds with extraordinary environments and complete immersion into a new culture.

HONORS PROGRAM: Gardner-Webb's unique Honors Program consists of a refined niche of dedicated students. This program encourages students to thrive in an active learning environment that fosters lively, engaging discussions in challenging, stimulating classes. The Honors Program, which has grown impressively since its founding in 1988, integrates students into their surrounding community through community service and aids their personal development through such out-of-classroom activities as dinners, exclusive trips, and conferences. Instructors of Honors courses are constantly reevaluating their teaching methods and improving their courses to best accommodate the accelerated, in-depth approach set by the high standard of the program. Students at Gardner-Webb say that their Honors classes are incredibly rewarding in the way they push them to grow as confident communicators and active learners.

DIMENSIONS: Each Tuesday morning within the walls of the University's Student Center, guest speakers invite students to listen to their proclamations of faith and their commitment to strong ethics. These weekly speeches allow a range of thought leaders to emphasize the importance and relevance of the Christian and Baptist values that are upheld within the campus community. Referred to as "Dimensions," the unique lectures promote religious growth, worship, and a strong intent of service to God. Gardner-Webb instills a strong sense of Christian community within its student body, allowing them to grow in spirit, intellect, and culture all throughout their college career.

INTERNSHIPS: Gardner-Webb encourages students to gain real-world experience, providing them ample assistance and guidance toward rewarding internships. By working side-by-side with professionals, students are able both to enrich their coursework at school and prepare them with invaluable skills for their future career. Students can participate in internships through Gardner-Webb to gain invaluable experience in their prospective fields. The Career Center for Development and Internships stands as a helpful resource that gives students a plan for integrating internship experience into their four-year plan, advising them to choose one of three categories that best suits their goals. Students can choose from internships through an academic department, internships through the University's certified program, or external internships. Regardless of their plan of action, students are supported with résumé and cover letter help and other resources for nailing the interview process.

http://gardner-webb.edu/
P: (704) 406-4000

PRIVATE - CHRISTIAN

STUDENT PROFILE

2,362 undergraduate students

81% of undergrad students are full time

39% male – 61% female

23.7% of students are from out of state

66.38% freshman retention rate

70.12% graduated in 6 years

FACULTY PROFILE

167 full-time faculty

196 part-time faculty

13 to 1 student/faculty ratio

ADMISSIONS

4,846 Total Applicants

1,294 Total Admissions

562 Total Freshman Enrollment

26.70% of applicants admitted

SAT Ranges: CR 430-550, M 440-560

ACT Ranges: C 18-24

TUITION & COSTS

Tuition: $30,310

Fees: $430

Total: $30,740

R&B: $10,080

Total: $40,820

FINANCIAL

$7,571 avg grant/scholarship amount (need)

$4,367 avg loan amount (need)

HIGH POINT UNIVERSITY

HIGH POINT, NORTH CAROLINA

High Point University is different. It's student-centered. It's values-based. It's a holistic learning environment whose recent transformation has already brought more than 25 new buildings to campus, doubled the number of faculty, and tripled the size of the freshman class.

FIRST-YEAR SUCCESS COACHES: At the beginning of freshman year, each student is assigned a First-Year Success Coach. The coach eases students through the transition into college by providing them with academic support and advising as well as opportunities to get comfortable and connected both inside and outside of the classroom.

EACH YEAR AN ADVENTURE: What makes High Point University distinctive are carefully crafted, holistic academic plans that merge classroom knowledge and experiences with the necessary life skills that make students highly competitive within the global marketplace. It begins right away with HPU President Nido Qubein's first-year Seminar on Life Skills and continues in more than 100 different ways throughout every student's four years at HPU.

EXPERIENTIAL LEARNING: High Point University's signature experiential learning program differs from the typical collegiate experience. Here, the world is anyone's laboratory. Students have opportunities to study abroad, hold off-campus internships, career shadow, conduct undergraduate research or independent study, participate in service-learning, and volunteer with nonprofit agencies. These avenues reinforce what they learn in the classroom, all while providing resources for professional networking and the practical knowledge within their fields of study.

HONORS SCHOLAR PROGRAM: The Honors Scholar Program is designed to provide enhanced educational opportunities for motivated and talented students from all majors. These enhanced educational opportunities are an array of in-class and out-of-class co-curricular experiences that promote academic, personal, and professional growth. Scholars in the program have the unique opportunity to participate in small group discussions with visiting scholars, conduct independent research with top faculty, and attend national honors conferences.

DIVERSE LEARNING COMMUNITY: HPU's Kester International Promenade is adorned with flags in support of the school's diversity, with students from 50 states and 37 countries. The residential communities are as diverse as the student population and even provide opportunities for honors housing and living and learning communities. All housing is new or recently renovated, with many dorms boasting high-end, apartment-style living. The campus is completely wireless, and students are able to check out complimentary iPads, Kindles, or GPS units from the Campus Concierge. Students may also schedule academic tutoring, reserve a bicycle, and receive complimentary tickets to all athletic events, concerts, speakers, and films.

PREPARATION: Throughout their years at High Point University, students are given real-world, practical learning opportunities. They develop etiquette and conversation skills at the 1924 Prime on-campus fine-dining restaurant. They also utilize a corporate boardroom and a stock-ticker room within the Plato S. Wilson School of Commerce, and they're given access to top-of-the-line technology throughout campus. The Office of Career and Professional Development Services team help students secure internships and externships with companies like: Apple, NASA, Animal Planet, Seventeen Magazine, Disney, MTV, PricewaterhouseCoopers LLP, and Merrill Lynch. The networking connections that students are exposed to during their internships help lead them to full-time positions after they graduate.

ALUMNI: Because High Point University takes such enormous strides to equip students for successful futures, it is no surprise that alumni are honored in leadership positions across the world. High Point University is called home by the COO of BB&T, Bloomberg's NYC Hedge Fund manager, the head men's basketball coach for the University of Memphis, many government officials, the former executive producer of the NBC Today Show, several authors, a Grammy Award winner, an Emmy Award winner, and many more.

http://www.highpoint.edu/
P: (336) 841-9216

PRIVATE

STUDENT PROFILE

4,362 undergraduate students

99% of undergrad students are full time

40% male – 60% female

78% of students are from out of state

81% freshman retention rate

65% graduated in 6 years

FACULTY PROFILE

276 full-time faculty

145 part-time faculty

13 to 1 student/faculty ratio

ADMISSIONS

10,910 Total Applicants

7,909 Total Admissions

1,362 Total Freshman Enrollment

72.49% of applicants admitted

SAT Ranges: CR 501-593, M 511-603, W 490-593

ACT Ranges: C 22-27, M 21-26, E 21-26

TUITION & COSTS

Tuition: $28,600

Fees: $3,830

Total: $32,430

R&B: $12,200

Total: $44,630

FINANCIAL

$2,910 avg grant/scholarship amount (need)

$5,091 avg loan amount (need)

LEES-MCRAE COLLEGE

BANNER ELK, NORTH CAROLINA

Lees-McRae College, founded in 1900, is a private, four-year institution that provides a well-rounded experiential education within the Blue Ridge Mountains of western North Carolina. Offering a diverse array of undergraduate degrees on the all-residential campus, as well as five programs online and at an extended-campus site at Surry Community College, Lees-McRae College fosters personal growth and exploration while providing a platform for environmental and community stewardship. As part of its core mission, Lees-McRae develops strong candidates for marketplace demands through creative, collaborative, and critical thinking with a focus on experiential learning. A Lees-McRae College education is hallmarked by the foundational belief that learning happens both in and outside of the classroom. During the school year, students across programs participate in experiential opportunities to deepen and hone their unique and individual skill sets. From working backstage in Hayes Auditorium to the mock crime scene event put on by the Criminal Justice program, students are encouraged to practice and apply their skills.

COMMON INTELLECTUAL EXPERIENCES: All Lees-McRae students complete several general education and core curriculum courses designed to develop a cutting-edge mindset in critical, creative, and collaborative inquiry. Lees-McRae students think differently, see the world differently, and see themselves differently. As students progress through the core curriculum, they create a foundation on which to build their specific field of study. This foundation is what prepares Lees-McRae students for a lifetime of learning and success. Each student who passes through Lees-McRae College is required to participate in four Core Liberal Arts courses designed to hone and further develop the skills needed to successfully complete an undergraduate degree. Their college career is formed around a foundational understanding of Self and the Environment, Career and Life Planning, and Global Citizenship and Ethics. In their senior year, they then apply this knowledge to their specific fields of study to a senior capstone project.

UNDERGRADUATE RESEARCH: In addition to research completed for each senior's required capstone project, many students are invited to participate in individual research by Lees-McRae faculty. Many of those research projects are presented at conferences and events across the U.S. Students within the Wildlife Biology program carry out research at the Elk Valley Preserve and Field Station. The college's property provides students with the opportunity to conduct real-world research in a natural environment. While there, students complete long-term research and gather data on various mammals, salamanders, snakes, and various fish.

SERVICE AND SOCIAL JUSTICE: Over the course of April, students across campus participate in events for Sexual Assault Awareness Month, working in coordination with the Lees-McRae Campus Life; Delta Zeta Nu, a community service-based sorority; and OASIS, a local nonprofit that serves survivors of sexual and domestic violence. Students also participate in such projects as the Clothesline Project, including Tea Week, a week-long event filled with presentations, films, and games in order to learn about a variety of topics related to sex, sexuality, and gender.

CAREER PREPARATION: Within Career Services at Lees-McRae College, students can begin exploring the possible career paths that fit their individual values, skills, and passions. At the Career Center, students can explore majors and programs, develop strong resumes and cover letters, participate in practice interviews, search for job openings, and explore the graduate and professional school application process. Students are also invited to participate in a formal dinner to practice important business-meeting etiquette. Other annual events include a Job Fair as well as the Career and Leadership Connections event, at which students participate in mock interviews and attend speaker sessions.

---

http://www.lmc.edu/

P: (828) 898-5241

PRIVATE - CHRISTIAN

STUDENT PROFILE

991 undergraduate students

99% of undergrad students are full time

34% male — 66% female

38% of students are from out of state

58.1% freshman retention rate

38% graduated in 6 years

FACULTY PROFILE

53 full-time faculty

86 part-time faculty

12 to 1 student/faculty ratio

ADMISSIONS

1,531 Total Applicants

965 Total Admissions

187 Total Freshman Enrollment

63.03% of applicants admitted

SAT Ranges: CR 440-580, M 450-560

ACT Ranges: C 18-23, M 17-23, E 16-23

TUITION & COSTS

Tuition: $24,878

Fees: $1,320

Total: $26,198

R&B: $10,758

Total: $36,956

FINANCIAL

$9,137 avg grant/scholarship amount (need)

$5,492 avg loan amount (need)

MEREDITH COLLEGE

RALEIGH, NORTH CAROLINA

Meredith College has been educating strong, confident women for more than a century. Students at Meredith identify and build upon their strengths, and classes are small so that students are seen as the unique individuals they are. And most importantly, Meredith's personal approach to education means that faculty and staff know when students are ready for the next challenge.

UNDERGRADUATE RESEARCH: The Undergraduate Research program at Meredith allows students to work on research projects one-on-one with a faculty member in their field. The program supports partnerships between faculty and students across all departments and may fund student travel to conferences where research is presented.

COMMUNITY-BASED LEARNING: Community-Based Learning connects classroom learning with service projects that benefit the community. Students who participate in community-based learning report strengthened academic performance, increased motivation to engage in their coursework, and heightened awareness of the issues that impact the community.

HONORS PROGRAM: The Meredith Honors Program gives students the opportunity to delve deeper into their areas of interest. Honors students complete 28 hours of Honors courses as well as an Honors senior project that is individually designed and then presented in a public forum. Honors students take at least two interdisciplinary, team-taught Honors colloquia, thereby allowing students to expand their knowledge and think about a subject through the perspective of multiple disciplines. Honors students participate in independent research, conferences, weekend trips, study abroad, and convocations.

TEACHING FELLOWS: The Meredith Teaching Fellows program offers a dynamic educational experience that is enriched with opportunities to gain hands-on classroom experience, learn from education professionals, participate in study abroad, and enroll in Honors courses. Teaching Fellows participate in a superior academic program that blends the liberal arts, a major in their chosen academic field, and professional courses that lead to their teacher licensure.

LEADERSHIP: Meredith students participate in such programs as the LeaderShape Institute, Emerging Leaders Seminar Series, Sophie Lanneau Women's Leadership Development Program, and the annual LEAD Conference. Additionally, women hold all of the more than 500 leadership positions available on campus.

IN-DEPTH, COLLABORATIVE LEARNING: Each program of study at Meredith incorporates interdisciplinary study, experiential learning, and global awareness. The Fashion Merchandising and Design program sponsors trips to Paris, New York's Garment District, and the Atlanta Merchandise Mart. Students in the education program select a major of their choice and earn education licensure alongside their degree. Health science students have access to the Human Performance Lab, and humanities students learn from Raleigh's archives, museums, and historic sites.

UNIQUE ON-CAMPUS FACILITIES: Meredith is home to the Meredith Autism Program, an early intervention program for children who have been diagnosed on the autism spectrum. It is one of the only programs of its kind in the U.S. to offer hands-on clinical course experience to undergraduates. Also available are the Ellen Brewer House, a five-star child care program that gives child development majors real-world experience, and the Human Performance Lab, at which exercise and sports science students conduct research and learn to administer fitness assessments.

INTERNSHIPS: Most students at Meredith complete not one but several internships. The Office of Career Planning and faculty internship coordinators work with students to identify their ideal internships as well as connect them with professionals within the community. Internships frequently turn into full-time jobs upon graduation.

MEREDITH COLLEGE

http://www.meredith.edu/
P: (919) 760-8600

PRIVATE

STUDENT PROFILE

1,679 undergraduate students

96% of undergrad students are full time

0% male – 100% female

79% freshman retention rate

62% graduated in 6 years

FACULTY PROFILE

157 full-time faculty

4 part-time faculty

12 to 1 student/faculty ratio

ADMISSIONS

1,721 Total Applicants

1,033 Total Admissions

439 Total Freshman Enrollment

60.02% of applicants admitted

SAT Ranges: CR 460-560, M 460-570

ACT Ranges: C 20-25, M 18-24, E 19-25

TUITION & COSTS

Tuition: $33,630

Fees: $100

Total: $33,730

R&B: $10,040

Total: $43,770

FINANCIAL

$18,481 avg grant/scholarship amount (total)

$7,966 avg loan amount (total)

PFEIFFER UNIVERSITY

MISENHEIMER, NORTH CAROLINA

Pfeiffer University is a private liberal arts university affiliated with the United Methodist Church. Its mission is to prepare leaders for lifelong learning and service. Pfeiffer's traditional undergraduate campus is in Misenheimer, N.C.—approximately 40 miles northeast of Charlotte—with additional locations in Charlotte and the Raleigh area. Since it's founding in 1885, Pfeiffer has continually grown in academic excellence, developing new programs to meet the needs of its students and emphasizing the ideals of Christian service.

ENGAGED AND INSPIRED: Pfeiffer University is a tremendous place to learn, filled with multi-talented students, dedicated faculty, and supportive administrators. It strives to foster personal connections among each and every member of the Pfeiffer family. The University provides its students with experiences to live, learn, worship, and serve as they grow into leaders inspired to change the world. Students learn to be effective group members and leaders as they plan and implement their own activities, programs, and events for their fellow Pfeiffer University students and staff.

THE PFEIFFER JOURNEY: Pfeiffer strives to provide a holistic education to each and every student. Sending students on the Pfeiffer Journey, the University dedicates each year to different levels of progression toward their postgraduate careers. In the first year, students get grounded with a foundational exposure to campus resources. Sophomores are then encouraged to explore their academic options, and juniors integrate their experiences with leadership and volunteer work. The senior year rounds off the Journey with culminating capstone projects and portfolios.

SCHOLARLY PROFESSORS: The University has approximately 80 outstanding, nationally-recruited faculty, many of whom hold doctorates or other terminal degrees in their teaching fields. While their primary focus is on their students' growth, the faculty are engaged in their own scholarly, creative, and public service initiatives. Pfeiffer seeks professors who value and contribute to students' intellectual and emotional growth, so it's no surprise that students are often invited to assist them with their exciting projects.

STUDENT ACTIVITIES: There are lots of things to do outside of the Pfeiffer classroom, and because the University is small, it is so easy to get involved. On campus, more than 30 student clubs and organizations, Falcon athletics, campus life, and leadership activities provide enriching college experiences that prepare students for professional and personal success. The Student Government Association (SGA), InterClub Council (ICC), and Campus Activities Board (CAB) are just some of the organizations that regularly serve the entire student population.

CONSTANTLY CONNECTED: During the Pfeiffer experience, many students find that their most important learning happens outside the classroom. Each of the campuses offer spaces for students to meet informally, share meals, and use access useful scholarly resources. They also have opportunities to meet with their professors and engage in professional societies and organizations that enhance their learning experiences. And they have even more opportunities to grow through a combination of high-quality academics and meaningful service abroad in countries all around the world.

CAREER SERVICES: Pfeiffer offers innovative services and guidance for its students' future careers in the global marketplace. Programs are continually updated to partner students with the best of the community's employers, including the Michelin tire manufacturer, which has supported students in all aspects of the company like data analysis and injury prevention. With an educational model that blends ideology, research, and practical application, students learn to collaborate through group work, refine their communication skills, and discover the value of civic engagement in a changing society.

---

http://www.pfeiffer.edu/

P: (800) 338-2060

PRIVATE

STUDENT PROFILE

917 undergraduate students

89% of undergrad students are full time

42% male – 58% female

69% freshman retention rate

43% graduated in 6 years

FACULTY PROFILE

97 full-time faculty

45 part-time faculty

12 to 1 student/faculty ratio

ADMISSIONS

1,627 Total Applicants

757 Total Admissions

160 Total Freshman Enrollment

46.53% of applicants admitted

SAT Ranges: CR 405-530, M 400-530

ACT Ranges: C 17-22, M 18-23, E 15-21

TUITION & COSTS

Tuition: $26,200

Fees: $925

Total: $27,125

R&B: $10,525

Room: $5,750

Board: $4,775

Total: $37,650

FINANCIAL

$19,521 avg grant/scholarship amount (total)

$10,683 avg loan amount (total)

SALEM COLLEGE

WINSTON-SALEM, NORTH CAROLINA

As the oldest educational institution for women in the United States, Salem boasts a proud history of fostering women's independence and confidence. Salem students have the freedom to explore who they are and who they want to be. Salem is a college where women from all over the world are encouraged to shine in every aspect of their lives. From the first moment students step on campus to the day they graduate, they are given the freedom to explore their skills and talents; be actively involved with the community; make lifelong friendships with fellow students; and learn from outstanding faculty members. Salem is confident that students will experience a vision of education that will shape their present and impact their future. Salem women can do anything. Becoming one of them means that, at graduation, students have not only the knowledge, but also the confidence and the vision to put that knowledge to work.

LEAD PROGRAM: All Salem students have a chance to lead on campus and in the community. Through Salem's four-year LEAD program, students identify their unique potential and develop their own signature leadership styles. Participating in workshops and local and national leadership conferences, they hone the skills that 21st-century employers value most. Their success begins with the Salem Signature curriculum, which sharpens their critical thinking and quantitative reasoning. And, ultimately, students graduate with 30 hours of community service and at least one professional internship.

CAMPUS TRADITIONS: Salem has many special traditions, among which include Fall Lawn, an annual dance held on campus; Fall Fest, when classes compete against one another in various activities; Christmas Candlelight Service; Founder's Day celebration; Opening and Closing Convocation; and the Leadership Banquet. Salem also features a Big Sister/Little Sister program in which juniors adopt a first-year student to introduce them to the college and facilitate the transition into college life. The program features a number of organized social activities to strengthen the bond of all Salem students.

JANUARY TERM. AN OPPORTUNITY TO FOCUS: In their first year, students take an on-campus course or faculty-sponsored travel program throughout the month of January. In following years, these options expand to include internships across the country and around the world. Jan Term is the perfect opportunity for students to work full-time in a professional field of interest, conduct an independent research project, or focus on one course in a specialty area. On-campus, intensive courses include Young Women's Activism: The Third Wave; Green Design: and Politics in Film.

ALUMNAE NETWORK: Salem's alumnae network is comprised of over 12,000 women and reaches across 49 states, two US territories, and 33 foreign countries. No matter the arena—business, media, international affairs, politics, education, medicine, science, the arts—Salem alumnae have long been recognized for service to and leadership in their communities. They are always ready to help new generations of Salem students and graduates with internships, career advice, mentoring, and a welcome into their cities and towns.

FOUR AREAS OF DISTINCTION: The college offers in-depth programming in four areas of distinction. The Center for Women Writers at Salem College provides an opportunity for writers to express their creativity all throughout the community, and the School of Music continues to shine since its early accreditation by the National Association of Schools of Music. Additionally, the Women in Science and Mathematics program and Women in Business and Economics program both get students in touch with professionals in their fields and provides a wealth of opportunities for research and other projects.

---

http://www.salem.edu/
P: (800) 327-2536

PRIVATE

STUDENT PROFILE

938 undergraduate students

82% of undergrad students are full time

4% male – 96% female

83% freshman retention rate

60% graduated in 6 years

FACULTY PROFILE

67 full-time faculty

79 part-time faculty

11 to 1 student/faculty ratio

ADMISSIONS

903 Total Applicants

562 Total Admissions

187 Total Freshman Enrollment

62.24% of applicants admitted

SAT Ranges: CR 470-640, M 470-600

ACT Ranges: C 21-29, M 20-29, E 20-30

TUITION & COSTS

Tuition: $25,870

Fees: $366

Total: $26,236

R&B: $11,824

Room: $5,840

Board: $5,984

Total: $38,060

FINANCIAL

$24,177 avg grant/scholarship amount (total)

$6,028 avg loan amount (total)

UNIVERSITY OF MOUNT OLIVE

MT. OLIVE, NORTH CAROLINA

The University of Mount Olive has become one of the most unique and fastest-growing universities in North Carolina. The University offers rigorous academic programs, over 60 majors and minors, experienced faculty, small class sizes, and Division II athletics with a winning tradition. Grounded in the liberal arts, the University of Mount Olive helps individuals realize their creative potential while preparing them for professional careers.

THE RIGHT START: In the first-year experience course, students explore a number of topics to help them adjust to college life and prepare them for successful futures. Students learn skills that assist them in assimilating to campus and community as well as how to navigate the technology used in courses.

FACULTY: The University of Mount Olive is committed to providing every student with a quality education in a safe and rewarding environment. Faculty serve both as experts within their area of study as well as mentors to their students as they prepare for successful careers. Classes are small and taught by professors who want to see each student develop into their personal best. The student-to-faculty ratio is 15:1, allowing for personal interaction between students and their professors.

HONORS PROGRAM: The Honors program gives students with outstanding high school achievements the opportunity to be intellectually challenged in a community with other advanced scholars. Honors students participate in an academic enrichment program that consists of seminars, forums, and projects. Throughout the program, students study the global aspect of classical literature and writing and then decide upon a country that they wish to visit. This program culminates in a ten-day international trip to the country of their choosing.

INTERNSHIP AND RESEARCH OPPORTUNITIES: Students at the University of Mount Olive are able to gain real-world experience from internships and research projects within their field of study. Internships are required in several majors, providing students the opportunity to apply practical knowledge in their day-to-day experiences. Research projects also provide students an opportunity to work hand-in-hand with faculty members in their field of study as they gain experience that will continue to benefit their future studies and career.

SPIRITUAL LIFE: As a denominational ministry of the Original Free Will Baptists, the University of Mount Olive is committed to educating students mentally, physically, and spiritually. Weekly chapel services are held, though not required. Several student-led groups are also available to help students grow in their faith and leadership.

CLUBS AND ORGANIZATIONS: The Campus Activities Board offers fun on-campus activities, including movie nights, socials, and fun games. Off-campus trips have included sporting events, skiing trips, and theatre outings. A wide variety of student organizations provide everyone the chance to get involved and grow as leaders. The University's clubs and organizations include performance groups, student-run interest groups, and organizations that are sponsored by various departments on campus.

PREPARATION FOR SUCCESS: The University of Mount Olive's holistic approach to education seeks to educate students and prepare them for life beyond the college classroom. Students are asked to adhere to the University's covenant, calling each person to demonstrate the virtues modeled by Jesus Christ, including honesty, trustworthiness, justice, courage, responsibility, gratitude, and respect. Capstone courses allow students to gain first-hand experience through a senior project that can provide the catalyst for further education or career exploration. Upon completion of their bachelor's degree, many graduates have enrolled in such graduate schools as University of North Carolina, East Carolina University, North Carolina State University, Duke University, Campbell University, Liberty University, Seton Hall, Lincoln Memorial University, and James Madison University.

University of
MOUNT OLIVE

http://www.umo.edu/
P: (800) 653-0854

PRIVATE

STUDENT PROFILE

3,251 undergraduate students

43% of undergrad students are full time

33% male – 67% female

13% of students are from out of state

58% freshman retention rate

39% graduated in 6 years

FACULTY PROFILE

93 full-time faculty

14 to 1 student/faculty ratio

ADMISSIONS

2,262 Total Applicants

1,143 Total Admissions

302 Total Freshman Enrollment

50.53% of applicants admitted

SAT Ranges: CR 395-500, M 400-520

ACT Ranges: C 17-21, M 16-22, E 15-21

TUITION & COSTS

Tuition: $18,400

R&B: $7,400

Total: $25,800

FINANCIAL

$12,474 avg grant/scholarship amount (total)

$5,916 avg loan amount (total)

UNIVERSITY OF NORTH CAROLINA – WILMINGTON

WILMINGTON, NORTH CAROLINA

UNCW is unique among public comprehensive universities because it offers effective learning environments for undergraduates that integrate teaching and mentoring with research and service. A UNCW education spans across several departments and disciplines, giving students a well-rounded academic experience. The skills gained from a UNCW education prepare students for postgraduate success, whether that be personal or professional. Located in Wilmington, North Carolina, UNCW also offers numerous outdoor and recreational activities for students to enjoy. Sitting within driving distance of the beach, Wilmington is a great city to learn in.

COMMITTED FACULTY: UNCW maintains a standard for its faculty and students. A college experience is about endless discovery, of both oneself and one's academic potential. With that standard in mind, an institution needs to be well-equipped with qualified professionals who are prepared to lead those journeys. At UNCW, professors demonstrate a sincere interest in their students. At the crux of this educational experience is the relationship between faculty and students. UNCW professors uphold a commitment to innovation. An education is meant to be molded, and its participants, whether professor or student, must be willing to push boundaries in an effort to discover academic and personal potentials.

CORNERSTONE LEARNING COMMUNITIES: The Cornerstone Learning Community option is only available to first-year students. Interested students have the opportunity to live and take classes with the same group of students. Participants in this program have the benefit of a close-knit learning and social community. Students involved in Cornerstone Learning Communities take courses that are linked to one another, and professors in the program collaborate with one another to enhance this unique, educational experience. As an added benefit, those students who participate enjoy smaller classroom dynamics, which leads to an increased sense of worth and individualized attention. Participation in this program means the completion of three University requirements, as well as the experience of practicing academic theories outside of the classroom.

STUDENT LEARNING CATEGORIES AND GOALS: The University bases its curriculum around four student learning categories: creative inquiry, critical thinking, thoughtful expression, and responsible citizenship. UNCW makes it a priority to provide a wealth of knowledge that is both foundational and diverse. With such a strong foundation, students are able practice creative and inventive inquiry, applying the information they study to various situations. The curriculum promotes their proficiency in communication, collaboration, and higher-level conceptualization. Ultimately, UNCW knows that its students have tools they need to fulfill their duties as responsible citizens of the global community.

RESOURCES FOR FUTURE SUCCESS: The UNCW Career Center is available with resources for all facets of the UNCW community, from alumni to undergrads. The purpose of the center is to provide guidance to participants looking to develop their career or career goals. UNCW students are also encouraged to join the alumni association for further benefits that bulk up their networks and professional portfolios. Even after they graduate, UNCW alumni have access to services and guidance to aid them as they pursue their career goals. And, through the association's built-in alumni network, the entire UNCW community has inside access to endless professional fields and employers.

UNCW

UNIVERSITY *of*
NORTH CAROLINA
WILMINGTON

http://www.uncw.edu/
P: (910) 962-3000

PUBLIC

STUDENT PROFILE

13,235 undergraduate students

88% of undergrad students are full time

39% male – 61% female

14% of students are from out of state

85% freshman retention rate

71% graduated in 6 years

FACULTY PROFILE

661 full-time faculty

300 part-time faculty

17 to 1 student/faculty ratio

ADMISSIONS

11,444 Total Applicants

6,976 Total Admissions

2,029 Total Freshman Enrollment

60.96% of applicants admitted

SAT Ranges: CR 560-630, M 560-630, W 520-620

ACT Ranges: C 23-27, M 22-26, E 21-27, W 6-8

TUITION & COSTS

Tuition: (In) $4,188 (Out) $18,054

Fees: $2,503

Total: (In) $6,691 (Out) $20,557

R&B: $9,466

Room: $5,706

Board: $3,760

Total: (In) $16,157 (Out) $30,023

FINANCIAL

$6,312 avg grant/scholarship amount (need)

$4,357 avg loan amount (need)

WAKE FOREST UNIVERSITY

WINSTON-SALEM, NORTH CAROLINA

One of the nation's most respected private schools, Wake Forest University is a collegiate university recognized for its outstanding academic reputation and challenging liberal arts curriculum. A Wake Forest education is concerned with the development of the entire individual. Students must grab their educational experience and run with it, testing the boundaries of their own potential and learning about the talents they possess. At the core of this new challenge higher education is their engaged interaction with their professors. Wake Forest professors are mentors and advisors who transform students and teach them to make higher-level, intellectual connections that transcend the classroom.

THE OFFICE OF SERVICE & SOCIAL ACTION: The Office of Service & Social Action provides students with the opportunity to give back to the community through various programs and organizations. Wake Forest has over 100 community partners, expanding student outreach and engagement far beyond the campus. There are also several leadership positions for students who are seeking increased responsibility.

A DIVERSE YET CONNECTED COMMUNITY: A Wake Forest education is about diversity—an amalgam of ideas, talents, ethnicity, socio-economic backgrounds, geographical differences, and all aspects of the human condition that differ from one individual to the next. That mixture makes for an ideal learning experience, where students can expand their wealth of knowledge to reach beyond what is easy and comfortable. They interact closely, both with one another and their professors. Such an intimate college environment allows students to get an individualized education experience, yet its concentration of diverse cultures enriches conversation with a world of perspectives.

THE OFFICE OF PERSONAL AND CAREER DEVELOPMENT: At the end of the day, it is the responsibility of every student to take ownership of their academic journey and ultimately their career. The Office of Personal and Career Development is a resource available to all students so that they make approach their postgraduate careers with success. It serves student needs to support them through academic challenges and provide them tools to thrive in their job pursuits and career development.

THRIVE: Aside from academic stress, students can find that staying healthy in both mind and body is a true challenge throughout college. Wake Forest has established a program to combat those difficulties. "Thrive," available to all students, consists of eight components that promote healthy living. Each component is concerned with the overall condition of the individual, providing resources for such areas as emotional and financial well-being.

TEACHER APPRECIATION: The average Wake Forest faculty member has been with the University for 12 years and, in their experience, has only grown in their desire to make incredible impacts on their students' lives. In many instances, students thank faculty members for their unfailing interest in both their academic and personal success. Students describe their educational experience in terms of their interactions with professors. When faculty adopt roles as mentors and advisors, they are enhancing the individual experience of each student.

ACADEMIC POTENTIAL AND INTELLECTUAL SERVICE: Wake Forest provides its students with a valuable educational experience—one that promotes service to others. Students are reminded that while their college experience is about discovering themselves, it is also about understanding one's duty to the global community. Students should ask themselves, 'How can I apply what I have learned to society, and how can that application bring about positive change?'

http://www.wfu.edu/

P: (336) 758-5000

PRIVATE

STUDENT PROFILE

4,871 undergraduate students

99% of undergrad students are full time

47% male – 53% female

70% of students are from out of state

93% freshman retention rate

88% graduated in 6 years

FACULTY PROFILE

1,859 full-time faculty

173 part-time faculty

10 to 1 student/faculty ratio

ADMISSIONS

13,281 Total Applicants

3,903 Total Admissions

1,284 Total Freshman Enrollment

29.39% of applicants admitted

TUITION & COSTS

Tuition: $47,120

Fees: $562

Total: $47,682

R&B: $14,260

Room: $8,496

Board: $5,764

Total: $61,942

FINANCIAL

$37,554 avg grant/scholarship amount (total)

$10,316 avg loan amount (total)

WESTERN CAROLINA UNIVERSITY

CULLOWHEE, NORTH CAROLINA

Western Carolina University is nestled in a beautiful mountain valley in proximity to Great Smoky Mountain National Park and the Blue Ridge Parkway. The university's rich, 129-year history is rooted in its quality and rigorous academic programs that serve the students of both the region and beyond. The natural scenic beauty of the campus in Cullowhee, North Carolina, provides an ideal study environment that also affords students the opportunity to apply their learning in real settings through service-learning and community engagement, highly selective internships, and rich campus programs.

FIRST-YEAR SEMINAR: Western Carolina University introduces its students to college through a dynamic set of courses that orient them to the style of collegiate coursework. As part of the Liberal Studies Program, First-Year Seminars integrate students into the college lifestyle while exposing them to topics across a variety of academic disciplines. The courses offered vary each semester, but they always are guaranteed to include exciting and interesting material. Seminar topics include "Black Death to Bioterrorism," "A User's Guide to Mass Media," "Crimes and Criminals," and "Creative Writing." First-Year Seminar professors are passionate about the subjects they teach as well as the students whom they get to introduce to WCU. They ensure that their class environments are friendly, comfortable, and intellectually stimulating.

STUDY ABROAD: With so many options for both the locations and lengths of time to study abroad, WCU students are sure to find the travel experience that's perfect for them. Universities that are partnered with WCU welcome students with open arms, immersing them in the coursework and culture of their programs. WCU can send students directly to more than 30 institutions throughout Europe, Asia, South America, Australia, and even the Caribbean. WCU is also proud to be one of more than 300 universities in the International Student Exchange Program (ISEP), a network of schools that exchange students at the most efficient prices possible.

UNDERGRADUATE RESEARCH: Fewer things are more valuable than putting one's skills to the test through the systematic process of discovery. Thanks to WCU's strong supply of resources and faculty support, every student has the opportunity to participate in fascinating research projects. These efforts are greatly recognized each year at WCU's campus-wide Undergraduate Research Exposition, a festival of engaging research presentations that is attended by hundreds of students and dozens of faculty. Not only do students get to present their research to their peers and professors at the Expo, but many also have the honor of taking their findings to the National Conference on Undergraduate Research (NCUR). This prestigious honor is not uncommon for WCU students; Western Carolina University has consistently ranked among the top 10 for the number of student projects taken to NCUR since 2006.

SERVICE AND COMMUNITY-BASED LEARNING: Service and community-based learning are hallmarks of an education earned at Western Carolina University. Students who enroll at WCU are afforded the opportunity to make a profound difference in their communities. The Center for Service-Learning, for example, is full of resources that connect students with philanthropic organizations in need of their help, opening up the chance for them to live out the caring, community-conscious mission of their university. The center also organizes Days of Service, which rally students together to volunteer all around Western North Carolina, as well as Alternative Breaks, which take advantage of long weekends and holidays by transporting students all around the world for acts of meaningful service and learning.

FINISH IN FOUR: WCU's Finish in Four initiative is the university's pledge to provide every resource necessary for students to complete their degrees within four years. Students who pledge to Finish in Four commit to meeting with their advisors every semester in order to stay on track to finish their undergraduate requirements in a timely manner. Advisers then, in turn, may direct them toward extraordinarily helpful tutors and counselors or programs to ensure their success.

https://www.wcu.edu/

P: (828) 227-7211

PUBLIC

STUDENT PROFILE

8,652 undergraduate students

86% of undergrad students are full time

46%male – 54% female

80% freshman retention rate

58% graduated in 6 years

8% of students are from out of state

FACULTY PROFILE

502 full-time faculty

188 part-time faculty

15.7 to 1 student/faculty ratio

ADMISSIONS

17,702 Total Applicants

7,127 Total Admissions

1,639 Total Freshman Enrollment

40.26% of applicants admitted

SAT Ranges: CR 470-560, M 470-570

ACT Ranges: C 20-24, M 19-24, E 19-24

TUITION & COSTS

Tuition: (In) $3,893 (Out) $14,286

Fees: $3,134

Total: (In) $7,027 (Out) $17,420

R&B: $8,864

Room: $4,438

Board: $4,426

Total: (In) $15,891 (Out) $26,284

FINANCIAL

$6,224 avg grant/scholarship amount (need)

$6,303 avg loan amount (need)

OKLAHOMA BAPTIST UNIVERSITY

SHAWNEE, OKLAHOMA

Oklahoma Baptist University is a highly ranked Christian liberal arts university in Shawnee, Oklahoma. Founded in 1910, OBU seeks to transform lives by equipping its students to pursue academic excellence, integrate faith within all areas of knowledge, engage a diverse world, and live worthily of the high calling of God in Christ.

WELCOMING WITH OPEN ARMS: During move-in day for freshmen, upperclassmen surround new students' vehicles, rock the car, chant, and welcome them to the family. Students also participate in the Unity Gathering, a candle-lit vigil designed to bring the diverse group of students together as one OBU family. This week culminates in The Walk, a traditional journey from the campus Oval to the front steps of Raley Chapel. It is similar to The Walk that they will eventually take on their final day as students when they attend commencement and receive their diplomas.

COMMON INTELLECTUAL EXPERIENCES: The core of OBU's liberal arts curriculum offers abundant opportunities for common intellectual experiences. This begins the first year, heightened by the January term experience, and continues throughout the student's undergraduate study. The sophomore year features two semesters of Western Civilization courses, providing all students with common study in history and literature. The liberal arts core helps to expand students' intellectual horizons, bringing them together and bonding them through their shared knowledge and learning.

UNDERGRADUATE RESEARCH: Students have numerous opportunities to grow their knowledge through research projects and internships. The Honors Program at OBU allows students the option to develop a senior thesis, an incredible opportunity that involves investigating a problem and delivering findings through a well-researched paper and public thesis presentation. Students also have ample opportunities for internships in numerous research capacities and are encouraged to develop their skills as they matriculate through their courses.

DIVERSITY/GLOBAL LEARNING: OBU seeks to encourage a diverse campus and embrace cultures from around the nation and the world at large. In the most recent academic year, OBU represented students from 40 states and 35 other countries. The University's mission statement includes the charge for students to "engage a diverse world," promoting a conscious level of respect and reverence for difference on a daily basis. Opportunities abound for students to learn and serve through Global Outreach service trips over six continents as well as study abroad opportunities throughout the world. The University likewise offers local and regional opportunities for service and learning within diverse cultural contexts, offering another way for students to embody OBU's mission.

INTERNSHIPS/CO-OPS/PRACTICUMS: Opportunities abound for internships and practical experience opportunities at OBU. Whether they engage in a summer internship, an on- or off-campus part-time job, or a trip to a study abroad destination, students have countless ways to gain experience in their field while attending OBU. Professors, having formed deep personal connections with their students, are invaluable resources for these enrichment opportunities,, as is the Career Development office, which assists current students and alumni with an array of career services.

CAPSTONE COURSES AND PROJECTS/SENIOR EXPERIENCE: OBU students have opportunities to demonstrate their expertise within their disciplines through capstone projects and courses. These experiences push students to apply all the knowledge they have gained and demonstrate their preparedness for applying their degree to a professional context. OBU's student experience culminates in not only the knowledge needed to succeed after college, but also in the development of character, faith, and integrity, setting graduates apart from other institutions.

https://www.okbu.edu/

P: (405) 585-5000

PRIVATE - CHRISTIAN

STUDENT PROFILE

1,953 undergraduate students

93% of undergrad students are full time

40% male – 60% female

30% of students are from out of state

74% freshman retention rate

55% graduated in 6 years

FACULTY PROFILE

94 full-time faculty

31 part-time faculty

15 to 1 student/faculty ratio

ADMISSIONS

4,785 Total Applicants

2,930 Total Admissions

556 Total Freshman Enrollment

61.23% of applicants admitted

SAT Ranges: CR 450-580, M 440-560

ACT Ranges: C 20-25, M 18-25, E 19-26

TUITION & COSTS

Tuition: $22,710

Fees: $2,600

Total: $25,310

R&B: $7,010

Total: $32,320

FINANCIAL

$8,276 avg grant/scholarship amount (need)

$4,154 avg loan amount (need)

OKLAHOMA CHRISTIAN UNIVERSITY

EDMOND, OKLAHOMA

Recognized as one of the best universities in the western United States, Oklahoma Christian University features a close-knit community in which students, faculty, and staff go the extra mile for each other. Its expert professors teach from a Christian worldview and are fiercely dedicated to high standards of scholarship.

FIRST-YEAR SEMINAR AND FRESHMAN EXPERIENCE: One of the University's most treasured traditions, Earn Your Wings, features a week-long introduction to OC for incoming freshmen. Led by more than 150 upperclassmen, students begin the Freshman Seminar Course, spend time in small groups with peer mentors, host local elementary students for a morning of campus kite-flying, and visit special sites across Oklahoma City. Theme days, concerts, and time for reflection altogether ensure that Earn Your Wings features something special for every incoming student.

STUDY EVERYWHERE: The mission of Oklahoma Christian University's Study Abroad program is to deepen and broaden students' intellectual, social, spiritual, and aesthetic awareness as they study, travel, and serve in other cultures. Students can choose from dozens of programs across the globe! For example, incoming freshmen can take their very first class in Europe with OC's President, and nursing students get to serve in the mountain clinics of Honduras. Summer trips to Asia include stops in Japan and China, and long-term exchange programs to Japan and Korea include cultural immersion and study at international universities. And university-owned Das Millicanhaus in Vienna, Austria, hosts students across all academic programs for fall, spring, or summer study opportunities. Students can also participate in a variety of Best Semester programs across the globe through OC's affiliation with the Council for Christian Colleges and Universities.

ENTREPRENEUR-IN-RESIDENCE AND CROSS-DISCIPLINARY STUDENT TEAMS: At OC, students can collaborate with an Entrepreneur-in-Residence to gain valuable information from a professional's perspective. Long-time entrepreneur Russ Maguire mentors individual students, teaming up to help ideas come to life. Cross-disciplinary student teams have successfully taken two products to market in the past two years and, for two years in a row, students have garnered awards at the Love's Entrepreneur's Cup, a competition for student teams from colleges and universities across the state of Oklahoma. The OC team took home first place in 2017.

PRESIDENT'S LEADERSHIP CLASS: Each year, 12 to 15 members of OC's freshman class are invited (after a competitive process of interviews) to join the President's Leadership Class (PLC). PLC students meet with President John deSteiguer on a weekly basis to learn in small group settings. These students also get to participate in a variety of special university events.

UNDERGRADUATE STUDENT RESEARCH: Students at Oklahoma Christian University have the opportunity to participate in undergraduate research initiatives across many academic programs. With abundant connections to the labs and companies in Oklahoma City's medical community, students get to participate in faculty research. Engineering students, too, partner with faculty for their own projects, including current research on wind energy. Students in other disciplines present papers and posters in a variety of conference and organization settings, both regionally and nationally.

ETHOS SPIRITUAL LIFE EXPERIENCE: Spiritual life is at the core of the Oklahoma Christian University experience. Through the Ethos program, students use their gifts and talents to practice spiritual disciplines in five dimensions: Community, Discipleship, Discovery, Servanthood, and Worship. Students take charge of their spiritual growth and earn "kudos" (spiritual life credits) by attending Big Chapel, small group Bible studies, community service projects, speaker events, and more. Engaging in endless combinations of activities, students can track their participation and document their journey via a University-developed phone application.

CAPSTONE COURSES AND STUDENT PROJECTS: Every OC student takes a senior-year capstone course in order to complete their studies. Guided by hands-on faculty, students see their four years of work culminate in a final project. Art collectives, scientific research, published articles, life-changing engineering projects, music compilations, and annual marketing plans for local companies—the possibilities are endless!

http://www.oc.edu/
P: (405) 425-5000

PRIVATE - CHRISTIAN

STUDENT PROFILE

1,987 undergraduate students

93% of undergrad students are full time

51% male – 49% female

53% of students are from out of state

79% freshman retention rate

49% graduated in 6 years

FACULTY PROFILE

106 full-time faculty

3 part-time faculty

13 to 1 student/faculty ratio

ADMISSIONS

2,597 Total Applicants

1,535 Total Admissions

452 Total Freshman Enrollment

59.11% of applicants admitted

SAT Ranges: CR 480-610, M 490-620,

W 490-580

ACT Ranges: C 21-28, M 21-29, E 20-27, W 6-8

TUITION & COSTS

Tuition: $19,890

R&B: $7,030

Room: $3,870

Board: $3,160

Total: $26,920

FINANCIAL

$11,677 avg grant/scholarship amount (total)

$7,256 avg loan amount (total)

UNIVERSITY OF SCIENCE AND ARTS OF OKLAHOMA

CHICKASHA, OKLAHOMA

The University of Science and Arts of Oklahoma is the state's only public liberal arts college, the mission of which is to provide the public with a distinctive and accessible liberal arts and sciences education. In combining an interdisciplinary core curriculum with superior instruction in major fields of study, USAO aims to provide a thorough education that prepares students for meaningful, purposeful lives.

THE BEST PROFESSORS FOR THE BEST EXPERIENCE: Beginning freshman year, USAO students are taught by Ph.D.s. Because USAO offers no graduate programs, undergraduate courses are never taught by graduate assistants, and students are always in touch with the most prestigious faculty they can find. Classes are small, and faculty devote themselves exclusively to providing students with the finest undergraduate learning opportunities anywhere.

IDS CORE: The Interdisciplinary Studies (IDS) core curriculum differs from other general education programs in several key ways: the breadth and structure of the program, its emphasis on interdisciplinarity, and its use of team teaching. Students commit 50 credit hours to the IDS program over the course of their college careers. This commitment fosters connections between faculty and students who, unable to completely withdraw into one academic department, interact with a wide range of people, ideas, and viewpoints on a daily basis.

A VARIETY OF EXPERIENCES: Much of campus life occurs outside the classroom. USAO promotes the idea that the total university experience cannot be realized through academic involvement alone, and that if a university education is a rehearsal for one's future, it should include a variety of experiences.

TOP-OF-THE-NOTCH FACILITIES: USAO's Lawson Hall apartments, which opened in fall 2002, are among the most elaborately appointed residence halls in the state, containing a hair and tanning salon, a pool, a volleyball court, a game room, and a movie theater. Additionally, a recent renovation of the Student Center makes it a great place for students to eat and meet friends. Nash Library not only serves as the primary research center, but it is also a great place to meet people and hang out. Computer labs in multiple halls are open to all students, and a special Writing Center provides help for students' writing assignments.

CHICKASHA: Chickasha, a small town of 17,000, is 35 miles from Oklahoma City's metro area, which features a variety shopping and arts events. The town is the proud home of the internationally recognized Festival of Light, a holiday extravaganza that features displays of more than 3.5 million Christmas lights. It draws more than 300,000 people to visit Shannon Springs Park, located just a few blocks from the USAO campus.

STUDENT ACTIVITIES: At USAO, the opportunities are endless! USAO works hard to keep the calendar filled with exciting—and yes, intellectually stimulating—events to get students out of their dorm rooms to have year-round fun. Popular events include dramatic and musical productions, Inter-Tribal Heritage Club powwows, guest speakers, entertainers, concerts, and sporting events. With more than 40 clubs and organizations from which to choose, students' campus experiences are customized according to their interests.

CAREER SERVICES: At USAO, individual students take responsibility for making decisions about their futures, all with the help of advisors who assist them in planning the path toward their degree. On campus, the university counselor, student life counselors, the staff of the student services office, resident assistants, and administrators provide students with information, motivation, and career-development opportunities.

http://www.usao.edu/

P: (405) 224-3140

PUBLIC

STUDENT PROFILE

873 undergraduate students

82% of undergrad students are full time

34% male – 66% female

63% freshman retention rate

40% graduated in 6 years

FACULTY PROFILE

62 full-time faculty

30 part-time faculty

12 to 1 student/faculty ratio

ADMISSIONS

706 Total Applicants

466 Total Admissions

223 Total Freshman Enrollment

66.01% of applicants admitted

SAT Ranges: CR 395-500, M 420-510

ACT Ranges: C 19-24, M 18-25, E 16-22

TUITION & COSTS

Tuition: (In) $5,100 (Out) $14,040

Fees: $1,170

Total: (In) $6,270 (Out) $15,210

R&B: $5,470

Room: $2,760

Board: $2,710

Total: (In) $11,740 (Out) $20,680

FINANCIAL

$9,487 avg grant/scholarship amount (total)

$3,569 avg loan amount (total)

UNIVERSITY OF TULSA

TULSA, OKLAHOMA

The University of Tulsa offers students a rare combination: the resources and opportunities of a large university with the personal attention and mentoring typically found at much smaller colleges. A warm classroom environment and state-of-the-art facilities give students an engaging college experience. It truly is a better fit for a better tomorrow.

A CUTTING-EDGE EDUCATION WITH A BROAD FOUNDATION: The university offers academic programs through the Henry Kendall College of Arts and Sciences, the Collins College of Business, the College of Engineering and Natural Sciences, the Oxley College of Health Sciences, and the College of Law. In addition to their major, every undergraduate must complete the Tulsa Curriculum, which includes a core curriculum focused on basic writing, math, and language competencies. The general curriculum requires students to take courses in three areas, including aesthetic inquiry & creative experience, historical & social interpretation, and scientific investigation.

EXPERIENTIAL LEARNING: TU students learn by doing. For example, the Student Investment Fund provides students real-world experience making investment decisions and managing a real portfolio currently valued at more than $5 million. In the School of Art, the student-run graphic design agency, Third Floor Design, provides award-winning promotional materials to Tulsa-area nonprofit organizations. The College of Arts and Sciences is also home to several major scholarly journals, all of which afford undergraduates opportunities to learn about the business of publishing. They can gain experience in editing, public relations, database management, and fact checking.

EVOLVING PROGRAMS FOR CONTEMPORARY INTEREST: Student interest in the burgeoning energy management field factored into the creation of the School of Energy Economics, Policy, & Commerce. This program prepares undergraduates for careers in upstream and midstream sectors of the global energy industry.

INTERDISCIPLINARY ARTS: TU has programs in film studies and arts management. The interdisciplinary arts management program combines study in the fine or performing arts with business and management courses. As a result of the university's management of the city-owned Gilcrease Museum, the two entities have developed a master of arts in both museum science and management program.

INFORMATION SECURITY: TU's reputation as a leader in information security education and research is well established, unique in its breadth and depth. The university trains federally certified computer security experts. Since 1996, its Institute for Information Security (iSec) has produced some of the country's leading professionals in information security, digital forensics, Internet security, and telecommunications security.

STUDY ABROAD: A partner in the Generation Study Abroad Initiative, TU is committed to doubling study abroad numbers over the next five years through educational opportunities for study, research, and internships. TU students from every major may participate in education abroad experiences that enhance their personal and professional growth. They have excellent means to do so, enjoying access to a network of preeminent and internationally known university exchange partners.

INTERNSHIPS: Internships are a significant part of TU's academic programs. The university has working relationships with many area and regional organizations and prominent businesses, giving students the chance to gain professional experience before they graduate. Most recently, students have interned with Tulsa Opera, ConocoPhillips, H.A. Chapman Institute of Medical Genetics, Samson, Indian Health Care Resource Center, the Oklahoma State Treasurer's Office, and WPX Energy, among many others.

THE UNIVERSITY of TULSA

http://utulsa.edu/
P: (800) 331-3050

PRIVATE

STUDENT PROFILE

3,473 undergraduate students

97% of undergrad students are full time

58% male – 42% female

39% of students are from out of state

88% freshman retention rate

70% graduated in 6 years

FACULTY PROFILE

344 full-time faculty

101 part-time faculty

11 to 1 student/faculty ratio

ADMISSIONS

7,636 Total Applicants

3,074 Total Admissions

764 Total Freshman Enrollment

40.26% of applicants admitted

SAT Ranges: CR 560-710, M 570-700

ACT Ranges: C 26-32, M 25-31, E 26-34

TUITION & COSTS

Tuition: $34,085

Fees: $320

Total: $34,405

R&B: $34,405

Room: $5,800

Board: $5,900

Total: $46,105

FINANCIAL

$21,679 avg grant/scholarship amount (need)

$9,085 avg loan amount (need)

CHARLESTON SOUTHERN UNIVERSITY

NORTH CHARLESTON, SOUTH CAROLINA

Charleston Southern University offers a well-rounded, practical liberal arts education that is taught in a stimulating Christian environment. At Charleston Southern, students are challenged academically, and each course of study integrates faith into the curriculum. Charleston Southern students study in small class settings that are led by professors who serve as caring mentors. Students also have the chance to experience opportunities that are typically found at larger universities, including dynamic campus ministries, a nationally recognized community service program, academic and service clubs and organizations, and Division I athletics.

LIBERAL ARTS CORE: The Liberal Arts Core curriculum, completed by all students pursuing a bachelor's degree, is designed to ensure that graduates leave with a basic understanding of human history, culture and relationships, the arts, literature, mathematics, and the natural sciences. The curriculum pushes students to reflect upon their studies in terms of a Christian vision of life.

UNDERGRADUATE RESEARCH: Opportunities for undergraduate research are available in multiple academic disciplines. Students are encouraged to collaborate with faculty, and several recent faculty/student research projects have received funding through the South Carolina Independent Colleges and Universities. Recent research projects presented at the annual Spring Symposium include research in biology, politics, business, English, computer science, Christian studies, music, graphic design, chemistry, psychology, and music therapy.

FRESHMAN SEMINAR: The Freshman Seminar is a one-hour course, the topic of which is decided upon students' academic majors. Through the seminar, freshmen are introduced to their fields of study and are oriented into the university experience.

HONORS PROGRAM: The most academically distinguished students have the option to enroll in the Honors Program, a highly respected community that combines academics with a variety of cultural and social activities.

THE BRIDGE PROGRAM: The Bridge Program makes an extra effort to give underprepared students the opportunity to earn their bachelor's degree. Through counseling and tutoring, students who may have not originally met the school's admissions requirements have the chance to develop their academic skills and gain the tools they need to succeed in college-level coursework.

SPECIAL SERIES: Charleston Southern University sponsors multiple annual lecture series, cultural events, and leadership training. Examples of annual events include the Student Leadership Academy, Values & Ethics Lecture Series, CSU Arts Week, The Lens Lecture Series, Welcoming Faith into the Science Classroom, and multiple music and theatre performances.

EXPERIENTIAL LEARNING INITIATIVE (ELI): The Experiential Learning Initiative, or ELI, provides enriched educational opportunities via internships, practicums, clinicals, field courses, and other real-world applications of classroom theory. Having commenced with the 2018 freshman class, the ELI asks students to earn experiential credits. Though this may be a requirement, the desire to stretch education beyond the classroom's walls is already thriving.

CLUBS AND ORGANIZATIONS: Charleston Southern University offers more than 25 academic clubs and student organizations. This is a great way to get plugged in, meet new friends, and make a difference. From business to nursing and athletics, Charleston Southern has social activities to interest everyone.

http://www.charlestonsouthern.edu/

P: (843) 863-7050

PRIVATE - CHRISTIAN

STUDENT PROFILE

3,112 undergraduate students

90% of undergrad students are full time

37% male – 63% female

16.72% of students are from out of state

65% freshman retention rate

39% graduated in 6 years

FACULTY PROFILE

163 full-time faculty

129 part-time faculty

15 to 1 student/faculty ratio

ADMISSIONS

4,197 Total Applicants

2,463 Total Admissions

756 Total Freshman Enrollment

58.68% of applicants admitted

SAT Ranges: CR 450-560, M 460-550

ACT Ranges: C 20-25, M 18-24, E 19-25

TUITION & COSTS

Tuition: $22,800

Fees: $40

Total: $23,200

R&B: $9,000

Total: $32,200

FINANCIAL

$4,343 avg grant/scholarship amount (need)

$3,503 avg loan amount (need)

COASTAL CAROLINA UNIVERSITY

CONWAY, SOUTH CAROLINA

Coastal Carolina University is a dynamic, public institution located in Conway, S.C., near the resort area of Myrtle Beach. The University is accredited by the Southern Association of Colleges and Schools Commission on Colleges to award the baccalaureate degree and master's degree and offers 71 areas of study toward the baccalaureate degree, 18 master's degree programs, and two specialist degrees and a Ph.D. in Coastal and Marine Systems Science.

INTEGRATED STUDENT ENGAGEMENT: A central focus of Coastal Carolina University's mission is to prepare students both to excel in the classroom as well as to succeed in life. An essential part of the educational mission is to engage students in hands-on learning that bridges the gap between theory and practice, providing them with the critical-thinking and problem-solving skills necessary for fruitful and fulfilling lives. In order to achieve this goal more effectively, the University has created Experienced@Coastal, an integrated approach to student engagement. This initiative brings experiential learning to the center of the educational culture, building upon its already strong tradition of active learning through undergraduate research, internships, international experiences, and community engagement.

UNDERGRADUATE RESEARCH: CCU students can expect to engage in collaborative research with faculty and peers in a number of venues. In a recent year, for example, nearly 600 undergraduate students enrolled in undergraduate research/senior thesis courses, yielding nearly 70 publications in peer-reviewed journals, on-campus research, fine arts journals, and 200 presentations both on campus and at regional, national, and international conferences. In addition, more than 200 students participated in public musical and theatrical performances, and many dozens more were recognized as award winners in regional and national academic competitions in visual arts, literature and poetry, Model United Nations, and Student Legislature.

GLOBAL PERSPECTIVES: To ensure that CCU students develop a global perspective in preparation for life in the 21st century, CCU offers a variety of opportunities for international studies and experiences, including programs abroad as well as on-campus programs. Every CCU student completes a global awareness-focused course as a part of the core curriculum, and they can further engage through a variety of minors that are dedicated to global studies, international business, French, German, or Spanish. CCU's commitment to experiential learning supports international education through more than $5,000 in support annually, the amount of which is further supplemented by more than $35,000 in internal study abroad scholarships.

UNDERGRADUATE PRESENTATIONS: The CCU Undergraduate Research Competition provides undergraduate students from all disciplines and majors the opportunity to present their University research at a venue outside their regular classroom. Presentations are judged by CCU faculty on such factors as significance, methodology, evidence of research, clarity, and organization. The cultural arts program at CCU complements the academic experience for students, enriching the quality of life in the community and region by offering a dynamic and diverse calendar of cultural events. Recent cultural events have included public performances, exhibits, theatrical productions, and musical entertainment.

INTERNSHIPS: Students in every major are encouraged to participate in at least one internship during their enrollment at CCU. There are nearly 120 internship courses offered to students that provide both academic credit and faculty supervision. In addition to the hundreds of local opportunities available, many students are taking advantage of national and international placements that provide them with an even more comprehensive résumé along with the skills necessary to compete for high-level positions in a competitive job market.

http://www.coastal.edu/
P: (800) 277-7000

PUBLIC

STUDENT PROFILE
9,460 undergraduate students
93% of undergrad students are full time
48% male – 52% female
55% of students are from out of state
69% freshman retention rate
42% graduated in 6 years

FACULTY PROFILE
448 full-time faculty
219 part-time faculty
18 to 1 student/faculty ratio

ADMISSIONS
17,768 Total Applicants
10,871 Total Admissions
2,249 Total Freshman Enrollment
61.18% of applicants admitted
SAT Ranges: CR 460-540, M 470-550
ACT Ranges: C 20-25

TUITION & COSTS
Tuition: (In) $10,696 (Out) $24,940
Fees: $180
Total: (In) $10,876 (Out) $25,120
R&B: $8,890
Room: $5,440
Board: $3,450
Total: (In) $19,766 (Out) $34,010

FINANCIAL
$4,846 avg grant/scholarship amount (need)
$9,136 avg loan amount (need)

COLLEGE OF CHARLESTON

CHARLESTON, SOUTH CAROLINA

At the College of Charleston, learning is not confined to the classroom. Students are encouraged to study abroad, participate in independent research projects, and engage in experiential learning opportunities that are typically only available at the graduate level. Opportunities provided by the city of Charleston and its environs are essential components of a College of Charleston education. Students can take advantage of a beautifully preserved historic city surrounded by a diverse natural environment, a vibrant arts community, an innovative business climate, and a consortium of area schools.

SERVICE-LEARNING: Service-learning courses allow students to learn through meaningful work with the community. Students' hands-on experiences help others and make classroom theory real and applicable to daily life. Opportunities change each year, but some examples of service-learning courses offered at the College include Exploration in Community Involvement and Global Awareness, Clinical Education Experience in Athletic Training, and Social Gerontology. A variety of volunteer opportunities also are available to College of Charleston students.

A LIBERAL ARTS EDUCATION: The College of Charleston offers more than forty majors; the school's most popular majors are business and economics, education, arts, and the strong biochemistry program. Building on its founding principles, the College also has rigorous general education requirements to support its liberal arts context. All students must take the equivalent of four semesters of a foreign language and numerous cultural studies programs, reflecting the College of Charleston's global focus and international orientation.

CHARLESTON, SOUTH CAROLINA: The College of Charleston is the oldest institution of higher learning in South Carolina and the thirteenth oldest in the country. Founded in 1770 (three of its founders were signers of the Declaration of Independence), the College became a state college in 1970. Its fifty-two-acre campus, outlined by herringbone-patterned brick sidewalks, is located in historic Charleston, also known as the Holy City. In addition to its historic significance and beauty, Charleston is an important seaport and has a population of about one hundred thousand. Spoleto Festival USA, the world-renowned cultural festival, is held in Charleston every spring, highlighting a wide range of performing arts. The College also hosts dozens of its performances each year as well.

STUDY AND SERVICE ABROAD: The College offers several study abroad options, including semester and summer programs, bilateral exchanges, and independent-study programs. Each year, the College's Center for International Education (CIE) offers six semester-long, faculty-led programs in places that range from Santiago, Chile, to La Rochelle, France, and Havana, Cuba. The College also offers a consortium program at Annot, France. College of Charleston students can also explore the world beyond Charleston by participating in alternative spring-break service projects, including helping the homeless in Chicago, doing environmental work in Seattle, and working with schools in the Dominican Republic.

CAREER PLANNING: Many College of Charleston alumni are willing to offer career assistance and advice to students through the College's Career Center. The Career Mentor Network allows students to connect with alumni and gather information about a particular position or field, including required skills and information on the employment market in a variety of geographical areas. Students can supplement their academic transcript with a co-curricular record of their campus involvement to showcase their skills and expertise when applying for jobs and graduate programs.

http://www.cofc.edu/

P: (800) 960-5940

PUBLIC

STUDENT PROFILE

10,468 undergraduate students

92% of undergrad students are full time

37% male – 63% female

43% of students are from out of state

79% freshman retention rate

68% graduated in 6 years

FACULTY PROFILE

624 full-time faculty

367 part-time faculty

15 to 1 student/faculty ratio

ADMISSIONS

11,722 Total Applicants

9,043 Total Admissions

2,237 Total Freshman Enrollment

77.15% of applicants admitted

SAT Ranges: CR 520-610, M 510-600

ACT Ranges: C 23-28, M 21-26, E 23-29

TUITION & COSTS

Tuition: $11,252

Fees: $70

Total: $11,322

R&B: $11,629

Room: $7,839

Board: $3,790

Total: $22,951

FINANCIAL

$8,834 avg grant/scholarship amount (total)

$6,707 avg loan amount (total)

ERSKINE COLLEGE

DUE WEST, SOUTH CAROLINA

Erskine College has been equipping young people to flourish in lives of learning, serving, and leading for 175 years. The institution's rich heritage of thoughtful scholarship, spiritual strength, and intentional community provides an academic experience that's as distinctive as its students, faculty, and graduates.

AUTHENTIC CHRISTIAN LIBERAL ARTS: Erskine College provides all students with a solid liberal arts education to help them see how knowledge and faith are interconnected, understand the unity of human experience, and define their unique calling. Part of an authentic Christian education is learning that knowledge never exists in a vacuum; to use the power of knowledge responsibly, a student must gain wisdom.

STUDENT-FACULTY RESEARCH: Erskine students across a variety of disciplines work in close partnership with faculty on professional-level research. Biology, chemistry, physics, and psychology majors participate in frontline research in their fields, work in conjunction with scholars at other institutions, and present their findings at conferences nationwide. Research opportunities aren't limited to the sciences–from education and business to the humanities, students are encouraged to develop their interests and dig deeply into research questions.

WINTER TERM: Erskine offers a Winter Term in January ("J-Term") to allow for concentrated study in a specific field or interest. J-Term options include independent study, externships, and travel. Education majors could spend the month working in local public school classrooms, while future business leaders might study how Disney trains its management at its famous theme parks. Biology students regularly travel to observe flora and fauna in native habitats around the world, and a group of Spanish students recently hiked El Camino Santiago in Spain. And students who elect to spend J-term on campus aren't left out. The course listing for J-Term changes each year as faculty tap into students' passions, hobbies, and core interests to offer unique classes like equestrian studies, filmmaking or film studies, Japanese culture, or the graphic novel. Many students can also schedule local internships in their preferred career fields for the month of January.

OPPORTUNITIES TO TRAVEL FOR STUDY OR MINISTRY: Semester-long opportunities to study abroad are available in Scotland, England, France, Spain, and Mexico. Students from all majors can benefit from these overseas experiences, especially with the help of faculty who can devise and plan a course of study that enables them to study abroad while still remaining on schedule for graduation. Other students can choose to engage in summer or J-term mission trips; for example, a dozen students from a variety of majors, two Erskine alumni, and an administrator spent a week during a recent summer bringing medical care to remote villages along the Amazon River.

SUPPORTIVE CHRISTIAN ATMOSPHERE: Erskine fosters an authentic Christian environment of caring, mentoring, and community building. At Erskine, student life is designed to encourage maturity by giving students increasing responsibility without ever abandoning them. Older students mentor younger students, while faculty and staff members mentor all of them. Erskine believes that, while everyone must learn responsibility and independence, maturity develops within a community.

NETVUE PROGRAM DEVELOPMENT GRANT: Erskine College recently received a grant from the Network for Vocation in Undergraduate Education (NetVUE), administered by the Council of Independent Colleges, making Erskine one of 36 institutions selected to deepen the intellectual and theological exploration of vocation among undergraduate students. Erskine's grant, "Flourishing and Vocational Excellence," seeks to bring the Christian concept of vocation into the heart of Erskine's identity and mission by providing programs and opportunities for faculty, staff, and undergraduate students. The ultimate goal of the grant is to see Erskine develop into a recognized center and site for vocational excellence.

http://www.erskine.edu/
P: (864) 379-8838

PRIVATE - CHRISTIAN

STUDENT PROFILE

622 undergraduate students

99% of undergrad students are full time

54% male – 46% female

61% freshman retention rate

62% graduated in 6 years

FACULTY PROFILE

49 full-time faculty

21 part-time faculty

12 to 1 student/faculty ratio

ADMISSIONS

991 Total Applicants

637 Total Admissions

219 Total Freshman Enrollment

64.28% of applicants admitted

SAT Ranges: CR 430-550, M 450-560, W 420-530

ACT Ranges: C 18-24, M 18-25, E 18-24

TUITION & COSTS

Tuition: $31,345

Fees: $1,970

Total: $33,315

R&B: $10,500

Room: $5,400

Board: $5,100

Total: $43,815

FINANCIAL

$34,864 avg grant/scholarship amount (total)

$6,952 avg loan amount (total)

FURMAN UNIVERSITY

GREENVILLE, SOUTH CAROLINA

Furman has emerged as a national leader among liberal arts colleges by giving students the chance to learn by doing through independent study, research projects with professors, study abroad, community service, and internships around the world. It has a picturesque campus with its own lake and, located in just 5 miles outside of downtown Greenville, students can enjoy the city and all it has to offer.

SIGNATURE PROGRAMS: Furman is noted for its integration of special learning programs into its core curriculum. These signature programs give students the chance to put academic theory into practice. Students are given the opportunity to participate in experiential learning, undergraduate research, and study abroad. Furman offers abroad programs in over 30 countries as well as faculty-led programs that are an awesome way for students to explore their new surroundings with the help of their professors. Professors are able to transfer the value of a Furman education to different locations, teaching students to remain well-rounded, adventurous learners.

LIBERAL ARTS EDUCATION: Furman is a liberal arts institution that places a dedicated focus on student-faculty interactions. The University recognizes the immense value of these interactions as a system of intellectual give and take. Students are taught to think critically, communicate effectively, and engage in higher-level conceptualization. A liberal arts degree is incredibly useful in today's global society. Furman provides its students with a well-rounded educational experience—one that transcends disciplines and departments. Ultimately, students still commit themselves to a specific area of study, but they are also equipped with a wide range of skills. They are given responsibility over their educations and are encouraged to take advantage of all the academic and personal resources that Furman has to offer.

STUDENT-FACULTY INTERACTION: Furman has 240 full-time faculty members, with a student-to-faculty ratio of 11:1. With this tightly knit community Furman makes student-faculty interactions the core of its educational experience. Communication between students and professors should be open and focused toward intellectual progress and innovation, and so Furman faculty take an interest in each student's individual interests.

ADVISING: Academic advising is taken seriously at Furman, putting students in close contact with all they need to succeed. Each student is assigned an advisor who provides academic and career counseling. The goal of this advising is to help students discover their intellectual and personal talents so that they may understand how their interests fit within their field and the workforce at large. Academic performance cannot be stretched to its greatest potential, however, unless a student maintains a healthy lifestyle. Furman's health services assist both the physical and emotional needs of students, offering guidance to anyone looking to improve their well-being. There are counseling services to help students sort out their academic and social stresses, nutrition advice for staying healthy, and more.

CAREER SERVICES: Career Services is dedicated to the progress of each student as they work toward their future goals. Furman provides services to help students prepare for their first interview, write a great résumé, and choose a career path. Students are encouraged to utilize these services for the many benefits they offer, including a competitive edge over other graduates. The student success rate at Furman is very high thanks to the dedication of both the faculty and the students themselves. Within six months of graduation, in fact, 97% of graduates find employment. Furman is committed to fostering meaningful, educational experiences as well as grooming students into responsible leaders and innovators.

---

http://furman.edu/

P: (864) 294-2000

PRIVATE

STUDENT PROFILE

2,731 undergraduate students

96% of undergrad students are full time

43% male — 57% female

69% of students are from out of state

89% freshman retention rate

83% graduated in 6 years

FACULTY PROFILE

247 full-time faculty

70 part-time faculty

11 to 1 student/faculty ratio

ADMISSIONS

5,143 Total Applicants

3,268 Total Admissions

672 Total Freshman Enrollment

63.54% of applicants admitted

TUITION & COSTS

Tuition: $45,632

Fees: $380

Total: $46,012

R&B: $11,522

Room: $6,202

Board: $5,320

Total: $57,534

FINANCIAL

$27,818 avg grant/scholarship amount (total)

$8,995 avg loan amount (total)

PRESBYTERIAN COLLEGE

CLINTON, SOUTH CAROLINA

Presbyterian College is quickly realizing its vision to become the leading liberal arts college of South Carolina and one of the ten best national liberal arts colleges in the Southeast. PC has crafted an academic program that bridges the gap between the world of academia and the real world; it combines the educational experience of a liberal arts college with practical preparation for the postgraduate world.

STUDY ABROAD: Study abroad is available either throughout the semester or during PC's "May-mester." Past "May-mester" programs, all of which have been annually crafted by PC's own faculty, have traveled to Vietnam, Europe, South America, and Ireland. A partnership with Ghuizhou University in China also offers students opportunities to study Chinese language and history on campus and then travel to fully immerse themselves in China alongside their professors. PC's Cuba study program is one of only fifteen in the country, providing students an experience that is especially unique for a small liberal arts institution. PC is also the only liberal arts college in the country to have been selected to host a Confucius Institute.

SERVICE: Service is the most highly emphasized form of experiential learning at PC. Whether they work in a children's home, at the Special Olympics, or at a local grade school, mentoring students, the vast majority of PC students contribute meaningful service to their community. Students have also rolled up their sleeves to work with a Habitat for Humanity house on McMillian Street in Clinton, and almost half of the student body is affiliated with Greek life, which naturally leads to copious amounts of service all year long.

RESEARCH OPPORTUNITIES: Students have many opportunities to perform research on either their own or with a professor, conducting an open dialogue with professors who act as personally invested mentors. PC also offers a Summer Fellows Research program, which provides stipends for students to work very closely with faculty in a concentrated manner on various research projects. All departments have opportunities for research, so every student has the chance to tackle a striking topic of interest and deepen their understanding of what they value most. Many students even present their research at national professional conferences.

HONOR CODE: Incoming students take a pledge that begins, "On my honor, I will abstain from all deceit." This honor code affects the campus atmosphere by giving students the freedom to trust one another, and professors testify themselves that such an oath weighs heavily on students' choices. With confidence in the honor code, professors will often allow students to take tests back to their rooms to complete, and PC students don't think twice about the safety of his or her laptop if it is left in the library during mealtime.

STUDENT/FACULTY INTERACTION: Professors have noted that they chose to teach at PC because of the great amount of contact they are able to have with their students. In the first year, for example, students participate in a small, twelve-student seminar that is led by a faculty member who works as their academic advisor. Of the professors at PC, 95 percent hold terminal degrees in their field, and PC has had six professors receive the CASE Professor of the Year award—more than any other school in South Carolina. The faculty-student relationships at PC are expressly unique: students are often invited to dine at faculty homes in a very informal manner, and they. Always feel comfortable stopping by a professor's office, knowing that they care about each of them as individuals. Lifelong friendships with faculty make the PC experience truly remarkable.

PRESBYTERIAN COLLEGE

http://www.presby.edu/
P: (864) 833-2820

PRIVATE

STUDENT PROFILE

1,064 undergraduate students

93% of undergrad students are full time

47% male – 53% female

32% of students are from out of state

81% freshman retention rate

70% graduated in 6 years

FACULTY PROFILE

105 full-time faculty

1 part-time faculty

11 to 1 student/faculty ratio

ADMISSIONS

2,072 Total Applicants

1,291 Total Admissions

262 Total Freshman Enrollment

62.31% of applicants admitted

SAT Ranges: CR 480-590, M 490-600, W 430-570

ACT Ranges: C 20-27

TUITION & COSTS

Tuition: $33,200

Fees: $2,930

Total: $36,130

R&B: $9,750

Room: $4,750

Board: $5,000

Total: $45,880

FINANCIAL

$28,806 avg grant/scholarship amount (total)

$6,797 avg loan amount (total)

WOFFORD COLLEGE

SPARTANBURG, SOUTH CAROLINA

Wofford's mission is to provide a superior liberal arts education that prepares its students for extraordinary and positive contributions to society. It is located in Spartanburg, South Carolina, the surrounding metropolitan area of which is best known as the home of BMW's assembly, seven higher education institutions, and two medical centers. Wofford offers an educational journey that is created for and tailored around the individual strengths of each student. For years, it has been highly respected as a leading liberal arts institution that offers over 51 major and minor programs.

THE CENTER FOR INNOVATION AND LEARNING: The Center for Innovation and Learning works to discover and implement resources into the Wofford learning community. The resources are identified and chosen for their capabilities to enhance the educational experience at the College. The incredible innovation and research are used to improve academia through a four-part plan, the first of which encourages innovation in teaching itself. Wofford recognizes the changing climate of education and, with that understanding, it seeks to keep up with the changes through new methods of teaching. Second, the plan supports co-curricular and curricular programming through written initiatives. Third, it provides an ideal educational environment for both students and faculty. And finally, Wofford then assesses each initiative to measure its actual impact on the community, working to improve them year after year.

STUDY ABROAD: Study abroad is a large part of the Wofford experience. Students have studied in 70 countries, spanning all 7 continents. Programs range from semester-long experiences to a full year. There are also opportunities for students to engage in international service-learning efforts, internships, and excursions. Abroad, students use International Program Blogs to keep the Wofford community informed of their travels and experiences, sharing in the joy of their adventures and helping underclassmen as they decide on their own future travel experiences.

INSTITUTE: Institute is a 4-week program that recreates the "real world,." designed to give students an idea of what to expect when they leave college. Institute is highly lauded as an ideal preparatory program that exposes students to the potential challenges they will face in the adult world.

IMPACT & LAUNCH COMPETITION: Wofford students have the opportunity to design and pitch projects that are aimed to make a positive impact on the community. Ideas are pitched, chosen, and employed with the help of the Wofford staff. These initiatives are a great way to give students the experience of leading life-changing work, all while effecting real change to the world around them.

THE SPACE: At The Space, students from all areas of study and discipline come together to share and gain marketable skills that are valued by employers and graduate programs. The Space is dedicated to preparing students for postgraduate success in any and all endeavors. Career Services assists with this effort by providing students with coaching and interviewing tips.

CAMPUS MINISTRY: Wofford's campus ministry provides a comforting community of faith and support. Students are encouraged to utilize campus ministry for their needs, academic and personal alike. Students are naturally pushed to tackle big questions while in college, and campus ministry is available to assist deep thought and large life decisions.

http://www.wofford.edu/

P: (864) 597-4000

PRIVATE

STUDENT PROFILE

1,660 undergraduate students

99% of undergrad students are full time

50% male – 50% female

48% of students are from out of state

87% freshman retention rate

81% graduated in 6 years

FACULTY PROFILE

131 full-time faculty

21 part-time faculty

11 to 1 student/faculty ratio

ADMISSIONS

2,792 Total Applicants

2,005 Total Admissions

442 Total Freshman Enrollment

71.81% of applicants admitted

SAT Ranges: CR 520-630, M 530-630, W 520-620

ACT Ranges: C 23-29, M 23-28, E 23-30, W 7-8

TUITION & COSTS

Tuition: $37,375

Fees: $1,330

Total: $38,705

R&B: $11,180

Room: $6,545

Board: $4,635

Total: $49,885

FINANCIAL

$25,987 avg grant/scholarship amount (need)

$7,871 avg loan amount (need)

BELMONT UNIVERSITY

NASHVILLE, TENNESSEE

Belmont University wants its students to succeed both inside and outside the classroom. With a liberal arts and sciences focus, as well as a mission based upon Christian ideals, Belmont develops well-rounded individuals who make significant contributions both domestically and abroad. Students can choose from over 90 diverse and challenging majors that encompass not only the arts and sciences, but pre-professional areas as well. On Belmont's beautiful campus, students enjoy the comforts of quaint surroundings and the action and excitement of a vibrant city.

THE BELL CORE: The Belmont Experience: Learning for Life (BELL) Core is a general education curriculum that showcases Belmont's belief in the importance of experiential learning. Through this curriculum, students complete their requirements through such activities as undergraduate research, study abroad, service-learning, internships, clinicals/practica, or recitals.

DOMESTIC AND INTERNATIONAL STUDY AWAY: The Office of Study Abroad connects undergraduate students from all majors with international study opportunities on six of the seven continents. Students can earn Belmont academic credits on year-long, semester, and short-term programs. Popular destinations include the United Kingdom, Ireland, Spain, Cambodia, Guatemala, South Africa, Australia, China, France, Japan, and Italy.

BELMONT LEARNING CENTERS: The Belmont Learning Centers (Math/Science Learning Center, the Language Learning Center, the Writing Center, and a Speech Practice Room) offer free tutoring and group study in math, writing, languages, and public speaking to all Belmont students. A one-on-one tutoring approach is used for connecting each student with his or her personal learning goals and techniques. The Belmont Learning Centers tutoring staff is diverse in their skill set, allowing students to find a delivery method that suits their speed and readiness. Group study is also encouraged so that students may help one another succeed in a direct peer-to-peer environment. Other services offered by The Belmont Learning Centers include study skill refreshers, textbook breakdowns, learning and note-taking guides, and easy scheduling.

GPS (GROWTH & PURPOSE FOR STUDENTS): All students have access to the GPS (Growth & Purpose for Students) program, which offers academic coaching, preparation, planning, and support. GPS staff coach students through the discernment of his or her unique path along with an identification of the best opportunities and resources available through their educational journey at Belmont.

COMMUNITY SERVICE: Students at Belmont meet needs in the community through a variety of service-learning activities, logging over 200,000 community service hours annually. English and education majors gain valuable teaching experience by tutoring students at local schools. Spanish majors team up with community role models in the Belmont-YMCA Hispanic Achievers program, a program designed to empower Hispanic youth through activities and mentoring specific to their career goals, and accounting students help neighborhood residents of all ages improve their computer skills. All these projects help Belmont students connect to and serve the community.

PRIME LOCATION FOR INTERNSHIPS: Belmont students are just miles from downtown, which means that they benefit greatly from being part of a larger community. Located in Tennessee's state capital, Belmont benefits from Nashville's thriving business community, which provides abundant internship opportunities for students in a variety of fields including entertainment, healthcare, and business, among many others. Seventy-three percent of all Belmont graduates hold at least one internship throughout their time as a student.

SERVICE-LEARNING: Belmont University seeks to be a meaningful community institution and thus highly encourages students to serve the community. This participation ensures that students learn the needs, challenges, and opportunities of working in diverse groups of people. Each year before the first day of the fall semester, all freshmen and transfer students participate in SERVE Nashville, an event in which students spend part of the day volunteering among various sites in the community.

BELMONT UNIVERSITY

http://www.belmont.edu/

P: (615) 460-6000

PRIVATE - CHRISTIAN

STUDENT PROFILE

5,983 undergraduate students

94% of undergrad students are full time

38% male – 62% female

74% of students are from out of state

83% freshman retention rate

69% graduated in 6 years

FACULTY PROFILE

342 full-time faculty

437 part-time faculty

13 to 1 student/faculty ratio

ADMISSIONS

6,145 Total Applicants

4,934 Total Admissions

1,387 Total Freshman Enrollment

80.29% of applicants admitted

SAT Ranges: CR 530-630, M 510-620

ACT Ranges: C 23-28, M 22-27, E 24-31

TUITION & COSTS

Tuition: $31,300

Fees: $1,520

Total: $32,820

R&B: $11,680

Total: $44,500

FINANCIAL

$17,550 avg grant/scholarship amount (total)

$13,131 avg loan amount (total)

CARSON-NEWMAN UNIVERSITY

JEFFERSON CITY, TENNESSEE

Carson-Newman University students experience the best of what higher education can be at this nationally recognized university, founded in 1851. This liberal arts-based institution integrates faith and learning in a nurturing and rigorous teaching environment where students come first. Carson-Newman offers the resources necessary for the enrichment of each student's education, from quality faculty and academic programs to state-of-the-art technology and facilities. Every day, Carson-Newman is preparing students to compete on the world stage.

STUDY ABROAD, THE WASHINGTON SEMESTER, AND MAY TERM: Students can spend an entire semester abroad by participating in the London Semester and other study abroad opportunities. Carson-Newman, along with International Enrichment, Inc., provides all academic and nonacademic support services so that students are given what they need to pursue their international adventures. The Washington Semester is available as an internship program primarily for political science and prelaw majors. Through the program, students earn credit while working in the nation's capital. Additionally, art and foreign language majors may earn credit while studying and traveling throughout Europe during the three-week May term.

COMMUNITY SERVICE: Students have numerous opportunities to explore community service. The Bonner Center for Service Learning and Civic Engagement prepares future-minded students to be servants and leaders in the community. Student volunteers are committed to building and sustaining a caring community through an integration of academic excellence and community engagement. The Appalachian Center serves the physical needs of rural Appalachia, and the Samaritan House provides housing for the homeless. Carson-Newman honors its twin pillars of academic excellence and Christian service, encouraging students to involve themselves actively with these sister organizations.

HONORS PROGRAM: Carson-Newman offers top-notch classroom experiences and cutting-edge programs. The Carson-Newman Honors Program provides academic challenges and opportunities for intellectually gifted and curious students through team-taught interdisciplinary classes and extracurricular events.

RESEARCH: Across all levels of campus, research is encouraged and actively cultivated. The annual Student Research, Creativity, and Performance Day showcases Carson-Newman's truly distinctive passion for intellectual inquiry through collaborative scholarship and creative endeavors between students and faculty alike.

THE FILM PROGRAM: Carson-Newman's film program offers students the opportunity to earn college credit while participating in internships with regional filmmakers. Through a partnership program with the Los Angeles Film Studies Center, accepted students also have an opportunity to live in L.A. and work directly with Hollywood filmmakers.

AN INTERNATIONAL COMMUNITY: Carson-Newman cultivates an international community on campus through its International Education program. Students from around the world study alongside traditional American students, giving both a mutually enriching experience that exposes them to each other's culture. International halls in dorms, language partners, and the International Club all seek to integrate multiple cultures and languages to help all students develop a broader worldview. For the 2016 fall semester, the University welcomed 143 international students from 34 countries to campus.

STUDENTS READY TO SUCCEED: Carson-Newman's exceptionally high placement rates in professional programs related to medicine, law, business, education, and theological study is a testimony to the excellence of its rigorous academic programs. Students leave the University prepared to enter the professional world, equipped with skills that extend beyond their academic program. Carson-Newman alumni constantly demonstrate the value of a liberal arts education through their success both in the professional world and in their personal lives.

---

http://www.cn.edu/

P: (800) 678-9061

PRIVATE - CHRISTIAN

STUDENT PROFILE

1,748 undergraduate students

98% of undergrad students are full time

42% male — 58% female

20% of students are from out of state

70% freshman retention rate

49% graduated in 6 years

FACULTY PROFILE

122 full-time faculty

132 part-time faculty

13 to 1 student/faculty ratio

ADMISSIONS

6,496 Total Applicants

4,111 Total Admissions

505 Total Freshman Enrollment

63.29% of applicants admitted

SAT Ranges: CR 400-560, M 440-560

ACT Ranges: C 20-26, M 18-25, E 20-26

TUITION & COSTS

Tuition: $26,200

Fees: $1,200

Total: $27,400

R&B: $8,630

Total: $36,030

FINANCIAL

$17,873 avg grant/scholarship amount (need)

$3,623 avg loan amount (need)

CHRISTIAN BROTHERS UNIVERSITY

MEMPHIS, TENNESSEE

Christian Brothers University is a private, Catholic, comprehensive university committed to preparing students of all faiths and backgrounds to become engaged global citizens. The University provides challenging educational opportunities in the arts, business, engineering, the sciences, and teacher education. CBU's commitment to the Lasallian ideals of faith, service, and community is reflected in an often-repeated phrase on campus: "Enter to Learn, Leave to Serve."

UNDERGRADUATE RESEARCH: Many students are engaged through mentored research programs at St. Jude Children's Research Hospital, the University of Tennessee Health Sciences Center, the Memphis Zoo, and the Minority Health Internship Research Training program. Others conduct mentored research with highly qualified CBU faculty members. The University offers numerous internship, externship, and co-op opportunities, enabling students to gather valuable real-life experience at many corporations and nonprofits.

STUDY ABROAD: CBU students take advantage of myriad study abroad programs. Popular destinations include Rome, Barcelona, London, Paris, and other great international cities. For students who wish to spend an entire semester or a summer steeped in another culture, CBU maintains partnerships with universities in Austria, Brazil, France, and Spain. The Lasallian International Programs Consortium invites CBU students to study in Argentina, Australia, China, Costa Rica, England, France, Germany, Ireland, Italy, Japan, Mexico, Nicaragua, Puerto Rico, South Africa, and Spain. Since the De La Salle Christian Brothers are present in 81 countries, students may also make arrangements to travel to even more countries than are listed above. These include virtually all nations in Central and South America, Singapore, the Philippines, Europe, and parts of Africa. CBU encourages its students to explore, as studying abroad has a positive, life-changing impact on students' perspectives and future careers.

LASALLIAN FELLOWS: Each year, five senior students are selected for the distinction of CBU Lasallian Fellow, having been recognized for the way they embody the values set forth by CBU's founder, St. John Baptist de la Salle. These students are nominated by CBU faculty and staff in recognition of their commitment to the underserved, their sensitivity to social and community needs, the active nature of their faith, and the difference that they make in the world. Each Lasallian Fellow is awarded $10,000 as a means of perpetuating their work in the community.

FIRST-YEAR EXPERIENCE: The First-Year Experience Program focuses on the transition that freshmen face from high school to college. It's designed to provide support and encouragement from student' first day of orientation all the way to the final day of their first year. CBU students start strong and, therefore, find success after graduation.

LIVING-LEARNING COMMUNITIES: CBU's five Living-Learning Communities offer a broad range of opportunities for students to take an active part in their learning, engage the city of Memphis, and explore new career paths. For example, students in the Business Living Learning Community have had dinner with CBU alumni who have successful careers in the sports industry. After the dinner, they attended a Memphis Grizzlies game to better understand the client acquisition and consumer behaviors that guarantee a successful sports event. These Living-Learning students often intern with alumni and form meaningful connections through their Learning Community experiences.

SUCCESSFUL CITIZENS: Upon graduation, CBU students possess all the skills to be successful in the workplace as well as in professional or in graduate school. They communicate effectively, think critically, and work well in teams. They have also developed a strong sense of value for their CBU bachelor's degree, which obliges its holder to work for the betterment of the community at large. CBU graduates have internalized the University's emphasis on faith, service, and community, often working through churches, civic organizations, clubs, neighborhood associations, employers, and government to affect positive change in the community. CBU's focus on educating the whole person thus pays rich dividends to the graduates themselves as well as to the communities in which they live and work.

---

http://www.cbu.edu/
P: (901) 321-3205

PRIVATE - CATHOLIC

STUDENT PROFILE
1,526 undergraduate students
92% of undergrad students are full time
47% male – 53% female
21% of students are from out of state
80% freshman retention rate
48% graduated in 6 years

FACULTY PROFILE
105 full-time faculty
101 part-time faculty
12.5 to 1 student/faculty ratio

ADMISSIONS
2,724 Total Applicants
1,447 Total Admissions
381 Total Freshman Enrollment
53% of applicants admitted

ACT Ranges: C 21-27, M 20-26, E 22-28

TUITION & COSTS
Tuition: $31,000
Fees: $870
Total: $31,870
R&B: $8,754
Total: $40,624

FINANCIAL
$18,357 avg grant/scholarship amount (need)
$3,754 avg loan amount (need)

FREED-HARDEMAN UNIVERSITY

HENDERSON, TENNESSEE

Freed-Hardeman University is dedicated to supporting its students with an extraordinary education that is backed and strengthened by students' individual God-given talents. Students serve God through their scholarship, service, and pursuit of lifelong learning.

INTERFACE: First-year students are given all they need to enter Freed-Hardeman University as smoothly as possible. The summer JumpSTART program gets incoming freshmen in touch with department faculty, providing them guidance and assistance as they register for their first semester of classes. Regardless of whether a student has declared a major, they have plenty of interaction with FHU faculty to explore their options and assess their skills and interests, all before their college career officially begins. Throughout the first week of school, these new students are welcomed into the community during a daily orientation, called INTERFACE. The entire class is divided into small INTERFACE groups, each led by upperclassmen peer advisors, and spend each day bonding and participating in fun events. Friendships form naturally through such activities as an afternoon of canoeing on the Buffalo River, a Carnival in the Commons, and the "INTERFACE Olympics."

UNIVERSITY SCHOLARS' DAY: University Scholars' Day is a recent tradition that exemplifies the value of research and academic exploration in the FHU community. Classes are canceled so that every student can gather for a day of presentations, discussions, and discovery. Headed by a guest keynote speaker, the event consists of multiple sessions that provide students and faculty the platform in which to share their independent projects.

GLOBAL LEARNING: FHU Abroad opens up the opportunity for students to travel all around the world, enriching their education and evolving as culturally aware, global citizens. Freed-Hardeman owns and operates a small campus within the town of Verviers, Belgium. Centrally located in Europe, this beautiful town acts as a hub for a whole semester's worth of adventure. FHU faculty enhance their lessons with trips around the continent, immersing students in culture and history to help their classes come alive. Excursions include a trip to Italy's historically rich Roman ruins, a tour of the Globe Theatre in the United Kingdom, and a journey through Germany's critical WWII-era landmarks.

SPIRITUAL LIFE: Spirituality is intrinsic to everything on FHU's campus. Such a strong, campus-wide faith is bolstered and reasserted through a daily chapel service in which the entire community gathers for prayer and worship. Later, each night, students have the option to attend devotionals and singings to strengthen their relationship with God and the faith-driven people around them. Mid-semester, students organize a series of lectures that gives them a chance to share their own insights, discoveries, and testimonies with their peers. The opportunity for student lectures is just one of many ways that anyone at FHU can practice leadership and grow as spiritually fulfilled adults.

A PLACE TO CALL HOME: As a residential university, Freed-Hardeman makes it easy for students to feel at home and part of a tightly knit community. Living on campus keeps everyone in touch with all FHU goings-on, and every student is made to gain a true sense of belonging. The Christian environment is inspiring, and anyone can always find support and friendship, whether they reach out to neighbors across the hall or share their experiences in dorm devotionals.

SERVICE-LEARNING: Because faith and scholarship are intertwined at FHU, it should come as no surprise that many professors incorporate meaningful service into their coursework. Nearly every academic department hosts a course that has service built into its curriculum, encouraging students to experience the broader meaning and impact of their studies. Some examples include mission trips to underprivileged neighborhoods, and fundraisers for cancer research. FHU faculty strive to raise their students not only as proficient scholars, but also as philanthropic community members who serve with a love for God and a compassion for others.

https://www.fhu.edu/
P: (800) 348-3481

PRIVATE - CHRISTIAN

STUDENT PROFILE

1,297 undergraduate students

95% of undergrad students are full time

44% male – 56% female

44% of students are from out of state

78% freshman retention rate

57% graduated in 6 years

FACULTY PROFILE

93 full-time faculty

64 part-time faculty

13 to 1 student/faculty ratio

ADMISSIONS

791 Total Applicants

762 Total Admissions

325 Total Freshman Enrollment

96.33% of applicants admitted

SAT Ranges: CR 480-558, M 435-518

ACT Ranges: C 21-27, M 19-26, E 21-30

TUITION & COSTS

Tuition: $21,950

R&B: $7,950

Total: $29,900

FINANCIAL

$13,949 avg grant/scholarship amount (need)

$3,829 avg loan amount (need)

KING UNIVERSITY

BRISTOL, TENNESSEE

King University is a Presbyterian, doctoral-level comprehensive university. Founded in 1867 as King College, the University offers more than 90 majors, minors, pre-professional degrees, and concentrations in such fields as business, nursing, law, medical and health sciences, pharmacy, education, and the humanities.

CLOSE FACULTY RELATIONSHIPS: Students navigate the college maze with the help of professors who are knowledgeable in their fields and innovative in their approaches to education. More than 67 percent of King professors hold doctorates from the finest colleges and universities in the world. They are a dedicated group, holding high distinctions in their respective fields. They each have exceptional professional—as well as personal—experiences to share. King's student-to-faculty ratio of 14:1 provides students with easily accessible professors in small class settings. This provides students with the personalized attention necessary for success. Students also have a their own student liaison, a major advisor, and career services staff who offer them guidance along the way.

CORE CURRICULUM: The Core curriculum at King is the academic foundation for the students' Quest. It gives students the skills, ideas, and knowledge they need to pursue their major and minor programs with confidence and good judgment. The Core, expressing King's values through the early exploration of the arts and sciences and a cross-cultural experience, helps King students understand their responsibilities to learn and serve. The Core's global emphasis, and the fact that senior faculty teach most courses, give advantages for King students both in the job market and in graduate school.

KING UNIVERSITY INSTITUTE FOR FAITH AND CULTURE: Through its thought-provoking lecture series, the King University Institute for Faith and Culture aims to address issues of faith, engaging the King community and audiences throughout the region. The Institute offers opportunities for focused consideration and reflection. Each year, the Institute welcomes a authors, artists, musicians, scholars, philosophers, historians, and others to interact with a regional and national audience. One notable highlight of the lecture series is a moving and enlightening lecture from a survivor of the Holocaust.

BRISTOL, TENNESSEE: King's campus is situated on 135 wooded acres with Georgian-style architecture buildings that provide a quiet, beautiful learning environment just two minutes away from bustling downtown Bristol. Bristol is known as the "Birthplace of Country Music." It is also home to the Bristol Motor Speedway, the world's fastest half-mile track, where thousands attend NASCAR races every year. Within an easy driving distance of campus, there is plenty to do. The area offers kayaking and canoeing, hiking trails and rock climbing, live music, concerts, festivals, and professional theatre productions at The Paramount Center for the Arts.

CAREER SERVICES: King's Career Services program offers a unique experience for students, integrating career identification with educational programs that are best designed to meet those goals. King graduates stand out when they begin looking for employment, having gone through a robust job- and internship-identification process. They are prepared to make meaning and significant contributions to their communities through their vocation after they complete their degrees.

OUTSTANDING PLACEMENT: At King, the University's goal is to prepare students for life after college, whether it be in a career or graduate school. King offers numerous opportunities for hands-on learning to better prepare students for whatever the future holds. Ninety-two percent of recent graduates were either employed or in graduate school six months after graduation, according to recent survey respondents.

http://www.king.edu/

P: (800) 362-0014

PRIVATE - CHRISTIAN

STUDENT PROFILE

2,343 undergraduate students

90% of undergrad students are full time

37% male – 63% female

61% of students are from out of state

69% freshman retention rate

44.4% graduated in 6 years

FACULTY PROFILE

129 full-time faculty

226 part-time faculty

13 to 1 student/faculty ratio

ADMISSIONS

1,601 Total Applicants

823 Total Admissions

159 Total Freshman Enrollment

51.41% of applicants admitted

SAT Ranges: CR 440-540, M 438-565

ACT Ranges: C 19.25-24, M 17-23, E 18-24

TUITION & COSTS

Tuition: $25,798

Fees: $1,478

Total: $27,276

R&B: $8,180

Total: $35,456

FINANCIAL

$12,095 avg grant/scholarship amount (need)

$4,509 avg loan amount (need)

LEE UNIVERSITY

CLEVELAND, TENNESSEE

Located in Cleveland, Tennessee, Lee University prides itself as a well-rounded, Christ-centered liberal arts institution. With 52 majors and 121 academic programs, and more than 100 clubs and organizations to get involved in, Lee's 5,041 students have ample opportunities to grow and learn as they navigate through their college experience. The majority of Lee's professors hold Ph.D.s and are always willing to assist their students in any way they can.

APPLIED LEARNING THROUGH SERVICE: Lee prides itself on not only community service, but also an overall lifestyle of service-learning. Students complete at least 80 hours of service during their four years at Lee, as the core of the University is built upon the philanthropic actions of its entire community. With more than 50 classes that are enhanced by community service, Lee University faculty enrich their material with tangible, impactful aid to others. For example, the Public Relations class creates a campaign for a local nonprofit; a drawing class makes portraits of people in an assisted care facility; and members of the Communication Capstone class do interviews and create videos about the lives of people in assisted care.

HANDS-ON OPPORTUNITY: At Lee, students have many opportunities to gain hands-on experience in their field of study. Education majors, as well as all majors that work toward teacher licensure, complete a semester's worth of student teaching that consists of two six-week placements. Majors including Accounting, Business, Church Music, Intercultural Studies, Communication, Public Relations, Telecommunication, Theatre, Political Science, Athletic Training, Children's Ministry, Discipleship Ministry, Youth Ministry, and Pastoral Ministry also require at least one internship, meaning that Lee students graduate with a major experiential advantage in the job market.

FACILITIES FOR HIGHER LEARNING: Most of the computer labs on campus are "social labs" that are arranged to allow collaboration on projects and research. There is also a "war room" in the Business Department that is equipped with a stock ticker and other instant financial information that students use to prepare for group presentations. Additionally, the University hosts a writing studio for every ENGL 105 class in which students can work collaboratively with peers to improve their writing under the guidance of carefully trained junior or senior English majors. All writing studios are seminar-style with enhanced technology. All of the new buildings on campus have comfortable group study spaces that encourage community, even while learning.

SPIRITUAL LIFE: Lee University believes that spiritual growth is vital to a well-rounded college experience. Every Tuesday and Thursday morning, the campus comes together to worship and hear from such challenging speakers as Louie Giglio, Reggie Dabbs, Ravi Zacharias, and Jentezen Franklin along with local pastors and Lee faculty. Lee also sets aside one week each semester to refocus on Christ and gather as a community of believers. This week, called Convocation, is dedicated to campus-wide spiritual renewal.

STUDY ABROAD: All Lee students complete a trip to study abroad, experiencing life in other cultures while getting credit in their areas of study. This incredible, school-wide privilege has been aptly recognized as among the top 5 study abroad programs in the nation. With over 30 trips to choose from, Lee students study abroad in places like Egypt, England, Scotland, China, Australia, Israel, South America, and more.

---

http://www.leeuniversity.edu/
P: (423) 614-8000

PRIVATE - CHRISTIAN

STUDENT PROFILE

4,560 undergraduate students

83% of undergrad students are full time

41% male – 59% female

50% of students are from out of state

79% freshman retention rate

52% graduated in 6 years

FACULTY PROFILE

196 full-time faculty

16 part-time faculty

17 to 1 student/faculty ratio

ADMISSIONS

2,141 Total Applicants

1,830 Total Admissions

835 Total Freshman Enrollment

85.47% of applicants admitted

SAT Ranges: CR 460-610, M 440-570

ACT Ranges: C 21-27, M 19-26, E 21-30

TUITION & COSTS

Tuition: $14,400

Fees: $600

Total: $15,000

R&B: $7,045

Room: $3,595

Board: $3,450

Total: $22,045

FINANCIAL

$11,041 avg grant/scholarship amount (total)

$6,930 avg loan amount (total)

MARYVILLE COLLEGE

MARYVILLE, TENNESSEE

Maryville is one of the 50 oldest colleges in the United States and is known for its academic rigor and focus on the liberal arts and sciences, offering nearly 60 pre-professional programs of study. Ideally located between the Great Smoky Mountains National Park and Knoxville, Maryville offers students the best of both worlds: quick access to hiking, cycling, and other outdoor activities as well as the vibrant Knoxville culture and resources. In many ways, Maryville College has always been ahead of its time. In the same year as its founding in 1819, the College admitted the first minority student to enroll in a Tennessee institution, George Erskine. Then, in 1875, Maryville became the first college in Tennessee to award a bachelor's degree to a woman, Mary Wilson.

MOUNTAIN CHALLENGE: The Mountain Challenge, unique to Maryville, is an exciting outlet for students to dive into nature and conquer the wilderness of Tennessee—no matter their experience in the great outdoors! As a one-credit class, this Challenge fosters a daring incentive to step outside of the box and try new experiences like biking, canoeing, caving, rafting, and much more! The fall and spring offerings vary season-by-season in order to follow the landscape's most valuable features. Students who take on the Mountain Challenge are bound to form a community with their adventurous group of peers, sharing their life-changing challenges alongside one another.

MODEL UNITED NATIONS: Maryville's long-standing Model UN program has spent years engaging students in the global political conversation. This intellectually charged program is famous for taking a hands-on approach to leadership, public speaking, and debate. Such a strong program exemplifies Maryville's history of global awareness and cultural respect, challenging students to role-play as citizens of other countries. One of the most distinctive programs in the nation, the College's Model United Nations also hosts a conference for high school students to learn more about the inner workings of international diplomacy.

EXPERIENTIAL LEARNING: The experiential learning requirement begins right when students step foot on campus, as all students take a freshman course that uses an experimental approach to analyze the effective change and growth of the environment. Experiential learning allows students to learn how to adapt to a new environment, to act without a customary support system, and to develop trust in their own resources of intelligence and discipline. And, even after freshman year, experiential learning is bound to find its way on every student's course schedule.

THE SENIOR STUDY: Maryville College is one of the nation's few colleges that require seniors to complete a comprehensive exam in their major and conduct an extensive Senior Thesis. This is the capstone of Maryville's academic rigor, which enables students to excel in "the real world." The Senior Study is a distinctive part of every Maryville student's studies. Under the guidance of a faculty mentor, seniors conclude their academic experiences by digging deeply into the majors and what has inspired them throughout their undergraduate careers.

A STRONG COMMUNITY OF EDUCATORS AND LEARNERS: Maryville College is, in essence, a community for learning. This community includes persons with a variety of interests, backgrounds, beliefs, and nationalities. Faculty emphasize effective teaching and strive to build supportive relationships with their students, challenging them to grow in academic competence, personal and social maturity, and spiritual discernment and commitment. In such an atmosphere of openness and caring, lasting friendships are formed. As they share a genuine concern for the world and work to fulfill the College's mission and purpose, directors, administration, staff, faculty, and students alike strive to build and strengthen the entire community.

---

http://www.maryvillecollege.edu/

P: (865) 981-8092

PRIVATE

STUDENT PROFILE

1,213 undergraduate students

97% of undergrad students are full time

46% male – 54% female

35% of students are from out of state

70.4% freshman retention rate

53% graduated in 6 years

FACULTY PROFILE

76 full-time faculty

43 part-time faculty

13 to 1 student/faculty ratio

ADMISSIONS

1,701 Total Applicants

1,136 Total Admissions

338 Total Freshman Enrollment

66.78% of applicants admitted

SAT Ranges: CR 440-560, M 440-540

ACT Ranges: C 20-26, M 18-26, E 20-28

TUITION & COSTS

Tuition: $32,746

Fees: $778

Total: $33,524

R&B: $10,868

Total: $44,392

FINANCIAL

$26,268 avg grant/scholarship amount (need)

$4,817 avg loan amount (need)

RHODES COLLEGE

MEMPHIS, TENNESSEE

Rhodes isn't just about learning; it's about learning to live, putting ideas and ideals into practice, and making it real. Students looking for a classic liberal arts education with a practical edge should consider the Rhodes reality: a beautiful campus, challenging academics, caring faculty, personal development, and all the opportunities of a culturally rich and vibrant city.

REAL EXPERIENCE: 60 percent of Rhodes students take advantage of the 150 academic internships offered each semester. Memphis is home to more than 100 medical, government, business, cultural, and artistic facilities. Through these, students have the chance to shape their skills for the future. Local options are as diverse as St. Jude Children's Research Hospital, FedEx, the FBI, the National Civil Rights Museum, the Blues Foundation, and the United States Attorney's Office.

REAL SERVICE: At Rhodes, more than 80 percent of the student body participates in community service. The Rhodes curriculum includes courses with service components as well as related internships for academic credit. Additionally, Rhodes students independently operate several service outlets, including a downtown soup kitchen and the country's first campus-based chapter of Habitat for Humanity. A large portion of the student body also volunteer as tutors and mentors in local schools and urban youth programs.

REAL WORLD: Rhodes offers a wide range of study abroad options, including its European Studies program, which gives students the opportunity to spend two weeks at the University of York in England; six weeks with British tutors at Lincoln College, Oxford; and five weeks of travel to major cultural centers on the continent. Other Rhodes-sponsored programs include special study in Argentina and Chile. Summer Programs include British Studies at Oxford, intensive language programs, and service-learning programs at several international locations.

REAL COMMUNITY: There are a number of social fraternities and sororities at Rhodes. Approximately 50% of the students are members of Greek organizations. The fraternity and sorority lodges are not, however, residential, and most Greek-sponsored parties and activities are open to the entire campus.

REAL INTERACTION: The Rhodes faculty is composed of gifted scholars who challenge, engage, and connect students in life-changing ways. With a student-to-faculty ratio of just 11:1, faculty members interact with students both inside and outside the classroom. The Rhodes faculty work with students to offer unique research experiences that are usually afforded only to graduate students at large research universities. In any one of 31 major programs, students have the opportunity for hands-on research and study.

INDEPENDENT RESEARCH: Flexible independent and off-campus study is encouraged at Rhodes. Choices include pre-designed or self-designed interdisciplinary majors, individualized study options, directed inquiry projects, the tutorial plan, and study abroad. State-of-the-art technology is everywhere on the wireless campus at Rhodes. "Smart" classrooms, located throughout the campus, offer Internet access and computer and video displays, and the college's science facilities have been recently updated to offer students top-of-the-line technology and instruments.

LIVING AT RHODES: The campus spans across 100 acres in midtown Memphis. It is right across Overton Park, which contains the Memphis Zoo, the Brooks Museum, and the Memphis College of Art. The campus design includes stone Gothic architecture buildings, 13 of which are currently listed on the National Register of Historic Places. A 140-foot bell tower was named in honor of explorer Richard Halliburton. There's more to Memphis than Graceland and Elvis Presley. From blues on Beale Street to stadium sports, Memphis offers a rich mix of entertainment options. Memphis, the 18th largest city in the United States, is renowned for its great food, outstanding museums, and rich Southern heritage.

http://www.rhodes.edu/
P: (800) 844-5969

PRIVATE

STUDENT PROFILE

2,046 undergraduate students

99% of undergrad students are full time

43% male – 57% female

72% of students are from out of state

91% freshman retention rate

83% graduated in 6 years

FACULTY PROFILE

196 full-time faculty

30 part-time faculty

10 to 1 student/faculty ratio

ADMISSIONS

4,666 Total Applicants

2,187 Total Admissions

562 Total Freshman Enrollment

46.87% of applicants admitted

SAT Ranges: CR 600-700, M 580-680

ACT Ranges: C 27-32, M 26-31, E 28-34

TUITION & COSTS

Tuition: $42,914

Fees: $310

Total: $43,224

R&B: $10,746

Total: $53,970

FINANCIAL

$25,584 avg grant/scholarship amount (total)

$5,876 avg loan amount (total)

SEWANEE: THE UNIVERSITY OF THE SOUTH

SEWANEE, TENNESSEE

"A place of academic adventure rooted in Southern tradition, Sewanee challenges students to explore the world within and beyond the classroom." The Mountain at Sewanee is much more than another pretty campus. It's a place for adventures of the mind, body, and spirit. It's a place where wilderness and culture intersect to provide answers. It's a place of deep peace, where students can seek what's true, real, and beautiful. Most of all, it's a place of transformation and a home away from home. Sewanee instills a love of adventure, both physical and mental, in its students. It's 10,000 acre campus is filled with activity and excitement, hosting a magnificent environment in which students can pursue their interests and investigate new problems.

FIRST-YEAR PROGRAM: Sewanee's First Year Program (FYP) allows new students to take an interdisciplinary seminar their first very first semester. Designed to ease their transition to college life, FYP builds communities of learning and friendship both inside and outside of the classroom. All courses are capped at 14 students, so those who participate get to know their professors and fellow classmates while engaging in lively discussions about topics that merge different areas of study. Past seminars have included Good and Evil: Fairy Tales in Literature and Music; Sex and Gender Around the World: Common Issues and Diverse Perspectives; and Philosophy through Film: Jesus, Socrates, and Cowboys.

INTERDISCIPLINARY STUDIES: Sewanee offers a number of programs that are unique in both topic and structure. Chief among them are their interdisciplinary majors, which allow students to study one subject from a wide cross-section of perspectives. A small sample of these majors includes American studies, Asian studies, environmentalism, French studies, and biochemistry. There is also the extraordinary chance for students to design their own majors with a variety of courses. Past examples include wildlife conservation, integrative environmental solutions, and early modern studies.

GREEK LIFE: Going Greek means making 100 new friends in a single night. Nearly 70% of Sewanee students pledge to one of 19 national fraternities and sororities, providing themselves a firm base for service, socialization, and leadership. Despite the strong presence of Greek life, however, there's no stark division between the community of Greek and non-Greek students. Fraternity and sorority houses are nonresidential, so all students live together in the residence halls. All Greek-sponsored parties and events are also open to everyone on campus, regardless of pledge status.

SERVICE: A Sewanee education provides much more than just technical training; it also prepares students to make positive impacts in the world. The University encourages the connection between mind and heart, establishing numerous service opportunities for the campus at large. The All Saints' Chapel and the student-run Community Service Council, for example, coordinate and supervise several service programs, including adult literacy work, AIDS awareness, alcohol education, mentoring and tutoring, staffing at homeless shelters, recycling, and providing companionship for senior citizens.

PRE-PROFESSIONAL SUCCESS: Sewanee provides an excellent foundation for pre-professional students. The University's pre-law program encourages strong oral and written communication skills, a critical understanding of societal institutions and values, and a logical approach to problem solving. The results speak for themselves: 95% of pre-law grads are accepted into law school, and pre-health grads boast acceptance rates to medical, dental, and veterinary schools well above the national average.

---

http://www.sewanee.edu/
P: (800) 522-2234

PRIVATE

STUDENT PROFILE

1,710 undergraduate students

99% of undergrad students are full time

48% male – 52% female

75% of students are from out of state

89% freshman retention rate

78% graduated in 6 years

FACULTY PROFILE

184 full-time faculty

29 part-time faculty

10 to 1 student/faculty ratio

ADMISSIONS

4,509 Total Applicants

1,830 Total Admissions

469 Total Freshman Enrollment

40.59% of applicants admitted

TUITION & COSTS

Tuition: $36,410

Fees: $272

Total: $36,682

R&B: $11,050

Room: $5,730

Board: $5,320

Total: $47,732

FINANCIAL

$20,461 avg grant/scholarship amount (total)

$5,823 avg loan amount (total)

TUSCULUM COLLEGE

TUSCULUM, TENNESSEE

Founded in 1794, Tusculum is uniquely equipped to offer an education that leads to engaged and effective citizenship, literally making this a one-of-a-kind experience in higher education. The mission of Tusculum, its innovative calendar, and an active, engaged learning environment all work together in an integrated way to prepare citizens for effective participation in professional, public, and personal life.

FIRST-YEAR EXPERIENCE: Every new freshman and transfer student kicks off the Pioneer Experience by participating in Tusculum's First-Year Experience program. The program runs through students' first fall semester and hosts Wednesday classes and fun activities. Each First-Year Experience Orientation Class is taught by an instructor and mentor who build their curriculum around a specific theme, organizing outings and activities outside of class that revolve around the theme.

CENTER FOR CIVIC ADVANCEMENT: Tusculum's Center for Civic Advancement (CCA) is dedicated to the mission of engaging the heart, mind, and soul of Tusculum by cultivating awareness of others and of self. The CCA seeks to accomplish this ambitious mission through the establishment of meaningful relationships with local, national, and global communities alike. The CCA's full-time staff support faculty and students in the planning and undertaking of service placements and projects.

BONNER LEADER PROGRAM: The Bonner Leaders at Tusculum are a group of students committed to serving the local community by using their talents and gifts where needed. Participants develop leadership skills by participating in meetings, trainings, internships, and service. Upon graduation, Bonner Leaders continue to seek ways to enrich their communities through the leadership of nonprofits and/or direct service.

SERVICE-LEARNING: Service-Learning is integral to Tusculum's General Education Curriculum, reflecting the institution's commitment to provide educational experiences that prepare its graduates for the demands of active and responsible citizenship. The service-learning graduation requirement may be fulfilled through a Service-Learning course, a Service-Learning practicum, an approved internship, or through an approved course with a significant service-learning component.

TALENT DEVELOPMENT: Tusculum is the only school in the state of Tennessee to offer programs specifically focused on the growing field of Talent Development, making the program a unique academic distinction. Tusculum offers a Bachelor of Arts, as well as a Master of Arts, in Talent Development. The BATD prepares students to work in organizations as entry-level training and talent-development employees. The MATD prepares graduates for a variety of careers, including corporate trainers, project managers, strategic planners, team developers, process analysts, and performance-improvement consultants.

NETTIE DAY: Annually, Tusculum's campus comes to life for Nettie Fowler McCormick Service Day, one of Tusculum's longest held traditions, which involves students spending time in service to others. This annual day of service honors the memory and selfless way of life of Nettie Fowler McCormick, who is recognized as Tusculum's first benefactor for funding the construction of several of the main campus's historic structures. Nettie Day began as day of cleaning the campus in honor of Nettie McCormick's generous contributions; however, the day has evolved into a time for the entire campus community to find ways to give back to those in need throughout the region.

SPIES: The SPIES program is an acronym that stands for Social, Physical, Intellectual, Emotional, and Spiritual. The purpose of SPIES is to encourage the entire Tusculum community to lead and maintain a healthy and balanced lifestyle while creating opportunities to meet new people, strengthen friendships, and grow. The SPIES program recognizes that there is more to becoming a successful individual than simply studying for a degree. Tusculum's community members are far more likely to achieve their goals and grow into well-rounded citizens when they actively strive to enrich and balance these five foundational areas.

http://tusculum.edu/
P: (423) 636-7300

PRIVATE

STUDENT PROFILE

1,585 undergraduate students

89% of undergrad students are full time

49% male – 51% female

51% of students are from out of state

68% freshman retention rate

41% graduated in 6 years

FACULTY PROFILE

72 full-time faculty

113 part-time faculty

15 to 1 student/faculty ratio

ADMISSIONS

2,238 Total Applicants

1,665 Total Admissions

324 Total Freshman Enrollment

74.40% of applicants admitted

SAT Ranges: CR 413-500, M 430-540

ACT Ranges: C 1823, M 17-23, E 17-23

TUITION & COSTS

Tuition: $23,700

R&B: $8,700

Total: $32,400

FINANCIAL

$9,629 avg grant/scholarship amount (need)

$4,098 avg loan amount (need)

UNION UNIVERSITY

JACKSON, TENNESSEE

Union University is a private, liberal arts-based, Christian university located in Jackson, Tennessee. Union is united in its love for Christ, for rigorous academics, and for biblical truth, integrating top-tier academics with Christian faith in more than 100 programs of study. Founded in 1823, Union is the oldest institution to be affiliated with the Southern Baptist Convention. Its mission is to provide a Christ-centered education that promotes excellence and character development in service to church and society.

RESEARCH: Research is required of all students in more than 100 programs of study. In addition, many majors require a capstone, thesis, or professional portfolio. Juniors and seniors have a chance to present their research on both local and national levels through the annual Scholarship Symposium and conferences of professional and honor societies. These requirements ensure that students gain the practical, applied knowledge of their fields, urging them to make the most of their spectacular education.

SCHOLARS UNITE: Union students have had the opportunity to hear from such world-renowned leaders as George H.W. Bush, Margaret Thatcher, Mikhail Gorbachev, and Condoleezza Rice. They can join in the important conversations of modern time with leading theologians and scholars from all over the United States at major Union-sponsored conferences.

STUDY ABROAD: Study abroad during the summer or semester terms have included such recent destinations as Oxford University, Jordan, Mexico, Italy, and France. Union University students also have the opportunity to go on short-term mission Global Outreach trips to locations in the United States, Europe, Asia, and Central America.

CLOSE PERSONAL CONNECTIONS: Union has a sense of closeness, and professors know their students by name. It is not unusual to find professors and students in the campus coffee house discussing common interests. And several times throughout the year, students are invited to be dinner guests in the homes of faculty and staff members. Outside the classroom, faculty and students interact in various arts and discussion groups. The Society for Critical Imagination, for example, provides a forum for a discussion of the arts and an evaluation of them from a Christian perspective.

TOP-NOTCH FACILITIES: Pharmacy, science, and nursing students benefit from state-of-the-art laboratories and simulation facilities. Communications students produce daily live programming from their HD television studio.

VOLUNTEER: In addition to ongoing community work, students, faculty, and staff set aside one day during the school year to serve the local community through more than sixty different volunteer projects. Named "Campus & Community," this day of service was initiated in 2009 to give back to the community as thanks for its support of the university throughout the academic year.

OPPORTUNITIES OUTSIDE OF THE CLASSROOM: Union offers more than 50 major student-produced music and theatre events each academic year and hosts 60 campus clubs, societies, fraternities, sororities and other organizations. The university also hosts a live news program, Jackson 24/7, and publishes The Cardinal & Cream student news publication and The Torch literary journal. Union's student newspaper, Cardinal & Cream, recently was named the best such magazine in the Southeast. In addition, students enjoy intramural sports, a variety of Student Life activities, and student-led Bible studies.

SUCCESSFUL STUDENTS: Union students enjoy impressive acceptance rates for graduate study at some of the world's top schools. In fact, 100% of the faculty-recommended students were accepted for graduate study in health sciences. Around 30 percent of Union students go on to graduate school immediately after graduation, and graduates have recently been accepted to graduate study at schools such as Yale, Notre Dame, Emory, Georgetown, Boston University, Northwestern, and Vanderbilt.

http://www.uu.edu/
P: (731) 668-1818

PRIVATE - CHRISTIAN

STUDENT PROFILE

2,520 undergraduate students

74% of undergrad students are full time

39% male – 61% female

28% of students are from out of state

84% freshman retention rate

64% graduated in 6 years

FACULTY PROFILE

236 full-time faculty

184 part-time faculty

10 to 1 student/faculty ratio

ADMISSIONS

1,830 Total Applicants

1,265 Total Admissions

342 Total Freshman Enrollment

69.13% of applicants admitted

SAT Ranges: CR 510-650, M 480-650

ACT Ranges: C 22-29, M 20-27, E 23-31

TUITION & COSTS

Tuition: $28,200

Fees: $990

Total: $29,190

R&B: $10,140

Room: $6,940

Board: $3,200

Total: $39,330

FINANCIAL

$19,746 avg grant/scholarship amount (total)

$7,010 avg loan amount (total)

ABILENE CHRISTIAN UNIVERSITY

ABILENE, TEXAS

ABILENE
CHRISTIAN

http://www.acu.edu/

P: (800) 460-6228

PRIVATE - CHRISTIAN

The ACU experience—whether on the Abilene campus, in Study Abroad programs, at education centers, or through an ACU virtual community—helps students develop intellect, grow closer to God, prepare for a meaningful career, and address global challenges with a Christian worldview. ACU is in Abilene, Texas, an All-American city of 115,000 people 150 miles west of the Dallas and Fort Worth area.

GLOBAL COMMUNITY: Many backgrounds, cultures, and ethnicities are represented at ACU. In fact, students from nearly every state and over 40 countries live and learn together, supporting each other's growth in a rich group environment. This global community creates an opportunity for students to expand their worldview as well as to understand the global nature of their lives as Christians and future leaders alike. Students are stretched intellectually as they involve themselves actively through undergraduate research, the Honors College, internships, and team projects.

STUDENT ACTIVITIES: Community life at ACU is energized by a variety of campus activities that have been borne out of its century-long university tradition. Student government, weekend and Spring Break campaigns, volunteer work, Habitat for Humanity, and a variety of student organizations all provide significant opportunities for further education and the development of students' leadership skills.

ATHLETICS: As a member of the National Collegiate Athletic Association and the Lone Star Conference, ACU competes in football, men's and women's basketball, baseball, men's golf, men's and women's cross country, men's and women's indoor and outdoor track and field, women's volleyball, men's and women's tennis, women's softball and women's soccer. ACU is an annual contender for the Learfield Sports Directors' Cup, recognizing the best all-around sports program in NCAA Division II.

INNOVATIVE STUDY: ACU students are served by more than 230 faculty members who focus on high-quality teaching, scholarship, and service. More than 97 percent of tenure-track faculty hold terminal degrees. The student-to-faculty ratio is 16:1, meaning that faculty members and administrators alike make dedicated commitments to their students growth. Professors are actively involved as leaders and presenters in many national professional associations, and ACU is an active member of both the Council for Christian Colleges and Universities as well as the Lilly Network of Church-Related Colleges and Universities. ACU was the first university to give iPhones and iPod touches to freshmen, and it continues to be a world leader in the study of mobile-learning technology for use in higher education.

UNDERGRADUATE RESEARCH: At ACU, students experience rare opportunities to prepare for their future careers. In the physics program, undergraduate students regularly participate with faculty members at national nuclear physics laboratories and make national and international presentations. Most universities only allow graduate students to participate in such high-level work, but ACU recognizes the benefit of these hands-on, awe-inspiring trips. Additionally, journalism students produce a twice-weekly newspaper, The Optimist, which has received All-American honors every year since 1975. Students of all majors are experiencing such unique opportunities as these, making ACU stand out as a hands-on institution.

SUCCESSFUL ALUMNI: For more than 100 years, ACU has challenged students academically, providing them with a strong liberal arts education and an environment in which Christ is front and center. Because of this powerful combination, ACU graduates are in high demand by employers and graduate schools all over the world. They are accepted into medical school at twice the rate of the national average, and their acceptance rate into law school tops 80 percent.

STUDENT PROFILE

3,760 undergraduate students

95% of undergrad students are full time

41% male – 59% female

79% freshman retention rate

61% graduated in 6 years

FACULTY PROFILE

285 full-time faculty

62 part-time faculty

15 to 1 student/faculty ratio

ADMISSIONS

10,804 Total Applicants

5,393 Total Admissions

1,072 Total Freshman Enrollment

49.92% of applicants admitted

SAT Ranges: CR 470-590, M 480-590, W 450-570

ACT Ranges: C 22-27, M 20-26, E 21-27, W 6-8

TUITION & COSTS

Tuition: $30,780

Fees: $50

Total: $30,830

R&B: $9,310

Room: $4,390

Board: $4,920

Total: $40,140

FINANCIAL

$18,356 avg grant/scholarship amount (total)

$10,456 avg loan amount (total)

DALLAS BAPTIST UNIVERSITY

DALLAS, TEXAS

Dallas Baptist University is a Christian liberal arts university that seeks to develop servant-leaders who have the ability to integrate faith and learning through their respective callings. With a student-to-faculty ratio of 12:1, DBU provides a world-class educational experience with 73 undergraduate majors as well as 62 accelerated bachelor's and master's degree programs, 29 master's programs, and 73 dual master's degree programs.

STUDENT WELCOME AND TRANSITION WEEK: Affectionately known as SWAT, Student Welcome and Transition Week is a three-day immersion experience in which incoming DBU freshmen and transfer students are introduced to life on University Hill. Over 100 student volunteers join forces to organize and lead SWAT week, making the transition into the DBU family easier for incoming students. SWAT also gives students the opportunity to make instant connections with other students, form lifelong friendships, and settle into their new college home.

COMMON INTELLECTUAL EXPERIENCES: DBU students have created a student chapter of the 21st Century Wilberforce Initiative for the purpose of advocating for religious freedom. Through advocacy, capacity building, and technical innovations, this group promotes global protections and reformation for the vulnerable and victimized around the world.

COLLABORATIVE ASSIGNMENTS AND PROJECTS: Collaborative Assignments may be utilized in every academic division, but the College of Business provides perhaps the best example of innovation: Strategic Management 4320, a senior-level capstone course, affords students the opportunity to analyze a business in the DFW area and write descriptive assessments of the company in the areas of industry, value chain, generic strategy, integration, international strategy, and execution.

UNDERGRADUATE RESEARCH: Students in Foundations of College Research courses, as well as some English courses, conduct research that is designed to contribute to the scholarly research in a variety of fields. Instead of a descriptive approach to research that strictly reports on what is known, students are taught a "Research Question" approach. With this approach, students pursue a topic to assess a problem that needs to be solved. Any subsequent papers or projects are created as a way to present findings that solve a stated research question.

PAIDEIA COLLEGE SOCIETY: The Paideia College Society challenges students to carry out their various callings in both public and private life with Christ-like knowledge, virtue, and wisdom. This group hosts a weekly symposium at which intellectuals present papers and give presentations with a view to serve as a catalyst for cultural transformation.

DIVERSITY/GLOBAL LEARNING: DBU is home to seventeen social organizations and many more service, spiritual, and academic organizations. Organizations like the International Chinese Fellowship, the South Asian Student Organization, and the African Students Union exist to promote unity and appreciation of cultural diversity among international students and the greater DBU community. These groups also provide an amazing amount of support to International students in their academic pursuits, helping them transition to life in the United States through a variety of activities.

WRITING-INTENSIVE COURSES: The DBU Writing Center provides students with guidance and tutoring as they learn the art of writing across the curriculum. The Writing Center is open all throughout the week to help students in need of extra support at any time and for any writing assignment. Each student who visits the Writing Center is tutored by a qualified writing consultant in the areas of Grammar, Research, Revising, Organization, and Documentation.

http://www.dbu.edu/
P: (214) 333-7100

PRIVATE - CHRISTIAN

STUDENT PROFILE

3,109 undergraduate students

76%of undergrad students are full time

43% male – 57% female

10.25% of students are from out of state

77% freshman retention rate

59% graduated in 6 years

FACULTY PROFILE

128 full-time faculty

531 part-time faculty

12 to 1 student/faculty ratio

ADMISSIONS

3,259 Total Applicants

1,405 Total Admissions

527 Total Freshman Enrollment

43.11% of applicants admitted

SAT Ranges: CR 520-600, M 510-590

ACT Ranges: C 19-25

TUITION & COSTS

Tuition: $25,380

R&B: $7,533

Total: $32,913

FINANCIAL

$3,975 avg grant/scholarship amount (need)

$4,126 avg loan amount (need)

HARDIN-SIMMONS UNIVERSITY

ABILENE, TEXAS

Academic excellence continues as a priority at Hardin-Simmons University as it has for more than a century. Small classes taught by experienced scholars give the opportunity for interactive learning, and the institution's commitment to excellence is best illustrated through the lives of graduates who have a tradition of excellence in any career they have chosen.

FIRST-YEAR SEMINARS: Designed especially for first-semester freshmen, "First-Year Seminar: Gateway" is the academic gateway to HSU's Christian liberal arts experience. This theme-based seminar offers incoming students the opportunity to dig into the topic of their choice while exploring their personal strengths and experiencing the intersection of faith and learning. Academic and social connections made in the course help students begin to build a support system that can support them through their entire HSU experience.

THE HONORS PROGRAM: The Hardin-Simmons University Honors Program, which serves as an integral part of the academic community, includes courses that are taught by selected faculty members who are interested in working with highly motivated students. The Honors Program expects participants to strive for excellence and assume personal accountability for their intellectual growth. The goal of Honors studies is to encourage students to engage more actively in pursuing knowledge, discussing ideas, and challenging themselves to grow both intellectually and spiritually.

THE LEADERSHIP STUDIES PROGRAM: The Leadership Studies Program at Hardin-Simmons University is a unique program devoted to the development of tomorrow's Christian leaders. Working with nonprofit organizations, leadership students implement and practice the concepts that they study in the classroom, creating and performing service projects that meet real community needs. In the Leadership Studies Program, learning occurs both in and out of the classroom.

HSU INTERNATIONAL STUDIES: HSU International Studies supports academic programs that foster an understanding of the global community, serving students, faculty, and departments by facilitating the development and implementation of quality international academic experiences. Study abroad programs at HSU vary in length from a full academic year to four weeks during the summer. At present, HSU hosts study programs in London, England, Salzburg, Austria, Florence, Italy, and many other destinations.

STAMPEDE WEEK: Stampede Week is a dedicated week intended for new students that is designed to help make the transition to Hardin-Simmons University smooth and comfortable. This is a great opportunity to learn about HSU traditions, make lifelong friendships, and participate in fun and exciting activities. It's the perfect way for freshmen to start their memorable years at HSU and, by the time classes start, they are already an intrinsic part of the community.

LIVING-LEARNING COMMUNITIES: While living on campus is one of the best decisions one can make as an HSU student, the Living-Learning Communities (LLCs) are "communities within a community" that make it an even bigger no-brainer! LLCs have been shown nationally and at HSU to assist students both academically and socially, leading to higher GPAs, more connections to the larger campus community, and higher retention rates than their peers. They are an ideal way to connect life on-campus with the academic experience.

CAREER SERVICES: Career Services at HSU provides students and alumni with services, activities, and an environment that enhances the opportunities to choose, prepare adequately for, and enter career fields in which they can serve as Christian leaders. HSU Career Services assists students with obtaining internships, fine-tuning résumés, and assisting students with finding jobs.

http://www.hsutx.edu/

P: (325) 670-1000

PRIVATE - CHRISTIAN

STUDENT PROFILE

1,599 undergraduate students

92% of undergrad students are full time

47% male — 53% female

4% of students are from out of state

68% freshman retention rate

53% graduated in 6 years

FACULTY PROFILE

134 full-time faculty

70 part-time faculty

12 to 1 student/faculty ratio

ADMISSIONS

1,595 Total Applicants

957 Total Admissions

413 Total Freshman Enrollment

60% of applicants admitted

SAT Ranges: CR 450-570, M 470-570

ACT Ranges: C 19-25, M 19-25, E 18-25

TUITION & COSTS

Tuition: $25,230

Fees: $600

Total: $25,830

R&B: $8,138

Total: $33,968

FINANCIAL

$6,910 avg grant/scholarship amount (need)

$4,126 avg loan amount (need)

LUBBOCK CHRISTIAN UNIVERSITY

LUBBOCK, TEXAS

Lubbock Christian University is committed to educating leaders whose lives will have a lasting effect on their family, church, community, and jobs. Because classes are small in number, LCU can provide a wide range of enriching and personal experiences.

LCU HONORS PROGRAM: The mission of the University Honors Program is to provide students of high academic ability an exceptional college experience that prepares them for lives of Christian service. The program offers challenging and provocative courses, colloquia and seminars, occasions for cultural enrichment, and assistance for semester internships and study abroad opportunities. One such internship opportunity, the LCU Washington Program, provides qualified students with a semester-long internship in the nation's capital. Students complete a full-time, entry-level professional internship in their chosen career field, participating in various professional development and academic learning experiences.

STUDY ABROAD: LCU recently launched its Semester in Spain program in fall 2016. This 14-week program brings LCU students and professors to the beautiful city of Avila in the heart of the Spanish countryside. Students take 15 hours of University Core-type credits with their LCU professors, immersing themselves in the culture within the medieval walled city.

SCHOLAR'S COLLOQUIUM: Each spring, LCU hosts an interdisciplinary forum to promote and highlight original scholarship. The colloquium is held as an academic conference with breakout presentations. LCU students, faculty, and staff present and field questions from the audience. Research posters are displayed in the Student Union Building and are accompanied by sessions for informal questions.

SIDE-BY-SIDE UNDERGRADUATE RESEARCH: LCU offers an innovative Undergraduate Research Program, the hallmark of which is the close involvement of faculty mentors. For undergraduate research opportunities, such as NCUR or the annual Scholar's Colloquium, faculty may approach students and request them to participate based on their performance on a paper or project. Students may also approach faculty members to ask whether they would be interested in mentoring their research and helping them develop their ideas. This process prepares students for graduate school or the work force, and the intimacy achieved when faculty and students work together forges ties that last long after students graduate.

COMMUNITY INVOLVEMENT: LCU's academic courses maintain a connection with the both surrounding community and around the globe. The LCU Praise Choir regularly travels to Ukraine for a mission trip of song, and LCU partners with Olive Branch Ministries to conduct an annual medical mission trip to Peru. Additionally, a variety of Spring Break trips allow students to spend their break experiencing culture and serving abroad. In 2016,for example, a group from the School of Education traveled to Ecuador to teach English. In addition to global trips, classes such as World Religions and various community service projects such as the annual Collide engage students in the varied cultures of the Lubbock community.

INTERNSHIPS: In addition to the LCU Washington Program, professors seek to help students find an internship that best supports their majors as well as their future careers. Many LCU students participate in internships during their college career, which often these provide them valuable on-the-job skills, workplace experience, and professional guidance.

SENIOR EXPERIENCE: Senior Capstones act as culminating experiences that require students nearing the end of their college years to create a project that integrates and applies what they've learned. The project can take the form of a research paper, a performance, a portfolio of "best work," or an exhibit of artwork. Capstones are offered both in departmental programs and, increasingly, in general education as well.

http://www.lcu.edu/
P: (800) 933-7601

PRIVATE - CHRISTIAN

STUDENT PROFILE
1,496 undergraduate students
85% of undergrad students are full time
41% male – 59% female
12% of students are from out of state
73% freshman retention rate
42% graduated in 6 years

FACULTY PROFILE
102 full-time faculty
81 part-time faculty
13 to 1 student/faculty ratio

ADMISSIONS
867 Total Applicants
833 Total Admissions
275 Total Freshman Enrollment
96.08% of applicants admitted
SAT Ranges: CR 440-550, M 430-555, W 420-548
ACT Ranges: C 19-25, M 18-25, E 18-25

TUITION & COSTS
Tuition: $20,160
Fees: $200
Total: $20,360
R&B: $6,070
Total: $26,430

FINANCIAL
$9,680 avg grant/scholarship amount (total)
$8,456 avg loan amount (total)

MIDWESTERN STATE UNIVERSITY

WICHITA FALLS, TEXAS

MSU is a vibrant, active residential university. With over 100 student organizations and a 17:1 student-to-faculty ratio, MSU is able to offer a personalized educational experience with the amenities of a large institution. Offering a private university experience at the affordability of a public university, MSU is unique in the state of Texas.

FIRST-YEAR SEMINARS AND EXPERIENCES: MSU offers incoming students learning communities in the fall term as well as first-year seminars in the spring term. It takes a structured approach that allows for greater engagement in the MSU community early on in freshmen's college careers. So as to not require students to take more courses than necessary, first-year seminar material is woven into core courses during the spring term. This integrated approach recognizes the value of streamlining students' paths to graduation.

COMMON INTELLECTUAL EXPERIENCES: MSU's 42-hour Core Curriculum is comprised of 8 Foundational Component Areas and 1 Component Area Option (CAO). The institution uses the CAO to create a Common Intellectual Experience for its students. Courses that count in the CAO reflect one of two themes: Cultural & Global Understanding and Inquiry & Creativity. Students are required to take a course from each theme, and while nearly 30 courses are available to choose from, they nevertheless share the experience of exploring the two themes.

COLLABORATIVE ASSIGNMENTS AND PROJECTS: The best examples of collaboration in research can be seen in MSU's commitment to Undergraduate Research and the Learning Communities. Students from different disciplines have the opportunity to band together and develop research projects to present in front of the campus community. Learning Communities also include integrative assignments, many of which are group projects. Not only do these assignments allow students to synthesize materials from the two courses that comprise the Learning Community, but they provide opportunities to learn valuable soft skills like teamwork and compromise.

UNDERGRADUATE RESEARCH: All students are invited to participate in MSU's undergraduate research initiative, EURECA (Enhancing Undergraduate Research and Creative Activities). Through EURECA, students work under the guidance of faculty mentors to develop a semester-long research project, propose the project for EURECA funding, and present their findings at the fall or spring research forum.

GLOBAL LEARNING: All students have the opportunity to participate in a variety of study abroad programs. MSU serves as the national consortium leader for the London-based British Studies summer program. This comparative study program offers students a range of classes from all six academic colleges, culminating with an international research project or portfolio. Students looking for a different opportunity through language or culture classes can choose to earn academic credits while studying in either Spain or London. Additionally, Health Science and Pre-Med/Pre-Vet students will soon have the opportunity to study Global Health & Wellness on the campus of an accredited medical school in Grenada, giving students a real opportunity to study global health issues while residing and experiencing what a medical school has to offer.

WRITING-INTENSIVE COURSES: Recognizing the importance of writing in success beyond college, MSU places significant emphasis on the development of mature and flexible writers. All students are required to take a first-year writing-intensive course that introduces them to research and writing in an academic setting. Additionally, several departments across campus—i.e. Biology, Business, Criminal Justice, Psychology—have a discipline-specific writing requirement.

LEARNING COMMUNITIES: At MSU, faculty collaborate to create academic learning communities, two paired courses that combine different Foundational Component Areas, and include several integrative assignments (assessments synthesizing knowledge from both disciplines). Many of these assignments include a co- or extra-curricular component, such as attending an election debate party, watching a documentary, handing out pocket Constitutions, or visiting area high schools to teach students about issues in education.

MIDWESTERN STATE UNIVERSITY

https://www.mwsu.edu/

P: (940) 397-4334

PUBLIC

STUDENT PROFILE

5,277 undergraduate students

77% of undergrad students are full time

43% male – 57% female

8% of students are from out of state

70% freshman retention rate

44% graduated in 6 years

FACULTY PROFILE

236 full-time faculty

109 part-time faculty

18 to 1 student/faculty ratio

ADMISSIONS

2,854 Total Applicants

2,169 Total Admissions

826 Total Freshman Enrollment

76% of applicants admitted

SAT Ranges: CR 450-540, M 450-550

ACT Ranges: C 19-24, M 18-24, E 18-24

TUITION & COSTS

Tuition: (In) $8,305 (Out) $10,255

Fees: $3,804

Total: (In) $12,109 (Out) $14,059

R&B: $8,027

Room: $5,001

Board: $3,026

Total: (In) $20,136 (Out) $22,086

FINANCIAL

$6,899 avg grant/scholarship amount (need)

$6,887 avg loan amount (need)

SAM HOUSTON STATE UNIVERSITY

HUNTSVILLE, TEXAS

Sam Houston State University's motto, "The Measure of a Life is its Service," thrives in the foundation of every program and every event on campus. SHSU is proud to provide an extraordinary education in the name of Sam Houston, a beacon of Texan excellence. Its historical honor stands strong to support contemporary students, providing an education from faculty who care about their students' success. Its programs thrive both on campus and off, as the University offers online courses that can be recognized as some of the best in Texas.

UNDERGRADUATE RESEARCH: SHSU hosts an Undergraduate Research Symposium in which student research is praised and acknowledged as a critical part of the campus' scholarly atmosphere. Students are given the opportunity to hone their public speaking and presentation skills. The Symposium acts as an efficient forum for networking and learning across a vast number of fields.

INTRODUCTION TO COLLEGIATE STUDIES: SHSU students begin their college careers with University 1301, a first-year writing intensive that prepares them for the rigor of collegiate coursework as well as the transition into their new lifestyles at school. The coursework for each session varies among disciplines, all designed to build a foundation of skills that continue to be useful throughout students' respective majors. Those who participate in University 1301 commonly have higher GPAs and stronger graduation rates, as they all begin college knowing that they are given direct access to academic survival tools and are instantly put in touch with their peers.

STUDENT SERVICES: Sam Houston State University offers a writing center, a math center, and online tutoring at no additional cost to every student. The university also provides students with advising, mentoring, and career planning through our Student Advising & Mentoring Center.

LEARNING COMMUNITIES: First-year students have the option to participate in SHSU's Freshman Learning Communities, living-learning communities that draw students together on the foundation of academic or extracurricular interests. These students get to know one another and act as great providers of support at every hour of the day; they spend so much of their time growing together, both out of the classroom and in the same core classes.

VOLUNTEER WORK: SHSU's tradition of service echoes throughout all that students and faculty do on campus. The school is roaring with a large number of annual volunteer events such as its Volunteer Opportunities Fairs and Alternative Spring Break trips. Most engaging is the "Bearkats: All Paws In" event in the spring, which is a campus-wide day for volunteer work and service. On this day, faculty suspend classes so that they may join their students in giving back to their community.

ACE COURSES: SHSU faculty strive to serve the world around them even through the courses they teach. Academic Community Engagement (ACE) courses combine service and academics, inspiring students to apply their knowledge to life-changing acts of kindness.

INTERNSHIPS: Many programs at SHSU strongly encourage students to pursue internships in and around Birmingham, an amazing city center that's filled with industry professionals who are looking for talented assistants. Internships build students' pre-professional work experience, all while supplementing their academic performance as well. Because internships are so beneficial for students both in and beyond college, they frequently reward students with credit toward graduation.

Sam Houston State University

http://www.shsu.edu/
P: (936) 294-1828

PUBLIC

STUDENT PROFILE

17,401 undergraduate students

81% of undergrad students are full time

39% male – 61% female

80% freshman retention rate

49% graduated in 6 years

FACULTY PROFILE

794 full-time faculty

236 part-time faculty

21 to 1 student/faculty ratio

ADMISSIONS

9,242 Total Applicants

6,720 Total Admissions

2,637 Total Freshman Enrollment

72.71% of applicants admitted

SAT Ranges: CR 450-550, M 440-540

ACT Ranges: C 19-24, M 18-24, E 19-25

TUITION & COSTS

Tuition: (In) $5,172 (Out) $14,532

Fees: $2,446

Total: (In) $7,618 (Out) $16,978

R&B: $8,676

Room: $4,896

Board: $3,780

Total: (In) $16,294 (Out) $25,654

FINANCIAL

$8,852 avg grant/scholarship amount (total)

$6,395 avg loan amount (total)

COLLEGE PROFILES: SOUTH

SOUTHERN METHODIST UNIVERSITY

DALLAS, TEXAS

SMU provides a great education for professionals who are interested in more than just their professions. It combines an expansive curriculum with general education requirements to ensure that students can immerse themselves in their particular interests while still benefiting from an exposure to different academic disciplines. Over the last decade, SMU has reaped the benefits of explosive growth while maintaining its sense of community. SMU is large enough to offer almost unlimited opportunities, but small enough for students to truly take advantage of them.

UNDERGRADUATE RESEARCH: The University provides several opportunities for undergraduates to conduct research. The Richter Fellowship awards grant money to support the costs that SMU students incur while researching international or multicultural topics. Students studying biomedicine can take advantage of summer research opportunities through the Biomedical Researchers in Training Experience Scholars Program, while psychology majors can start researching and conducting experiments as early as their sophomore year.

AN EDUCATION THAT GOES AS FAR AS YOU TAKE IT: SMU students have the opportunity to explore a wide assortment of subjects in an innovative, interdisciplinary way. Described as "open-minded, outgoing, and friendly," SMU students are known to be forward-looking with an appreciation of a traditional lifestyle.

AN ACADEMIC PROGRAM THAT'S INNOVATIVE AND COMPREHENSIVE: "One-on-one interaction is the heart of an SMU education," says one faculty member. Every first-year student takes a rhetoric class that is made up of 18 or fewer students, ensuring that everyone benefits from active participation in a close group community. The SMU faculty are known for their bring accessible to students outside of their scheduled office hours. Some professors even offer their home or cell phone numbers for students who need assistance after hours.

A-LEC: The Altshuler Learning Enhancement Center (A-LEC) offers an array of programs to help students stay on track, including seminars for time and stress management, writing tutorials from full-time faculty, and a course titled ORACLE (Optimum Reading, Attention, Comprehension, and Learning Efficiency).

RESIDENCE COMMUNITIES: Honors students have the opportunity to live in special communities. The Hilltop Scholars Program is a live-and-learn community for first-year students. These students live together in Perkins Hall and take up to three classes together. The University Honors Program also offers honors students the option to live in Virginia-Snider, a hall dedicated to the honors community. Students interested in community service can live in the Service House, paying for room and board through volunteer work.

A THRIVING NEIGHBORHOOD: In addition to all the exciting activities on campus, there's plenty to do both in the neighborhood across the street as well as within the city, which is easily accessible by train. There are numerous shops and restaurants within walking distance of campus. Some of the best shopping, art, and cultural activities in the world can be found in Dallas. SMU's Meadows Museum houses one of the finest and most comprehensive collections of Spanish art outside of Spain. The Dallas area is also home to the Dallas Cowboys, Dallas Mavericks, Dallas Stars, Texas Rangers, and FC Dallas.

CAREER SERVICES: Whether students are planning to attend graduate school or join the workforce, the SMU Hegi Family Career Development Center is prepared to help. The center provides comprehensive testing services, academic guidance, seminars on résumé building, and mock interviews. The career center also has a job and internship placement program and is proud to say that there are more internships available to SMU students than there are students to fill them.

http://www.smu.edu/

P: (800) 323-0672

PRIVATE

STUDENT PROFILE

6,411 undergraduate students

96% of undergrad students are full time

50% male – 50% female

56% of students are from out of state

90% freshman retention rate

79% graduated in 6 years

FACULTY PROFILE

787 full-time faculty

376 part-time faculty

11 to 1 student/faculty ratio

ADMISSIONS

12,992 Total Applicants

6,360 Total Admissions

1,374 Total Freshman Enrollment

48.95% of applicants admitted

SAT Ranges: CR 600-690, M 620-720, W 600-690

ACT Ranges: C 28-32, M 27-31, E 28-33, W 8-9

TUITION & COSTS

Tuition: $42,770

Fees: $5,420

Total: $48,190

R&B: $15,575

Room: $10,045

Board: $5,530

Total: $63,765

FINANCIAL

$27,113 avg grant/scholarship amount (total)

$10,785 avg loan amount (total)

364   COLLEGES OF DISTINCTION | **2018**

SOUTHWESTERN UNIVERSITY

GEORGETOWN, TEXAS

Changing lives since 18840, Southwestern University is a private, selective national liberal arts and sciences institution, committed to maintaining a dynamic residential community where students are challenged, supported, and engaged. Southwestern fosters a community whose values and actions encourage meaningful contributions to the wellbeing of humanity.

PAIDEIA CURRICULUM: Paideia, Southwestern's uniquely designed curriculum is interdisciplinary, integrative, and intentional. Courses are organized as "Paideia Clusters" in order to draw.focus around thematic questions. These cluster courses help students become more aware of the ways that different disciplines consider the same questions. Interdisciplinary exploration begins in the Paideia Seminar, where students and faculty integrate various perspectives all together. Paideia moves student and faculty understanding beyond the disciplines themselves, forming connections between learning experiences as they seek creative solutions to the global challenges of today.

INQUIRY INITIATIVE: The Southwestern Inquiry Initiative, funded by a grant from the Howard Hughes Medical Institute, is transforming science and math at Southwestern University. Faculty throughout the Natural Sciences are incorporating the process of inquiry into introductory classes and laboratories, and a new cadre of specially-trained peer mentors, the SCI Guides, help students maximize their learning and critical thinking skills. Learning through discovery continues especially for students who conduct research with faculty mentors in SCOPE, the Inquiry Initiative's summer research program. Through intentional, evidence-based practices, Southwestern builds an ever-growing scientific community that is increasingly strong and exploratory. The Inquiry Initiative supports Southwestern's natural sciences in generating a creative, accomplished, and diverse pool of Southwestern student scientists.

STUDY ABROAD: More than a third of Southwestern students study abroad at least once throughout their college career. A London experience is available each fall along with summer programs in locations such as Argentina, Costa Rica, Jamaica, Peru, and Spain. Students have access to universities around the world through the International Student Exchange Program. In addition, Southwestern also offers opportunities semester-length studies in New York and Washington, D.C., as well as both national and international internships.

GUEST LECTURES AND SYMPOSIA: Students also have the opportunity to attend several lectures and symposia throughout the year. The Paideia Connections: Engaging in Scholarly Conversations series is a new series on campus that features short talks by two faculty members from diverse fields about their recent scholarly work. Following their talks, members of the campus community and the general public are encouraged to engage in thought-provoking discussions and share connections they make between the presentations. "Paideia Connections" takes its name from Southwestern's Paideia curriculum, which encourages students and faculty members to make connections between various disciplines and disparate ideas.

COMMUNITY ENGAGEMENT: At a rate that is twice the national average, Southwestern students give more than 39,000 service hours annually to more than 100 local nonprofits and agencies. Students can enact change and have loads of fun in approximately 100 student organizations that span topics across scholastic and honorary, government, Greek, special interests, and departmental fields of interest.

GRADUATE SUCCESS: In a recent survey, 91 percent of Southwestern graduates reported having obtained employment or having been accepted into graduate or professional school within 10 months. Southwestern's Office of Career Services collected several testimonials from alumni, discovering that the University's graduates leave feeling satisfied and inspired by their college experience.

Southwestern University

http://www.southwestern.edu/
P: (512) 863-6511

PRIVATE

STUDENT PROFILE

1,515 undergraduate students

99% of undergrad students are full time

43% male – 57% female

14% of students are from out of state

87% freshman retention rate

75% graduated in 6 years

FACULTY PROFILE

113 full-time faculty

49 part-time faculty

12 to 1 student/faculty ratio

ADMISSIONS

3,736 Total Applicants

1,652 Total Admissions

359 Total Freshman Enrollment

44.22% of applicants admitted

SAT Ranges: CR 520-640, M 520-630

ACT Ranges: C 23-29, M 22-27, E 23-30

TUITION & COSTS

Tuition: $37,560

R&B: $11,324

Room: $5,350

Board: $5,974

Total: $48,884

FINANCIAL

$23,691 avg grant/scholarship amount (total)

$9,094 avg loan amount (total)

ST. EDWARD'S UNIVERSITY

AUSTIN, TEXAS

Established in 1885 and located in the heart of Austin, Texas, St. Edward's is a private, liberal arts Catholic university in the Holy Cross tradition. With over 90 academic programs, St. Edward's continues its founding tradition of academic excellence and educating the whole person. The University sits on a hill with a commanding view of downtown Austin.

AUSTIN: St. Edward's is located in Austin, TX. Because the University is so close to the city, students have access to amazing professional opportunities as well as endless recreational activities. Austin is known for its live music, outdoor activities, and tech industry. There are plenty of attractions, including Austin City Limits, South by Southwest, and Fun Fun Fun Fest.

GLOBAL PERSPECTIVE: St. Edward's recognizes global perspective as an integral part of the undergraduate experience. The university believes that each student has a duty to the global community, and should therefore understand the issues and opportunities our world faces. In order to reach this goal, each student is required to take Cultural Foundations classes. These courses are designed to expand students' understanding of other cultures and practices. The Global Understanding Certificate is an additional opportunity for students to demonstrate their dedication to global citizenship and engagement, recording their experiences abroad and in interculturally focused courses.

CAREER PREPARATION: St. Edward's works very hard to prepare each student for postgraduate success—whether that's entering into a career, applying for graduate school, or becoming a volunteer. In order to reach that goal, St. Edward's provides a handful of services and resources to prepare students for post-graduate life. The university has Career and Professional Development counselors, who are available to guide student decisions and answer tough questions. St. Ed's also hosts career and internship fairs, which allow students to begin the networking process right on campus. Other services include an online database for job postings, résumé workshopping, and a variety of career-searching events and fairs.

LIVING LEARNING COMMUNITIES: Living Learning Communities (LLCs) bring together students from different backgrounds who share common interests or academic goals. These students have the unique opportunity to live and learn among similarly minded peers 24 hours a day. This structure allows students to collaborate both in and out of the classroom, thus enhancing the educational experience through the participation in special events, discussions, and service projects. Examples of St. Edward's University's LLCs include Active Living, Honors, Leadership, Natural Sciences, and "Wicked Problems," a community dedicated to approaching complex social issues.

ALTERNATIVE SPRING BREAK: Alternative spring break is a great opportunity for students to give back to the community. During the break, students travel to areas of need within the United States, working alongside community members to enact positive change. In the past, students have traveled to Arizona, Kentucky, Oregon, New Mexico, New York, and Illinois.

HONORS PROGRAM: The Honors program brings together academically gifted students from all majors and schools. Alongside faculty, these students create an intellectually stimulating community that promotes both academic and personal growth. Most of the Honors seminars are taught in a team-teaching style, boosted by professors who teach from different disciplines. Their work culminates in an Honors Senior Thesis, which stands as a reflection of each student's passions and academic capabilities.

---

http://www.stedwards.edu/

P: (512) 448-8400

PRIVATE - CATHOLIC

STUDENT PROFILE

4,023 undergraduate students

88% of undergrad students are full time

39% male – 61% female

17% of students are from out of state

85% freshman retention rate

63% graduated in 6 years

FACULTY PROFILE

203 full-time faculty

254 part-time faculty

14 to 1 student/faculty ratio

ADMISSIONS

5,034 Total Applicants

3,899 Total Admissions

873 Total Freshman Enrollment

77.45% of applicants admitted

SAT Ranges: CR 530-620, M 510-600, W 500-600

ACT Ranges: C 23-27, M 21-26, E 22-29

TUITION & COSTS

Tuition: $38,320

Fees: $400

Total: $38,720

R&B: $11,664

Room: $6,734

Board: $4,930

Total: $50,384

FINANCIAL

$26,691 avg grant/scholarship amount (total)

$8,770 avg loan amount (total)

ST. MARY'S UNIVERSITY

SAN ANTONIO, TEXAS

ST. MARY'S UNIVERSITY

St. Mary's University, founded by Marianist brothers in 1852, is the first higher education institution to have been established in San Antonio. It offers a strong educational experience through an integration of the liberal arts, professional preparation, and ethical commitment. St. Mary's students receive the value of quality programs, holistic learning, and community support, helping graduates discover what they love to do and how to apply their knowledge in meaningful ways. They are truly given an edge for a successful future.

FIRST-YEAR SEMINAR: The First-Year Seminar assists students in deriving maximum benefit from their undergraduate experience. Instructors facilitate the transition from high school to life on a college campus with a focus on both classroom success and personal development. The course is offered to general sections of students as well as through affinity groups (e.g., Living Learning Communities; Honors; STEM; etc.). A unique feature is the ability for students to build relationships with faculty and staff, providing a new support contact for their collegiate years.

UNDERGRADUATE RESEARCH: St. Mary's encourages and supports undergraduate research. The senior capstone course in the core curriculum requires students to engage in individual research and apply knowledge and skills learned throughout the core curriculum to problems at the local, regional, national, or international level. Numerous majors have research projects as the final requirement for graduation. The university hosts a research symposium every spring in which students are provided an opportunity to share their findings to the public. Student research is supported through Summer Undergraduate Research Fellowships and Undergraduate Research Travel Funds.

DIVERSITY/GLOBAL LEARNING: Students are provided numerous opportunities to extend the horizons of their learning. The St. Mary's Center for International Programs offers study abroad programs, international service-learning opportunities, and international internships. These programs permit students to immerse themselves in their international host communities while engaging in academically challenging studies. Programs are offered in a number of formats including short-term, faculty-led programs to semester-long exchange programs in a variety of locations, including Japan, China, Spain, Brazil, and London. Numerous student organizations support non-U.S. students and provide opportunities for cross-cultural activities and co-curricular learning.

FACULTY ACADEMIC MENTOR (FAM) PROGRAM: In 2010, St. Mary's implemented a Faculty Academic Mentor (FAM) program, which was developed to provide first-generation students with both faculty and student mentors. These mentors quickly become trusted advisors, making college life easier and more comfortable by checking in periodically and providing helpful support.

LIVING-LEARNING COMMUNITIES: Living-learning communities (LLCs) are academic- or interest-themed living communities primarily for students with similar majors or interests. There are eight LLCs at St. Mary's: Biology, Political Science, Psychology, the Honors Program, the Marianist Leadership Program, Rattler Athletics fans, and health and wellness enthusiasts. Students in LLCs not only live together, but they also go to class and study together. The cultivation of peer mentoring in LLCs has led to greater student success and retention. Students who live and study together also succeed together.

SURROUNDING CITY AND COMMUNITY: San Antonio has long been known as "Military City, USA," a place that exemplifies hospitality and warmth not only to its men and women in uniform, but also to its culturally diverse citizens. San Antonio has been increasingly expanding, especially in its business sector, but the people will nevertheless say that it feels like a big small town—in the best possible way. At St. Mary's, community service is part of the Marianist Charism that defines the university. Students devote countless hours to local volunteer opportunities, service-learning classes, advocacy work, and liturgical ministry.

https://www.stmarytx.edu/

P: (210) 436-3126

PRIVATE - CATHOLIC

STUDENT PROFILE

2,268 undergraduate students

96% of undergrad students are full time

47% male – 53% female

9% of students are from out of state

76% freshman retention rate

55% graduated in 6 years

FACULTY PROFILE

210 full-time faculty

189 part-time faculty

11 to 1 student/faculty ratio

ADMISSIONS

4,346 Total Applicants

3,375 Total Admissions

587 Total Freshman Enrollment

77.66% of applicants admitted

SAT Ranges: CR 470-560, M 480-570

ACT Ranges: C 19-25, M 18-25, E 18-24

TUITION & COSTS

Tuition: $27,520

Fees: $680

Total: $28,200

R&B: $9,300

Total: $37,500

FINANCIAL

$18,310 avg grant/scholarship amount (need)

$5,016 avg loan amount (need)

STEPHEN F. AUSTIN STATE UNIVERSITY

NACOGDOCHES, TEXAS

SFASU is a comprehensive institution dedicated to excellence in teaching, research, scholarship, creative work, and service. Within driving distance of the beach, the Dallas area, and Louisiana, SFASU students have numerous activities to choose from both on and off campus.

FIRST-YEAR EXPERIENCE: The First-Year Experience (FYE) is an introductory program that welcomes new students to university life. The transition from high school into college can be difficult for students, with many needing a little extra time to get used to the campus community and new academic standards. The FYE aims to ease this transition period by providing students with the necessary resources to succeed. SFA 101 is an introductory course that is additionally designed to transition first-year students into college-level academics. While the course is not mandatory, it is highly recommended. Many incoming freshmen do not realize how different college is than high school, and this can leave many feeling underprepared or overwhelmed. SFA 101 is perfect for easing students into their new academic standards. The course is capped at 25 students per class, which allows for a more intimate, discussion-based learning environment. Some of the topics covered in SFA 101 include: career planning, study skills, and time management.

THE HONORS PROGRAM: The SFASU Honors Program was created to further challenge academically gifted students. Individuals enrolled in the Honors Program have the benefit of small classes that promote advanced skills in critical thinking, problem solving, writing, communication, and higher-level conceptualization. Honors students also take a series of interdisciplinary courses that explore topics from multiple viewpoints. They profit from close interaction with faculty, an association with other highly-motivated students, and access to valuable resources. For qualifying students, the Honors Program is an advantageous track full of opportunity.

RESIDENTIAL LEARNING COMMUNITIES: RLCs provide the unique opportunity for students to live and learn among peers with similar goals and interests. Participation in an RLC has incredible benefits that ultimately enhance the educational experience. RLC members typically perform better in school because they are provided with an environment that has a concentrated focus on academic and personal growth. Students in an RLC also benefit from close interaction with faculty, built in academic support, access to extra-curricular activities, and discussion groups. SFA currently has RLC options for both freshmen and upperclassmen. Examples include communities that focus on Natural Resource Management, Outdoor Experiences, Community Service, and Honors.

STUDY ABROAD: Study abroad is considered one of the most rewarding experiences of an undergraduate career. Students who go abroad gain incredibly valuable skills in cross-cultural communication and global engagement. Many also gain a greater sense of independence and educational responsibility. They have many options to choose from so that they can cater their experience for themselves, going on short excursions through faculty-led trips, participating in an independent exchange program, or accessing a program that is offered through provider programs at another university.

CAREER SERVICES: Career Services is the best resource for all things, school, internship, and career related. Students are faced with many challenging questions during college: What will they major in? Where and how will they secure an internship? What is the true trajectory of the career they have chosen? Career Services has trained career coaches to guide students through these and many other tough questions. Sometimes, all a student needs is a guiding hand to see all the possibilities and even answers. Some of the services offered include: résumé assistance, internship and job search, interview assistance, and workshops.

http://www.sfasu.edu/
P: (936) 468-2011

PUBLIC

STUDENT PROFILE

10,899 undergraduate students

87% of undergrad students are full time

37% male – 63% female

2% of students are from out of state

71% freshman retention rate

41% graduated in 6 years

FACULTY PROFILE

554 full-time faculty

136 part-time faculty

19 to 1 student/faculty ratio

ADMISSIONS

11,382 Total Applicants

7,008 Total Admissions

2,282 Total Freshman Enrollment

61.57% of applicants admitted

SAT Ranges: CR 440-550, M 450-550

ACT Ranges: C 19-24, M 17-24, E 17-24

TUITION & COSTS

Tuition: (In) $5,652 (Out) $15,012

Fees: $1,908

Total: (In) $7,560 (Out) $16,920

R&B: $8,868

Total: (In) $16,428 (Out) $25,788

FINANCIAL

$8,960 avg grant/scholarship amount (total)

$6,848 avg loan amount (total)

TEXAS CHRISTIAN UNIVERSITY

FORT WORTH, TEXAS

With 8,800 students from across the country and around the world, TCU offers many benefits of large universities, including rigorous academic programs, over 100 undergraduate majors, excellent high-tech facilities, professors who are leaders in their fields, and Division I athletics. Grounded in the liberal arts, TCU can help individuals realize their creative potential, assuring that graduates are well prepared for professional careers.

FIRST-YEAR EXPERIENCE: Students flock to TCU knowing that they are right to expect an endless range of experiences from the beginning of their first year to beyond. The Summer Frog Camp orientation primes new students with an introduction to the skills they need to be successful in college. It introduces new students to their classmates, university history and traditions, and the concept of ethical leadership and citizenship. First-year students have the additional opportunity to take freshman seminars that are designed to help them develop both a sense of belonging and the self-confidence needed for academic success.

IT'S NOT ALL ACADEMIC: With more than 200 student organizations, students can find the group that's just for them, from the High Adventure Club to the Young Republicans and TCU Democrats. Students can also participate in an award-winning student newspaper, magazine, and radio station. Those who are musically inclined can join a spirited marching band, orchestral groups, and choral groups that perform at Carnegie Hall and around the world.

WORLD-CLASS ARTS: The College of Fine Arts provides hands-on learning for its students through public performances and festivals. Additionally, the biennial Latin American Music Festival draws world-renowned artists, musicians, and composers to the Metroplex. TCU choirs have performed at Carnegie Hall on multiple occasions, while the ballet and modern dance department regularly offers students opportunities to perform internationally. The theatre department also collaborates on productions with professional theaters in Fort Worth, and the art history program offers study at internationally recognized museums such as the Kimbell Art Museum, the Amon Carter Museum, and the Modern Art Museum of Fort Worth. These achievements in the arts highlight TCU's efforts to let their talented students shine.

WORLD-CLASS RESEARCH: As a major teaching and research university, TCU receives research funding from more than seventy-five agencies. The Institute of Behavioral Research is one of the oldest and most respected evidence-based addiction treatment research institutes in the world.

FROGS ARE FAMILY: At TCU, each student is part of a family—a family that wants to help them succeed. The Careers Services Center does more than host job fairs and help with graduate school applications. It provides serious help for students, including résumé and interviewing workshops as well as "Major in Success," which explores the activities that students should be pursuing while still in school in order to ensure their success after graduation.

ALUMNI NETWORK: Not only can TCU students use Career Services for guidance into the real world, but they can also keep in touch with a helpful network of fellow Frogs. Alumni can be found around the world as leaders of companies, cities, and even countries. This network gives TCU students easy access to internships, graduate school applications, or mentorships in future careers. With 75,000 members and 19 alumni chapters nationwide, one can find a Frog wherever they go.

http://www.tcu.edu/

P: (800) 828-3764

PRIVATE

STUDENT PROFILE

8,894 undergraduate students

97% of undergrad students are full time

40% male – 60% female

51% of students are from out of state

90% freshman retention rate

76% graduated in 6 years

FACULTY PROFILE

649 full-time faculty

9 part-time faculty

13 to 1 student/faculty ratio

ADMISSIONS

18,423 Total Applicants

7,974 Total Admissions

2,073 Total Freshman Enrollment

43.28% of applicants admitted

SAT Ranges: CR 530-630, M 550-650, W 530-640

ACT Ranges: C 25-30, M 25-29, E 25-32

TUITION & COSTS

Tuition: $40,630

Fees: $90

Total: $40,720

R&B: $11,800

Room: $7,100

Board: $4,700

Total: $52,520

FINANCIAL

$22,431 avg grant/scholarship amount (total)

$12,895 avg loan amount (total)

TRINITY UNIVERSITY

SAN ANTONIO, TEXAS

Trinity University is one of the nation's top private undergraduate institutions. Noted for its superior academic quality, outstanding faculty, and exceptional academic resources, Trinity is committed to the intellectual, civic, and professional preparation of its students.

THE PLUNGE: The Plunge is a four-day excursion that takes place before new student orientation. This trip, sponsored by Trinity's Chapel Fellowships, involves a mixture of mission work, reflection, and worship. The Plunge is a great way for new students to meet and connect with future peers and upperclassmen. After the trip has ended, students can choose to remain involved with the Chapel Fellowships, which are Christian faith groups that meet weekly on campus.

UNDERGRADUATE RESEARCH: Trinity students are constantly involved in undergraduate research, benefitting from side-by-side collaboration with talented faculty. In some cases, students are even published in journals as co-authors. Trinity offers research opportunities across most disciplines, allowing the majority of students to get involved before graduation.

SUMMER RESEARCH PROGRAM: Trinity selects a group of students to stay on campus over the summer months to immerse themselves in comprehensive research. Most students receive a stipend and free housing for their work, and all projects are closely overseen by a faculty member. At the end of the summer program, students get to present their findings at a research symposium.

COMMUNITY SERVICE: A college education extends beyond academics; it's much more holistic than that. Because service to the community is an integral part of the undergraduate experience, students reach beyond their educational responsibilities and address their duties to the both the local and global communities. Trinity offers several different service opportunities, ranging from volunteerism to alternative breaks.

SUSTAINABILITY AND CAMPUS: Trinity is highly dedicated to practices and lifestyles that promote sustainability. This dedication can be seen not only in volunteer and service efforts, but also in the curriculum itself. Ultimately, Trinity wants to reduce its global footprint and promote the benefits of sustainable practices. Trinity's Environmental Studies program is an exciting opportunity to address the challenges of sustainability. Students enrolled in the program take a variety of courses in the sciences, arts, humanities, and social sciences. On top of coursework, students are also involved in service initiatives, fieldwork, and internships that deal with the environment. The program also offers the unique opportunity to participate in summer research. Chosen students travel to High Lonesome Ranch on the Western Slope of the Colorado Rockies, studying conservation in an outdoor laboratory.

SAN ANTONIO: San Antonio is the 7th largest city in the U.S., and it is filled with cultural, athletic, and recreational opportunity. Because Trinity is so close to the downtown area, students are given amazing access to the city's many attractions. San Antonio has museums, theme parks, the Alamo, 4 professional sports teams, The River Walk, and so much more to offer!

THE CENTER FOR EXPERIENTIAL LEARNING & CAREER SUCCESS: Memorizing information and reading course material will only get one so far. Trinity recognizes that a truly marketable student needs to have hands-on experience prior to graduation. The Center for Experiential Learning & Career Success, therefore, is responsible for connecting students to opportunities through which they can apply academic theory to real-life situations. In many cases, the center connects students with opportunities where they can practice leadership and management skills.

https://new.trinity.edu/
P: (210) 999-7011

PRIVATE

STUDENT PROFILE

2,233 undergraduate students

98% of undergrad students are full time

48% male – 52% female

19% of students are from out of state

90% freshman retention rate

83% graduated in 6 years

FACULTY PROFILE

262 full-time faculty

63 part-time faculty

9 to 1 student/faculty ratio

ADMISSIONS

5,563 Total Applicants

2,672 Total Admissions

602 Total Freshman Enrollment

48.03% of applicants admitted

SAT Ranges: CR 580-690, M 580-680

ACT Ranges: C 27-32, M 26-30, E 26-33

TUITION & COSTS

Tuition: $37,296

Fees: $560

Total: $37,856

R&B: $12,362

Room: $7,972

Board: $4,390

Total: $50,218

FINANCIAL

$27,899 avg grant/scholarship amount (need)

$5,616 avg loan amount (need)

UNIVERSITY OF DALLAS

IRVING, TEXAS

UNIVERSITY OF DALLAS

Founded in 1956 through a unique partnership between the Diocese of Dallas and a group of dedicated lay people, the University of Dallas is a private, Catholic, co-educational university open to students of all faiths. Offering nearly 30 undergraduate majors, 30 master's programs, 4 doctoral programs, and 10 graduate certificate programs, the university provides an academically rigorous environment with a supportive community of faculty, staff, and students from diverse backgrounds.

COMMON INTELLECTUAL EXPERIENCES: UD students share a formative experience in studying the great deeds and words of Western civilization. The Core is an opportunity to inquire into the fundamental aspects of being and the person's relationship with God, nature, and fellow human beings. The Core curriculum embodies the University of Dallas' dedication to the pursuit of wisdom, truth, and virtue as the proper and primary ends of education. It is a shared sequence taken by all undergraduates that consists of 19 courses in English, history, philosophy, theology, economics, politics, science, mathematics, language, and fine arts. During their course of study, students read the great works that have shaped Western civilization and discuss them with their peers in small classes. A 10:1 student-to-faculty ratio allows professors and students to engage in thoughtful, meaningful dialogue that inspires a love of intellectual inquiry.

DIVERSITY/GLOBAL LEARNING: Most UD students spend a semester of their sophomore year at the University of Dallas' Rome campus, which is located just south of Rome. The courses in Rome are Core courses, ensuring the academic integrity of the university's program and keeping students on track for graduation. As part of their studies, students enjoy frequent outings through which they can walk in the footsteps of the greatest thinkers in Western civilization, stroll among the ruins of Ancient Rome and Greece (during the 10-day Greece trip), and visit some of the most beautiful and momentous sites of the Roman Catholic Church. Students can also perform recitations of the Greek tragedies they've been studying in the actual theaters at which the dramas were once performed, and they have the chance to see the fields where ancient heroes fought and died in the battles that shaped the course of history.

WRITING-INTENSIVE COURSES: All courses across the Core curriculum emphasize writing. Students are encouraged to read texts, analyze concepts, and incorporate what they learn across multiple disciplines to draw insightful conclusions.

VIBRANT COMMUNITIES: While pursuing their undergraduate degrees, University of Dallas students grow spiritually, intellectually, socially, and creatively through various student organizations and activities. Over 50 extracurricular activities are available on both campuses, representing diverse interests through organizations like the Chess Club, the rugby team, the Investment Club, and the Jane Austen Society. Numerous service opportunities, theatrical performances, concerts, and art shows also available for students to participate in and enjoy throughout the year.

INTERNSHIPS/COOPS/PRACTICUMS: The Office of Personal and Career Development aids students in securing internships that can additionally qualify for academic credit. All business majors are required to complete a 400-hour internship. 98.5% of the Class of 2016 was either employed or enrolled in graduate school within six months of graduation.

CAPSTONE COURSES AND PROJECTS/SENIOR EXPERIENCE: All students, regardless of major, complete either a thesis, research project, or other culminating experience that brings together all they have learned throughout their four years.

http://www.udallas.edu/
P: (972) 721-5266

PRIVATE - CATHOLIC

STUDENT PROFILE

1,336 undergraduate students

98% of undergrad students are full time

44% male – 56% female

54% of students are from out of state

81% freshman retention rate

70% graduated in 6 years

FACULTY PROFILE

143 full-time faculty

84 part-time faculty

10 to 1 student/faculty ratio

ADMISSIONS

2,228 Total Applicants

1,436 Total Admissions

393 Total Freshman Enrollment

64.45% of applicants admitted

SAT Ranges: CR 540-690, M 540-650

ACT Ranges: C 24-30, M 23-29, E 24-32, W 6-9

TUITION & COSTS

Tuition: $34,650

Fees: $2,580

Total: $37,230

R&B: $11,540

Room: $6,450

Board: $5,090

Total: $48,770

FINANCIAL

$25,113 avg grant/scholarship amount (need)

$5,748 avg loan amount (need)

UNIVERSITY OF MARY HARDIN–BAYLOR

BELTON, TEXAS

MARY HARDIN-BAYLOR

Founded in 1845, the University of Mary Hardin-Baylor is dedicated to to the proposition that an educated person is one who not only has mastered a chosen field of study, but has also gained an understanding of and appreciation for the intellectual and cultural traditions of a diverse world. Through traditional liberal arts programs and professional programs at both the undergraduate and graduate levels, the university seeks to develop graduates of strong Christian character and integrity who are able to communicate effectively, think critically, and solve complex problems. UMHB strives to inspire a lifelong love for learning so that graduates may face challenges successfully in an ever-changing world.

FRESHMAN SEMINARS: All new students are enrolled in Freshman Seminars, courses taught by experienced faculty members who are recognized as outstanding teachers. The seminars are designed to give new freshmen the tools they need to transition from high school to college. Professors emphasize that students are now "in charge" of their own destinies in many ways and that the choices they make in college will impact their futures. The seminars give freshmen a way to meet students who share their interests and to build strong relationships with their professors.

UP-TO-DATE FACULTY: UMHB is known as a university at which outstanding teachers provide not only great classroom experiences, but also the personal attention that students need to learn and grow. Professors are encouraged to learn about the latest teaching techniques and incorporate activities that help students connect with their coursework. The university's Center for Effectiveness in Learning and Teaching offers ongoing courses and seminars where professors discuss topics like best teaching practices, how to engage students in discussions, and the scholarship of teaching and learning.

UNDERGRADUATE RESEARCH: Undergraduate research projects enable interested students to pursue a research topic in collaboration with their professors and other students. Each spring, the university observes Scholar's Day, during which students read their scholarly papers or present their research to showcase the talent of the UMHB community.

STUDY ABROAD: The UMHB study abroad program offers ways for students to include an international travel experience as a part of their coursework. Opportunities range from a full semester in the London Studies Program to one-week study trips to locations in Europe, South America, Africa, or the Middle East. Study abroad scholarships are offered to enable students to clear the way for a truly outstanding opportunity beyond the limits of the university's walls.

STUDENT LIFE AND CAMPUS TRADITIONS: UMHB is the oldest continually operating university in Texas, so it comes as no surprise that the campus has many unique traditions. Like knights of old, first-year students are "dubbed" with a real sword, making them "Crusaders for Life." For over a century, students have shown off their talents when the freshmen, sophomores, juniors, and seniors vie for top honors at Stunt Night. Easter Pageant, Homecoming, Charter Day, and the Midnight March connect today's students with generations past and provide great opportunities for making new friends.

SERVICE-LEARNING: UMHB combines the foundation of a Christian, liberal arts education with the training needed for the jobs of tomorrow. Many courses include a service learning component, in which students work in teams on projects that benefit groups in surrounding communities—from building a website for a local nonprofit agency to organizing one-day clinics that administer free flu shots.

https://www.umhb.edu/
P: (800) 727-8642

PRIVATE - CHRISTIAN

STUDENT PROFILE

3,173 undergraduate students

92% of undergrad students are full time

37% male – 63% female

2% of students are from out of state

69% freshman retention rate

43% graduated in 6 years

FACULTY PROFILE

167 full-time faculty

111 part-time faculty

19 to 1 student/faculty ratio

ADMISSIONS

7,504 Total Applicants

6,033 Total Admissions

726 Total Freshman Enrollment

80.40% of applicants admitted

SAT Ranges: CR 460-560, M 470-570

ACT Ranges: C 20-26, M 19-26, E 20-26

TUITION & COSTS

Tuition: $24,300

Fees: $2,350

Total: $26,650

R&B: $7,300

Total: $33,950

FINANCIAL

$13,144 avg grant/scholarship amount (need)

$4,477 avg loan amount (need)

UNIVERSITY OF TEXAS AT DALLAS

RICHARDSON, TEXAS

The University of Texas at Dallas is a collaborative institution with a strong emphasis on research. The University offers a wide range of programs, affording students several opportunities to find their niche. UT Dallas is quickly progressing and turning out students that are well equipped to succeed.

INTERNSHIPS: UT Dallas recognizes co-ops and Curricular Practical Training (CPT) as existing under the umbrella, "Internship." In all cases, students apply what they have learned in the classroom to real world experience. In order to be eligible, students must be enrolled at UT Dallas and have a declared major. Students must also have completed at least one semester in school and have a GPA of 2.0 or higher. Comet Careers, an online student portal, is a great resource for finding and securing positions. But before a student can become an intern, they must first attend an internship information session, report their position to Comet Careers, and make an appointment with a career consultant.

EXTERNSHIPS: Externships involve riveting job-shadowing experiences. When students job shadow, they get a firsthand look at what a career has to offer, as well as the demands of the job. Externships allow participants to gain industry knowledge without a long term commitment. Some of the activities one might experience during an externship include: tours of the facilities, staff meetings, and observation of customer/client interactions. Externships happen over spring break. Interested students can contact a career consultant early in their college career, allowing them to explore their options as soon as possible.

UNDERGRADUATE RESEARCH: The Vice President for Research evaluates undergraduate research and awards students for their original work. All projects are eligible for entry, but every student's work must be supervised by a faculty member and cover a serious topic within the corresponding area of study. Recipients of this award have the chance to share their work at the Undergraduate Research Poster Contest in the spring. At this event, students have the opportunity to receive additional awards for their work. Through participation in undergraduate research, students gain experience in creating their own work; interact with grad students, faculty, and other researchers; and deeply explore a topic to develop their passion and understanding of the world around them.

LIVING LEARNING COMMUNITIES: LLCs take learning outside of the classroom and into the residence halls. The result is a community of young scholars that can bond over academics and similar interests. UT Dallas offers 6 different living learning communities: Arts and Technology, Computer Science, Engineering, Management, Pre-Health, and Social Sciences.

STUDY ABROAD AND EXCHANGE PROGRAMS: There are several different study abroad options available at UT Dallas, including internships and exchange programs. UT Dallas' partnerships with international institutions afford students countless benefits, as they develop cross-cultural communication skills and learn to become independent thinkers in foreign environments. Just a few of the available exchange program partnerships include Dublin City University, City University of Hong Kong, and Universidad de Lima. And, if a student identifies a study abroad program not offered through the school, they can find opportunities through third-party providers.

CORE CURRICULUM: UT Dallas' liberal arts education is designed to build students' functional competency in a range of subjects so that they may be prepared for any challenge thrown at them. The core curriculum guides students through communication, mathematics, natural and social sciences, philosophy and culture, history and political science, and the arts. Such a holistic education enables students to examine how they fit in a complex world, readying themselves for long, successful lives after college.

http://www.utdallas.edu/

P: (972) 883-2111

PUBLIC

STUDENT PROFILE

15,575 undergraduate students

82% of undergrad students are full time

57% male – 43% female

4% of students are from out of state

84% freshman retention rate

66% graduated in 6 years

FACULTY PROFILE

855 full-time faculty

290 part-time faculty

23 to 1 student/faculty ratio

ADMISSIONS

11,237 Total Applicants

6,909 Total Admissions

2,728 Total Freshman Enrollment

61.48% of applicants admitted

SAT Ranges: CR 560-670, M 600-700, W 520-650

ACT Ranges: C 25-31, M 26-32, E 24-32, W 7-8

TUITION & COSTS

Tuition: (In) $10,864 (Out) $26,894

R&B: $9,944

Room: $6,336

Board: $3,608

Total: (In) $20,808 (Out) $36,838

FINANCIAL

$14,345 avg grant/scholarship amount (total)

$6,604 avg loan amount (total)

BETHANY COLLEGE

BETHANY, WEST VIRGINIA

A quality life is built of many parts. It's the same with a college. That's why a sure measure of a school's lasting value is its blend of distinctions. At Bethany, the expected and the surprising combine with both the traditional and the innovative. It's one way that it creates an environment in which everything is possible. Bethany students are fully engaged in their education, learning both inside and outside of the traditional classroom setting through close interaction with the faculty and the community alike. Students are presented with opportunities for self-expression and growth through seminars, lectures, state-of-the-art technology, and numerous clubs and activities.

OPPORTUNITIES ABOUND: At Bethany College, students do more than learn the liberal arts; they live them, exercising their minds so that they become stronger and better prepared for a fast-changing, networked, and global world. Bethany strengthens character and graduates students with sound tools for judgment, a reliable ethical compass, and the backbone required to make smart choices. Bethany teaches students how to think so that they can decide how to live. For more than 167 years, Bethany has been refining this approach to education and giving students "permission to dream." Bethany believes that every dream and the life it inspires grows from a bedrock of meaningful learning and support.

A SCHOOL OF EXPLORERS: Bethany has well-established affiliations with study abroad programs in a number of countries around the globe. Bethany maintains programs at the Sorbonne in Paris, France; the Pädagogische Hochschule in Heidelberg, Germany; and the University of Navarra in Pamplona. There is no additional tuition cost to participate in these programs. Students' scholarships and financial aid apply, and student airfare costs are included. Many student clubs and academic departments also feature short-term travel. The Model United Nations club, for example, makes trips every semester to locations in Africa, the Caribbean, Central America, or South America. Several clubs in the department of political science offer two-week trips to such locations as Panama, China, Europe, and Africa. Some Bethany students have even visited as many as a dozen different countries during their college careers.

VALUABLE, PRACTICAL LEARNING: A traditional liberal arts program, low student/teacher ratios, and innovative programs make Bethany a great place to learn. The Bethany faculty are a blend of senior faculty and young scholars, and the academic programs provide the strongest possible learning experience for each student. Great students emerge with the help of dynamic teachers and mentors. Bethany's faculty have chosen to put teaching first and to be at a school in which one-on-one engagement with students is the top priority. Similarly, faculty consider students a vital part of any research effort. Bethany faculty invite students to collaborate, and students gain invaluable opportunities for discovery, publishing, and presentation. With a fourteen-to-one student-to-faculty ratio and small classes, Bethany fosters close working relationships between professors and students.

SENIOR CAPSTONE: The senior project and senior comprehensive exams serve as practical capstones and give seniors the opportunity to demonstrate the breadth and depth of the knowledge they have acquired. The senior project is a required, faculty-directed research presentation, while the comprehensive exams include a one-hour oral exam and an eight-hour written exam. Students consider the comprehensive exams to be great confidence-builders, and many students have published their work and presented the results of their research at such meetings as the undergraduate research day in Charleston, West Virginia.

http://www.bethanywv.edu/
P: (800) 922-7611

PRIVATE

STUDENT PROFILE

710 undergraduate students

99% of undergrad students are full time

59% male – 41% female

87% of students are from out of state

64% freshman retention rate

41% graduated in 6 years

FACULTY PROFILE

58 full-time faculty

31 part-time faculty

11 to 1 student/faculty ratio

ADMISSIONS

1,168 Total Applicants

820 Total Admissions

208 Total Freshman Enrollment

70.21% of applicants admitted

SAT Ranges: CR 380-490, M 400-510, W 370-470

ACT Ranges: C 17-22, M 16-22, E 14-21

TUITION & COSTS

Tuition: $25,580

Fees: $920

Total: $26,500

R&B: $9,800

Room: $5,000

Board: $4,800

Total: $36,300

FINANCIAL

$20,718 avg grant/scholarship amount (total)

$8,849 avg loan amount (total)

DAVIS & ELKINS COLLEGE

ELKINS, WEST VIRGINIA

Davis & Elkins College is an energized and beautiful place—a place that prepares and inspires students for success and thoughtful engagement in the world. Just hours from Pittsburgh and Washington, D.C., D&E is home to a vibrant arts community as well as leading programs in entrepreneurship, sustainable studies, health care, education, the sciences, and much, much more. Safe and supportive, stimulating and friendly, it's a small school at which big things happen.

AN OPEN MIND: At D&E, students don't have to choose their majors right away. In fact, D&E prefers that people come with an open mind. They are encouraged to explore classes that they may have never dreamed of liking. No matter what, they can count on their professors and mentors to help them realize their goals and plan their success. Participation comes naturally thanks to D&E's small classes and hands-on learning opportunities.

MULTICULTURALISM: The Augusta Heritage Center is internationally renowned for its programs in traditional music, dance, folklore, and crafts. It is best known for its workshops, which are held on campus every summer. In addition, the Appalachian studies course work connects D&E students to the art and magic of America's roots and traditions throughout Augusta. This diverse array of events highlight just small part of D&E's rich arts community.

SUSTAINABILITY: Davis & Elkins College is a leader in sustainability studies, offering West Virginia's first Bachelor of Arts program in the field. Through the Center for Sustainability Studies, D&E students have encouraged recycling in the city of Elkins, helped the College reduce energy consumption with three different solar panel projects, developed several community gardens, and consulted on the construction of a LEED-certified housing project. Ongoing activities of the GreenWorks! student organization engage students, faculty, and the broader community to ensure a viable world for future generations.

PERSONAL RELATIONSHIPS WITH FACULTY: Great teaching is a hallmark of what sets Davis & Elkins College apart. The D&E faculty focus primarily on teaching, helping students discover their passions and potential. Students really know their professors at D&E, spending time with them in and out of class, dining together, enjoying special events, going on field trips, and even traveling abroad. A student is never a number. Great teaching at D&E has everything to do with each individual.

STUDENT ACTIVITIES: Whether a student likes sports, theatre, music, rock climbing, politics, or poetry, they can find a wide range of events and activities happening at D&E. Faculty and students alike lead events with the help of the Campus Activities Board (CAB). CAB brings leading entertainment to campus all year long, starting with orientation weekend and continuing through the annual Déjà vu music festival at the end of the academic year.

SENIOR CAPSTONE: Every D&E senior is required to complete a senior capstone experience. These projects vary from program to program, but the expectations are the same. Students integrate learning in their chosen fields with the general academic skills they study in other classes.

CAREER SERVICES: D&E's Office of Career Services & Student Employment offers career counseling and a variety of other vocational services that are devoted to preparing students for successful careers upon graduation. Emphasis is also placed on networking and the effective and proper use of social media to develop and present oneself. Students are encouraged to begin career planning from day one; by their senior year, they are well on their way to professional success in the career of their choice.

http://www.dewv.edu/

P: (304) 637-1900

PRIVATE

STUDENT PROFILE

796 undergraduate students

97% of undergrad students are full time

44% male – 56% female

41% of students are from out of state

65% freshman retention rate

41% graduated in 6 years

FACULTY PROFILE

53 full-time faculty

32 part-time faculty

12 to 1 student/faculty ratio

ADMISSIONS

2,175 Total Applicants

1,273 Total Admissions

209 Total Freshman Enrollment

58.53% of applicants admitted

SAT Ranges: CR 410-530, M 390-520

ACT Ranges: C 17-22, M 16-21, E 16-22

TUITION & COSTS

Tuition: $27,000

Fees: $492

Total: $27,492

R&B: $9,250

Total: $36,742

FINANCIAL

$17,816 avg grant/scholarship amount (total)

$7,783 avg loan amount (need) (total)

SHEPHERD UNIVERSITY

SHEPHERDSTOWN, WEST VIRGINIA

Shepherd University takes students on an extraordinary academic journey to master the knowledge and skills necessary for personal and professional success. The Shepherd path begins with a liberal arts education, advances to a nationally recognized degree, and leads to outstanding career preparation.

LIBERAL ARTS IN A CARING COMMUNITY: Every undergraduate (and graduate) student is known by name at Shepherd. Students have the benefit of individual relationships with professors as they pursue a rigorous academic experience and find personal inspiration. Shepherd is the right fit for students looking to make the most of a university that has thriving arts and humanities, cutting-edge science, and professional degree programs. A Shepherd education is liberal arts in action. It encourages students to explore a wide range of subjects and experiences, discovering how different disciplines intertwine.

INSPIRED TO EXPLORE: Students find new passions at Shepherd, both inside and outside of the classroom. They explore by taking courses outside their major or join a weekend trip to museums in D.C. The university provides students ample opportunity to discover new and surprising sides of themselves, asking students to open themselves up to new worlds and viewpoints that they may not have previously understood or even knew existed. Some of these subjects may not interest students long-term, and that's okay. Part of the process of personal and academic growth is recognizing and making the most of individual interests and strengths.

ENCOURAGED TO LEAD: Shepherd students make a difference in the world. Chances are that, somewhere on campus today, a music student is providing free lessons, someone is preparing for the next Contemporary American Theater Festival, and one of the NCAA Division II teams is celebrating a win. In various forms, student leadership and service-learning activities are a vital component of the Shepherd experience, providing interactions that build self-realization, confidence, leadership, teamwork, and negotiation skills.

EQUIPPED TO SUCCEED: The proof of a Shepherd liberal arts education comes as students encounter an ever-changing world upon graduation. The Shepherd graduate is well equipped to succeed in their career and is able to adapt—and flourish—with integrity regardless of whatever uncertainties lie ahead of them.

SHEPHERDSTOWN: Shepherdstown is a cosmopolitan enclave with a variety of restaurants, plenty of meeting places, and lots to do. Located just outside Washington, D.C., and Baltimore, MD, students have easy access to the excitement and cultural life of the nation's capital. In addition, the university's location has the advantage of historic sites and outdoor recreation in its backyard. Faculty and students capitalize on all these resources to make the most of their Shepherd experience.

ACCESS TO OPPORTUNITY: Throughout the year, the university hosts several opportunities for students to explore the region and try new things. Shepherd partners with prestigious businesses to connect students and alumni with internship and employment opportunities. Shepherd University provides the room and time for students to grow, celebrating their motivation to contribute to the surrounding community.

GUARANTEED SUCCESS: Shepherd has been recognized by the national Collegiate Learning Assessment (CLA) as an institution that "provides value to its students." This means that Shepherd advances its students' reasoning and communications skills beyond those of their peers. In fact, Shepherd scored higher than 96 percent of the 234 participating colleges and universities in the CLA, a worthy representation of how far its students have progressed in their self-realization during their collegiate experience. Shepherd students are rated "superior" in demonstrating critical thinking and reasoning to their peers attending other prestigious institutions. Shepherd students' CLA scores confirm the University graduates strong communicators, team leaders, creative thinkers, problem solvers, and well-rounded, experienced human beings.

---

http://www.shepherd.edu/

P: (800) 344-5231

PUBLIC

STUDENT PROFILE

3,649 undergraduate students

80% of undergrad students are full time

42% male – 58% female

39% of students are from out of state

66% freshman retention rate

48% graduated in 6 years

FACULTY PROFILE

179 full-time faculty

170 part-time faculty

15 to 1 student/faculty ratio

ADMISSIONS

1,648 Total Applicants

1,481 Total Admissions

638 Total Freshman Enrollment

89.87% of applicants admitted

SAT Ranges: CR 440-553, M 430-540

ACT Ranges: C 19-24, M 17-23, E 18-25

TUITION & COSTS

Tuition: (In) $4,918 (Out) $13,766

Fees: (In) $1,912 (Out) $2,862

Total: (In) $6,830 (Out) $16,628

R&B: $9,070

Room: $4,500

Board: $4,570

Total: (In) $15,900 (Out) $25,698

FINANCIAL

$6,523 avg grant/scholarship amount (total)

$10,328 avg loan amount (total)

PRESCOTT COLLEGE

PRESCOTT, ARIZONA

Prescott College offers experientially centered undergraduate and graduate degrees both on campus and via distance learning. Collaboration is emphasized over competition, and interdisciplinary inquiry proceeds alongside professional skill development. Its courses are problem based and solution oriented; students work together to solve both local and global issues and help shape a more environmentally sustainable and socially just world.

NEW STUDENT ORIENTATION - WILDERNESS AND COMMUNITY BASED: Students in the on-campus undergraduate program are introduced to Prescott College, the Southwest, and their learning community through an immersive 21-day Orientation course. Many students choose to enroll in Wilderness Orientation, an expedition in the remote canyons and mountains of Arizona. Other students choose to enroll in Community Based Orientation, which is carried out as a set of multiple mini-expeditions throughout Arizona, exploring the state's ecological, political, and cultural boundaries.

FIRST-YEAR EXPERIENCE: Prescott College's first-year experience courses provide support and guidance to on-campus students throughout the first semester of their freshman year. After their Orientation course, students can choose from a variety of interdisciplinary classes that are linked and co-taught by faculty members from various disciplines. For example, courses like Wilderness and Civilization, Creative Expressions, and Yoga Philosophy are all linked to the common Writing Workshop course, which emphasizes the exploration of self. Each student reflects deeply on their personal history, culture, values, and sense of place, working with their peers to develop a sense of curiosity, engagement, and purpose. Courses emphasize writing, relationship development, and community building through collaborative projects, wilderness expeditions, and/or team projects with community organizations. A co-curriculum and peer-mentoring program support students' human development as they explore greater independence and deeper collaborations in new communities.

CREDIT FOR LIFE EXPERIENCE: Prescott College holds an immense amount of respect for students' prior learning, whether they learned in non-college settings or in extended, demanding professional experiences. Students are able to earn credit for their prior education by creating a portfolio that documents their experiences from before college. Credit earned through a Prior Learning Assessment can greatly accelerate the path to students' degrees.

A GLOBAL CAMPUS WITHOUT WALLS: Prescott College's undergraduate and graduate distance learning programs allow students to stay in their home community while earning their degree. Through these programs, students work with Prescott College faculty to design a personally and professionally fulfilling degree path. Students can earn their degree from wherever they live, work, or travel, allowing them to conduct research and complete their studies in remote locations. They develop strong connections to the College community both through online forums and by making periodical visits to campus for residency events.

COMMUNITY LUNCH–A WEEKLY GATHERING: Community lunch is a proud tradition at Prescott College. Every Wednesday, the community comes together for free soup and bread provided by the café on campus. Students, faculty, staff, and other community members gather to talk, make announcements, and connect to discuss the issues of the day.

SUSTAINABILITY SYMPOSIUM: The Prescott College Symposium on Sustainability Education is an annual conference that brings scholars, practitioners, and students together to learn about the latest work in the emerging field of sustainability education. All members of the community are invited to attend the conference and learn from students in the Ph.D. in Sustainability Education program, all of whom collaborate to organize the symposium theme, invite the keynote speaker, and present their research findings.

Prescott College

http://www.prescott.edu/
P: (877) 350-2100

PRIVATE

STUDENT PROFILE

350 undergraduate students

75% of undergrad students are full time

43% male – 57% female

98% of students are from out of state

71% freshman retention rate

49% graduated in 6 years

FACULTY PROFILE

66 full-time faculty

49 part-time faculty

9 to 1 student/faculty ratio

ADMISSIONS

314 Total Applicants

215 Total Admissions

47 Total Freshman Enrollment

68.47% of applicants admitted

SAT Ranges: CR 480-620, M 440-580

ACT Ranges: C 21-28, M 19-24, E 20-28

TUITION & COSTS

Tuition: $28,976

Fees: $1,635

Total: $30,611

R&B: $7,700

Total: $38,311

FINANCIAL

$15,202 avg grant/scholarship amount (need)

$4,576 avg loan amount (need)

AZUSA PACIFIC UNIVERSITY

AZUSA, CALIFORNIA

AZUSA PACIFIC
U N I V E R S I T Y

Azusa Pacific University is a four-year, comprehensive Christian, evangelical university founded in 1899. It stands proudly as an evangelical Christian community of disciples and scholars who seek to advance the work of God. Through academic excellence in the liberal arts and professional programs of higher education, students develop a Christian perspective of truth and life.

SERVICE AS A CORNERSTONE: Azusa Pacific places a high priority on service-learning projects. The Center for Academic Service-Learning and Research provides programs for Azusa Pacific students to engage with the surrounding community. The programs vary from teaching local school children to reading with the Azusa Reads program. Students can be involved in the College Headed and Mighty Proud (C.H.A.M.P.) program, which introduces the idea and benefits of college to over 700 local at-risk fourth graders, and the Azusa Conservatory of Music, which provides free music lessons to area youth.

HIGH SIERRA SEMESTER: APU's High Sierra Semester offers students the unique opportunity to step away from the typical college experience and study in the High Sierras, just south of Yosemite National Park. Each semester, around 50 students embark on the adventure of a lifetime as they enter into this small, nature-rich community. The High Sierra Program holds each student to high academic standards, challenging them as scholars while nourishing them as explorers. Classes are taught as part of the University's Great Works Option, which allows students to learn through the integration of all their classes, all while meeting General Studies and Upper Division Elective requirements. This means that they do not need to worry about exploring new opportunities at the expense of their four-year plans.

NURSING AND THE COMMUNITY: The Neighborhood Wellness Center is a collaborative project between the city of Azusa and APU's School of Nursing to improve the health and wellbeing of the predominantly underserved families of Azusa and the surrounding area. The center's community drop-in center offers health screening, bilingual health education, and referrals. Also, in partnership with various community agencies, the center develops a multitude of activities that address the identified health needs of local residents, including stress reduction, exercise, healthy eating, and child safety.

A COMMUNITY OF AWARENESS: The Office of Multi-Ethnic Programs (MEP) seeks to contribute to a campus climate that is sensitive to the values of ethnic diversity. MEP promotes student development through ethnic organizations (Latin American Student Association, Black Student Awareness, and the Pacific Islander Organization). In addition, it coordinates the Multi-Ethnic Leader Scholarship Program. As a further pursuit to keep the campus fully aware of the issues and happening around them, APU's The Clause publication is distributed after chapel on a weekly basis. It is filled with student perspectives on the university and world news, entertainment, sports, and campus issues.

STUDY ABROAD: Azusa Pacific has more than 40 national and international study abroad opportunities through the Center for Global Learning & Engagement. One of the most popular, the Azusa Oxford Semester, sends 25 junior and senior students to become associate students at Oxford University in Oxford, England. Here, the 12-15-unit curriculum includes lectures, tutorials, and a weekly Colloquium on Faith and Learning. The APU South Africa Semester offers students an exciting opportunity to learn, serve, and engage the unique culture of South Africa in Cape Town and Pietermaritzburg.

---

http://www.apu.edu/

P: (626) 969-3434

PRIVATE - CHRISTIAN

STUDENT PROFILE

5,883 undergraduate students

91% of undergrad students are full time

35% male – 65% female

23% of students are from out of state

88% freshman retention rate

68% graduated in 6 years

FACULTY PROFILE

480 full-time faculty

727 part-time faculty

11 to 1 student/faculty ratio

ADMISSIONS

6,084 Total Applicants

4,922 Total Admissions

1,202 Total Freshman Enrollment

80.90% of applicants admitted

SAT Ranges: CR 480-590, M 470-590

ACT Ranges: C 21-27, M 20-27, E 21-28

TUITION & COSTS

Tuition: $34,174

Fees: $580

Total: $34,754

R&B: $9,218

Room: $5,438

Board: $3,780

Total: $43,972

FINANCIAL

$18,181 avg grant/scholarship amount (total)

$7,821 avg loan amount (total)

CALIFORNIA BAPTIST UNIVERSITY

RIVERSIDE, CALIFORNIA

California Baptist University (CBU), located in Riverside, California, is a private, comprehensive university affiliated with the California Southern Baptist Convention. It offers traditional and online undergraduate study programs, including more than 175 majors, minors, and concentrations. CBU students enjoy smaller class sizes where the student-to-professor ratio is 18:1, a setting that allows for more mentoring opportunities, personal interactions with professors, and meaningful academic support. Faculty members may be involved in research and publication, but their first priority is teaching. No matter the academic program, students actively participate in an environment of integrated faith and learning, all under the guidance of top-notch professors who mentor them both inside and outside the classroom.

STUDY ABROAD: Study abroad opportunities during the summer or semester terms include more than 30 different international locations. CBU has educational exchange partnership agreements in China, South Korea, Russia, and Rwanda. In addition, the University partners with Cultural Experiences Abroad, International Studies Board, Hong Kong Baptist University, and the Council for Christian Colleges and Universities (CCCU) to provide additional study opportunities all around the world. The CCCU's off-campus study programs include the American Studies program in Washington, D.C.; the Contemporary Music Program; the Los Angeles Film Studies Center; and the Washington Journalism Center.

ENGAGED FACULTY: California Baptist University's goal is to help students reach their highest potential in scholarship, leadership, and service as well as to live the purpose for which they were intended. CBU faculty members focus primarily on teaching, genuinely striving for their students to learn. Small class sizes allow opportunities for students to participate actively in the educational process. In addition to classroom instruction, faculty advise and mentor students, conduct field trips and travel courses, and engage students in service learning and research projects.

DESIRED STUDENT OUTCOMES: CBU provides academic programs that prepare students for professional careers as well as co-curricular programs that foster the intellectual, physical, social, and spiritual development of each student. Within these arenas of the student experience, the University's faculty and administration have identified the student outcomes they find desirable and reflective of the impact they seek to have on the lives of their students. These student outcomes are distilled as the "Core 4": Academically Prepared; Biblically Rooted; Globally Minded; and Equipped to Serve. They are taught to demonstrate spiritual literacy and an understanding of Baptist values alongside respect for diverse religious, cultural, philosophical, and aesthetic perspectives. They also build their skills in critical thinking, learning to communicate their proficiency in both oral and written media and apply their knowledge to professional settings. Ultimately, they learn to implement a personal and social ethic that results in informed participation in multiple levels of community.

ACTIVITIES IN AND AROUND CAMPUS: The CBU college experience is much more than academic. The most memorable years of a student's life will likely be made discovering his or her purpose alongside close friends. At CBU, it's possible to go to class, the mountains, the beach, and the desert in the same day. California Baptist University students never get bored; there is so much to do all around the area. On campus, CBU community life provides quite a journey! A wide variety of campus organizations allow students to have fun while interacting with others of similar interests. In addition, CBU offers campus-wide activities that bring joy to the entire student body.

cbu

http://www.calbaptist.edu/
P: (951) 689-5771

PRIVATE - CHRISTIAN

STUDENT PROFILE

6,630 undergraduate students

86% of undergrad students are full time

37% male – 63% female

8% of students are from out of state

76% freshman retention rate

60% graduated in 6 years

FACULTY PROFILE

306 full-time faculty

334 part-time faculty

18 to 1 student/faculty ratio

ADMISSIONS

4,180 Total Applicants

2,734 Total Admissions

1,107 Total Freshman Enrollment

65.41% of applicants admitted

SAT Ranges: CR 420-540, M 410-540, W 410-530

ACT Ranges: C 17-24, M 16-24, E 17-24

TUITION & COSTS

Tuition: $28,574

Fees: $1,810

Total: $30,384

R&B: $9,870

Room: $5,110

Board: $4,760

Total: $40,254

FINANCIAL

$15,492 avg grant/scholarship amount (total)

$8,062 avg loan amount (total)

CALIFORNIA COLLEGE OF THE ARTS

SAN FRANCISCO, CALIFORNIA

California College
of the Arts

Students at California College of the Arts (CCA) discover cross-disciplinary opportunities, innovative courses with real-world applications, outstanding faculty, successful alumni, and a world-class campus environment. Wherever their art takes them—designing sustainable products, painting outside the canvas, producing animated films, or shaping the city of the future through architecture—CCA offers an ideal environment to make it happen.

COMMUNITY ENGAGEMENT: ENGAGE at CCA, one of CCA's signature initiatives, is a family of courses open to students in any major. The students in each ENGAGE class work with a faculty leader, outside experts, and established firms and community organizations to seek solutions to particular, identified issues. Another initiative is the IMPACT Social Entrepreneurship Awards. Multiple $10,000 awards are given each year to interdisciplinary teams of students, enabling them to undertake a major project over the summer, anywhere in the world. The college also offers Kinetic Micro Grants of up to $500 to students who wish to launch small-scale creative projects with members of a local community.

STUDY ABROAD OPPORTUNITIES: Study abroad and exchange opportunities expand students' worldviews and cultural understanding. Participants in the International Exchange Program spend a semester at one of more than 30 colleges of art and design around the globe. Or, through the Association of Independent Colleges of Art and Design (AICAD) exchange program, students can spend a semester at one of 32 other art schools in the United States. There are also numerous study abroad course offerings for undergraduate and graduate students throughout the summer.

DISTINGUISHED VISITORS COME TO CAMPUS: An incredible array of distinguished artists, designers, architects, and critics have visited the college, including film directors Michael Moore and John Waters, architect Renzo Piano, artist Joan Jonas, philosopher Judith Butler, and writers David Sedaris and Anne Waldman. Their visits may involve public lectures, master classes, critiques of student work, and even artist residencies that last up to several months. These visitors offer access to the international art world, and students benefit greatly from one-on-one exposure to prominent and successful practitioners in their chosen fields.

PROXIMITY TO DESIGN AND TECH COMPANIES: Depending on their major, second-year students may choose to stay in Oakland or to move their base to the San Francisco campus, which is located in the city's Design District. This fantastic area is home to design firms, art galleries, high-tech startups, and such companies as Adobe, Twitter, fuseproject, and Zynga. It is also very close to the new biotech and medical research area, anchored by UCSF's Mission Bay campus.

EXTERNSHIPS AND INTERNSHIPS: CCA CONNECTS is an annual structured "externship" experience in which 40 students are given the chance to work at outside organizations like design firms, schools, or architectural offices and make real, substantive contributions to ongoing projects. CCA also offers all kinds of other internship programs that enable students to gain practical experience and make professional connections while earning academic credit. Internships are required by some majors and are at least strongly encouraged by all of CCA's programs. CCA students graduate with the specific tools and knowledge to be successful in their chosen field as well as critical thinking skills that will be invaluable in any future pursuit. CCA's particular emphasis on interdisciplinarity sets it apart from other art schools. CCA is also distinguished by its many connections with creative industries, thanks in part to its fortuitous location in the San Francisco Bay Area. Major corporations, arts organizations, and nonprofits sponsor academic courses, offer internships to students, and employ alumni.

---

http://www.cca.edu/

P: (800) 447-1278

PRIVATE

STUDENT PROFILE

1,504 undergraduate students

95% of undergrad students are full time

38% male – 62% female

39% of students are from out of state

82% freshman retention rate

FACULTY PROFILE

99 full-time faculty

400 part-time faculty

7 to 1 student/faculty ratio

ADMISSIONS

1,713 Total Applicants

1,364 Total Admissions

241 Total Freshman Enrollment

79.63% of applicants admitted

SAT Ranges: CR 470-598, M 460-640, W 453-600

ACT Ranges: C 21-28, M 19-28, E 21-26

TUITION & COSTS

Tuition: $44,976

Fees: $490

Total: $45,466

Room: $9,320

Total: $54,786

FINANCIAL

$24,678 avg grant/scholarship amount (need)

$4,968 avg loan amount (need)

CALIFORNIA STATE UNIVERSITY, STANISLAUS

TURLOCK, CALIFORNIA

The 9,000-strong student body of Stanislaus is housed at two locations: across a 228-acre campus in Turlock and at Magnolia District's Stockton Center. The University is renowned for its 100+ academic programs for undergraduates, including specific concentrations within some majors. Stanislaus is part of the California State University system, one of the largest and most varied systems in the country. It aims to make higher education accessible to everyone with an affordable cost of attendance, all while equipping them with skills that are applicable and valuable in the workforce.

LEARNING WITHOUT BORDERS: Stanislaus State has many options available for students who want to extend their classroom experience to a location abroad. The California State University International Program organizes for students the academic trips of a lifetime, all without any additional charge to their tuition. More options abound through the University Studies Abroad Consortium, the adventures of which can still count toward college credit! Previous students have studied in Australia, China, Denmark, Germany, France, and many others. Some programs ask that students have junior class status, though many programs are available to students at any level in their college career. Because of the wide range of financial aid that Stanislaus State offers, studying abroad is an opportunity for everyone.

FIRST-YEAR EXPERIENCE: Stanislaus State offers a first-year experience program in order to help ease students into the brand-new college lifestyle. Much of this program focuses on developing strong writing and communication skills, supplementing assignments with immersive activities into the campus culture and traditions. Students are also provided a toolbelt of practical skills, such as time management, critical thinking, and stress management. The program's small class sizes create a warm environment in which students are free to approach teachers whenever they need to and bond with friends who are going through the same process of transition. Beyond the course's emphasis on writing, teachers help students participate in meaningful activities on campus and cultivate a support network for social, educational, and professional development.

GIVING BACK: Warriors Giving Back is Stanislaus State's multiannual community service initiative. This project is made up of three campaigns— two in the fall and one in the spring—each of which are run by Associated Students Inc. and the University Student Union. The fall campaign makes a meaningful impact through the Back 2 School Supply Drive, which collects school supplies for local elementary students, and Project Giving Tree, which operates under a similar premise to collect items and goods for local children's wish lists. The spring initiative gathers students and alumni to venture into the local Turlock community in order to repair structures, clean facilities, and beautify the area.

STUDENT SUCCESS FROM THE START: At Stanislaus State, the Career Services Office maintains an active partnership with Student Affairs in order to aid the academic and professional success of every student. Freshman students are given special advising from the start of their college career, helping them establish the academic path that is best for them. As students progress through college, they are able to access services for their career development. They benefit from hands-on assistance as they decide their majors, search for jobs, or begin their search for graduate school. Career Services also hosts an annual career fair at which many students find professional-level positions and internships. To complement this fair, the Office also hosts year-round résumé workshops and mock interviews.

https://www.csustan.edu/

P: (209) 667-3122

PUBLIC

STUDENT PROFILE

8,099 undergraduate students

84% of undergrad students are full time

36% male – 64% female

81% freshman retention rate

55% graduated in 6 years

FACULTY PROFILE

294 full-time faculty

260 part-time faculty

22 to 1 student/faculty ratio

ADMISSIONS

7,081 Total Applicants

5,001 Total Admissions

1,270 Total Freshman Enrollment

70.63% of applicants admitted

TUITION & COSTS

Tuition: (In) $5,472 (Out) $16,632

Fees: $1,232

Total: (In) $6,704 (Out) $17,864

R&B: $10,089

Room: $6,346

Board: $3,743

Total: (In) $16,793 (Out) $27,953

FINANCIAL

$8,990 avg grant/scholarship amount (total)

$4,974 avg loan amount (total)

CHAPMAN UNIVERSITY

ORANGE, CALIFORNIA

Chapman University offers the best of both worlds: a classic liberal arts foundation and pre-professional programs of distinction with strong ties to their industries. The university is known for providing a uniquely personalized education (with a student-to-faculty ratio of 14:1) and extraordinary learning experiences that begin right at the first day a student arrives on campus. The University's variety of academic opportunities spans everywhere from performing arts, humanities, and business to economics, film, and the sciences.

STUDY ABROAD: Part of the mission at Chapman is to foster global citizenship. Chapman makes a globally focused approach easy, offering thousands of courses in hundreds of locations worldwide in which students can explore new cultures. Students can select from semester- and year-long programs; short-term, faculty-led Travel Courses; and summer international internships. Approximately 42% of students participate in some form of global education before they graduate. The Center for Global Education at Chapman University is a proud member of NAFSA: Association of International Educators, the Forum on Education Abroad, the Institute for International Education, and International Student Exchange Programs.

UNDERGRADUATE RESEARCH: The Office of Undergraduate Research and Creative Activity (OURCA) is available to everyone, allowing each student to go beyond the classroom in every discipline. It provides students one-on-one faculty contact so that they may develop inquiry-based learning approaches through high-level, independent research. Through OURCA's many funding and grant opportunities, students get support to present at conferences, publish peer-reviewed journals, and gain valuable skills for future careers. One of the benefits of Chapman's medium-size institution is that it is able to offer greater access to research than smaller schools without sacrificing its funding in the same way that larger universities do.

LIVING-LEARNING COMMUNITIES: Students' journeys at Chapman begin with living-learning communities. First-year students who choose to live on campus are assigned to residence halls based upon their academic program and the college of their major, assisting them in forging connections with like-minded friends. These communities help encourage students to engage in interdisciplinary, university-level, critical inquiry, which can include off-campus excursions or visits from faculty to help deepen their understanding of course material.

WHERE DIVERSITY THRIVES: Diversity, equity, and mutual respect are rooted in Chapman's heritage and community. There are 14 different committees composed of more than 250 student, staff, and faculty volunteers in the Chapman Diversity Project. These committees are focused on strategic institutional change related to diversity, inclusion, and the strengthening of the campus climate for all members of the Chapman community. Additionally, the "I Am Chapman" campaign was established to build compassion through education about diversity, equity, and social justice by encouraging students to celebrate their individuality and diversity through various forms of storytelling.

ORANGE COUNTY OPPORTUNITIES: Orange County is America's sixth-largest county with more than 3 million people, making Chapman's location a valuable goldmine for connections to internships and job opportunities. Many of America's largest corporations such as Allergan, Disney, Ford Motor Co., and Blizzard Entertainment call Orange County their home or U.S. headquarters. Furthermore, most of the Fortune 500 companies also have an Orange County office, providing ample opportunities for students who seek internships or employment.

INTERNSHIP OPPORTUNITIES: Students can and are taking advantage of the internship opportunities made available to them through the outstanding resources at Chapman. Some 76% of Chapman students report that they have held an internship during their undergraduate experience, having enjoyed the opportunities provided to them through professors, departments, the Chapman Connect network, and the Career Development Center.

---

http://www.chapman.edu/
P: (888) 282-7759

PRIVATE

STUDENT PROFILE

6,281 undergraduate students

96% of undergrad students are full time

39% male – 61% female

36% of students are from out of state

90% freshman retention rate

79% graduated in 6 years

FACULTY PROFILE

417 full-time faculty

534 part-time faculty

14 to 1 student/faculty ratio

ADMISSIONS

13,670 Total Applicants

6,504 Total Admissions

1,426 Total Freshman Enrollment

47.58% of applicants admitted

SAT Ranges: CR 550-640, M 550-650

ACT Ranges: C 25-30, M 24-29, E 25-32

TUITION & COSTS

Tuition: $48,310

Fees: $400

Total: $48,710

R&B: $14,368

Total: $63,078

FINANCIAL

$16,096 avg grant/scholarship amount (need)

$4,876 avg loan amount (need)

DOMINICAN UNIVERSITY OF CALIFORNIA

SAN RAFAEL, CALIFORNIA

Dominican University of California's mission is to educate and prepare students to be ethical leaders and socially responsible global citizens who incorporate the Dominican values of study, reflection, community, and service into their lives. The University is committed to diversity, sustainability, and the integration of the liberal arts, the sciences, and professional programs.

FIRST-YEAR EXPERIENCE: Dominican is the only university in the United States to offer a multidisciplinary First-Year Experience course based on Big History. Big History is an emerging academic discipline that provides a unifying overview of the 14 billion-year history of the universe, from the Big Bang to the present day. Big History synthesizes history, astronomy, chemistry, biology, geology, sociology, and other fields to provide a cohesive picture of the history of the human race and its relationship to the planet.

STUDY ABROAD: As part of the university's mission of fostering an appreciation of cultural diversity and global interdependence, students are encouraged to participate in study abroad opportunities while attending Dominican. Students can arrange to study in virtually any country where an accredited study abroad program exists. Opportunities are available for every major on campus and range from one week to one year in length.

SERVICE-LEARNING: Dominican's reach extends throughout the San Francisco Bay Area through service-learning and internships. Dominican's Service-Learning (SL) Program, now in its 10th year, offers more than 40 courses a year across the curriculum. Of 250 students participating in a recent survey, 92 percent said they felt that service-learning enhanced their learning of class content and theories.

AN OUTSTANDING LOCATION: The 80-acre campus is at the center in a historic neighborhood located close to downtown San Rafael's restaurants, sidewalk cafés, movie theaters, live music venues, and a seasonal farmer's market. Although only 30 minutes from San Francisco, Dominican's quiet and safe campus is set at the edge of some of the best hiking and mountain biking trails in the Bay Area. Marin County's popular Stinson Beach is less than an hour from campus, while Lake Tahoe's mountain resorts are a favorite weekend destination for skiers and snowboarders.

STUDENT ACTIVITIES: The Associated Students of Dominican University (ASDU) is the primary group to help students plan and provide campus activities, distribute activity funds, initiate changes in policy, and represent themselves to the University's administration and the broader community. This group of elected student representatives serves both as the student activities association and the student government board. The members of the ASDU Senate are composed of representatives from all four class levels of regular day-program students.

SENIOR THESIS: Special characteristics of a Dominican education include the Senior Thesis, an intensive research project that provides all students the opportunity to shine in their chosen fields of study. The Senior Thesis can also provide the final distinguishing feature to ensure their admission to graduate school or the offer of an appealing job.

INTERNSHIPS: Internships are available through the University's Internship and Career Services Office, giving students the opportunity to explore employment options with local companies. The center also offers workshops and individual counseling on career and job search strategies, résumé writing, and interviewing skills. Internship sites include business, nonprofits, and public agencies that also benefit from the program. Students are required to make a formal presentation regarding their experience, what they learned, and what skills they were able to cultivate. They are asked to explain how their experience enriched their understanding of both their major and their future career goals.

http://www.dominican.edu/
P: (415) 457-4440

PRIVATE

STUDENT PROFILE

1,358 undergraduate students

86% of undergrad students are full time

28% male – 72% female

14% of students are from out of state

82% freshman retention rate

66% graduated in 6 years

FACULTY PROFILE

111 full-time faculty

174 part-time faculty

9 to 1 student/faculty ratio

ADMISSIONS

2,178 Total Applicants

1,717 Total Admissions

255 Total Freshman Enrollment

78.83% of applicants admitted

SAT Ranges: CR 480-560, M 470-580

ACT Ranges: C 21-25, M 19-26, E 20-26

TUITION & COSTS

Tuition: $42,950

Fees: $450

Total: $43,400

R&B: $14,220

Total: $57,620

FINANCIAL

$22,028 avg grant/scholarship amount (need)

$4,702 avg loan amount (need)

HOLY NAMES UNIVERSITY

OAKLAND, CALIFORNIA

Holy Names University is a regional, residential university with an academic program of 20 majors in the arts and sciences. Innovative programs such as sports management and self-designed majors instill in students the desire to be lifelong learners and responsible world citizens.

CONNECTIONS PROJECT: The HNU Experience involves connecting learning to social justice and service. Students begin their experience with the "Connections Project," part of a comprehensive first-year experience that prepares them to become lifelong learners, critical thinkers, and responsible citizens. Inherent in the HNU Experience is an emphasis on the total development of students, promoting academic success through action and reflection as they make connections between their activities inside and outside of the classroom. Students are encouraged to explore their own interests, strengths, and challenges, to embrace multiple perspectives, to engage in meaningful dialogue with others, and to be active participants in creating a good and just community.

SERVICE-LEARNING: HNU's Center for Social Justice and Civic Engagement works with faculty members to facilitate service-learning courses. These courses integrate classroom learning with action alongside some of HNU's many nonprofit community partners. Service-based learning offers students the opportunity to apply the theories learned in class to real-life social justice work in the Oakland community, which is a vibrant source of social justice activity.

LEARNING FROM THE BEST: Faculty members at HNU are just as passionate about the educational experience as they are about the classes they teach. They share, explore, and cultivate their academic interests with students through a balance of real-world experience and academic research. Students have opportunities to take courses that are taught by published novelists, social justice advocates, and professionals in accounting and marketing who own their own companies. HNU professors are passionate and engaged in their disciplines, eager to share their knowledge and enthusiasm with students. HNU faculty members have gained wide recognition for their scholarship and teaching, and over 90 percent hold doctorates or the highest degree in their field.

SERVICE AND ADVOCACY: HNU's students are activists, mentors, and leaders. Holy Names University is committed to inspiring students to take action and go beyond just attending class, listening to lectures, and reading textbooks. Students are encouraged to engage the world at every stage of their education. For instance, students can participate in actions and service projects, like helping out at the Oakland Catholic Worker, walking for breast cancer research, and traveling to Tutwiler, Mississippi, to build houses with Habitat for Humanity. The commitment that students make to these projects is what makes the HNU vision of service actually happen. HNU is a living lab of how a diverse community can come together and celebrate their similarities and differences, reflecting a safe environment in which students live and work. Students are encouraged and supported by staff and faculty to host events that are born of the inspiration they receive in the classroom. These include the 24-hour Relay for Life fundraiser and celebration, which is organized by student-athletes in coordination with the American Cancer Society, and the Jim Durbin Entrepreneurship Speaker Series, hosted by students from the Business program.

INTERNSHIPS: HNU encourages hands-on learning and job preparation through internship opportunities in the local community and beyond. Many majors, such as Business, Sociology, Communications Studies, and Sports Biology either require or strongly encourage students to enroll in at least one internship course as a way to explore, experience, and reflect on their chosen fields of study.

CAREER SERVICES: Students at HNU benefit from the Career Center's focus on preparing graduates for meaningful work and supporting them in the transition to the workplace or postgraduate education. Services include individualized career counseling and job search preparation, career interest inventories and assessments, support in internship search and application process, industry spotlight events, and alumni networking events. Career Services also offers assistance with graduate school research and applications and encourages postgraduate study through such events as the Bay Area Forum for Diversity in Graduate Education.

HOLY NAMES

http://www.hnu.edu/
P: (800) 430-1321

PRIVATE - CATHOLIC

STUDENT PROFILE

656 undergraduate students

83% of undergrad students are full time

35% male – 65% female

8% of students are from out of state

60% freshman retention rate

40% graduated in 6 years

FACULTY PROFILE

42 full-time faculty

110 part-time faculty

10 to 1 student/faculty ratio

ADMISSIONS

872 Total Applicants

375 Total Admissions

119 Total Freshman Enrollment

43% of applicants admitted

SAT Ranges: CR 390-470, M 380-470

ACT Ranges: C 15-21, M 15-20, E 15-21

TUITION & COSTS

Tuition: $35,166

Fees: $500

Total: $35,666

R&B: $12,072

Room: $6,290

Board: $5,782

Total: $47,738

FINANCIAL

$25,411 avg grant/scholarship amount (total)

$5,882 avg loan amount (total)

HUMBOLDT STATE UNIVERSITY

ARCATA, CALIFORNIA

COLLEGE PROFILES: WEST

HUMBOLDT
STATE UNIVERSITY

Surrounded by a stunning natural landscape, the students at Humboldt State University have access to the beach, mountain ranges, redwood forests, and more. But beyond the beauty, Humboldt offers something even more spectacular: an abundant array of options to learn both on and off campus. Founded in 1913, Humboldt State University consists of over 8,500 students who are engaged in 51 majors and 69 minors. Small class sizes, with an average student-teacher ratio of 21:1, provide Humboldt's students with numerous opportunities to create personal relationships with their professors. These engaged students have access to over 190 student organizations and are constantly participating in community service and other activities in and outside the classroom.

STUDY ABROAD: Humboldt's expansive study abroad program provides students with the chance to explore the world, all while racking up class credit. The University hosts informational meetings that provide the resources and materials needed to make the most cognizant decision about studying abroad. They allow for all students to learn and take advantage of the most possible experiences that Humboldt has to offer. Additionally, students can meet with study abroad advisors and apply for scholarships in order to make going abroad an achievable possibility. Students have traveled to a variety of places, including Australia, Italy, the United Kingdom, France, Thailand, and Argentina. With options to go away for 10 weeks in the summer or an entire school year abroad, the travel programs can be altered to fit students' preferences as they embark on an experience of a lifetime.

REDWOOD COAST MARINE SCIENCE SUMMER PROGRAM: Humboldt offers a unique program that gives students the chance to gain hands-on experience aboard the University's own ship, the Coral Sea. Throughout their studies, students learn about climate change, the ocean en masse, tides, animal and plant life, and much more. Courses in the Marine Science program even offer field trips to beaches and rivers at which students learn firsthand the inner workings of the complex natural biosphere. And, through an introductory course made up of a tightly knit group of 24 students, curious explorers work on research projects with extremely qualified staff who are highly experienced in such subjects as biochemistry and oceanography. These professors lead students each summer through the Redwood Coast Marine program on the Coral Sea, embarking on exciting adventures into the marine world.

LIVING-LEARNING COMMUNITIES: Humboldt strives for inclusivity, acceptance, and a strong, caring community. With access to themed residence halls, students can apply to live alongside like-minded individuals, choosing from such themes as academic-intensive living, upperclassmen housing, veteran housing, a community for LGBTQ+ students, international living, gender-inclusive housing, and a community for those looking to explore further into the liberal arts. Humboldt's diverse configurations of themed Living-Learning Communities create a welcoming environment for all people and all interests.

SERVICE-LEARNING: Humboldt's service-learning program aims to create a communal, actively caring voice within the student body. Encouraging students to coordinate with outside organizations, create a feeling of loyalty, and connect to the needs of others in the surrounding community, Humboldt's service-learning program makes it easy to learn and contribute to society at the same time. Through this program, students foster a sense of responsibility, reciprocity, and communal development.

Sidebar

https://www.humboldt.edu/
P: (707) 826-3011

PUBLIC

STUDENT PROFILE

8,259 undergraduate students

93% of undergrad students are full time

44% male – 56% female

7% of students are from out of state

75% freshman retention rate

46% graduated in 6 years

FACULTY PROFILE

280 full-time faculty

271 part-time faculty

23 to 1 student/faculty ratio

ADMISSIONS

13,018 Total Applicants

10,024 Total Admissions

1,420 Total Freshman Enrollment

77% of applicants admitted

SAT Ranges: CR 440-560, M 430-550

ACT Ranges: C 18-24, M 17-24, E 16-24

TUITION & COSTS

Tuition: (In) $5,472 (Out) $16,632

Fees: $1,723

Total: (In) $7,195 (Out) $18,355

R&B: $12,250

Room: $5,900

Board: $6,350

Total: (In) $19,445 (Out) $30,605

FINANCIAL

$9,212 avg grant/scholarship amount (total)

$5,325 avg loan amount (total)

LA SIERRA UNIVERSITY

RIVERSIDE, CALIFORNIA

La Sierra University, a Christian institution nationally acclaimed for its diverse campus and service to others, sustains a supportive and nurturing environment for students. In small classes, professors lead students in exploration, investigation, and discussion that are altogether designed to encourage curiosity and growth.

FIRST-YEAR EXPERIENCE: The La Sierra University faculty and staff care about helping students to think for themselves—a major component of which is guiding first-year students through their initial college experience. The La Sierra Center for Student Academic Success (CSAS) provides undergraduate academic advising and support with the goal of empowering students to achieve educational milestones. CSAS is joined by other first-year programs like IGNITE, which is a freshman orientation event designed to introduce new students to the university community, teaming them up with others in a unique family group and acquainting them with workshops, worship services, and team-building games. Popular workshop classes include "College Readiness" and "Fully Alive," which explore everything from Studying 101 to Title IX.

FIRST-YEAR WRITING INTENSIVE: A first-year college experience is about more than learning the ins and outs of university life. During the first-year College Writing Sequence, each student practices and gains the skills necessary for self-expression and coherency through the written word. These three writing-intensive courses give students the tools necessary for the remainder of their college careers, developing expertise in basic creative writing, argumentative writing, and research writing that are utilized in various other courses at La Sierra.

UNDERGRADUATE RESEARCH: There are multiple occasions for undergraduate research in each department, but such scholarly pursuits are especially encouraged for students who are members of the Honors program or Sigma Tau Delta. Prior to graduation, Honors students complete a scholarship project in which they develop an original research and/or creative project to present to the public. Students who are part of Sigma Tau Delta are invited to submit research essays that are honored at annual conference presentations.

GLOBAL LEARNING: La Sierra University students have a chance to take a gap or bridge year during which they can serve as student missionaries in countries like India, the Philippines, and Papua New Guinea. Many students also choose to take an extra year in order to study abroad in Argentina, Austria, Brazil, England, France, Germany, Italy, Lebanon, or Spain. Through Adventist Colleges Abroad, anyone can completely immerse themselves in another culture, become fluent in another language, and gain an appreciation for the history and communities of others.

SERVICE-LEARNING: At La Sierra University, service to others is an integral part of the college experience. The Service-Learning program is integrated into specific classes, allowing for a hands-on approach to community service that ties back to the cornerstones of academics and faith. Students can tutor elementary children, read to the elderly, and take part in various other community outreaches.

CAREER SERVICES: La Sierra students have access to the Career Services Center, which hosts an annual Career Expo at which students can connect with organizations, network with potential employers, and make a lasting impression in the professional world. Attending the expo can also help build résumés by connecting students to part- and full-time job opportunities as well as internships and shadowing possibilities.

SENIOR CAPSTONE: Events like Service-Learning and the Career Expo help lead students toward successful senior experiences. Seniors at La Sierra take a capstone course specific to their majors in which they demonstrate that they have achieved the student learning outcomes set out by their departments.

---

https://lasierra.edu/

P: (800) 874-5587

PRIVATE - CHRISTIAN

STUDENT PROFILE

2,020 undergraduate students

91% of undergrad students are full time

41% male – 59% female

60% of students are from out of state

78% freshman retention rate

49% graduated in 6 years

FACULTY PROFILE

102 full-time faculty

15 part-time faculty

14 to 1 student/faculty ratio

ADMISSIONS

4,328 Total Applicants

1,931 Total Admissions

442 Total Freshman Enrollment

44.62% of applicants admitted

SAT Ranges: CR 420-510, M 420-520

ACT Ranges: C 16-22, M 16-23, E 15-22

TUITION & COSTS

Tuition: $30,600

Fees: $990

Total: $31,590

R&B: $8,100

Total: $39,690

FINANCIAL

$20,938 avg grant/scholarship amount (need)

$4,820 avg loan amount (need)

LOYOLA MARYMOUNT UNIVERSITY

LOS ANGELES, CALIFORNIA

Loyola Marymount University is rooted in its Roman Catholic tradition—a relationship that is directly connected to the school's goals and overall success. LMU promotes both the intellectual and personal growth of each student, embracing Catholicism in the development of social consciousness and contribution to the global community.

FIRST-YEAR EXPERIENCE: LMU's first-year experience takes a holistic approach to preparing students for successful college careers. Students get to know themselves while also engaging with their peers, all while learning how to utilize different resources and explore the foundations of critical thinking. Every incoming freshman is also required to finish a common reading assignment prior to arriving on campus. Students get the chance to attend a presentation by the author themselves within the first two weeks of school. The common reader is a shared experience among students, acting as a foundation of the critical scholarship that each one of them will experience at LMU.

SERVICE AT LMU: Every month, LMU takes on a new service initiative with a local nonprofit agency, communicating its project to the entire LMU campus community. Because the projects change on a monthly basis, LMU is able to touch several different parts of the community and spread its love to multiple outlets. One ongoing, particularly distinctive service initiative is El Espejo. Here, El Espejo, or "mirror" in Spanish, is used to emphasize reflection, inviting volunteers work to find a common connection between themselves and those they are helping. El Espejo connects LMU students with at-risk middle school students in the community, educating and mentoring students on the importance and potential of intellectual and personal growth.

INTERNSHIPS: Internships allow students to apply the concepts and theories they have learned at the academic level to a professional position. Because all students are encouraged to complete an internship at some point throughout their undergraduate experience, they are given the opportunity to verify their work as academic credit toward their degree.

LIVING LEARNING COMMUNITIES: Living Learning Communities synthesize academics and residence life into one shared experience. Those who participate in an LLC enjoy academic support from their peers as well as frequent interaction with faculty, enjoying a community of scholars who share similar interests and areas of study. Three of LMU's LLCs are geared specifically toward first-year students in certain majors. Freshmen in Psychology, Engineering, and the Life Sciences can live together and enroll in exclusive courses that immerse them in their fields of study in ways that are not typically offered to other college underclassmen. Other LLCs include residences for Honors students, residences for students looking for a community that fosters graduate school and career preparations, and "The Global City," which brings students together to focus on topics that pertain to international politics.

ALTERNATIVE BREAKS: An alternative break is a way for students to engage in volunteer work during their school breaks. Whether they serve locally, domestically, or internationally, participants are exposed to a community in need and are called upon to enact positive change. The efforts of alternative breaks may change from year to year based on the most pressing needs of society at the time. Recently, for example, LMU spent alternative breaks focusing on Ecological Justice, Education, Farm Workers, Human Trafficking, Immigration, Indigenous Communities, Public Health, Land Rights, and Refugee Issues.

LMU|LA
Loyola Marymount University

http://www.lmu.edu/
P: (310) 338-2700

PRIVATE - CATHOLIC

STUDENT PROFILE

6,259 undergraduate students

96% of undergrad students are full time

44% male – 56% female

29% of students are from out of state

91% freshman retention rate

79% graduated in 6 years

FACULTY PROFILE

654 full-time faculty

542 part-time faculty

11 to 1 student/faculty ratio

ADMISSIONS

13,288 Total Applicants

6,748 Total Admissions

1,354 Total Freshman Enrollment

50.78% of applicants admitted

SAT Ranges: CR 550-640, M 560-660, W 550-650

ACT Ranges: C 25-30, M 24-29, E 25-32, W 8-9

TUITION & COSTS

Tuition: $41,876

Fees: $693

Total: $42,569

R&B: $13,630

Total: $56,199

FINANCIAL

$19,970 avg grant/scholarship amount (need)

$5,771 avg loan amount (need)

NOTRE DAME DE NAMUR UNIVERSITY

BELMONT, CALIFORNIA

Notre Dame de Namur (NDNU) features small classes that average 17 students, personal attention, quality courses and instructors, and a range of majors. Professors at NDNU are not only gifted instructors, but they are also committed to advising and mentoring students through the college journey. Individual learning is a key feature of an NDNU education, and the university strives to give students the tools, knowledge, and inspiration to engage and expand their talents successfully. NDNU's location also presents learning opportunities through community engagement and internships that can't be found elsewhere.

FRESHMAN SEMINARS: The small Freshman Seminar courses provide an introduction to university-level academic life, allowing students and their professors to grapple with complex questions while simultaneously learning about themselves as learners and members of the NDNU campus community. Students also work alongside community partner organizations to apply their academic knowledge and skills to practical community needs. All freshmen read and discuss one book in common as part of a shared academic experience that melts them into the inspiring learning community.

STUDENT LEADERSHIP PROGRAMS: NDNU offers multiple opportunities for students to develop and exercise leadership skills. Governance experience includes the Associated Students of Notre Dame de Namur University, the official student government. Juniors and seniors can serve as Resident Advisors (RAs) who function as peer mentors, emergency responders, program and event planners, and community creators in all of the campus' residential communities. Student leaders also serve on the Programming Board, which creates and provides quality programs and events to engage students with the greater NDNU community. The Spirituality Team works with the Office of Spirituality to promote the personal and spiritual development of NDNU students, and The Bonner Leader Program and the Alternative Spring Break help interested NDNU students acquire the skills and knowledge to become effective social activists.

STUDY ABROAD OPPORTUNITIES: Students at Notre Dame de Namur University are able to participate in a variety of study abroad programs that offer courses for all majors as well as internships, community service, and travel opportunities. NDNU students have taken part in programs all throughout the world in such places as India, China, Africa, Australia, and Europe. Some of the most popular choices are European universities in London, Prague, Geneva, Madrid, Barcelona, Rome, and Florence. Eligible students receive financial assistance for study abroad through financial aid, program scholarships, and NDNU study abroad scholarships.

NEW VIRTUAL REALITY LEARNING LAB: NDNU has recently added a new virtual reality 3D learning lab. The lab features holographic computing with the Microsoft Hololens, virtual reality headsets and hands by Oculus Rift and VIVE, mixed reality using zSpace specialized computers, and Double Robotics and Swivl telepresence robots. With this state-of-the-art learning technology, students can study the anatomy of the human heart in three dimensions, inside and out. For example, students can actually see and feel a heartbeat while it is both at rest and in action.

WRITING CENTER AND TUTORING: NDNU offers a drop-in Writing Center in which students can receive assistance for any of their writing-focused course assignments. Friendly, dedicated instructors and capable tutors bring a high-quality level of instruction to tutor and train students, committed to NDNU's mission to help students succeed.

CAPSTONE COURSES: Almost all majors at NDNU culminate in capstone courses that give students the opportunity to integrate and demonstrate the knowledge and skills that they have acquired throughout their studies. These courses generally involve student projects, papers, or presentations. Final products have included live performances, new community organizations, research papers, and start-up business plans.

http://www.ndnu.edu/
P: (650) 508-3600

PRIVATE - CATHOLIC

STUDENT PROFILE

982 undergraduate students

75% of undergrad students are full time

34% male – 66% female

10% of students are from out of state

83% freshman retention rate

51% graduated in 6 years

FACULTY PROFILE

54 full-time faculty

154 part-time faculty

12 to 1 student/faculty ratio

ADMISSIONS

1,234 Total Applicants

1,193 Total Admissions

157 Total Freshman Enrollment

96.68% of applicants admitted

SAT Ranges: CR 400-508, M 400-510

ACT Ranges: C 17-22, M 16-24, E 15-23

TUITION & COSTS

Tuition: $33,926

Fees: $270

Total: $34,196

R&B: $13,656

Total: $47,852

FINANCIAL

$21,049 avg grant/scholarship amount (need)

$4,283 avg loan amount (need)

OCCIDENTAL COLLEGE

LOS ANGELES, CALIFORNIA

Known as 'the little giant' for its academic prowess and size, Occidental is a four year, undergraduate-focused institution with a unique core program developed by faculty to unify and enhance the liberal arts education offered.

LIBERAL ARTS AND JOINT ACADEMICS: Occidental students develop their personal and academic potentials, all while supporting the endeavors of their peers. They can choose from 31 majors as well as supplementary learning opportunities like research and experiential learning. Occidental motivates it students to push past their boundaries to elevate their college experiences and extend their growth beyond the classroom. It is a liberal arts institution, offering its students a well-rounded education that spans multiple disciplines. Students are also given the option to take classes at Caltech or the Art Center in order to have the best possible array of courses for their academic pursuits. Some students go on to earn joint degrees from Columbia University, Keck Graduate Institute, and Caltech.

PROFESSORS AND THEIR ROLES: Occidental faculty work tirelessly, fulfilling roles far beyond those as lecturers. Professors serve as mentors, advisors, and guides to their students. They are genuinely interested in their students, firmly and enthusiastically encouraging them to explore concepts outside of their comfort zones. With a student-to-faculty ratio of 10:1, such a challenge is achievable with the help of an individualized and intimate learning experience for every student. The relationships between faculty and students are much stronger, creating a more meaningful educational experience for both parties.

COMMUNITY ENGAGEMENT: Occidental has three offices that are wholly dedicated to community engagement and service. The Center for Community-Based Learning brings together groups from the campus community to bring awareness to issues of social justice, and the Office of Community Engagement hooks students up with service opportunities through which they can apply Occidental's values to the greater community. The Urban & Environmental Policy Institute links social initiatives with environmental needs, helping students to bring about change with regards to sustainability.

JOB SHADOWING: Occidental offers a job-shadowing program to its students called "Walk In My Shoes" (WIMS). This program connects students with alumni and community members, exposing them to professional, applied methods in their chosen fields of study. A designated host works individually with students in order to place them in the proper shadowing program that best prepares them for the future goals. Before students embark on their shadowing experience, they complete a series of preparatory tasks like pre-site training and writing reflective essays.

LOS ANGELES: Occidental is located in the city of Los Angeles, affording students access to the amenities and attractions of the famed, thriving city. L.A.'s warm climate makes it easy to enjoy the great outdoors year-round. What's more, the proximity to the city gives students many chances to intern for and work at major institutions and businesses.

DIVERSITY: Occidental is committed to diversity. Every member of the campus community is reminded to keep the College's commitment to inclusion at heart. The nuance of diversity is constantly changing shape, and Occidental makes it a mission to stay abreast of issues so as to serve the needs of the community. At the forefront of this effort are the faculty members who strive to set a positive example for their students. One effort to increase multicultural awareness and respect for the global society is the College's offering of international programs. Such experiences, like study or research abroad, is a great way for students to develop valuable skills like cross-cultural communication and independence.

https://www.oxy.edu/
P: (800) 825-5262

PRIVATE

STUDENT PROFILE

2,021 undergraduate students

99% of undergrad students are full time

43% male – 57% female

52% of students are from out of state

93% freshman retention rate

88% graduated in 6 years

FACULTY PROFILE

171 full-time faculty

76 part-time faculty

10 to 1 student/faculty ratio

ADMISSIONS

5,911 Total Applicants

2,652 Total Admissions

518 Total Freshman Enrollment

44.87% of applicants admitted

SAT Ranges: CR 600-690, M 600-690, W 605-690

ACT Ranges: C 28-31, M 26-31, E 28-33

TUITION & COSTS

Tuition: $48,690

Fees: $558

Total: $49,248

R&B: $14,236

Room: $7,936

Board: $6,300

Total: $63,484

FINANCIAL

$33,159 avg grant/scholarship amount (total)

$7,078 avg loan amount (total)

PACIFIC UNION COLLEGE

ANGWIN, CALIFORNIA

Pacific Union College, located in California's Napa Valley, is a four-year liberal arts college accredited by the Western Association of Schools and Colleges. Founded in 1882 by the Seventh-day Adventist Church, PUC offers a Christian approach to comprehensive undergraduate education. PUC's reputation for academic excellence is highlighted by consistent rankings among the top baccalaureate colleges in the West.

RESEARCH: PUC provides opportunities for academic research in the fields of biology, psychology, physics, and others, earning PUC students various awards and honors at major national conventions. Recently, students have presented groundbreaking research at the Association of Baccalaureate Social Work Program Directors; the International Conference on Phototonic, Electronic, and Atomic Collisions; the American Association of Cancer Research; and the Western Psychological Association Convention.

STUDY ABROAD: Each year, a number of PUC students study abroad in countries like Argentina, Austria, Brazil, France, Germany, Greece, Italy, Japan, Mexico, Spain, and Thailand through the Adventist Colleges Abroad (ACA) program. While abroad, students can even continue to complete their degree requirements. Study abroad allows students to be immersed in the culture and life of another country while becoming conversant in its language.

SERVICE: PUC students have developed a strong reputation for their commitment to service. Students have volunteered as student missionaries all over the world in places as diverse as South America, Micronesia, the Middle East, and their own communities closer to home. PUC offers more than a dozen campus ministries that focus on growing students in faith and service. In any given week, community-conscious students can be found making a difference in their local community at a variety of ministry and service opportunities.

HIGH-IMPACT PRACTICES: PUC professors engage students in a broad range of high-impact educational practices. These include first-year seminars as well as common intellectual experiences that highlight the "big questions" that matter both within and outside of the academic setting. Tight-knit learning communities, writing-intensive classes, collaborative projects, and undergraduate research top off the PUC experience, all of which contribute to students' exposure to diverse and global perspectives.

TALENTED FACULTY: The Herber Family Endowment grants $10,000 to PUC's talented faculty members in order to help them achieve and sustain innovative, quality instruction. These grants finance developmental opportunities that range from attending workshops to presenting papers all over the world. Over the years, PUC's faculty has included Fulbright scholars, published authors, and renowned artists, all of whom have converted this wealth of experience into unmatched expertise in the classroom.

CAMPUS MINISTRIES: As a college built on a foundation of faith, perhaps the most important aspect of PUC is its strong community of Christian believers. The campus offers many official opportunities for worship every week, including church services, evening vespers, and sacred music programs. In addition, the campus is home to innumerable small groups that meet frequently for prayer, Bible study, worship, and support.

SOCIAL EVENTS: PUC's Student Association offers a constant lineup of social and entertainment programming. Frequent activities include film screenings, music concerts, and game nights as well as major quarterly and annual events like banquets, seasonal festivals, and talent shows. In addition, events hosted by the college's more than 30 social, cultural, and special interest clubs ensure that there is always something to do at PUC.

THE ARTS ON CAMPUS: PUC's campus is home to Rasmussen Art Gallery, the Alice Holst Theater, and the Paulin Center for the Performing Arts, all of which allow students to experience an ever-changing stream of cultural exhibits and performances. Such inspiring showings range from student recitals and original plays to performances and exhibitions by world-class and internationally known artists.

---

http://www.puc.edu/
P: (800) 862-7080

PRIVATE - CHRISTIAN

STUDENT PROFILE

1,508 undergraduate students

90% of undergrad students are full time

43% male – 57% female

13% of students are from out of state

76% freshman retention rate

44% graduated in 6 years

FACULTY PROFILE

97 full-time faculty

46 part-time faculty

13 to 1 student/faculty ratio

ADMISSIONS

2,041 Total Applicants

923 Total Admissions

251 Total Freshman Enrollment

45.22% of applicants admitted

SAT Ranges: CR 420-560, M 430-570

ACT Ranges: C 18-23, M 17-25, E 17-22

TUITION & COSTS

Tuition: $27,999

Fees: $630

Total: $28,629

R&B: $5,728

Total: $34,357

FINANCIAL

$14,927 avg grant/scholarship amount (need)

$3,861 avg loan amount (need)

PEPPERDINE UNIVERSITY

MALIBU, CALIFORNIA

Since its founding in 1937, Pepperdine University has excelled in its high standards of academic achievement and its commitment to preparing students for fulfilling futures. A private university grounded in Christian values and ethics, Pepperdine bolsters lives of leadership by way of its inspiring faculty and friendly community.

FIRST-YEAR SEMINAR: All undergraduates at Pepperdine begin their college careers enrolled in one of many First-Year Seminars. These semester-long courses prepare students for everything, easing freshmen into the college lifestyle both socially and academically. While topics of study vary by seminar each year, every course is aimed to heighten students' literacy and critical-thinking skills. Through these common learning experiences, every student gets equipped with the tools they need to apply their vocation to research, current issues, cultural understanding, and self-development.

UNDERGRADUATE RESEARCH: Undergraduates of any major have many available opportunities to conduct research. Both internal and external grants are offered to curious students looking to put their education in practice. Scholars in all of Pepperdine's five schools are constantly buzzing with new ideas and new expeditions into unexplored intellectual territory. The Summer Undergraduate Research Program (SURP) bolsters students by helping them understand the logistics and processes necessary for research studies. Students learn to hypothesize, design experiments, and present data, all while building friendly communities around their shared interests of study. The Cross-Disciplinary/Interdisciplinary Undergraduate Research Program (CDIUR) promotes a collaborative society of student researchers from different disciplines. Students from different areas of study are sorted into "research clusters" that meet in the summer to apply varied perspectives to a single subject of research. By bringing separate points of view together, students in these clusters explore topics with a degree of complexity they would never have imagined on their own. By the start of the fall semester, they are ready to present their findings at the annual Undergraduate Research and Scholarly Achievement Symposium at Seaver College.

STUDY ABROAD: Pepperdine is proud to admit more the 50 percent of its Seaver College students to study abroad programs all around the world. Education abroad expands students' perspectives and makes them personally aware of a whole world of varied cultures and issues, and so the school works hard to make international opportunities accessible and comfortable. Pepperdine-owned residential programs are offered all year (including during the summer) in Argentina, China, Switzerland, Italy, England, and Germany. Each program is fully loaded with educational field trips and cultural outreach initiatives. Students get the opportunity to work with local organizations, delving fully into the culture while serving the new community around them.

JUNIOR WRITING PORTFOLIO: The General Education program requires that all students maintain a writing portfolio made up of formal assignments and papers from their first four semesters at Pepperdine. The Junior Writing Portfolio is graded on a scale from 1-5 with an evaluation of clarity, organization, and depth of thought. Because all students have a portfolio to submit, they are all encouraged and trained through their growth as writers.

THEME HOUSE PROGRAM: Pepperdine sophomores are given the option to be involved in the Theme House program, which houses students in communities that are centered around a common interest. The most popular is the Adventure House, which takes its residents out into the beautiful Malibu landscape for a variety of outdoor activities such as hiking and kayaking. Other Theme Houses foster community around topics of faith, academic excellence, global advocacy, the fine arts, and more.

WAVES OF SERVICE: Waves of Service is rooted in Pepperdine's Christian commitment to service and leadership. Many volunteer opportunities are available to students who are looking to serve. They can travel during their spring breaks on community service trips around the country, raise money for different charities, and even work with the graduate schools of business and law to plan initiatives for social and environmental advocacy.

PEPPERDINE UNIVERSITY

http://www.pepperdine.edu/
P: (310) 506-4000

PRIVATE - CHRISTIAN

STUDENT PROFILE

3,533 undergraduate students

91% of undergrad students are full time

41% male – 59% female

44% of students are from out of state

94% freshman retention rate

84% graduated in 6 years

FACULTY PROFILE

415 full-time faculty

3 part-time faculty

13 to 1 student/faculty ratio

ADMISSIONS

9,923 Total Applicants

3,781 Total Admissions

745 Total Freshman Enrollment

38.10% of applicants admitted

SAT Ranges: CR 550-650, M 550-670, W 550-650

ACT Ranges: C 25-30, M 24-30, E 25-32, W 8-9

TUITION & COSTS

Tuition: $48,090

Fees: $252

Total: $48,342

R&B: $16,610

Room: $10,610

Board: $6,000

Total: $64,952

FINANCIAL

$29,761 avg grant/scholarship amount (total)

$7,722 avg loan amount (total)

POINT LOMA NAZARENE UNIVERSITY

SAN DIEGO, CALIFORNIA

PLNU's location is a big part of what makes it distinctive—and not just because of the dormitories and classrooms' ocean view. The campus' proximity to the coast, downtown San Diego, and an international border helps PLNU students experience a holistic, balanced approach to their growth.

STUDY ABROAD OPPORTUNITIES: Students in any year and any major are able to study abroad while at PLNU. The university offers faculty-led programs that take students around the world with their professors, and students have the additional opportunity to study through carefully vetted partner programs all over the world. Study abroad courses are all pre-approved, ensuring that students who go abroad are still taking courses that fit right into their four-year graduation track. Better yet, the only additional costs to study abroad are usually limited to airfare—financial aid travels with students!

CENTER FOR JUSTICE AND RECONCILIATION: Because PLNU is located in a border-town, social justice is a definite priority. The Center for Justice and Reconciliation (CJR) provides countless ways for students to support others within their community. The CJR studies fair trade and worker rights, immigration and racial justice, and human trafficking through research, education, and advocacy.

HONORS SCHOLARS PROGRAM: PLNU's Honors Scholars program is an opportunity for college seniors to prepare themselves for the rigor of postgraduate research and scholarship. If accepted to the program, students choose a topic for original research, pair up with faculty mentors, conduct their research, go through peer-evaluation and, finally, transform their work into a scholarly presentation to be presented at the Honors Conference. Several Honors Scholars have gone on to have their research published, even before completing their studies at PLNU

EMPHASIS ON WRITING: PLNU faculty understand that every student, regardless of major, requires a certain level of proficiency as communicators. Because of that, every incoming freshman is required to take a useful writing-intensive course. An honors writing course is also available for students who have existing writing credits. Beyond this specific course, however, each of PLNU's GE courses also have strong writing components, whether they be on biology or religion.

COASTAL CAMPUS: Because campus is literally on the Pacific Ocean, PLNU students are able to reap the benefits of a climate that makes a slew of activities available year-round. There's never a bad time to be outdoors! Formally, PLNU has dozens of clubs, athletic teams, rec teams, and outdoor adventure activities that take full advantage of the San Diego sunshine. Students can wake up early for a Surfing 101 class (students get PE credit to learn to surf!), go rock climbing with Great Escapes Adventures, catch a game with the university's nationally ranked Rugby Club, and so much more.

OFFICES OF STRENGTH AND VOCATION: The Offices of Strengths and Vocation (OSV), PLNU's career services center, is available to help students take their next steps. For undeclared students, OSV offers assessments and counseling appointments to help them better understand their strengths and passions. And, when it comes time for students to put their calling into practice, OSV is key in connecting students to potential internships. OSV also maintains an alumni mentor database, as well as active ties to the San Diego community, fostering countless internship opportunities each semester. In preparation for graduation, OSV also hosts networking events for students in each major, connecting them with professionals and showing them how their degree can work in the real world. Additionally, they have countless practical services to help build students' confidence: résumé-writing workshops, a business attire fashion show, mock interviews, and more.

https://www.pointloma.edu/
P: (619) 849-2273

PRIVATE - CHRISTIAN

STUDENT PROFILE

3,053 undergraduate students

85% of undergrad students are full time

36% male – 64% female

24.6% of students are from out of state

86.1% freshman retention rate

70.9% graduated in 6 years

FACULTY PROFILE

135 full-time faculty

283 part-time faculty

15 to 1 student/faculty ratio

ADMISSIONS

3,162 Total Applicants

2,195 Total Admissions

594 Total Freshman Enrollment

69.42% of applicants admitted

SAT Ranges: CR 510-620, M 520-620

ACT Ranges: C 23-28, M 23-28, E 23-30

TUITION & COSTS

Tuition: $34,000

Fees: $600

Total: $34,600

R&B: $10,150

Total: $44,750

FINANCIAL

$17,325 avg grant/scholarship amount (need)

$4,792 avg loan amount (need)

SANTA CLARA UNIVERSITY

SANTA CLARA, CALIFORNIA

Santa Clara University

Santa Clara University, a comprehensive Jesuit, Catholic university, offers its students rigorous undergraduate curricula in arts and sciences, business, and engineering as well as engineering Ph.D.s and master's and law degrees. Distinguished nationally by one of the highest graduation rates among all U.S. master's universities, SCU strives to educate citizens and leaders who will build a more just, humane, and sustainable world. Today, the University is committed to promoting academic excellence, enriching its educational experience through the Jesuit philosophy of educating the whole person, fostering an engaged community, and realizing opportunities available through its location in the San Francisco Bay Area and Silicon Valley.

COMMUNITY-BASED LEARNING: Santa Clara students work with and learn from marginalized groups both in the region and farther afield. They earn course credit through partnerships for community-based learning, choosing opportunities like tutoring elementary-school students in San Jose or assisting at an immigration law clinic. Through these partnerships, students work at more than 50 sites in and around Silicon Valley—in schools, clinics, health-care centers, church parishes, and homeless shelters. Here they learn with and from community partners and engage in research and collaboration around social justice.

INTEGRATED STUDIES: Three interdisciplinary Centers of Distinction engage faculty and students with society in the areas of Jesuit values and community-based learning; applied ethics; and science, technology, and social entrepreneurship. As part of the core curriculum, all students select and complete a "Pathway," which is a cluster of 3-4 courses that center around a common theme. Topics like health, humanities, justice, and social issues promote integrative, intentional learning. These concentrated, collaborative courses can also provide unique opportunities for undergraduate research.

LIVING & LEARNING: One unique aspect of Santa Clara life is the Residential Learning Communities. Upon entering Santa Clara, all students select a Residential Learning Community (RLC) in which to live and share classes with peers who have many common interests. Students select an RLC based on their interest in topics such as natural history, diversity, sustainability or social justice, excited to combine their academic, residential, and social components of campus life.

TEACHING-SCHOLARS: SCU faculty members are award-winning scientists, economists, artists, and writers, but they are first and foremost teachers. Students get the research experience and one-on-one access they need, as SCU's small classes enable professors to know them each by name. Learning in the classroom is only the first step of an SCU education. Students gain and practice new skills through such real-world applications in their field as isolating DNA for biochemistry research, interviewing residents at a shelter, and helping produce a professional musical.

CLUBS & ORGANIZATIONS: More than 150 student-run clubs and organizations exist on campus, including a student newspaper, yearbook, literary magazine, and radio station. Popular campus events include the Student Activity Programming Board's fall concert, the Hawaii club's spring luau, the Multicultural Center's annual Global Village event and various cultural nights, and basketball games against rival teams from Saint Mary's and Gonzaga.

INTERNSHIPS & FELLOWSHIPS: Over 70% of SCU students engage in at least one internship before they graduate. These work or volunteer experiences engage students in the process of exploring career goals and fields of interests. SCU also offers undergraduate students several paid fellowships that involve local and international projects justice, ethics, and technology. Santa Clara graduates enter their personal and professional lives prepared not only with knowledge, but also with a commitment to making ethical decisions that serve the needs of humankind. With an education based on the Jesuit heritage, graduates are well prepared to lead, shape, and transform the world.

Sidebar

http://www.scu.edu/
P: (408) 554-4700

PRIVATE - CATHOLIC

STUDENT PROFILE

5,385 undergraduate students

98% of undergrad students are full time

51% male – 49% female

38% of students are from out of state

95% freshman retention rate

84% graduated in 6 years

FACULTY PROFILE

536 full-time faculty

360 part-time faculty

12 to 1 student/faculty ratio

ADMISSIONS

14,899 Total Applicants

7,270 Total Admissions

1,261 Total Freshman Enrollment

48.80% of applicants admitted

SAT Ranges: CR 590-690, M 620-710

ACT Ranges: C 27-32

TUITION & COSTS

Tuition: $45,300

R&B: $13,425

Total: $58,725

FINANCIAL

$22,507 avg grant/scholarship amount (total)

$7,362 avg loan amount (total)

UNIVERSITY OF CALIFORNIA, SANTA BARBARA

SANTA BARBARA, CALIFORNIA

UC Santa Barbara is a noted research institution located on the edge of the Pacific. Students benefit from the natural research environment, enjoying a serene atmosphere that is conducive to academic success as well as many outdoor and recreational activities offered by the University.

FRESHMAN SEMINARS: Incoming first-year students at UCSB have the opportunity to participate in freshman seminars. Class sizes for freshman seminars are capped at 20 students, allowing for small-group settings that foster student-faculty interaction. Seminars cover interesting topics that allow students to explore areas of study outside of their declared majors. Examples include "Latin America in Film;" "Death, Revenge, and Madness in Icelandic Literature and Culture;" and "The Creationism, Intelligent Design, and Evolution Controversy." These seminars serve as riveting introductions to college-level thought, bringing students together with complex questions and tightly knit discussions.

EUREKA! UNDERGRADUATE RESEARCH: EUREKA! is an awesome, hands-on program that introduces first-year STEM students to the greater science community. Students involved in EUREKA! have the opportunity to explore career options and network with faculty and peers who are deeply interested and involved in STEM. EUREKA! also offers opportunities for undergraduate research, a privilege most often awarded to upperclassmen.

UCSB SUSTAINABILITY PROGRAM: UCSB Sustainability gives interested students the chance to learn about smart environmental practices both in and around their community. Students gain hands-on experience, working as interns to aid innovative sustainability projects. Participants of the program learn from mentors, leaders within the field, and like-minded peers, all of whom are passionate about the health of the world around them. There are two projects in connection with the Service Learning Program: ECOalition and Partners in Environment. ECOalition is a network of shared information regarding student-led organizations and projects, enabling the UC community to be informed about how they can help their peers. The Partners in Environment is based on three foundational values: environmentalism, volunteerism, and collaboration. Members of this project focus on recruiting volunteers for organizational events.

INTERNSHIP SCHOLARSHIP PROGRAM: An internship is a great way to get hands-on experience and gain industry-related knowledge. Many employers consider internships a necessary first step to choosing a career and securing a position, demonstrating a student's ability to apply academic theories to work settings. There is, however, no standard for payment when it comes to internships; some positions are paid, while others for not. Unpaid positions can turn away talented students who cannot financially bear the experience without compensation. The Internship Scholarship Program addresses this problem by awarding select students for securing positions and performing research.

UNIVERSITY OF CALIFORNIA EDUCATION ABROAD PROGRAM: The UC Education Abroad Program supports global education and internships for all University of California schools. There are 393 programs in 43 countries, providing students with plenty of options to choose from. Some of the most popular destinations include Australia, France, Hong Kong, Mexico, Morocco, Russia, Singapore, and Spain. There is also a one-of-a-kind internship program that provides the unique opportunity to gain an up-close look at the political governing body in Edinburgh, Scotland. Students enrolled in this program serve as full-time interns and work side-by-side with a member of the Scottish Parliament.

THE UNIVERSITY OF CALIFORNIA CENTER IN SACRAMENTO: The University of California Center in Sacramento coordinates and supports internship and coursework opportunities for students within the UC system. One of the major attractions of the UCCS is the surrounding area of the state's capital. Because the center is located in Sacramento, students have the amazing opportunity to observe public policy processes as they happen. The two programs offered by UCCS are Public Policy and Summer Journalism.

http://www.ucsb.edu/
P: (805) 893-8000

PUBLIC

STUDENT PROFILE

20,607 undergraduate students

98% of undergrad students are full time

47% male – 53% female

6% of students are from out of state

93% freshman retention rate

81% graduated in 6 years

FACULTY PROFILE

923 full-time faculty

180 part-time faculty

17 to 1 student/faculty ratio

ADMISSIONS

70,536 Total Applicants

23,026 Total Admissions

4,473 Total Freshman Enrollment

32.64% of applicants admitted

SAT Ranges: CR 530-660, M 560-700, W 510-630

ACT Ranges: C 26-31, M 26-32, E 26-33

TUITION & COSTS

Tuition: (In) $11,220 (Out) $35,928

Fees: $2,748

Total: (In) $13,968 (Out) $38,676

R&B: $14,594

Total: (In) $28,562 (Out) $53,270

FINANCIAL

$17,948 avg grant/scholarship amount (need)

$6,250 avg loan amount (need)

UNIVERSITY OF CALIFORNIA, SANTA CRUZ

SANTA CRUZ, CALIFORNIA

UC Santa Cruz has a steadfast commitment to the intellectual growth of its students. The University promotes active engagement with the community as well as environmental stewardship. Faculty work closely with students providing individualistic attention that drives real results.

10 COLLEGES: There are ten different colleges at UC Santa Cruz—each with its own distinctive community and academic focus. UCSC's colleges function as living learning communities and provide amazing benefits like academic support, student-faculty collaboration, and social activities. Students can indicate their college preference during the admissions acceptance process. Examples of each college's areas of focus include the self and society, cultural identities and global consciousness, the environment and society, and the role of science and technology in society.

UCDC PROGRAM: The UCDC program allows qualified students the chance to study or intern in Washington DC for a quarter. The program is highly competitive and only open to juniors and seniors. Students of all majors are invited to apply. On top of the general application, individuals must submit academic records, a written statement, and letters of recommendation. Selected students live, study, and work in the nation's capital. The program places UCSC students among participants from other UC campuses, creating a professional and socially thriving network among students. Through UCDC, students get firsthand experience among political powerhouses.

EDUCATION FIELD PROGRAMS: The Education Field Programs are not limited to students that are pursuing careers as educators. In fact, students can enroll if they just want to expand their liberal arts experience to appreciate the institution of education. Field study in education explores topics like learning theory, educational thought and philosophy, and diversity. Students take what they learn from these topics and apply them to different situations that they encounter while they are gaining hands-on experience.

PSYCHOLOGY FIELD STUDY PROGRAM: UCSC invites select students to participate in the Psychology Field Study Program. Qualified students have the chance to apply academic theories to professional experience, applying theoretical coursework to real, effective work. Participants commit 10 hours a week to a community agency, aiding professional experts in psychology as they gain a vast amount of knowledge that aids them both in their coursework and future work in their careers.

GENERAL EDUCATION: UC Santa Cruz is dedicated to graduating strong, well-rounded individuals. In order to prepare students for the challenges they'll face after graduation, every student is exposed to coursework in cross-cultural analysis, ethnicity and race, interpreting media, textual analysis, and an exploration of controversial perspectives. These out-of-the-box general education requirements are also joined by mathematics, statistics, science, and composition courses that prepare them with a foundation of skills and knowledge.

THE CHANCELLOR'S UNDERGRADUATE INTERNSHIP PROGRAM: The Chancellor's Undergraduate Internships Program allows undergraduates to build important job skills like leadership and time management while working on a campus project. Under the direction of a mentor, students take an active leadership role that allows them to step out of their comfort zone and test their boundaries. The program requires students to work 15 hours a week and provides a scholarship to pay for a large portion of the registration fees.

http://www.ucsc.edu/
P: (831) 459-0111

PUBLIC

STUDENT PROFILE

16,231 undergraduate students

97% of undergrad students are full time

47% male – 53% female

5% of students are from out of state

88% freshman retention rate

78% graduated in 6 years

FACULTY PROFILE

567 full-time faculty

260 part-time faculty

18 to 1 student/faculty ratio

ADMISSIONS

45,532 Total Applicants

22,897 Total Admissions

3,620 Total Freshman Enrollment

50.29% of applicants admitted

SAT Ranges: CR 510-630, M 540-670, W 510-630

ACT Ranges: C 25-30, M 24-29, E 24-31

TUITION & COSTS

Tuition: (In) $11,220 (Out) $35,928

Fees: $2,241

Total: (In) $13,461 (Out) $38,169

R&B: $14,952

Total: (In) $28,413 (Out) $53,121

FINANCIAL

$16,599 avg grant/scholarship amount (total)

$5,820 avg loan amount (total)

UNIVERSITY OF LA VERNE

LA VERNE, CALIFORNIA

Located outside Los Angeles, California, the University of La Verne is one of the oldest colleges in the state. Founded in 1891, the campus is home to 2,800 undergraduate students who study a variety of academic majors. The university's liberal arts, education, business, and science programs prepare graduates for lifelong learning.

A PROGRAM FOR EVERYONE: The University of La Verne is comprised of four colleges: College of Arts and Sciences, College of Business & Public Management, College of Education & Organizational Leadership, and College of Law. La Verne offers over 70 undergraduate majors that empower students to combine their academic interests with potential career choices. Many majors like criminology, Kinesiology, child development, movement & sports science, and e-commerce are uncommon at other universities, and the flexibility to double major, minor, or establish a concentration allows La Verne students to choose from all of the academic offerings at the University. No matter what, they are certain to be prepared for successful and productive lives after college.

OFF-CAMPUS LEARNING: Whether studying abroad, performing original research in the sciences, or engaging in hands-on internships, students often find themselves in stimulating environments that foster a better understanding of both themselves and the world around them.

HONORS PROGRAM: Intellectually curious and creative honors students engage in activities that venture beyond traditional academia. They delve into the rich resources of greater Los Angeles, including film studios, technology centers, museums, churches, concerts, exhibitions, and lectures.

MENTORSHIPS: La Verne students have the opportunity to not only pursue their academic interests, but also to gain tangible and valuable experiences in their future careers. Faculty who are renowned in their respective fields work closely with students to guide and mentor them through their professional endeavors. Mike Bennett, for example, credits much of his success as an internationally known percussionist to his time spent with his La Verne music professor. Examples like this abound in various programs at the University of La Verne; the strong one-on-one and small-group interactions between faculty and students are the backbone of what makes any University of La Verne student successful.

FORWARD-THINKING: The University of La Verne is located in beautiful Southern California. While it enjoys a rich 120-year history, it feels brand new due to its vibrant, spirited, and forward-thinking atmosphere. Excitement is in the air, and history is being made at the University of La Verne. In 2011, Dr. Devorah Lieberman was installed as the first female President of the University, which is just one of the many stepping stones of La Verne's ever-forward movement.

CAMPUS DIVERSITY: Diversity is an integral component of life at La Verne, making it stand out from other institutions. More than 50% of undergraduate students enrolled at the University identify themselves as Hispanic, African American, or Asian American. In addition, international students from all over the globe enhance the campus community.

ALUMNI IN EVERY FIELD: La Verne alumni can be found in every state of the union as well as in 66 countries across the globe. Thirty-four judges hold a J.D. from the College of Law, and many alumni have distinguished themselves as business owners, CEOs, or presidents who serve national and international corporations alike. City managers, police chiefs, city and county department heads, and many public management and law enforcement officials hold public administration degrees from La Verne. And, reflecting the high value that the University places on service, many alumni are teachers, ministers, psychologists, and counselors. La Verne is also proud to have showcased its leadership in the field of education by producing 25% of California's school superintendents.

---

http://www.laverne.edu/

P: (909) 392-2800

PRIVATE

STUDENT PROFILE

5,214 undergraduate students

72% of undergrad students are full time

42% male – 58% female

85% freshman retention rate

64% graduated in 6 years

FACULTY PROFILE

272 full-time faculty

440 part-time faculty

17 to 1 student/faculty ratio

ADMISSIONS

8,179 Total Applicants

3,859 Total Admissions

724 Total Freshman Enrollment

47.18% of applicants admitted

SAT Ranges: CR 470-560, M 470-570, W 460-560

ACT Ranges: C 20-24, M 19-25, E 19-25

TUITION & COSTS

Tuition: $37,100

Fees: $1,460

Total: $38,560

R&B: $12,510

Room: $6,580

Board: $5,930

Total: $51,070

FINANCIAL

$24,377 avg grant/scholarship amount (total)

$7,669 avg loan amount (total)

UNIVERSITY OF REDLANDS

REDLANDS, CALIFORNIA

A private liberal arts and sciences institution in the heart of Southern California, University of Redlands is committed to educating the hearts and minds of its students through an emphasis on service, study abroad, and experiential learning. In addition to more than 50 programs of study in the arts and sciences, University of Redlands also offers impressive pre-professional opportunities in pre-health, pre-law, and education.

FIRST-YEAR SEMINAR: Every first-year student at University of Redlands enrolls in a first-year seminar that is designed to be an academic bridge between high school and college. In addition to acting as students' initial academic advisors, first-year seminar professors help students teach valuable critical thinking, reading, writing, and communication skills. Recent seminar offerings have included Global Issues for American Business; The Science of the Sea; and Harry Potter and the Widely Applicable Skillset.

STUDY ABROAD: Redlands strongly encourages its students to study abroad and, currently, more than 50 percent of undergraduates take advantage of an international program. At University of Redlands, cross-cultural learning is respected as an integral component of a liberal arts education. Since 1960, the University has even hosted its own program in Salzburg, Austria. Students in this program live in the Marketenderschössl, a nearly 500-year-old Renaissance building that overlooks the historic city of Salzburg.

MAY TERM: May Term is an optional, one-month semester in which students take one immersive, hands-on class. Students who participate can choose to stay on campus and take a unique academic course, get involved in a community service project, or embark on a faculty-led travel course with a small group of fellow students. The latest May Term courses includes Service-Learning in Cambodia; Policy Making in Washington, D.C.; and Baseball, Business, and American Life.

SERVICE: Every year, University of Redlands students extend their learning beyond the classroom by completing more than 120,000 hours of community service. From mentoring local youth to building houses for homeless families in Mexico, students immerse themselves in endless opportunities to make the world a better place. These experiences broaden students' awareness, empower their contribution, and strengthen their connection to the larger community.

UNDERGRADUATE RESEARCH: The annual Summer Science Research program gives Redlands students the opportunity to focus on a research project alongside a faculty mentor. They spend 10 weeks of their summer on campus to research such topics as "Distribution and Behavioral Analysis of Marine Mammals in Southern California" and "New Ruthenium complexes for Anticancer Activity: Synthesis, Spectroscopic Characterization, and Reactivity with CT-DNA."

CAMPUS TRADITIONS: Redlands students and alumni find themselves chanting the "Och Tamale" as a greeting or congratulatory cheer. It starts, "Och Tamale Gazolly Gazzump, Deyump Deyatty Yahoo…" This nonsensical chant was written in the 1910s as a rebuttal to a rival school's Latin chant and has been a tradition ever since. Students learn it on their first day of orientation, and it's not easily forgotten! Members of the University have been known as the Redlands Bulldogs ever since its first official live bulldog mascot, Deacon, joined the community in 1946. There have been four other official mascots since then, and the community recently commemorated Deacon with a statue on campus. Students like to rub his nose for luck on their way to a sporting event or challenging test.

SENIOR CAPSTONE: Prior to graduation, all students complete a capstone project that is the culmination of their academic accomplishments. Capstone courses typically vary, but all offer students a way to synthesize their knowledge of their field of study, whether that be in the form of a 30-page paper or a research project. Students find their senior capstone useful when applying for graduate schools or seeking employment.

UNIVERSITY OF

http://www.redlands.edu/
P: (909) 748-8074

PRIVATE

STUDENT PROFILE

2,402 undergraduate students

99% of undergrad students are full time

42% male – 58% female

34% of students are from out of state

87% freshman retention rate

74% graduated in 6 years

FACULTY PROFILE

169 full-time faculty

139 part-time faculty

12 to 1 student/faculty ratio

ADMISSIONS

4,562 Total Applicants

3,410 Total Admissions

591 Total Freshman Enrollment

74.75% of applicants admitted

SAT Ranges: CR 490-590, M 490-600

ACT Ranges: C 22-27

TUITION & COSTS

Tuition: $47,722

Fees: $350

Total: $48,072

R&B: $13,862

Total: $61,934

FINANCIAL

$28,598 avg grant/scholarship amount (need)

$6,556 avg loan amount (need)

UNIVERSITY OF SAN DIEGO

SAN DIEGO, CALIFORNIA

USD is dedicated to the values originally articulated by its founders, Bishop Charles Francis Buddy of the Diocese of San Diego and Mother Rosalie Hill of the Society of the Sacred Heart, reflecting in the University's rich Catholic intellectual tradition. USD's community of scholars are committed to educating the whole person—intellectually, physically, spiritually, emotionally, socially, and culturally. The University provides a character-building education that fosters independent thought, innovation, integrity, analytical thinking, and an open-minded and collaborative world view.

THE FRESHMAN PRECEPTORIAL PROGRAM: The Freshman Preceptorial program begins each USD student's academic career with a combination of advising, orientation, and an introduction to college-level scholarship. The preceptor, a faculty member in the student's intended area of study, has frequent contact with each advisee and continues advising throughout the student's general education program. Once students declare a major by the end of their sophomore year, the responsibility of advising shifts to a department faculty member who provides specialized guidance.

THE FIRST-YEAR EXPERIENCE: The University of San Diego's First-Year Experience (FYE) strives to build a community of engaged student learners who value academic excellence; intellectual, personal, and spiritual development; inclusion; ethical conduct; and compassionate service. It integrates two core components: the Preceptorial Program and the residential living-learning environment.

RESEARCH: Research at USD is a year-round process. Each semester, each summer, and even during Intersession, the act of research is a full-time, invested commitment for Torero undergraduate and graduate students and faculty. USD students are eager to explore, engage, and add value to what is already a solid academic offering. Faculty who are active in research and publishing also apply for grants that enable them to be research mentors for collaborative student projects. Students commonly generate ideas for innovative ventures that respond to a social or environmental issue of their choice and then compete for funding to launch or expand their ventures. Social ventures may be for-profit, non-profit, or hybrid models with a domestic or international focus.

CREATIVE COLLABORATIONS: "Creative Collaborations" is an event that showcases the vibrant student-faculty interactions that continually stand as a hallmark of a USD education. This conference celebrates the intellectual life at USD and provides all undergraduate students an opportunity to present their projects in an environment with other students and faculty. Working side-by-side with their faculty mentors, USD students gain lifelong experiences that extend well beyond the classroom.

CAMPUS COMMUNITY: One of the best things about being a University of San Diego student is the ability to experience an enriching life on campus. The friendly and energetic atmosphere guarantees that there is always something to do and someone to do it with. The active, thriving community offers plenty of opportunities to get involved with fellow students both on and around the beautiful 180-acre Alcalá Park campus.

RESIDENCE LIFE: Over 95% of freshmen live on campus, and on-campus housing is available for all four years. Almost half of all students live on campus for the duration of their time at USD, which provides for an active student life. Students participate in over 200 clubs and organizations, residence hall activities, community service and University Ministry programs, and gain valuable leadership skills as part of Associated Students. Additionally, USD offers a world-class theater, events that feature nationally respected speakers, Greek life, honor societies, and much more.

---

http://www.sandiego.edu/
P: (619) 260-4506

PRIVATE - CATHOLIC

STUDENT PROFILE

5,604 undergraduate students

97% of undergrad students are full time

46% male – 54% female

48% of students are from out of state

87% freshman retention rate

78% graduated in 6 years

FACULTY PROFILE

440 full-time faculty

466 part-time faculty

14 to 1 student/faculty ratio

ADMISSIONS

14,413 Total Applicants

7,406 Total Admissions

1,133 Total Freshman Enrollment

51.38% of applicants admitted

SAT Ranges: CR 540-650, M 560-660

ACT Ranges: C 26-30, M 25-29, E 25-32

TUITION & COSTS

Tuition: $44,000

Fees: $586

Total: $44,568

R&B: $12,042

Total: $56,62

FINANCIAL

$25,655 avg grant/scholarship amount (need)

$7,061 avg loan amount (need)

UNIVERSITY OF THE PACIFIC

STOCKTON, CALIFORNIA

Offering a variety of useful resources and unique experiences, University of the Pacific is committed to helping students succeed. The Four-Year Graduation Guarantee facilitates each student's goal to earn their Bachelor's Degree within four years. Competitive accelerated programs go even further to prepare very dedicated and talented freshmen for their professional degrees. Alumni leave Pacific equipped to make their mark and practice their professions at the highest level.

STUDY ABROAD: Pacific students benefit from a robust Study Abroad program that offers programs in many different countries throughout six continents. Exchange programs, which focus on cultural immersion and language-intensive courses, are offered during the semester or academic year, while other faculty-led programs are offered during the summer. A number of Pacific faculty members also offer embedded courses, which are typical semester courses that include an additional short-term study abroad component (often at the end of the term).

PACIFIC SEMINAR: Pacific Seminar I (PACS I) is a small, writing-intensive first-year seminar that asks students "What is a good society?" PACS I serves as an introduction to general education, strengthening students' writing, critical thinking, and reading skills. It also allows all freshmen to share common intellectual experiences, drawing them together with readings, lectures, and a special art experience. Pacific Seminar II is composed of different topical seminars that examine specific problems or themes of society that are introduced in PACS Seminar I. Students take Pacific Seminar III: What is an Ethical Life? (PACS III) in their senior year. In the third and final PACS course, they learn about and analyze ethical concepts and theories to better understand their moral development, values, and behavior.

RESIDENTIAL LEARNING COMMUNITIES: Residential Learning Communities provide students with programming opportunities that go hand-in-hand with what they are studying in the classroom. The First-Year Honors Community, designed for freshmen in the Honors Program, offers easy access to faculty resources, added social and academic support through "Honors Peers," and structured programs and activities that are organized to coincide with classroom learning. Students who live in the First-Year Residential Living Community are assigned to common Pacific Seminar sections, allowing the same cohort of students to live and learn together. The Engineering & Computer Science Learning Community's location allows students to have easy access to services in the immediately adjacent School of Engineering and Computer Science building. These services include free drop-in tutoring as well as the 24-hour Engineering and Computer Science open labs.

FRESHMAN HONORS PROGRAM: The Freshman Honors Program is a vibrant intellectual and social community designed for academically talented students across all majors. Students in the program are invited to apply for space in the Honors Residence Hall (see above) in order to immerse themselves fully into their active community.

INTERNSHIPS AND JOBS: There are many great internship experiences available to Pacific students. The Career Resource Center, for example, offers a number of services including Tiger Jobs, the center's online job database. Tiger Jobs even includes a list of alumni mentors who want to connect with students. There are also internships available through specific schools. For example, Cooperative Education (CO-OP) is an experiential internship program for students in the School of Engineering and Computer Science that allows them to reinforce classroom experience by relating theory to practice. Students strengthen and reinforce their academic engineering knowledge and skills, acquire hands-on industry experiences and programming skills, learn how to navigate in a corporate environment, and build confidence.

UNIVERSITY OF THE PACIFIC

http://www.pacific.edu/
P: (209) 946-2211

PRIVATE

STUDENT PROFILE

3,474 undergraduate students

97% of undergrad students are full time

47% male – 53% female

7% of students are from out of state

85% freshman retention rate

68.3% graduated in 6 years

FACULTY PROFILE

443 full-time faculty

406 part-time faculty

12 to 1 student/faculty ratio

ADMISSIONS

8,870 Total Applicants

5,853 Total Admissions

726 Total Freshman Enrollment

65.99% of applicants admitted

SAT Ranges: CR 500-630, M 530-670

ACT Ranges: C 23-30

TUITION & COSTS

Tuition: $44,068

Fees: $520

Total: $44,588

R&B: $12,858

Total: $57,446

FINANCIAL

$25,217 avg grant/scholarship amount (need)

$9,224 avg loan amount (need)

WESTMONT COLLEGE

SANTA BARBARA, CALIFORNIA

Students receive a rigorous liberal arts education and grow spiritually on a campus that is filled with natural beauty. After four years, they graduate as men and women with intellect and character who have reaped the rewards of an outstanding faculty and first-rate experiential learning opportunities.

ENGAGED IN FAITH AND ACADEMICS: Westmont seeks to provide a first-rate liberal arts education to intellectually curious students who foster a strong sense of faith. Professors are always in the classroom, and no graduate assistants conduct classes. The average class size is 23 students, allowing faculty to focus solely on their undergraduates.

STUDY ABROAD: Westmont's study abroad programs include semesters of travel in Europe, Israel, and more. Westmont offers England semester for English literature, an Asian studies summer program for business and economics, and the World Vision International Relief and Development Internship program for sociology majors. Biology majors are also given the opportunity to study in the Global Stewardship Study program. Faculty members are increasingly offering a number of May-term and summer programs that feature extensive travel, and students can enroll in programs sponsored by the Council for Christian Colleges & Universities (CCCU). Students can also spend a semester in Los Angeles to learn about the film industry, explore contemporary life in San Francisco through the college's urban program, or spend a semester of government study in Washington, D.C.

ENTREPRENEURS FOR THE FUTURE: Westmont is proud of the entrepreneurial focus of its programs. Recently, professor David Newton, was even invited to speak on CNN as a featured college with strong entrepreneurial programs. Westmont students take part in the Spirit of Entrepreneurship and Enterprise Development (SEED) Venture Forum, which requires students to create business plans and offers them the opportunity to receive advice from local businesspeople.

SUMMER RESEARCH: During the summer, students can work with faculty through a research assistance program that enables them to focus solely on their projects. Through the program, students are invited to stay on campus for the summer, gain active assistance from faculty members, and present their findings at an annual symposium.

A BEAUTIFUL CAMPUS: Set on 133 acres in the foothills of the Santa Ynez Mountains, Westmont's wooded and scenic campus is an ideal residential college atmosphere. The campus includes buildings and land that have been acquired from two former estates and the historic Deane School for Boys. The grounds feature the pathways, stone bridges, and garden atmosphere that are typical of Montecito, a suburb of Santa Barbara. It is also located three miles uphill from the ocean, which can be seen from certain spots on campus.

UNITED IN FAITH: The Christian faith is intertwined into every aspect of the Westmont community. The college encourages and supports the spiritual growth of its students through informal interactions and formal initiatives. One example is the acclaimed Leadership and Character Development Program, which pairs students with a faculty mentor to engage them in four years of close Bible study, prayer, conversation, and counsel.

SERVICE: Serving others is an important part of the Westmont experience. Students have countless service opportunities on campus, in the community, and in other countries. Every year, around four hundred students travel to Ensenada, Mexico, to work with twenty churches on hundreds of projects. They also work with faculty and staff on construction projects, in orphanages, vacation Bible school programs, and ministry through theater and athletics. Other international ministries have traveled to Costa Rica, India, and Israel.

http://www.westmont.edu/
P: (800) 777-9011

PRIVATE - CHRISTIAN

STUDENT PROFILE

1,297 undergraduate students

100% of undergrad students are full time

39% male – 61% female

27% of students are from out of state

83% freshman retention rate

77% graduated in 6 years

FACULTY PROFILE

128 full-time faculty

88 part-time faculty

12 to 1 student/faculty ratio

ADMISSIONS

2,077 Total Applicants

1,687 Total Admissions

338 Total Freshman Enrollment

81.22% of applicants admitted

SAT Ranges: CR 520-650, M 530-650, W 520-640

ACT Ranges: C 23-29, M 23-28, E 23-31, W 7-10

TUITION & COSTS

Tuition: $40,320

Fees: $1,040

Total: $41,360

R&B: $13,040

Room: $8,110

Board: $4,930

Total: $54,400

FINANCIAL

$22,375 avg grant/scholarship amount (total)

$7,986 avg loan amount (total)

WHITTIER COLLEGE

WHITTIER, CALIFORNIA

The essential heart of Whittier College was formed at its founding by Quakers in 1887, a true distinction apart from California colleges. Even though Whittier hasn't been religiously affiliated since the 1930s, it is still driven by a mission that emphasizes the belief that no one is inherently superior to anyone else—that everyone has unique gifts that should be respected, developed, and shared. One illustration of this mission is the way that Whittier has always welcomed students irrespective of gender, race, religion, or social status. Few Whittier students fit stereotypes; even fewer want to.

PERSONALLY DESIGNED MAJORS: For 40 years, the Whittier Scholars Program (WSP) has offered a unique option for students to construct personalized programs of study as well as original majors. In addition to the wide array of seminars and classes offered across the academic spectrum, the WSP incorporates off-campus learning opportunities and culminates in a substantial senior capstone project. With helpful, attentive advisement and support, the program allows students to customize their education plans so that they may prepare for their goals more directly than they would with a standard catalog major.

STUDY ABROAD: Within four years, a single student could manage to study in nine other countries. Whittier offers plenty of study abroad options in addition to the typical junior-year or semester abroad concept that is common to other schools. Whittier's partner programs are located in Australia, Scotland, England, and Hong Kong, but that doesn't mean that the options are limited. In fact, Whittier's staff works to cater to students' ambitions by arranging studies as essentially any school in the world. Briefer travel opportunities are regularly offered throughout the "mini-terms," which are offered 3-4 weeks before and after each spring semester. Examples of these courses have included Environmental Science in the Amazon; International Business in Hong Kong; Theatre in London; Latin Jazz in Havana; Philosophy in Greece; and Art in Paris.

FRESHMAN WRITING: Whittier understands that students have greater chances for success (both in college and after) if they are able to write well, whether they become novelists, veterinarians, math teachers, or stockbrokers. The challenge, therefore, is to make a writing course that is interesting and relevant regardless of a student's major or intended profession. To navigate this challenge, Whittier approaches writing with an attractive twist. Incoming students get to pick a specific topic that goes on to serve as the primary context in which to sharpen their writing skills. These courses could be taught by professors of biology, business, political science, psychology, English, or anything else. Each course is then paired with another class that is thematically linked to the original topic, expanding upon the subject in a dynamic, skill-building way.

RESEARCH AND FIELDWORK: Whittier students work in close collaboration with world-class thinkers and doers. While their professors have the powerful credentials that are typically found at mega-universities, they are nevertheless uniquely dedicated teachers who actually enjoy working with undergraduates. They regularly act as advisors and assist students who may be breaking new ground on their own research. Each year, more and more Whittier students are able to present their ideas and achievements at academic and professional conferences nationwide.

A RECORD THAT SPEAKS FOR ITSELF: The value of a Whittier education is clear in the achievements of its students and alumni. Many have been state and regional finalists for the elite Rhodes Scholarship; four have actually won it. The College has also produced impressive numbers of NCAA Scholar Athletes as well as Marshall, Fulbright, and Mellon scholarship winners.

http://www.whittier.edu/
P: (888) 200-0369

PRIVATE

STUDENT PROFILE

1,645 undergraduate students

98% of undergrad students are full time

44% male — 56% female

81% freshman retention rate

66% graduated in 6 years

FACULTY PROFILE

116 full-time faculty

72 part-time faculty

12 to 1 student/faculty ratio

ADMISSIONS

5,192 Total Applicants

3,251 Total Admissions

445 Total Freshman Enrollment

62.62% of applicants admitted

SAT Ranges: CR 463-580, M 470-590

ACT Ranges: C 20-26

TUITION & COSTS

Tuition: $44,184

Fees: $590

Total: $44,774

R&B: $12,902

Total: $57,676

FINANCIAL

$31,278 avg grant/scholarship amount (need)

$5,519 avg loan amount (need)

WOODBURY UNIVERSITY

BURBANK, CALIFORNIA

Established in 1884, Woodbury University is a small, private, fully-accredited nonprofit institution known for its highly regarded, practice-based professional and liberal arts undergraduate and graduate majors, many of which are nationally and regionally ranked. Woodbury University's degree programs transform students into innovative professionals who also learn the value of social responsibility. Academic excellence is achieved by focusing on purposeful student engagement, establishing external partnerships, and enriching the overall student experience. Students who choose Woodbury reflect the cultural diversity of Southern California and, through the university's transformative educational programs, are empowered to put their talents to work toward extraordinary things.

INDIVIDUALIZED ATTENTION: Woodbury takes pride in providing its students with individual attention. Faculty members, many of whom are practicing professionals themselves, understand that students need to satisfy the high standards that their professions expect. They also take to heart the fact that what distinguishes Woodbury graduates from others is their ability to employ their own experiences and voices. Students are taught to see themselves as makers of knowledge, and their faculty members empower, support, and nurture students in support of their process.

ONE CAMPUS–ONE COMMUNITY: Student life is what truly makes Woodbury a vibrant campus. Whether it manifest in the casual culture of the 24/7 studios or the formal culture of the annual architecture conference of project and discussions, the integration of academic and personal development is present everywhere on campus. Woodbury is a diverse community of students from more than 40 countries and dozens of regional and national ethnicities. From the outset, students come together as a community through the "One Book, One Campus" program, which engages students and faculty in campus-wide discussions around a single book. The campus community also expands when the student group La Voz Unida brings parents to campus, inviting them to shadow their students for a day.

PROBLEM- AND PROJECT-BASED LEARNING: At Woodbury University, the student experience is at the center of learning. Problem- and project-based learning strategies are integrated throughout Woodbury University's curriculum, often in community settings where individual and collaborative contributions make a significant difference. Some examples include a designated studio space for first-year architecture students, logo and banding projects for graphic design students, and collaborative marketing strategy and management projects between business students and corporate partners.

INTERNSHIPS: All students engage in significant internships and work experiences that are intended to lead them to successful jobs. Using Burbank and Hollywood as a real-world lab, students gain career experiences with such companies as Cartoon Network, Comcast/NBC Universal, The Walt Disney Company, Warner Bros. and PricewaterhouseCoopers, to name a few.

FINALS PROJECTS FOR THE REAL WORLD: Woodbury University's education emphasizes quality, creativity, innovation, communication in many media, social responsibility, personal and professional growth, and collaborative problem solving. Before graduation, each student undertakes a significant project, either alone or as a member of a team. Typical assignments might be creating a new app, designing a new solar building, or serving as CEO of a simulated business. It is through the capstone, along with many other initiatives, that faculty and staff direct their students toward an embodiment of the university's principles.

WOODBURY
UNIVERSITY
FOUNDED IN 1884

http://www.woodbury.edu/
P: (818) 767-0888

PRIVATE

STUDENT PROFILE
1,245 undergraduate students
87% of undergrad students are full time
51% male – 49% female
82% freshman retention rate
46% graduated in 6 years

FACULTY PROFILE
92 full-time faculty
189 part-time faculty
8 to 1 student/faculty ratio

ADMISSIONS
1,342 Total Applicants
773 Total Admissions
117 Total Freshman Enrollment
57.60% of applicants admitted

SAT Ranges: CR 430-540, M 430-520

ACT Ranges: C 16-21

TUITION & COSTS
Tuition: $35,808
Fees: $600
Total: $36,408
R&B: $10,668
Room: $6,604
Board: $4,064
Total: $47,076

FINANCIAL
$18,983 avg grant/scholarship amount (total)
$5,349 avg loan amount (total)

COLORADO CHRISTIAN UNIVERSITY

LAKEWOOD, COLORADO

Founded in 1914, Colorado Christian University is the flagship Christian university in Colorado and the Rocky Mountain region as a whole, delivering a world-class education to thousands of students. The University's primary goal is to produce graduates who think critically, live faithfully, and impact their spheres of influence. With a steadfast commitment by dedicated faculty, hardworking administration, and students who hunger for academic and Biblical learning, CCU is in a class of its own.

FIRST-YEAR SEMINARS AND EXPERIENCES: The First-Year Integration (FYI) program is a required course for all first-time freshmen in the College of Undergraduate Studies. CCU's unique approach to the First-Year Integration program encourages students to explore their spiritual gifts, individual strengths, and their own personal mission statement, all while developing lifelong, personal connections and mentorships with their instructors. In addition to FYI, students at CCU benefit from a unique academic advising model through the Life Directions Center (LDC). The LDC connects students with advisors who guide them throughout all four years of their CCU experience.

COMMON INTELLECTUAL EXPERIENCES: The mission of CCU's general education program is to build a broad, foundational knowledge of the humanities, philosophy, reformation theology, and the study of western civilization and democracy. These general education requirements attempt to sharpen students' knowledge of American politics and economics, Christian church history, and philosophy in western society. In addition, studies in scientific thought and mathematics stimulate inquiry, critical thinking, and problem solving, encouraging students to learn how to make logical and ethical decisions.

DIVERSITY AND GLOBAL LEARNING: Colorado Christian University encourages students to experience other cultures and expand their academic experience by participating in study abroad programs and other off-campus opportunities. The University's study abroad and Best Semester programs provide students with more than a dozen Christian-based academic opportunities in such countries as Australia, China, England, and Uganda. There are also opportunities to participate in off-campus study programs within the U.S., including the American Studies Program in Washington, D.C.; the Film Studies Center in Los Angeles, CA; and the Contemporary Music Center in Nashville, TN.

STUDENT DISCIPLESHIP: Discipleship groups (D-Groups) at CCU offer freshmen the chance to get to know other students on a deeply spiritual level. D-Groups offer consistent communities for encouragement, accountability, and support in a safe place that welcomes questions and prayer requests. Ultimately, each group's focus is to grow closer to Jesus while also growing closer to one another in authentic relationships.

SERVICE LEARNING: CCU's unique ministry hours requirement showcases the University's commitment to preparing graduates for Christian leadership and service. In order to graduate from the College of Undergraduate Studies, every student must complete 45 hours per academic year at CCU, encouraging them to develop lifestyles of service and a drive to pursue their vocational callings. The ministry hours requirement pushes students to branch out of their comfort zones and explore ways to serve outside of their immediate circles of influence. For this reason, a maximum of 25% of students' ministry hours are permitted to be service within the CCU community. Ministry hours may otherwise be completed at church, in organizations and businesses, and through domestic and overseas missions.

Colorado Christian
UNIVERSITY

http://www.ccu.edu/
P: (303) 963-3000

PRIVATE - CHRISTIAN

STUDENT PROFILE

1,218 undergraduate students

100% of undergrad students are full time

40% male – 60% female

47% of students are from out of state

93% freshman retention rate

40% graduated in 6 years

FACULTY PROFILE

53 full-time faculty

109 part-time faculty

9 to 1 student/faculty ratio

ADMISSIONS

1,414 Total Applicants

1,010 Total Admissions

439 Total Freshman Enrollment

71.43% of applicants admitted

TUITION & COSTS

Tuition: $28,860

Fees: $500

Total: $29,360

R&B: $5,158

Room: $3,465

Board: $2,549

Total: $34,518

FINANCIAL

$13,692 avg grant/scholarship amount (total)

$8,166 avg loan amount (total)

COLORADO MESA UNIVERSITY

GRAND JUNCTION, COLORADO

Colorado Mesa University in Grand Junction, Colorado, has always been an institution dedicated to exceptional education at an affordable price. CMU administration and staff are all committed to the highest quality of service to the university community. In spite of the many changes in the university's 89-year history, its dedication to providing the highest quality education in a student-centered environment has always remained. This principle is sure to continue the momentum of Colorado Mesa University into the future.

HANDS-ON LEARNING EXPERIENCE: Students ultimately hold the key to their own futures, but it is through Colorado Mesa University that they get the opportunity to learn more about their obstacles through practical, applied learning experiences that engage their disciplines. Learning doesn't solely revolve around lectures; students rather take the reins of their own education through scenario-based projects and student-operated organizations. Whether performing on the main stage, being a team leader in a group project, or managing and operating a student media outlet, CMU students step up and do what they came to do: learn and grow.

STUDY ABROAD: Colorado Mesa University is a member of the International Student Exchange Program, which allows students to pay CMU tuition while studying abroad for a semester or academic year. This program gives students the chance to immerse themselves in a global academic experience in locations across more than 50 countries. In addition, Colorado Mesa University faculty lead students, alumni, and community members on tours and research opportunities around the globe. Recent trips have included immersion courses in China, Costa Rica, Ecuador, Japan, Germany, and Spain.

ONE-ON-ONE: With a student-to-faculty ratio of 23:1, faculty have the ability to involve undergraduates actively in challenging research experiences that are usually found only in graduate programs. In-class instruction is also supplemented by a variety of out-of-class opportunities that range from fieldwork in Western Colorado to study groups that travel the globe.

PROFESSOR ACCESSIBILITY: All classes at the university are taught by professors who put copious time and energy into the classroom. Instead of lectures that are led by teacher's assistants in classes of hundreds, CMU's classes are small and led by by professors who know their students by name. Professors are more than teachers—they become mentors, advisors, and partners who benefit the success of their students.

LEARNING SUPPORT: Students are supported by a full range of academic services that are designed to help them achieve their goals. Programs and services include academic advising, career services, tutoring, and disability services. The vast Tomlinson Library is also available to provide additional support and helpful resources.

OUTDOOR RECREATION CENTER: Situated at the base of the world's largest flat-topped mountain and surrounded by hills, canyons, and mountains, Grand Junction provides more opportunity for outdoor adventure than anywhere in the country. Organizations like the CMU Outdoor Program allow students to explore their own backyard throughout the year or even trek around the world during winter and summer breaks. Trips and activities include ice climbing, visits to natural hot springs, cross-country skiing and snowshoeing, whitewater rafting, kayaking, rock climbing, and skydiving. Many activities require no previous experience, but students who progress have the chance to pursue more extreme adventures as well.

INTERNSHIPS: Colorado Mesa University lies in the heart of a growing business community. With a vibrant downtown area of small businesses, a dynamic industrial workforce, and the headquarters of several large companies, opportunities abound for students to gain real-world experience in their fields before graduation.

http://www.coloradomesa.edu/
P: (800) 982-6372

PUBLIC

STUDENT PROFILE

9,299 undergraduate students

77% of undergrad students are full time

46% male – 54% female

15% of students are from out of state

70% freshman retention rate

37% graduated in 6 years

FACULTY PROFILE

271 full-time faculty

279 part-time faculty

22 to 1 student/faculty ratio

ADMISSIONS

6,670 Total Applicants

5,540 Total Admissions

2,120 Total Freshman Enrollment

83.06% of applicants admitted

SAT Ranges: CR 430-540, M 430-540

ACT Ranges: C 17-23, M 16-23, E 16-24

TUITION & COSTS

Tuition: (In) $6,706 (Out) $17,304

Fees: $768

Total: (In) $7,474 (Out) $18,072

R&B: $10,176

Room: $5,750

Board: $4,426

Total: (In) $17,650 (Out) $28,248

FINANCIAL

$5,379 avg grant/scholarship amount (total)

$8,609 avg loan amount (total)

NAROPA UNIVERSITY

BOULDER, COLORADO

Naropa University is a non-traditional liberal arts university in Boulder, Colorado. Its approach is grounded in the belief that personal discovery precipitates both inner and outer change and fosters both compassion and creativity. Naropa purposefully creates an environment rich in self-discovery by combining traditional academics with experiential education and mindfulness practice.

INHERENTLY ENGAGED: A Naropa education goes beyond traditional academics, offering a curriculum that includes interactive engagement both inside and outside the classroom. Such opportunities as internships, service-learning, and special community events challenge students to engage more deeply both with each other as well as with their studies. Students are also encouraged to help build a stronger university community as a whole by organizing new student groups and campus events.

CONTEMPLATIVE EDUCATION: Naropa University practices contemplative education, an approach to learning and teaching that combines traditional academics with experiential learning and mindfulness practice to help students develop self-awareness alongside other crucial real-world skills. Like most schools, Naropa makes it easy for students to engage in research, write papers, and take exams. The experience is further enhanced, however, by the addition of experiential opportunities like field study, internships, and volunteerism, and even further through such mindfulness practices as sitting meditation, t'ai chi ch'uan, and yoga.

PERSONALIZED STUDIES: Naropa's Interdisciplinary Studies program offers students the opportunity to design their own custom major by integrating two to three disciplines taught at the school. Students receive support in designing their course of study and work with faculty mentors throughout their academic journey. The program also affords students the opportunity to engage in independent study and research.

STUDY ABROAD: Valuing active engagement both locally and globally, Naropa University offers a number of options to study abroad. A powerful tool in expanding their worldview, studying abroad helps students better understand the differences and interdependencies that characterize the world as a whole. The University notably offers an opportunity in South Asia through an exclusive partnership with the Royal University of Bhutan as well as a trip to the Andes and Amazon through a partnership with "Where There Be Dragons." Naropa also offers study abroad opportunities in China, India, and the Himalayas, and the "School for International Training" affiliate program offers more than 55 programs in Asia, Africa, Latin America, the Middle East, Europe, and the Pacific.

BOLDER AND BOULDER: Both Naropa University and the surrounding Boulder, Colorado, community place strong emphasis on innovative thinking, social and environmental justice, spiritual development, and artistic expression. For this reason, community activities go beyond the expected college town happenings. While Boulder offers plenty of nightlife, many Naropa students find themselves more attracted to engaging in activism, outdoor recreation, spiritual practice, and volunteerism; attending concerts, readings, and lectures; and organizing their own community events.

PRACTICING IN COMMUNITY: Each semester, Naropa hosts Community Practice Day, a full day during which classes are canceled and the entire community engages in a variety of contemplative practices. The day includes sitting and walking meditation, guest speakers, and the opportunity to engage in mindfulness practices from a diversity of cultural and religious traditions. Such practices include Japanese tea ceremony, Hindu chanting, walking a labyrinth, contemplative prayer, and many more.

CELEBRATION, ECO-STYLE: Naropa hosts a number of events that celebrate the environment, green solutions, and sustainable practices. Each year, the university celebrates Sustainability Day in the fall and Earth Day in the spring. These events include guest speakers, eco-activities, student performances, dialogues around improving personal and campus sustainability, and engagement with local environmental groups and start-ups. Additionally, the Naropa community participates in the annual RecycleMania, a national competition for universities to divert waste from landfills.

http://www.naropa.edu/
P: (303) 444-0202

PRIVATE

STUDENT PROFILE

397 undergraduate students

93% of undergrad students are full time

35% male – 65% female

56% of students are from out of state

78% freshman retention rate

31% graduated in 6 years

FACULTY PROFILE

46 full-time faculty

117 part-time faculty

14 to 1 student/faculty ratio

ADMISSIONS

181 Total Applicants

144 Total Admissions

45 Total Freshman Enrollment

79.56% of applicants admitted

TUITION & COSTS

Tuition: $30,400

Fees: $170

Total: $30,570

R&B: $9,465

Total: $40,035

FINANCIAL

$24,862 avg grant/scholarship amount (need)

$11,519 avg loan amount (need)

UNIVERSITY OF DENVER

DENVER, COLORADO

As the only campus in the country to require a face-to-face interview for every admission candidate, the University of Denver is focused on admitting students who are most likely to get the most out of their DU experience. The University of Denver is the perfect choice for students looking to join a community of adventurous learners, offering exceptional preparation for the professional world, lively and energetic friendships with students from across the globe, and the opportunity to make lifelong connections with professional faculty.

IF THE SCHOOL FITS...: DU strongly encourages all applicants to complete a Hyde Interview in which they have a conversation with one to three members of DU's community who travel to more than thirty cities each year. Though grades and test scores play the largest role in admission decisions, the interview helps DU admit students who are motivated, honest, and open to new ideas. These interviews also serve to show prospective students that personal attention is more than a catchphrase at DU—it is a practice.

STUDY ABROAD: DU has a strong commitment to internationalizing its undergraduate education, sending students abroad to every continent except Antarctica. For qualified students, the Cherrington Global Scholars program offers undergraduates the chance to study abroad in their junior or senior year at no cost above normal DU tuition, room, and board. DU also pays for additional transportation costs, visa application fees, mandatory insurance abroad, application fees, programs fees, and the International Student Identity Card. Through this program, students can take courses at one of 80 universities around the globe and have their credits transferred back to DU. Over 70 percent of students study abroad, ranking DU as second out of all doctoral/research institutions for undergraduate participation in study abroad.

SERVICE-LEARNING: Each year, about 1,500 DU students participate in service-learning courses. From courses on philosophy and social justice to intensive Spanish language and Mexican/Mayan cultural immersion, students can choose from a broad range of topics. Some service-learning courses are travel courses, while others stay in Denver to serve the community closest to home.

ACCESSIBLE PROFESSORS: Undergraduate students benefit from experienced professors who do not solely rely on textbooks, but rather bring their own knowledge and experiences into the classroom. Professors are genuinely involved in students' educations and are accessible outside of the classroom. Some DU professors even extend their accessibility by printing their home phone numbers on class syllabi.

PARTNERS IN SCHOLARSHIP PROGRAM: DU's Partners in Scholarship (PinS) program pairs students with professors to help with research projects, making the opportunity to perform collaborative research with a faculty partner available to students of all majors. PinS supports undergraduate research, creative projects, and funding for travel by distributing quarterly grants through an application process. Students can also present their work in a symposium, and some are even invited to publish their work or participate in national symposia.

LIVING AND LEARNING IN THE COMMUNITY: Located in a residential community eight miles from downtown, DU offers a 130-acre campus and a scenic view of the mountains. Students can make the fifteen-minute drive downtown or hop on the light rail, which has a station on campus and is free for DU students and faculty. Popular for its location and rigorous academics, DU also offers a people-friendly campus and an openly caring environment. Great weather and mild winters are great factors in what draws students to DU.

INTERNSHIPS: Around 70 percent of DU alumni participate in internships before graduating. DU's location provides internship options in a number of disciplines, and the Denver metro area includes 39,000 DU alumni.

http://www.du.edu/
P: (800) 525-9495

PRIVATE

STUDENT PROFILE

5,758 undergraduate students

95% of undergrad students are full time

46% male – 54% female

30% of students are from out of state

86% freshman retention rate

77% graduated in 6 years

FACULTY PROFILE

726 full-time faculty

585 part-time faculty

11 to 1 student/faculty ratio

ADMISSIONS

15,036 Total Applicants

10,938 Total Admissions

1,426 Total Freshman Enrollment

72.75% of applicants admitted

SAT Ranges: CR 550-660, M 560-660, W 530-630

ACT Ranges: C 26-30, M 25-29, E 25-32, W 8-9

TUITION & COSTS

Tuition: $43,164

Fees: $1,014

Total: $44,178

R&B: $11,498

Room: $6,958

Board: $4,540

Total: $55,676

FINANCIAL

$25,047 avg grant/scholarship amount (total)

$7,466 avg loan amount (total)

WESTERN STATE
COLORADO UNIVERSITY

WESTERN STATE COLORADO UNIVERSITY

GUNNISON, COLORADO

The Western experience includes personalized attention from faculty, lifelong friendships with classmates, and academic programs that are enhanced by the university's surrounding natural laboratory. And with a student-to-faculty ratio of just 17 to 1, professors handcraft each student's education to fit their interests and prepare them for a career.

HANDS-ON LEARNING: From their first year on campus, Western Mountaineers are immersed in academic adventure. Whether they are strapping on waders to study stream ecology, researching the effects of elevation on athletes in the High-Altitude Performance Lab, or building a business plan for a local ski area, Western students embrace their school's emphasis on hands-on learning.

FIRST-YEAR SEMINARS: Freshmen at Western are enrolled in the first-year experience seminar, Headwater 100, which begins meeting during orientation to provide students with a seamless transition into college. At orientation, students take part in service-learning projects and participate in field experiences while they attend other social events and workshops that introduce them to the campus' resources. Throughout the fall, students then spend Headwater 100 examining the "place" surrounding Western and its community. It is a discussion-based seminar that includes an introduction to the liberal arts, community sustainability, and the social, natural, and cultural surroundings of the region. Through dynamic studies, students are introduced to college-level coursework as well as the academic support services that they can utilize throughout the remainder of their college careers.

UNDERGRADUATE RESEARCH: Western believes that active participation in original scholarship is essential to a high-quality undergraduate education. For this reason, Western faculty are constantly engaged in scholarly work. From the laboratory to the field, the concert hall to the studio, Western professors pursue novel questions and explore creative expression. Western sustains many different kinds of opportunity for student research, including faculty-led, student-led, and collaborative projects, all of which are showcased each semester during the Celebration of Scholarship presentations. Here, students are given the platform on which to present their talents and passions through exhibitions of their research and creative work.

STUDY ABROAD: Whether they're journeying to Egypt to study emerging democracies in conflict zones or taking advantage of Western's relationship with Harlaxton University in England–the No. 1-ranked study abroad program for Americans–Mountaineers take their travels seriously. Western's Master in Environmental Management program has also partnered with the Peace Corps Preparation Program to help Western students earn their master's degrees while serving overseas.

WILDERNESS PURSUITS: Western is located just 30 minutes from some of the nation's best opportunities to ski at the Crested Butte Mountain Resort and Monarch Mountain Ski Area. Rafting, kayaking, boating, sailing, windsurfing, mountain biking, cycling, and world-class fishing are also all within minutes of campus. Furthermore, the 1.7 million acres of the Gunnison River Territory encompass some of the wildest and most beautiful terrain in the world, including the Blue Mesa Reservoir, Hartman Rocks, and the Black Canyon of the Gunnison National Park. With so many outdoor recreational activities to choose from, Western helps provide the tools for any interested student to make the most of their surroundings. Wilderness Pursuits provides fun, low-cost, and professional outdoor expeditions and resources for students, giving them free reign over the university's massive gear room. This incredible resource provides rental access to kayaks, mountain bikes, camping gear, snow sports equipment, and more. Students can even join guided trips through the surrounding mountains, exploring the beautiful Colorado landscape to its full potential.

http://www.western.edu/
P: (800) 876-5309

PUBLIC

STUDENT PROFILE

1,951 undergraduate students

76% of undergrad students are full time

60% male – 40% female

68.97% freshman retention rate

42% graduated in 6 years

FACULTY PROFILE

117 full-time faculty

47 part-time faculty

16 to 1 student/faculty ratio

ADMISSIONS

1,631 Total Applicants

1,592 Total Admissions

467 Total Freshman Enrollment

97.61% of applicants admitted

SAT Ranges: CR 460-580, M 450-560

ACT Ranges: C 17-23, M 16-24, E 16-24

TUITION & COSTS

Tuition: (In) $5,844 (Out) $16,848

Fees: $2,607

Total: (In) $8,451 (Out) $19,455

R&B: $9,307

Room: $4,923

Board: $4,384

Total: (In) $17,758 (Out) $28,762

NORTHWEST NAZARENE UNIVERSITY

NAMPA, IDAHO

NORTHWEST NAZARENE UNIVERSITY

Northwest Nazarene University believes that education should be about the transformation of the whole person—intellectual, social, physical, and spiritual. A Christian liberal arts university, NNU offers over 60 areas of study, 18 master's degrees, and 2 doctoral degrees. In addition to its 90-acre campus in Nampa, Idaho, the University also offers programs online as well as in Boise, Idaho Falls, and in cooperation with programs in 35 countries.

FRESHMAN RETREAT: Building relationships to last a lifetime takes time, so NNU actively helps freshmen get the ball rolling as they transition to their new home away from home. The entire freshman class gets to bond with one another on a trip to Trinity Pines Camp & Conference Center over Labor Day weekend for a Freshman Retreat. There, students are able to come together as a class, forming new friendships without the distraction of classes and homework.

STUDY ABROAD: A longstanding partnership with the Council for Christian Colleges and Universities (CCCU) allows students to see the world. Students have access to programs in Australia, China, Costa Rica, Jordan, Oxford, Uganda, and more. NNU also offers connections to domestic programs in Washington, D.C., Los Angeles, and Nashville.

RESEARCH OPPORTUNITIES: Recent research projects that students have conducted have included such focus areas as NASA RockSat and CubeSat Engineering; agricultural drones; hyperbaric oxygen treatment of breast cancer cells; Alzheimer 's disease; and Lake Titicacan frogs and native cat species in Costa Rica. Mentoring faculty work alongside students to enrich the research experience, and many students have also gone on to present their research at such national conferences as the Murdock College Science Research Program Conference.

STUDENT-FACULTY INTERACTION: Students have direct access to talented faculty members in all disciplines who become their research partners, mentors, tablemates in the cafeteria, and spiritual sounding boards. Undergraduates at NNU are able to build relationships with their professors, the luxuries of which are usually only afforded to graduate students. These relationships allow professors and students to work side-by-side.

FRESHMAN AND SENIOR EXPERIENCES: Students begin their freshman year at NNU in Freshman Seminar, a class designed to build a foundation of skills and habits that encourage success all throughout college. After three years, students are prepared to take on the challenge of their senior capstone class, internship, or research project. NNU seniors are discovering exciting methods and places to put their education into practice, producing professional, Hollywood-style films, crafting franchise-winning business plans, designing Idaho's first satellite, testing new computer software with million-dollar companies, and so much more!

STUDENT GOVERNMENT ASSOCIATION: Staple campus traditions would not be possible without the Student Government Association (SGA) and other student leadership positions. SGA gives students opportunities to get involved both on campus and in the surrounding community. NNU has standard clubs and organizations (more than 40!) as well as a handful of traditions and campus characters that are unique to the university.

DIVERSITY: 16 percent of NNU students come from a culturally diverse background. The Office of Multicultural Affairs works to increase awareness, cooperation, and understanding concerning ethnic, religious, and cultural diversity both on campus and in the local community.

INTERNSHIPS: Students dive into research and internship opportunities both throughout the country and around the world. NNU's strong connections and industry relationships have opened doors for students to explore their disciplines in a professional arena. NNU students have interned at ESPN, Fox Sports, Unilever, Campbell's, Centennial Job Corps, St. Luke's, Wal-Mart Headquarters, U.S. Embassy in Belgium, Micron, Hewlett Packard, Scentsy Headquarters, Lawrence Livermore National Lab, Simplot, and Disney.

---

http://www.nnu.edu/

P: (208) 467-8011

PRIVATE - CHRISTIAN

STUDENT PROFILE

1,524 undergraduate students

77% of undergrad students are full time

43% male – 57% female

49% of students are from out of state

74% freshman retention rate

49% graduated in 6 years

FACULTY PROFILE

104 full-time faculty

1 part-time faculty

15 to 1 student/faculty ratio

ADMISSIONS

1,589 Total Applicants

870 Total Admissions

258 Total Freshman Enrollment

54.75% of applicants admitted

SAT Ranges: CR 460-580, M 460-570, W 440-560

ACT Ranges: C 21-25, M 22-25, E 21-25, W 21-27

TUITION & COSTS

Tuition: $27,750

Fees: $400

Total: $28,150

R&B: $7,000

Room: $3,000

Board: $4,000

Total: $7,400

FINANCIAL

$14,234 avg grant/scholarship amount (need)

$9,241 avg loan amount (need)

THE COLLEGE OF IDAHO

CALDWELL, IDAHO

A College of Idaho education empowers students to gain transformational, relevant experiences that prepare them to lead productive and fulfilling lives. The College enjoys a vibrant campus of 1,000 students with more than 50 student organizations, 20 sports teams, seven fraternities and sororities, and outstanding performing and visual arts programs.

FIRST-YEAR EXPERIENCE: The C of I's First-Year Experience Program introduces new students to the intellectual challenges, personal growth, and self-discovery they are sure to experience at the College. It also provides tools to help students succeed both academically and socially. Every student meets with an academic advisor at the beginning of freshman year to begin charting their academic plan. The First-Year Theme and Book help develop a sense of community among first-year students by featuring guest speakers, films, debates, theatrical productions, and other programming to which they can all relate.

PEAK CURRICULUM: The C of I's innovative PEAK Curriculum—inspired by the independent spirit of its unique Idaho setting—is designed to provide an education that is both broad and deep. Through PEAK, every student earns a major and three minors spread across the four knowledge peaks of the fine arts and humanities, natural sciences, social sciences, and professional studies. Each student designs an individualized academic path based on his or her own passions and goals, rather than taking a checklist of courses.

UNDERGRADUATE RESEARCH: Undergraduate research and creative work are integrated throughout all fields of study at the C of I. Nearly half of all C of I students do research with a faculty member during their time at the College. Additionally, an annual Student Research Conference celebrates the numerous scholarly and creative projects completed by students.

STUDY ABROAD: The College of Idaho's four-week January term offers numerous opportunities for off-campus study. In recent years, C of I students have studied tropical ecosystems in Australia, history and culture in London, environmental literature and wilderness in Idaho's Sawtooth Mountains, and international business in Paris. In addition to these faculty-led study experiences, C of I students can study for a semester or longer in more than 50 countries through partner institutions.

ENACTUS: Students of all majors can participate in the College's chapter of ENACTUS, which connects students and local business leaders who are committed to using the power of entrepreneurial action to transform lives and shape a more sustainable world. With support from the C of I's business faculty, students in ENACTUS have collaborated with businesses on a variety of economic development projects.

DIVERSITY: The College of Idaho enjoys a campus community that reflects the world. Nearly 10 percent of students are international, representing more than 40 countries. Another 20 percent of students are American students of color, and more than 30 percent identify themselves as first-generation students. Clubs such as the International Student Organization, Association of Latino Americano Students, and AFRO Club are among the most active on campus. The C of I believes a broad understanding of other cultures, customs, and peoples is essential for a quality education. This has all become a beacon of cultural and racial diversity in the Intermountain West.

INTERNSHIPS: Students receive assistance in finding internships through the College's PEAK Center. Nearby Boise provides high-tech industries, regional businesses, and cultural centers with numerous internship opportunities. C of I students have interned at NASA, Deloitte, Lawrence Berkeley National Laboratory, Boise Art Museum, Hewlett-Packard, Bank of China, and at the U.S. Capitol with Idaho's senators and representatives.

http://www.collegeofidaho.edu/
P: (208) 459-5305

PRIVATE

STUDENT PROFILE
1,039 undergraduate students

97% of undergrad students are full time

50% male – 50% female

25% of students are from out of state

82% freshman retention rate

68% graduated in 6 years

FACULTY PROFILE
84 full-time faculty

56 part-time faculty

10 to 1 student/faculty ratio

ADMISSIONS
955 Total Applicants

863 Total Admissions

201 Total Freshman Enrollment

90.37% of applicants admitted

SAT Ranges: CR 460-590, M 470-600

ACT Ranges: C 20-26, M 19-26, E 20-26

TUITION & COSTS
Tuition: $26,670

Fees: $755

Total: $27,425

R&B: $8,990

Total: $36,415

FINANCIAL
$5,243 avg grant/scholarship amount (need)

$4,831 avg loan amount (need)

CARROLL COLLEGE

HELENA, MONTANA

Located in Montana's state capital, Helena, Carroll College is a private, four-year, Catholic diocesan college that provides a first-rate undergraduate education to nearly 1,500 students. Founded in 1909, Carroll has distinguished itself as a preeminent and award-winning leader in its academic programs, including pre-medical, natural sciences, nursing, engineering, mathematics, the social sciences, and the liberal arts. Students choose Carroll for its combination of exceptional academic programs, affordable tuition with generous financial aid and scholarship opportunities, and the strong, close-knit community that exists on the beautiful Rocky Mountain campus.

GLOBAL OUTREACH: Service-learning and education abroad are important attributes of a Carroll education, as much of the Carroll community extends across the globe. Many students study, intern, and serve internationally. The College's Engineers Without Borders chapter, Carroll Outreach Team, and Campus Ministry all offer regular trips to Latin America, South America, Europe, and Africa. All around the world, Carroll students work alongside their professional mentors to help mitigate local problems, improving public health and building infrastructure. Carroll is pleased to offer direct exchange programs in Chile, France, Japan, Ireland, South Korea, and Spain, and it works in additional partnerships with college and universities across six continents.

LEARNING TOGETHER: At Carroll, students are immersed in a community that learns together, celebrates together, and serves others together. The community at Carroll supports students to excel in any of their 60 fields of study. It is impossible not to make intellectual, imaginative, and social strides on a daily basis at Carroll. Students are always examining the challenges of modern society and asking life's fundamental questions in their Catholic college setting, challenging and collaborating with each other as they foster a curiously charged community. They connect ideas across disciplines in active and new ways, whether they are sitting in a lecture, working in one of the College's cutting-edge laboratories, or even exploring Montana's diverse ecosystem and natural beauty as an extension of the classroom.

STUDENT ACTIVITIES: Student life thrives at Carroll. Many clubs and organizations give everyone the outlet through which to explore their passions and showcase their talents. And, alongside all the student-run fun, the Student Activities office brings the College together with 340 campus-wide events, such as the ever-popular Softball Weekend, musical performances, swing dances, open mic nights, Slip N' Slide down Guad Hill, and more!

SMALL CLASSES FOR BIG RESULTS: Carroll's professors believe that every individual plays an important part in everyone else's learning process. Each student is invited to engage in their small classes, bringing their own perspectives to the overall classroom understanding. The ecumenical culture of Carroll creates a common ground in the classroom where each student is held in esteem—both by professors and their peers—while they uncover knowledge and gain a deeper understanding of themselves as scholars. As a result, Carroll students are driven to be involved. The College paves the way for its active learners to take advantage of a diverse range of local opportunities, such as working as an intern at the State Capitol, conducting research on the West Nile virus in Montana's various ecosystems, and even taking part in organizing an annual literary festival that attracts authors from around the world.

ALUMNI PLACEMENT: Carroll graduates are highly valued in the professional job market and are accepted to the nation's best medical, law, and graduate schools. In fact, they boast some of the highest per-capita admission rates in the nation. Under grants from the Howard Hughes Medical Institute, the National Institutes of Health, and the U.S. Centers for Disease Control, Carroll students are conducting groundbreaking research into infectious diseases, including West Nile Virus.

---

http://www.carroll.edu/
P: (800) 992-3648

PRIVATE - CATHOLIC

STUDENT PROFILE

1,469 undergraduate students

96% of undergrad students are full time

42% male – 58% female

79% freshman retention rate

64% graduated in 6 years

FACULTY PROFILE

88 full-time faculty

53 part-time faculty

13 to 1 student/faculty ratio

ADMISSIONS

3,513 Total Applicants

2,252 Total Admissions

387 Total Freshman Enrollment

64.10% of applicants admitted

SAT Ranges: CR 480-600, M 490-600, W 460-590

ACT Ranges: C 22-27, M 22-27, E 21-27, W 6-9

TUITION & COSTS

Tuition: $30,104

Fees: $650

Total: $30,754

R&B: $9,218

Room: $4,688

Board: $4,530

Total: $39,972

FINANCIAL

$18,616 avg grant/scholarship amount (total)

$7,381 avg loan amount (total)

CORBAN UNIVERSITY

SALEM, OREGON

Corban University is committed to preparing students to be Christian thought leaders in today's culture, thriving as part of society in a wide variety of careers while living for Christ. Students are challenged to ask questions, search for answers, and build a biblically-based worldview so that they can lead with conviction, integrity, and intelligence.

ACADEMIC FOUNDATION: All Corban students take core courses that set a foundation for success, including American Thought & Culture and World Thought & Culture. These courses uniquely blend history, literature, and fine arts to help students understand how all aspects of culture impact the events of history and, in turn, how history influences art and literature. Students are challenged to think critically about the development of their worldview and to appreciate the interconnectedness of the academic disciplines. Each student also takes at least 24 credit hours of Bible and theology classes, which leads to a Bible minor. This lays the foundation for the biblical integration in every class and equips students to live authentically and boldly for Christ.

UNDERGRADUATE RESEARCH: Original student research is highly valued at Corban, even at the undergraduate level. By participating in relevant research, Corban undergraduates get to be part of breakthroughs in science and gain a significant advantage in preparing for medical school or grad school. Health science majors might conduct live animal research in the mouse lab or natural product synthesis in the chemistry lab, while exercise science students focus on fitness research. They work closely with expert faculty and present their findings at Corban's Annual Science Symposium. Some students have even had their research published.

INTERNATIONAL OPPORTUNITIES: Corban students are encouraged to develop a global perspective. Each year, teams serve in medical missions in Haiti, sports outreach in Cuba, and church ministry in Cameroon, among other mission trips and service experiences. Faculty-led study tours let students explore Europe, Israel, and Southeast Asia. Study abroad options include Corban's AMBEX program in Germany as well as semesters in Spain, Israel, and any of CCCU's BestSemester programs.

WRITING EXCELLENCE: Through college writing classes, capstone projects, and upper-division courses, Corban students develop above-average writing skills and outperform national comparison groups in writing competency. Courses challenge students to research well, think critically, and articulate clearly their ideas through written communication. This gives them a significant advantage for success in any career field.

PRACTICAL EXPERIENCE: Internships, practicums, and capstone projects give students the opportunity to put their learning into practice even before they graduate. Education majors complete their observation and student teaching in at least three different types of schools so that the may be ready for any school setting. Exercise science students earn their personal trainer certification and coach clients while they're in college. Business majors collaborate with area businesses to create and implement strategies for marketing, increasing revenue, or launching new products. Ministry majors actively serve in local churches. Media arts majors create videos for local non-profits. Political science majors take advantage of Corban's location in the state capital to serve as interns to state legislators.

MAKING A DIFFERENCE: Students who attend Corban for four years volunteer at least 160 hours in the community with churches and nonprofit organizations through Corban's REACH program. This program emphasizes Corban's mission "to educate Christians who will make a difference in the world for Jesus Christ," as students serve in organizations that focus on education and literacy, hunger and housing, dignity and justice, conservation, or mentoring and coaching.

---

https://www.corban.edu/

P: (503) 581-8600

PRIVATE - CHRISTIAN

STUDENT PROFILE

1,022 undergraduate students

95% of undergrad students are full time

40% male – 60% female

57% of students are from out of state

80% freshman retention rate

58% graduated in 6 years

FACULTY PROFILE

55 full-time faculty

76 part-time faculty

13 to 1 student/faculty ratio

ADMISSIONS

2,474 Total Applicants

855 Total Admissions

237 Total Freshman Enrollment

34.56% of applicants admitted

SAT Ranges: CR 490-590, M 460-580

ACT Ranges: C 20-26, M 18-25, E 20-26

TUITION & COSTS

Tuition: $30,980

Fees: $660

Total: $31,640

R&B: $10,060

Total: $41,700

FINANCIAL

$17,920 avg grant/scholarship amount (need)

$4,392 avg loan amount (need)

EASTERN OREGON UNIVERSITY

LA GRANDE, OREGON

Founded in 1929, Eastern Oregon University prepares students for the world beyond college with high-quality liberal arts and professional programs. As one of the best values in higher education today, EOU offers small classes, flexible programs, and a low tuition to help graduates get ahead with an education personalized to meet their goals.

FIRST-YEAR SEMINARS AND EXPERIENCES: Student success is a priority at EOU, where First-Year Experience programs help guide students through their academic and co-curricular experiences. These programs assist students with developing critical thinking skills, healthy behaviors, an understanding of their own values and beliefs, and an awareness of values and beliefs that may differ from their own. Student success advocates also help to navigate the ever-changing world of college life, academics, and finances.

COLLABORATIVE ASSIGNMENTS AND PROJECTS: Many talented and creative people work together in EOU's music, theatre, art, and English writing programs. This collaboration yields impressive results, including the university's honor of becoming the first in the U.S. to produce an amateur version of "Phantom of the Opera." Students are regularly writing and creating pieces for publication in the university's literary magazine, "Oregon East," and the Nightingale Gallery on campus offers even more opportunities that showcase student and faculty work.

UNDERGRADUATE RESEARCH: Students are receiving hands-on experience as early on as their freshman year at EOU. They build their résumés through work alongside faculty, present undergraduate research, and participate in internships. Such practices are valued highly by employers and graduate schools. Undergraduates also have unparalleled access to cutting-edge science and technology labs in which they can sequence DNA or design new software. Each year, students from across disciplines come together to present their original research and creative accomplishments at the Spring Symposium. Opportunities also include presenting at national conferences both independently as well as with faculty research partners.

DIVERSITY/GLOBAL LEARNING: EOU students are embarking on exciting international travel through a variety of study abroad programs around the world. Back on campus, the International Dinner and Show and Island Magic Lu'au are annual events organized entirely by students. The Indian Arts Festival and Spring Powwow is another celebration EOU's Native American Student Council plans each year. Featuring dancing, drumming, crafts, and a traditional friendship feast, the community event is a great opportunity to participate in and learn about the culture and traditions native to the eastern Oregon region.

GREAT OUTDOORS: When students want to get outside, there are four seasons of recreation waiting in EOU's backyard. The Outdoor Adventure Program can help them plan a successful trek and access equipment rentals that are free for the EOU community. Snowboarding at Oregon's highest base elevation ski area, kayaking Class III rapids, rock climbing, and mountain biking are all available within minutes of campus.

LEARNING COMMUNITIES: EOU students majoring in biology, chemistry-biochemistry, computer science, and mathematics can become ASTEO Scholars and live in a STEM community in the campus residence halls. ASTEO stands for Advancing Science and Technology in Eastern Oregon, the scholarship of which is funded by a grant from the National Science Foundation's S-STEM Program. Recipients of the award participate in hands-on learning beginning their first year of study, attend regular activities with STEM faculty, become eligible for summer internships, and sometimes qualify for paid positions as an ASTEO Ambassador for EOU.

---

http://www.eou.edu/

P: (800) 452-8639

PUBLIC

STUDENT PROFILE

2,721 undergraduate students

62% of undergrad students are full time

41% male – 59% female

31% of students are from out of state

72% freshman retention rate

31% graduated in 6 years

FACULTY PROFILE

111 full-time faculty

86 part-time faculty

16 to 1 student/faculty ratio

ADMISSIONS

1,043 Total Applicants

1,012 Total Admissions

352 Total Freshman Enrollment

97.03% of applicants admitted

SAT Ranges: CR 410-520, M 420-520, W 390-490, E 6-8

ACT Ranges: C 17-23, M 16-24, E 15-22, W 5-8

TUITION & COSTS

Tuition: (In) $7,020 (Out) $18,429

Fees: $1,449

Total: (In) $8,469 (Out) $19,878

R&B: $8,930

Room: $5,375

Board: $3,555

Total: (In) $17,399 (Out) $28,808

FINANCIAL

$8,241 avg grant/scholarship amount (need)

$4,154 avg loan amount (need)

GEORGE FOX UNIVERSITY

NEWBERG, OREGON

George Fox offers undergraduate students personal attention, subsidized overseas experiences, and an education that emphasizes spiritual development and service.

STUDY ABROAD: The university's commitment to outreach, study abroad, and social justice issues has helped to create a learning environment that emphasizes global awareness and engagement, as more than half of the school's undergraduates study abroad before graduation. Additionally, the university hosts the annual Juniors Abroad program, three-week subsidized study trips that are led by faculty mentors. Other students can choose to spend whole semesters studying overseas or join service trips with organizations like Food for the Hungry.

SERVING CHRIST, SERVING THE COMMUNITY: George Fox takes seriously Christ's challenge for people to be agents of love and reconciliation in the world. Every fall, the university closes campus for its annual Serve Day, sending more than 1,500 students, professors, and employees to volunteer in the community. The school also hosts spring, winter, and May service trips that allow students to serve in diverse, cross-cultural settings that range from Los Angeles to Swaziland. Some programs, such as engineering and nursing, even integrate service into the curriculum.

THE RICHTER SCHOLARS PROGRAM: Students at George Fox enjoy a challenging curriculum that encourages significant scholarship and application. Undergraduate and graduate students in the Richter Scholars program, for example, conduct original research with faculty mentors. During these projects, they research issues such as cures for breast cancer, cellular-level diabetes information, or trauma and cognitive development. George Fox is one of only 11 colleges to participate in this prestigious program.

ATHLETICS: Competitive students get the chance to face off at George Fox. Many have formed intramural flag football, 3-on-3 basketball, and volleyball teams. Others thrive in the school's nationally successful intercollegiate programs. George Fox offers 15 varsity sports—eight for women, seven for men—and competes in the nine-member Northwest Conference at the NCAA Division III level. The university has won two national titles in the past decade: a 2004 World Series championship in baseball and a 2009 women's basketball crown.

PERFORMING ARTS: The university's Department of Performing Arts is a close-knit community of musicians, artists, and actors. The university's bands, choirs, orchestras, and ensembles perform in Bauman Auditorium, which is renowned for its acoustics and used by the Oregon Symphony for recordings. Theatre students perform three mainstage productions a year, ranging from Greek tragedies to contemporary plays. Art students pursue painting, printmaking, ceramics, photography, and digital art with access to two on-campus galleries.

FELLOWSHIP: At George Fox, faith is a verb. The university wants to help students pursue their passions and calling and, as their relationships with God grow deep and wide, so too do their desires to engage the world and do the work of Jesus. Through chapel, small-group study, service trips, and everyday living on campus, students have the opportunity to make their spiritual journeys ones of great adventure.

ONTO FURTHER EDUCATION: George Fox students have previously had a medical school acceptance rate 30 percent higher than the national average. Furthermore, recent graduates have gone on to such graduate schools as Boston University School of Medicine, Harvard University School of Education, Princeton Seminary, Stanford University, and University of Oregon School of Law. In 2011, 100 percent of George Fox's nursing students successfully passed the NCLEX, the National Credential Licensure Exam, while more than 70 percent of those who graduated from the nursing program in 2010 are employed and practicing as professional nurses.

GEORGE FOX
UNIVERSITY

http://www.georgefox.edu/
P: (503) 554-2240

PRIVATE - CHRISTIAN

STUDENT PROFILE

2,587 undergraduate students

91% of undergrad students are full time

44% male – 56% female

81% freshman retention rate

70% graduated in 6 years

FACULTY PROFILE

201 full-time faculty

234 part-time faculty

14 to 1 student/faculty ratio

ADMISSIONS

2,903 Total Applicants

2,224 Total Admissions

620 Total Freshman Enrollment

76.61% of applicants admitted

SAT Ranges: CR 480-600, M 480-600, W 460-590

ACT Ranges: C 21-27, M 20-27, E 20-26, W 6-8

TUITION & COSTS

Tuition: $32,430

Fees: $356

Total: $32,786

R&B: $10,152

Room: $5,922

Board: $4,230

Total: $42,938

FINANCIAL

$17,207 avg grant/scholarship amount (total)

$7,931 avg loan amount (total)

LEWIS & CLARK COLLEGE

PORTLAND, OREGON

At Lewis & Clark, students can find graduate-level research options, opportunities to work with nationally recognized professors, and top-ranked overseas programs. While the school's campus (regularly ranked among the most beautiful in the nation) is located in Portland, Oregon, Lewis & Clark intellectually spans the globe, offering one of the strongest international education programs in the United States.

A GLOBAL COMMUNITY: Lewis & Clark is one of America's most international colleges, with a student body representing more than 80 countries and 47 states. More than half of the college's students participate in off-campus and overseas study programs, commonly to countries that lie outside of Western Europe. Additionally, every year since the inception of the national 100 Projects for Peace Initiative, Lewis & Clark students have won a highly competitive grant that supports their grassroots projects around the world.

PARTNERS IN LEARNING: At Lewis & Clark, academic rigor means academic collaboration. Professors work directly with students in pursuit of original inquiry and research at levels that are usually restricted to graduate school programs. Over the past five years, for example, more than 120 undergraduate students have coauthored articles in peer-reviewed academic journals.

COMMUNITY SERVICE: Nationally lauded for its programs that contribute to the public good, Lewis & Clark makes community service a priority. The Office of Student Leadership and Service gives students the chance to engage, learn, and lead through ongoing and one-time service projects, immersion programs, and academic civic engagement.

CENTER FOR ENTREPRENEURSHIP: Complementing Lewis & Clark's diverse academic offerings, the Center for Entrepreneurship provides students with expertise, resources, and structured opportunities for applying what they know across a range of endeavors: start-ups, creative enterprises, science and technology, and nonprofits, bringing innovation to existing businesses and workplaces.

ACADEMIC SYMPOSIA: Nationally recognized academic symposia organized and managed by students have been a hallmark at Lewis & Clark for more than 50 years, providing opportunities for personal engagement with leading thinkers and policy makers. Signature symposia include International Affairs (established in 1962), Gender Studies (1981), Environmental Affairs (1997), and the Ray Warren Symposium on Race and Ethnic Studies (2003).

COLLEGE OUTDOORS: College Outdoors, founded in 1979, recently ranked among the country's top 10 programs at colleges and universities of all sizes for its variety of available trips. The program is so popular and its offerings so rich and diverse that 9 out of 10 students take at least one College Outdoors trip. And with millions of acres of natural wonders, the Pacific Northwest abounds with opportunities to explore.

IN AND OF PORTLAND: A vibrant incubator for new ideas, Portland offers exciting possibilities to all who live and study at Lewis & Clark. The city is brimming with international organizations as well as smaller businesses and nonprofits looking to make the world a better place. Lewis & Clark's Career Development Center and Office of Student Leadership and Service connect students with learning opportunities throughout the region.

CAREER DEVELOPMENT: The Lewis & Clark Career Development Center offers programs and services to students from the day they start on campus, including workshops, visits to local employers, networking events, career fairs, and individual career counseling. Additionally, the school's Center for Entrepreneurship offers courses, workshops, a mentoring program, and an incubator and launch fund for student-led ventures to help students build entrepreneurial skills for any career path.

---

http://www.lclark.edu/

P: (503) 768-7000

PRIVATE

STUDENT PROFILE

2,209 undergraduate students

99% of undergrad students are full time

39% male – 61% female

82% of students are from out of state

83% freshman retention rate

72% graduated in 6 years

FACULTY PROFILE

237 full-time faculty

205 part-time faculty

12 to 1 student/faculty ratio

ADMISSIONS

7,368 Total Applicants

4,629 Total Admissions

654 Total Freshman Enrollment

62.83% of applicants admitted

TUITION & COSTS

Tuition: $44,744

Fees: $360

Total: $45,104

R&B: $11,314

Room: $6,130

Board: $5,184

Total: $56,418

FINANCIAL

$23,631 avg grant/scholarship amount (total)

$6,692 avg loan amount (total)

PORTLAND STATE UNIVERSITY

PORTLAND, OREGON

Portland State University is a public research university whose mission is rooted in sustainable living, accessibility, and community engagement. Its location within the city inspires students to solve problems and promote prosperity within rapidly changing, urban environments.

FRESHMAN INQUIRY: The University Studies Program starts with Freshman Inquiry, a year-long series of interactive courses based around one of ten themes. Recent themes include Design & Society, Power & Imagination, Sustainability, and The Work of Art. Each theme is approached from a variety of different angles that take on life's big questions and involve students in hands-on activities.

SOPHOMORE INQUIRY: The University Studies Program continues the second year with Sophomore Inquiry, which prepares students for upper-division courses and lets them explore topics of interest that are different from—yet complementary to—their majors.

UPPER-DIVISION CLUSTER: Upper-Division Cluster is the third-year segment of the University Studies Program. Based around the student's chosen Sophomore Inquiry theme, cluster courses build upon the knowledge and core skills that students develop in their first two years.

SENIOR CAPSTONE: University Studies culminates in the fourth year with the Senior Capstone, which connects the classroom to the community by immersing teams of students in community-based learning projects that address real-world issues. PSU offers more than 200 capstones each year, which have included teaching English as a second language to adults, finding solutions to social justice disparities, working with people with disabilities, and helping design gardens for a women's prison. In all cases, students are engaged with each other and the outside world.

PEER MENTORS: PSU provides opportunities for student engagement and co-creation in the classroom through its mentoring program. Juniors and seniors also have the opportunity to be peer mentors to students in the Freshman Inquiry courses, providing every student with someone near their age to help them figure out their experiences and courses at the university. Graduate students, too, can be peer mentors for students in the Sophomore Inquiry. In addition to gaining valuable leadership experience, peer mentors receive awards and stipends, tuition reimbursement, skill training, and professional development.

THE CENTER OF THE CITY: Portland State is a vibrant campus located within an equally vibrant city. With some 50 academic buildings, the campus boundaries dovetail almost seamlessly with the rest of downtown. Portland's bus and light rail lines, as well as its ubiquitous bike paths, give students easy access to the campus and the surrounding city, which is a magnet for foodies, book store lovers, and microbrew enthusiasts. PSU's Urban Plaza, occupied by the College of Urban and Public Affairs and the Academic and Student Recreation Center, is Portland's busiest transit hub.

COMMUNITY ENGAGEMENT: One of PSU's distinguishing features is its engagement with the greater community. Through community-based projects and internships, PSU students live the university's urban-serving mission. Faculty regularly bring businesses, nonprofits, government, and citizens into their classrooms. Such connections enable students to earn a quality education while learning how to apply it.

PROFESSIONAL CONNECTIONS: PSU has formed strong partnerships with such large players in the business community as Daimler, Nike, and Intel. It is with these connections that students have direct access to life-changing internships as well as promising job prospects after they graduate.

ALUMNI ACROSS THE WORLD: Last year, PSU granted nearly 5,800 degrees and in previous years has had the largest graduation numbers in Oregon. Portland State has 171,000 alumni throughout the world, and most of them—more than 100,000—live in the Portland metropolitan area.

https://www.pdx.edu/
P: (503) 725-3000

PUBLIC

STUDENT PROFILE

19,119 undergraduate students

72% of undergrad students are full time

46% male – 54% female

17.4% of students are from out of state

73% freshman retention rate

46.5% graduated in 6 years

FACULTY PROFILE

889 full-time faculty

706 part-time faculty

20 to 1 student/faculty ratio

ADMISSIONS

6,373 Total Applicants

5,699 Total Admissions

1,797 Total Freshman Enrollment

89.42% of applicants admitted

SAT Ranges: CR 470-590, M 460-570

ACT Ranges: C 19-25, M 17-25, E 18-26

TUITION & COSTS

Tuition: (In) $5,616 (Out) $18,828

Fees: $1,317

Total: (In) $6,933 (Out) $20,145

R&B: $12,822

Room: $9,204

Board: $3,618

Total: (In) $19,755 (Out) $32,967

FINANCIAL

$5,798 avg grant/scholarship amount (need)

$4,188 avg loan amount (need)

UNIVERSITY OF PORTLAND

PORTLAND, OREGON

An education at the University of Portland is guided by knowledge that is imparted by award-winning professors, enhanced by real-world experiences, and underscored by the values that the University has embraced since its founding in 1901. University of Portland has a commitment to service and the unwavering belief that the mind is little without the heart.

FIRST-YEAR SEMINAR: During freshman year, students take three classes with the same group of approximately a dozen students, fostering relationships that tend to remain strong throughout the undergraduate years and beyond. Sophomores and juniors lead freshman seminars and give first-year students personal introductions to college life and new learning strategies.

DRIVEN TO SERVE: In keeping with the University's mission of "teaching, faith, and service," the University and the Archdiocese of Portland offer many opportunities for volunteer service. Students can work in meal programs, children's centers, HIV centers, hospitals, and environmental cleanup facilities.

STUDY ABROAD: The University offers numerous study abroad programs with options for summer, semester-long, or full-year opportunities. University of Portland faculty accompany students on most programs, taking students to such locations as Japan, Italy, Mexico, Australia, England, and Austria.

INTERNSHIPS: A number of majors require students to complete internships. In many cases, professors and the university's career services department help students find internships in their areas of interest. Additionally, the University's Center for Entrepreneurship promotes professional relationships among students and the local business community. With the center's support and funding, students launch and manage their own entrepreneurial ventures.

TEACHING THE MIND, EMPOWERING THE HEART: Relatively small classes help professors discover the strengths and needs of their students. One faculty member notes, "Activity, creativity, discovery—those are the habits of mind I am trying to teach my students." University of Portland faculty members are recognized for their willingness to meet one-on-one with students outside class hours. They are also more than willing to support their students on service days and even during other University activities.

UNIVERSITY BROTHERHOOD: The University has no fraternities or sororities, but students say they feel bonded to their fellow students "in brotherhood." Small class sizes and residence life programs in the campus residences allow students to form many successful social networks. The University holds evening prayer sessions three times a week as well as staggered schedules for Mass that allow students with busy schedules to attend services. Those who choose not to participate in religious observances say they do not feel pressured to conform.

EVENTS FOR ALL: A steady assortment of interesting guest speakers, fiction and poetry readings, dialogues on faith and justice, theatrical offerings, and other activities fill the campus calendar. Throughout the school year, students actively cheer for their competitive Division I athletic teams.

CURIOUS EXPLORERS: The Outdoor Pursuits Program offers rentals for camping gear and organizes outdoor trips like snowshoeing and kayaking. Students take advantage of the campus' location, which is in close proximity to the mountains. They can go on skiing and snowboarding trips or even take to the Oregon coast for adventures on the beach.

GOALS IN REACH: The office of career services helps students turn their educations into bright futures. From freshman year to graduation and beyond, the University's career services provides career counseling, help with résumés, and listings of available openings for jobs and internships. The office also offers workshops and training sessions, including mock interviews, to prepare students for the job market.

http://www.up.edu/

P: (888) 627-5601

PRIVATE - CATHOLIC

STUDENT PROFILE

3,770 undergraduate students

98% of undergrad students are full time

41% male – 59% female

92% freshman retention rate

78% graduated in 6 years

FACULTY PROFILE

256 full-time faculty

195 part-time faculty

14 to 1 student/faculty ratio

ADMISSIONS

11,200 Total Applicants

6,939 Total Admissions

941 Total Freshman Enrollment

61.96% of applicants admitted

SAT Ranges: CR 540-660, M 550-640

ACT Ranges: C 24-28, M 23-29

TUITION & COSTS

Tuition: $40,080

Fees: $2,208

Total: $42,288

R&B: $11,902

Total: $54,190

FINANCIAL

$22,336 avg grant/scholarship amount (total)

$6,624 avg loan amount (total)

WARNER PACIFIC COLLEGE

PORTLAND, OREGON

Warner Pacific's Christ-centered, liberal arts approach invites students to seek answers to difficult questions and challenges them to expand their comfort zones in order to explore the ways in which they understand society, community, and faith.

SERVICE-LEARNING: Students at Warner Pacific experience all the benefits of a private, Christ-centered liberal arts college, along with the opportunities afforded by an urban setting. Warner Pacific's scenic campus is centrally located in the eclectic neighborhood of SE Portland, where students enjoy the intimacy of a small college along with the cultural and career-building possibilities of a major city. The Warner Pacific Office of Service-Learning works with students, faculty, staff, and community partners to create volunteer service opportunities that benefit the city of Portland. Warner Pacific highlights this commitment to the community through annual events like the Common Day of Service, when all classes are cancelled and the entire campus community devotes a day to serving agencies throughout Portland.

MURDOCK SCHOLARS: Warner Pacific Murdock Scholars are young scientists who spend ten weeks during the summer between their junior and senior years working full-time on a scientific project under the direction of an established research scientist at Oregon Health and Sciences University (OHSU). During their senior year, the scholars continue to work on a part-time basis with their mentors to complete their research projects, write their scientific theses, and present their research at local conferences. The Murdock Scholars Program is funded by the trustees of the M.J. Murdock Charitable Trust and directed by Dr. David Farrell at the OHSU Heart Research Center. It brings the brightest science majors from local, private institutions of higher education to work in the nationally recognized laboratories of the OHSU Heart Research Center and the Knight Cancer Institute.

INDIVIDUALIZED MAJORS: Individualized majors and minors are available for students who seek to graduate with an interdisciplinary degree. Students work with a faculty member to plan an individualized course of study, providing them the opportunity to focus their learning in a specialized field that is not otherwise available through the College's regular programs.

CAMPUS MINISTRIES: The Campus Ministries team cultivates the love of God by providing quality pastoral care, developing transformational leaders, and building community by serving the campus and the city alike. Through chapel, small groups, student leadership, service, music, and arts, Warner Pacific students are engaged in a journey of spiritual growth and development.

PREPARED FOR THE FUTURE: Regardless of their academic path, Warner Pacific students are well prepared for both challenging graduate study and meaningful professional careers. The Warner Pacific community has helped them develop the intellectual capacity, practical leadership skills, and spiritual perspective necessary to excel in their chosen field and find personal fulfillment in their lives.

PORTLAND AND INTERNSHIPS OPPORTUNITIES: Portland offers a wide range of internship, service, and research opportunities. Warner Pacific students are stretched as they encounter diverse opinions and have eye-opening experiences through meaningful connections with the people and cultures found in Portland. Internships are a vital part of the academic program at Warner Pacific. Recent internships include Wells Fargo, Boeing, Columbia Sportswear, Intel, Nike, the City of Portland, and Multnomah County.

CAREERS AND GRADUATE SCHOOL: Warner Pacific students have embarked on careers around the world and are making a difference in their respective fields of business, education, music and the performing arts, humanities, natural science, medicine, religion, social science, urban planning, and more. Recent graduates have been accepted into the prestigious graduate and pre-professional programs at Lewis and Clark College, Reed College, the New School (NYC), Duke Divinity School, Vanderbilt Divinity School, Johns Hopkins University, and Oregon Health and Science University, just to name a few.

http://www.warnerpacific.edu/
P: (800) 804-1510

PRIVATE - CHRISTIAN

STUDENT PROFILE

552 undergraduate students

95% of undergrad students are full time

44% male — 56% female

32% of students are from out of state

63.4% freshman retention rate

55% graduated in 6 years

FACULTY PROFILE

27 full-time faculty

48 part-time faculty

12 to 1 student/faculty ratio

ADMISSIONS

948 Total Applicants

500 Total Admissions

85 Total Freshman Enrollment

52.74% of applicants admitted

TUITION & COSTS

Tuition: $19,640

Fees: $660

Total: $20,300

R&B: $8,230

Room: $3,340

Board: $4,890

Total: $28,530

FINANCIAL

$10,132 avg grant/scholarship amount (total)

$6,682 avg loan amount (total)

WILLAMETTE UNIVERSITY

SALEM, OREGON

Whether pursuing innovative research, interning with a business or nonprofit, working one-on-one with a professor, studying abroad, or leading a campus organization, Willamette University students hone their creativity, global perspective, and critical thinking for a lifetime of success.

FIRST-YEAR PROGRAM: Students are introduced to the intellectual life of Willamette from the moment they arrive on campus through College Colloquium. This first-year program allows students to hone their critical reading and writing skills, actively discuss issues in a small class setting, and broaden their worldview. Students have many Colloquium topics to choose from, and they can even reach out to their Colloquium professor as their academic advisor until they choose a major.

AN EDUCATION THAT GOES FAR BEYOND CLASSROOM WALLS: Willamette offers competitive, funded undergraduate research opportunities in all subject areas, providing students with the opportunity to explore their interests and build a valuable set of skills for the future. About 28% of undergraduates conduct faculty-mentored research through a variety of programs, and at least 75 competitive Willamette grants are available annually for student research.

STUDENT INITIATIVES: Willamette students are always looking for new ways to make their mark on the world. They frequently launch new endeavors both on campus and in the community, learning valuable skills of teamwork and productivity. The Bistro coffee shop on campus, the Wulapalooza art and music festival, and Zena Farm are just a few examples of the University's student-created initiatives.

STUDENTS OF SERVICE: Undergraduates are engaged in communities both locally and internationally (about 50% study abroad before they graduate!). In 2010, the president's higher-ed honor roll named Willamette one of the top six schools in the country for exemplary service. Undergraduates build upon this honor by volunteering almost 33,000 hours annually. Willamette is also strongly dedicated to sustainability: the National Wildlife Federation ranked us first in the nation for sustainability activities.

JOINT DEGREES: In addition to 48 undergraduate academic programs, Willamette students may also choose to enroll in a joint degree program, pairing their liberal arts education with a master's degree so that they may stand out from the competition and get a jump-start on their career. Willamette offers three joint degrees: a bachelor of arts/master of business administration (BA/MBA), a BA/master of arts in teaching (BA/MAT), and a BA/juris doctor (BA/JD).

LIFE IN THE NORTHWEST: Willamette enjoys all the benefits of the Pacific Northwest: beautiful landscapes and the nearby ocean, environmental consciousness, and a relaxed, creative, and civic-minded culture. The school is located in Salem, Oregon's capital and the epicenter of state government, law, and business. Downtown Salem, next to campus, offers numerous restaurants, coffeehouses, concerts, and other activities.

CAREER SERVICES: Willamette's Career Services office provides numerous programs to help students explore their career possibilities in any field. Apart from offering drop-in office hours and a popular online job board, the office also hosts events and activities that assist with everything from building résumés to searching for schools.

INTERNSHIPS: Politics, biology, economics, and psychology are among Willamette's top majors, but students nevertheless explore a wide spectrum of interests. About 68% of students investigate their academic interests and career possibilities through one or more internships—from the Oregon State Capitol across the street to Intel to the Art Institute of Chicago—as they gain work experience that enhance their job and grad school applications.

---

http://www.willamette.edu/

P: (877) 542-2787

PRIVATE

STUDENT PROFILE

2,123 undergraduate students

92% of undergrad students are full time

43% male – 57% female

82% of students are from out of state

87% freshman retention rate

79% graduated in 6 years

FACULTY PROFILE

242 full-time faculty

51 part-time faculty

10 to 1 student/faculty ratio

ADMISSIONS

6,332 Total Applicants

4,935 Total Admissions

521 Total Freshman Enrollment

77.94% of applicants admitted

SAT Ranges: CR 550-670, M 550-660, W 550-650

ACT Ranges: C 25-30, M 24-29, E 24-32

TUITION & COSTS

Tuition: $45,300

Fees: $317

Total: $45,617

R&B: $11,400

Room: $5,800

Board: $5,600

Total: $57,017

FINANCIAL

$24,877 avg grant/scholarship amount (total)

$7,904 avg loan amount (total)

SOUTHERN UTAH UNIVERSITY

CEDAR CITY, UTAH

Designated as Utah's masters university with full accreditation, Southern Utah University provides experiential education in a variety of disciplines. With 140 undergraduate and 19 graduate programs, SUU professors help students explore, engage, and excel inside and outside the classroom.

FYE AND ORIENTATION: The First-Year Experience and Orientation program at SUU provides personal attention to each incoming student. Support is provided by student ACES (Assistant Coaches for Excellence) who help new students with their class schedule, find clubs to participate in, and become acquainted with campus.

EDGE PROGRAM: Every SUU student plans, executes, and analyzes a long-term comprehensive project, supplementing their undergraduate education. Refining soft skills and preparing viable portfolio content, the EDGE (Education Designed to Give Experience) Program is student centered and faculty mentored. With five centers, students focus their projects on global, community, leadership, creative, or outdoor engagement.

RESEARCH: With fellowships and grants available to undergraduate students, opportunities abound for in-depth research projects across all disciplines. Professors act as mentors outside of the classroom to provide project-based learning to passionate students. During annual symposia, students and faculty showcase their extracurricular research and prepare for future presentations at the Utah Conference on Undergraduate Research, the Festival of Excellence, and the Utah Academy of Sciences, Arts, & Letters.

LEARNING ABROAD: The Office of Learning Abroad follows SUU's core themes of "explore, engage, and excel." Students have opportunities to travel during a full semester, a summer session, or winter and/or spring break. SUU boasts an International Affairs office, welcoming students from more than 30 different countries on campus. With more than 44 partnerships with universities around the world, classrooms are rich with diversity and global perspectives.

BACHELOR'S TO MASTER'S SEGUE: In the Graduate Bridge Program, undergraduate students get a headstart on their graduate courses while working toward their bachelor's. Saving time and money are only two of the many educational benefits that come to students who pursue this curriculum track.

AVIATION: SUU's Professional Pilot Aviation Program offers rotor-wing (helicopter) and fixed-wing (airplane) pilot training in a partnership with SkyWest Airlines. The Professional Pilot Program offers licenses and ratings in areas ranging from Private Pilot to Certified Flight Instructor. This partnership creates industry-leading career options for prospective pilots. Resources to students include tuition reimbursement, access to pilot mentors, and advanced company seniority.

WRITING CENTER: The Writing Center helps students with writing across all disciplines. Staffed with student tutors, the center has resources available to assist students with grant proposals, persuasive essays, research papers, and class writing assignments. Tutors walk students through each step of the writing process, from brainstorming to sentence construction and grammar.

SPEECH AND PRESENTATION CENTER: The Speech and Presentation Center offers personalized help and feedback on all verbal, nonverbal, and visual aspects of a presentation. From class projects to interview skills, the staff of graduate students and interns help students, faculty, staff, and community members strengthen delivery strategies and reduce speech anxiety.

CAPSTONE COURSES AND PROJECTS/SENIOR EXPERIENCE: Regardless of a Thunderbird's major, they are encouraged to enhance their senior year with a capstone or senior project. The senior capstones give students a hands-on project that they can then display to future employers. Department heads and faculty help students develop and execute their capstone experiences. Science majors may spend time on research based projects that can be displayed at an annual symposium, while visual arts majors will spend more time on a BFA exhibition.

---

https://www.suu.edu/

P: (435) 586-7741

PUBLIC

STUDENT PROFILE

6,523 undergraduate students

88% of undergrad students are full time

46% male – 54% female

21% of students are from out of state

64% freshman retention rate

39% graduated in 6 years

FACULTY PROFILE

308 full-time faculty

194 part-time faculty

18 to 1 student/faculty ratio

ADMISSIONS

8,387 Total Applicants

6,050 Total Admissions

1,427 Total Freshman Enrollment

72.14% of applicants admitted

SAT Ranges: CR 450-590, M 450-570

ACT Ranges: C 20-27, M 19-26, E 20-27

TUITION & COSTS

Tuition: (In) $5,774 (Out) $19,054

Fees: $756

Total: (In) $6,530 (Out) $19,810

R&B: $7,067

Room: $3,167

Board: $3,900

Total: (In) $13,597 (Out) $26,877

FINANCIAL

$4,468 avg grant/scholarship amount (need)

$3,807 avg loan amount (need)

WESTMINSTER COLLEGE OF UTAH

SALT LAKE CITY, UTAH

At Westminster, education is not just about landing a first job, it's also about paving a path to a meaningful life. Westminster challenges its students to see the world through others' eyes—celebrating diversity of thought. Westminster provides transformational learning experiences in a truly student-centered environment that empowers and inspires students to live meaningful lives. Faculty focus on teaching, learning, and developing distinctive, innovative programs that blend the liberal arts with professional skills. Westminster is a private, independent, and comprehensive college in Salt Lake City, Utah.

NOT SO GENERAL GEN-ED: WCore is Westminster's liberal education program. Westminster students have exciting choices for their Gen Ed, including "Counting Votes," a look at U.S. voting methodology that puts mathematics to use in new ways, or "Bust that Psych Myth," which exposes such legends as the power of hypnosis. WCore gives students the opportunity to explore new subjects and ideas through unique courses, offering small group settings and a focus on synthesis, communication, and disciplinary research. Because WCore has fewer requirements than standard general education structures, students have more room in their schedules to pursue minors and electives.

LEARNING COMMUNITIES: Learning communities function to pair two traditionally different subject areas (like art and business) with a common theme. These communities are team-taught by two professors each, inspiring the discovery of two disciplines in the context of contemporary times. Students make connections between courses, see how ideas intersect, and take ownership of their first year in college. These linked courses fulfill a piece of Westminster's WCore requirements.

SERVICE-LEARNING: More than 1,900 Westminster students participate in service-learning activities that are sponsored by the college. In a recent year, Westminster students contributed more than 95,000 hours of community service. The Katherine W. Dumke Center for Civic Engagement is a campus resource that facilitates volunteer opportunities, student-run service programs, service-learning, and other civic engagement activities in which the Westminster community can get involved.

UNDERGRADUATE RESEARCH: There are many opportunities to participate in research as an undergraduate at Westminster. Some disciplines even allow students to receive academic credit for their work. There are also a number of positions available through work-study. Each summer, funds are made available from a variety of sources to support students who conduct undergraduate research with their faculty mentors.

MAY TERMS: May Term is a month of offbeat and inspiring classes, laid-back trips around Utah, and exciting international adventures. After a year of hitting the books, May Term is a truly unique experience taking students outside of the classroom and outside of themselves. Students stay as close as Utah's national parks and go as far away as Thailand or the Netherlands. May Term study experiences cover topics that range from cats in pop culture to a deconstruction of capitalism.

SUGAR HOUSE, SALT LAKE, AND BEYOND: Sugar House features an eclectic collection of shops, coffeehouses, restaurants, and cafés, all of which are within a 10-minute walk from campus. In downtown Salt Lake, just 10 minutes away from campus, students can take advantage of internship and employment opportunities with business firms, high-tech companies, health care facilities, financial institutions, and state and local government. The state of Utah offers access to skiing, snowboarding, mountain biking, rock climbing, backpacking, kayaking, canyoneering, and just about every other outdoor activity a student could want. In fact, Westminster is just 30 minutes from six world-class mountain resorts, including Snowbird, Alta, Park City Mountain, and Deer Valley. Westminster is also just a few hours' drive from Zion, Arches, Bryce Canyon, and Yellowstone National Parks. The College's Outdoor Recreation program helps students take advantage of such amazing resources.

---

http://www.westminstercollege.edu/

P: (801) 832-2200

PRIVATE

STUDENT PROFILE

2,135 undergraduate students

95% of undergrad students are full time

44% male – 56% female

82% freshman retention rate

62% graduated in 6 years

FACULTY PROFILE

151 full-time faculty

237 part-time faculty

9 to 1 student/faculty ratio

ADMISSIONS

2,001 Total Applicants

1,920 Total Admissions

468 Total Freshman Enrollment

95.95% of applicants admitted

SAT Ranges: CR 500-620, M 503-618

ACT Ranges: C 22-27, M 21-27, E 22-28

TUITION & COSTS

Tuition: $30,720

Fees: $808

Total: $31,528

R&B: $8,712

Total: $40,240

FINANCIAL

$19,482 avg grant/scholarship amount (need)

$4,144 avg loan amount (need)

GONZAGA UNIVERSITY

SPOKANE, WASHINGTON

At Gonzaga University, students discover a stunning array of opportunities to develop the kind of knowledge, skills, experience, and character that lead to fulfilling lives of purpose and principle.

HOGAN ENTREPRENEURIAL LEADERSHIP PROGRAM: Students in any major who are interested in business can take advantage of Gonzaga's innovative Hogan Entrepreneurial Leadership Program. The program, which includes intensive seminars, lectures, site visits, internships, projects, and mentoring, immerses students in the challenges of starting a new venture in the public or private sector. This program has a strong emphasis on service and ethics and offers a $500-per-year scholarship to those who participate. Students in the program receive such additional benefits as the opportunity to participate in a special summer program as well as potential funding for an original business plan. Participants graduate with an Entrepreneurial Leadership Concentration along with their regular major.

SCHOLARLY COMPETITION: Gonzaga students aren't shy about putting what they have learned to the test. For example, a group of mechanical engineering students entered and won a hydropower engineering efficiency competition for their senior project. Each member of the team won a scholarship from the American Society of Mechanical Engineering. Gonzaga engineering students have also won awards at the international Student Safety Engineering Design Contest for six straight years. Additionally, Gonzaga's curricular emphasis on persuasive oral communication has produced an exceptional debate team that has soared as high as first place in national rankings.

STUDY ABROAD: Education at Gonzaga knows no boundaries thanks to great study abroad programs in Australia; Baja, Mexico; the British West Indies; Canada; China; Costa Rica; Cuernavaca, Mexico; England; France; Ireland; Italy; Japan; Kenya; and Spain. Students do more than simply take in the sights (though there is plenty of time for that!); many of Gonzaga's study abroad programs are rigorous enough to require academic prerequisites.

GREAT STUDENT-PROFESSOR RELATIONSHIPS: Students have the opportunity to develop a close working relationship with their professors. After collaborating in the lab, for example, Professor Maria Bertagnolli recently helped her student land a position in cancer research at the prestigious Brigham & Women's Hospital in Boston, MA. Chemistry department chair and professor David Clearly actively involves students with his cutting edge research on lasers, and students who are interested in industry's impact on the environment can get involved with Associate Biology Professor Hugh Lefcort's research on the effects of mining companies releasing heavy metals into water systems. No matter what, Gonzaga students and professors always have a respected peer with whom they can collaborate and achieve amazing things.

SERVICE-LEARNING: Service-learning is a big part of the student experience at Gonzaga. Every year, students complete approximately 12,000 hours of community service through course-based service-learning initiatives. At the start of every year, for example, the Center for Community Action and Service-Learning (CCASL) organizes a Community Service Fair at which as many as 50 different nonprofit agencies recruit student volunteers. CCASL also funds student-run service organizations and helps students who wish to initiate new groups. Service-learning experiences like these frequently lead to an enhanced desire to serve that goes far beyond the boundaries of the academic programs themselves.

INTERNSHIPS: Internships and other hands-on learning opportunities are plentiful at Gonzaga. For example, marketing students in the School of Business Administration can take advantage of a General Motors internship program or help invest $75,000 in a portfolio management class, and engineering students can work in small groups to complete senior design projects under supervision from an industry professional. Recent projects have been done for such companies as Boeing and Hewlett Packard.

---

http://www.gonzaga.edu/
P: (800) 322-2584

PRIVATE - CATHOLIC

STUDENT PROFILE

5,062 undergraduate students

98% of undergrad students are full time

46% male – 54% female

54% of students are from out of state

95% freshman retention rate

83% graduated in 6 years

FACULTY PROFILE

446 full-time faculty

322 part-time faculty

12 to 1 student/faculty ratio

ADMISSIONS

6,729 Total Applicants

4,945 Total Admissions

1,337 Total Freshman Enrollment

73.49% of applicants admitted

SAT Ranges: CR 540-640, M 550-650

ACT Ranges: C 25-29

TUITION & COSTS

Tuition: $37,480

Fees: $510

Total: $37,990

R&B: $10,780

Room: $5,170

Board: $5,610

Total: $48,770

FINANCIAL

$18,333 avg grant/scholarship amount (total)

$7,546 avg loan amount (total)

NORTHWEST UNIVERSITY

KIRKLAND, WASHINGTON

Northwest University (NU) is located near Seattle, Washington, a region that offers a thriving economy, technological innovation, and natural beauty. Established in 1934, NU is a regionally accredited, Christian institution awarding associate, bachelor's, master's, and doctoral degrees. As a liberal arts college, NU meets the needs of an ever-changing society and offers multiple ways for students to achieve their academic goals—including online courses that can be taken anywhere, anytime.

A CHRIST-CENTERED UNIVERSITY EXPERIENCE: Northwest University began as a Bible College in 1934. While NU has grown into a liberal arts university offering over 70 majors and programs, the institution has not wavered from its Christian roots. Students are encouraged to grow in their faith via Chapel, small groups, mission trips, and the support of its Christian community. Professors are hired not only for their academic prowess, but also for their love of students and God. NU provides a rigorous education where faith and academics intersect. As a result, nearly 90% of NU students report growing in their faith while attending the institution.

LOCATED IN A THRIVING ECONOMY: Northwest University is located in the Pacific Northwest, home to Microsoft, Amazon, Boeing, Starbucks, and other successful companies. Students at NU are able to spend their 4 years not only developing relevant job skills, but also building their career network in a region that is booming. Additionally, nearly 70% of all majors at Northwest University offer local internships as part of their program. At NU, students find real-world experience that brings classroom teaching to life. And many are set up with jobs once they graduate.

PROVEN ACADEMIC EXCELLENCE: Northwest University is accredited at the highest institutional level possible. Professors at NU have written best-selling books and have been published in prestigious journals. NU has received Murdoch grants to purchase state-of-the-art equipment for its science labs. The nursing program has a first time NCLEX pass-rate of 97%—well above the national average of 87%. And the director of NU's Music Production program has won two Grammys and produced 30 gold records. NU offers a combination of academic rigor, spiritual vitality, and communal support that is hard to find elsewhere.

BUILDING A SUPPORTIVE COMMUNITY: The Student Development Department has a mission to provide an engaged, collaborative environment in which students participate, take ownership, and apply their learning to God's call in their life. The Student Development staff work together with faculty in the unified purpose of enabling Northwest students to integrate their faith, learning, and living. From classroom to chapel, and from student center to residence hall room, Northwest University is committed to maturing and developing the whole human being.

EDUCATION THROUGH GLOBAL EXPERIENCES: As an institution, NU believes that each student has been uniquely created to impact his or her world for God. This belief is put into practice by international trips—a requirement of many majors. NU students have served in places like Cambodia, India, Guatemala, South Korea, Prague, Italy, and other locations around the world. These trips are designed to broaden students' cultural perspectives and help them to see their connection to all of humanity regardless of nationality, location, creed, or color.

CAREER DEVELOPMENT THAT WORKS: The Northwest University Career Development Center serves students in the life calling discernment process by means of assessment, skill development, and life coaching. The Career Development Center assists students in identifying strengths, passions, and skills through personality tests, and then provides personal coaching in resume-building, interviewing skills, and other critical areas. The Career Development Center has also formed meaningful relationships with local business and can align student interests with internships and employment opportunities.

https://www.northwestu.edu/

P: (425) 822-8266

PRIVATE - CHRISTIAN

STUDENT PROFILE

897 undergraduate students

99% of undergrad students are full-time

35% male – 65% female

26% of students are from out of state

77% freshman retention rate

56% graduated in 6 years

FACULTY PROFILE

57 full-time faculty

237 part-time faculty

9 to 1 student-to-faculty ratio

ADMISSIONS

308 Total Applicants

280 Total Admissions

125 Total Freshman Enrollment

90.91% of applicants admitted

SAT Ranges: CR 480-610, M 460-580

ACT Ranges: C 20-26, M 18-26, E 20-26

TUITION & COSTS

Tuition: $29,900

Fees: $420

Total: $30,320

R&B: $8,400

Total: $38,720

FINANCIAL

$14,107 avg grant/scholarship amount (need)

$3,831 avg loan amount (need)

PACIFIC LUTHERAN UNIVERSITY

TACOMA, WASHINGTON

With distinctive international programs and close student-faculty research opportunities, PLU seeks to educate its 3,300 students for lives of thoughtful inquiry, service, leadership, and care—for other people, for their communities, and for the Earth. The distinctive tradition of Lutheran higher education helps students from all faiths and backgrounds discern their life's vocation through coursework, mentorship, and internships at world-class Puget Sound-area businesses and institutions. Located in the Parkland neighborhood of Tacoma, Washington, PLU is located in a region that also offers vast opportunities for outdoor recreation, culture, and sports.

STUDY ABROAD: The first American university to have Study Away classes on all seven continents simultaneously, PLU is also the first private university on the West Coast to receive the prestigious Senator Paul Simon Award for Campus Internationalization. PLU students have access to financial aid and scholarships while studying away, earning class credit through a semester, year, or short-term program. The Wang Center for Global Education supports students during exploration, pre-departure, while they are away, and when they return. Nearly half of PLU students study away at some time in their academic careers. By contrast, the comparable national average is only 3 percent.

STUDENT-FACULTY RESEARCH: PLU graduates often point to a specific person—invariably, a professor—who had a profound influence on their intellectual development. Their satisfaction is a result of what PLU calls "learning together." At PLU, there are very few large lecture classes; and all classes are taught by professors, not teaching assistants. Most of a student's time in class will be spent in close-up, hands-on work with professors and fellow classmates. This ability to work closely with faculty is something undergraduate students at most large universities do not experience.

SERVICE LEARNING: PLU's Center for Community Engagement & Service mobilizes PLU students and faculty to work collaboratively with community partners. CCES allows students to develop hands-on knowledge of the community, fulfill service-learning requirements, and build a résumé with extensive experience. Community-engaged learning courses state explicit learning objectives that are linked to student engagement in the community. Inviting students to critically examine the term, "service," these opportunities provide ongoing critical reflection, continual integration of community experiences with course readings, and multiple forms of assessment that invite students, faculty, and community partners to evaluate learning.

FIRST-YEAR EXPERIENCE PROGRAM: PLU's unique, one-of-a-kind program offers incoming students a chance to learn more about themselves and improve their academic skills as they enter the university system. Specially crafted courses and opportunities for off-campus expeditions provide an atmosphere of discovery and learning beyond typical coursework. Students learn the crucial skills of thinking, speaking, and writing by applying them to a thought-provoking topic. All First-Year Writing and Inquiry seminars are focused on important and compelling themes like "Stem Cell Research," "Reinventing the American High School," "The Beauty Myth," and "Eat my Words: Writing and Food."

INTERNSHIPS: PLU's Career Connections Center connects students and employers with quality internship experiences that open doors to professional opportunities. Bridging the gap between classroom learning and the professional workplace, academic internships are a meaningful way to discover vocation, explore career goals, and gain a competitive edge in the job market. Career Connections maintains an opportunity board with hundreds of internships, on- and off-campus paid positions, state work study positions, and volunteer opportunities.

http://www.plu.edu/
P: (800) 274-6758

PRIVATE

STUDENT PROFILE

2,809 undergraduate students

98% of undergrad students are full time

38% male – 62% female

28% of students are from out of state

83% freshman retention rate

68% graduated in 6 years

FACULTY PROFILE

223 full-time faculty

116 part-time faculty

12 to 1 student/faculty ratio

ADMISSIONS

3,623 Total Applicants

2,737 Total Admissions

643 Total Freshman Enrollment

75.55% of applicants admitted

SAT Ranges: CR 480-620, M 500-610

ACT Ranges: C 22-28

TUITION & COSTS

Tuition: $36,180

Fees: $350

Total: $36,530

R&B: $10,230

Total: $46,760

FINANCIAL

$21,449 avg grant/scholarship amount (need)

$4,963 avg loan amount (need)

SEATTLE UNIVERSITY

SEATTLE, WASHINGTON

Seattle University consistently ranks among the top universities in the West, offering a full range of outstanding undergraduate and graduate programs. Founded in 1891, Seattle U has more than 7,400 students on its 55-acre, carbon-neutral campus. Set in the heart of a city of commerce, community, global engagement, and forward-thinking industries, this University is undoubtedly full of opportunity.

OFFICE OF FELLOWSHIPS: Seattle University has an impressively strong record of supporting SU students and alumni in their applications to nationally competitive scholarship and fellowship programs. The Office of Fellowships strives to support students in their search for prestigious awards and opportunities to enrich their education at both the undergraduate and graduate level. SU is among the most elite schools in the country for the number of Truman and Fulbright Scholars that it produces.

EDUCATION ABROAD: At Seattle University, students understand that the best way to learn about another country or culture is to be immersed in it. With more than 50 countries just a plane trip away, approximately 550 students each year are able to travel, learn, and make a positive impact through internships, academic programs, and service projects in places far and wide. In Seattle University's distinctive International Development Internship Program (IDIP), participants are able to work with NGOs in the developing world while also gaining invaluable professional formation. Past placements include Tanzania, Bolivia, Senegal, India, Guatemala, Cambodia, Morocco, and many more.

PERSONAL EDUCATION: Located in the heart of one of the most advanced cities in the nation, Seattle University attracts faculty at the top of their fields. Students at Seattle U experience a deep intellectual life, working on research projects alongside these accomplished faculty members. With an average class size of 19 and a student-to-faculty ratio of 13:1, Seattle U offers an interactive classroom experience in which every student's voice is heard, enabling truly transformative growth. Faculty members often say they come to a university of this size because they want to make undergraduates their focus. Partnering with students in groundbreaking research and mentoring them as they grow from novices into experts is as important as their own scholarship.

CORE CURRICULUM: At the center of Seattle University's Jesuit academic experience is the Core Curriculum. With an emphasis on rigorous, engaging courses, the Core develops students into critical thinkers and global-minded citizens who are able to tackle any challenge they encounter. Through their Core classes, students develop confidence and communication skills as they grow into the leaders of tomorrow, empowered to be agents of change in their careers and their communities. Classes are typically comprised of no more than 20 students, and faculty are engaged and highly accessible. Some Core classes available to students include: What does "America" Mean Now?; Rhetoric of Sustainable Food; God, Money, and Politics; The Genetics of Disease; Literary Bad Boys; and more.

AREAS OF STUDY: With more than 60 undergraduate degree offerings, incoming students are sure to find their niche. New programs develop each year, including the Bachelor of Business Administration in Business and Law, which allows students to begin courses in the Seattle University School of Law as an undergraduate and effectively save on a full year of undergraduate tuition. A Bachelor of Science in Marine and Conservation Biology allows students to study marine environments while researching successful conservation efforts. And those who haven't quite decided on a major still have amazing opportunities to grow and settle on the program that is best for them. The Pre-Major Studies Program pairs students with an advisor who helps plan a series of courses that can help guide students closer toward their academic calling.

SEATTLEU

http://www.seattleu.edu/
P: (206) 220-8040

PRIVATE - CATHOLIC

STUDENT PROFILE

4,602 undergraduate students

96% of undergrad students are full time

40% male – 60% female

63% of students are from out of state

84% freshman retention rate

79% graduated in 6 years

FACULTY PROFILE

537 full-time faculty

246 part-time faculty

11 to 1 student/faculty ratio

ADMISSIONS

7,806 Total Applicants

5,700 Total Admissions

1,002 Total Freshman Enrollment

73.02% of applicants admitted

SAT Ranges: CR 530-650, M 530-630, W 530-630

ACT Ranges: C 25-29, M 24-28, E 24-32

TUITION & COSTS

Tuition: $38,970

Fees: $720

Total: $39,690

R&B: $11,326

Room: $7,092

Board: $4,234

Total: $51,016

FINANCIAL

$19,407 avg grant/scholarship amount (total)

$7,396 avg loan amount (total)

WESTERN WASHINGTON UNIVERSITY

BELLINGHAM, WASHINGTON

Western Washington University is a public, four-year university located in Bellingham, Washington. Western is known for having the best of both worlds: the faculty access and student focus of a smaller institution in addition to the resources, choices, and diversity found at larger research universities.

FIRST-YEAR INTEREST GROUPS (FIGS): Incoming freshmen are highly encouraged to begin their academic career in a First Year Interest Group (FIG). A FIG is a combination of three courses—2 Gen Eds and 1 seminar. The seminar is highly beneficial because it is much smaller in class size than the Gen Ed courses. Smaller classes typically lead to more in-depth class discussion, peer interaction, and increased comprehension of the material. In general, FIGs make the transition into college easier. The university believes that students benefit greatly from participation, locking in their classes early, learning from top university professors, and making solid connections with new friends.

CAMPUS 2 COMPASS: Campus 2 Compass is a mentoring program that connects Western Washington students to local schools. The initiative addresses the needs of underrepresented and underprivileged students with the intent of pushing them toward opportunities in higher education. WWU students provide various services to the local schools, including one-on-one mentoring, group discussion, and teacher support. WWU also works with students during recess, after school, during lunch, and any time in between. The ultimate goal of the program is to ignite educational goals and show how they can be attained.

STUDY ABROAD: Any form of abroad education is considered highly beneficial. WWU offers plenty of options to choose from and encourages all students to get involved in whatever way best suits their interests. In general, students who study abroad gain valuable skills in global citizenship and tolerance, independence, and cross-cultural communication. Options include traditional study abroad programs that highlight cultural immersion, exchange programs for independent experiences, international internships for global experience in the professional world, and third-party study abroad programs that are customized for the most fulfilling experience possible. Faculty from various fields also initiate Global Learning Programs, leading a group of students through a single, immersive course that is supplemented by international travel.

MARINE SCIENCE SCHOLARS PROGRAM: The Marine Science Scholars Program (MSSP) is a unique, 2-year program offered to a select group of incoming freshmen. Invited students join a competitive, academic community that is designed to engage them with the sciences and prepare them for fruitful careers. Participants are given incredible benefits like exclusive internship opportunities, research experiences, and working with faculty and marine scientists from the Shannon Pointe Marine Center.

GUR STRANDS: GUR Strands are highly involved learning communities that span over the course of a year. Strands link 2-3 Gen Ed courses together, providing beneficial context to each course's perspective. Through a structured strain of classes, freshmen can build upon skills throughout the year, greatly enhancing their educational experience. GUR Strands take an interconnected approach to academics, enabling students to draw from what they have learned and link it to new ideas.

BELLINGHAM: Western Washington students truly have the world at their fingertips. For students who enjoy time outdoors, Bellingham offers everything from waterways to mountains. And for students who like to explore music and recreational activities, the city hosts many concerts, theatre productions, and more! Students are highly encouraged to step outside of campus and enjoy all that Bellingham has to offer.

http://www.wwu.edu/
P: (360) 650-3000

PUBLIC

STUDENT PROFILE

14,402 undergraduate students

92% of undergrad students are full time

45% male – 55% female

14% of students are from out of state

82% freshman retention rate

71% graduated in 6 years

FACULTY PROFILE

662 full-time faculty

337 part-time faculty

18 to 1 student/faculty ratio

ADMISSIONS

9,933 Total Applicants

8,183 Total Admissions

2,809 Total Freshman Enrollment

82.38% of applicants admitted

SAT Ranges: CR 500-620, M 500-600, W 470-590

ACT Ranges: C 22-27, M 21-27, E 21-28, W 7-8

TUITION & COSTS

Tuition: (In) $7,734 (Out) $20,086

Fees: $877

Total: (In) $8,611 (Out) $20,963

R&B: $10,342

Room: $6,512

Board: $3,830

Total: (In) $18,953 (Out) $31,305

FINANCIAL

$7,020 avg grant/scholarship amount (total)

$5,840 avg loan amount (total)

WHITMAN COLLEGE

WALLA WALLA, WASHINGTON

Whitman College is a vibrant, residential learning community widely known for its unique combination of academic excellence, culture, and engaging community. It is renowned for combining academic excellence, a humble Northwest culture, and an engaging community. A Whitman education liberates minds, inspires spirit, and unleashes imagination, and its scholars are characterized as individuals who foster a love of learning, burst with a passion for fun, and embrace the value of working together. Whitman College attracts active engaged students with its broad offering of 88 off-campus study and study abroad programs, a myriad of internship connections, community service opportunities, and planning services for postgraduate success.

SEMESTER IN THE WEST: An environmentally focused expedition across America, Whitman's unique Semester in the West program takes an interdisciplinary approach to understanding the country's ecosystems and the public policies related to them. This exhilarating experiential course takes students on an 8,000-mile journey across the Great Basin, meeting with environmentalists, energy experts, government officials, and other professionals who play a major role in the conservation of the environment. This program is full of camping, political and scientific analysis, and service, all of which enrich students with a well-rounded perspective of the land in the American West.

MENTORS IN RESEARCH: Whitman faculty are known for their desire to mentor students, and so the College goes the extra mile to make out-of-classroom experiences accessible. The College encourages its faculty to pursue new findings within their field, knowing that students are involved every step of the the way. Through both the academic year and summer intersession, faculty can access the resources needed to conduct research and give students hands-on experiences in methodology and practice. As research fellows, students are given the chance to establish themselves alongside professional academics.

GUEST SPEAKERS: The College hosts innumerable speakers and programs throughout the academic year, demonstrating its institutional commitment to bringing the world to Southeastern Washington. Recent speakers have included Humorist David Sedaris; Physicist Neil Degrasse Tyson; Columnist, Professor, and former U. S. Secretary of Labor Robert Reich; U.S. Secretary of the Interior Sally Jewell; Author Sherman Alexie; and Actor/Author Eric Idle. In such intellectually stimulating events as the Visiting Writers Series, the guests invited to Whitman challenge students with complex ideas and thought-provoking questions. Their perspectives enrich the community, adding to the already vibrant education that Whitman professors provide.

SUCCESS FOR ALL: Whitman College is known for graduating students who become ethical leaders in their communities and careers. Whitman ranks highly in its percentage of graduates who enter the Peace Corps, Teach for America, and service to the country, and approximately 70% of Whitman students enter graduate school. The Student Engagement Center acts as the umbrella campus office that oversees the numerous programs offered to students preparing for graduate school and career success.

THE GLOBAL STUDIES INITIATIVE: A signature program of Whitman College, the Global Studies Initiative is a solid foundation for students in a variety of career paths, including humanitarian work, education, and business. This program is an exploration of both historical and contemporary issues around the world, analyzing the global impact of national decisions. With an understanding of the way countries all around the world interact with one another, students involved in the Global Studies initiative learn to communicate effectively with people from different cultures.

WHITMAN COLLEGE

http://www.whitman.edu/

P: (509) 527-5176

PRIVATE

STUDENT PROFILE

1,470 undergraduate students

97% of undergrad students are full time

42% male – 58% female

93% freshman retention rate

87% graduated in 6 years

FACULTY PROFILE

186 full-time faculty

45 part-time faculty

9 to 1 student/faculty ratio

ADMISSIONS

3,790 Total Applicants

1,619 Total Admissions

364 Total Freshman Enrollment

42.72% of applicants admitted

SAT Ranges: CR 600-720, M 600-700, W 600-700

ACT Ranges: C 27-32, W 8-9

TUITION & COSTS

Tuition: $45,770

Fees: $368

Total: $46,138

R&B: $11,564

Room: $5,348

Board: $6,216

Total: $57,702

FINANCIAL

$21,334 avg grant/scholarship amount (total)

$5,673 avg loan amount (total)

WHITWORTH UNIVERSITY

SPOKANE, WASHINGTON

Since 1890, Whitworth has held fast to its founding mission of providing "an education of mind and heart" through rigorous intellectual inquiry guided by dedicated Christian scholars. Recognized as one of the top regional colleges and universities in the West, Whitworth University has an enrollment of nearly 3,000 students and offers 60 undergraduate and graduate degree programs.

TAKING LEARNING TO NEW HORIZONS: Whitworth students develop intercultural competence by participating in study abroad programs over the January term or during a full semester through the university's innovative 4-1-4 academic calendar. Whitworth's 30 international study programs include ancient philosophy in Europe, computer science in India, women's studies in Thailand, politics and culture in South Africa, and Latin American Studies at the university's new Costa Rica Center.

A STRONG FAITH: While some Christian universities limit engagement with challenging ideas or secular scholarship, Whitworth encourages tough questions and a fearless search for answers. And though many other institutions deny the role of faith in the pursuit of truth, Whitworth consistently affirms Christian conviction and intellectual curiosity as complementary rather than competing values. These dual commitments set Whitworth University apart in the higher education landscape.

DISTINGUISHED SCHOLARS. INDIVIDUAL ATTENTION: Whitworth combines high-quality academic instruction with personal attention to create a sense of belonging that's often lost at larger institutions. With the university's student-faculty ratio of 11:1, students are not just numbers in professors' grade books. Professors frequently meet students for coffee or lunch or invite them to their homes. It is this kind of one-on-one interaction that results in Whitworth's personalized learning environment.

ENGAGED RESEARCH: Scholarly activity is viewed at Whitworth as an aid, rather than an obstacle, to great teaching. In fact, many professors engage students fully in the daunting enterprise of discovery, the dissemination of new knowledge, and the creation of original contributions to their fields. Students work alongside faculty on research ranging from assessing the impact of micro-lending in low-income neighborhoods and developing countries to exploring the theological insights of early Christian aesthetics.

STUDENT LEADERSHIP: Whitworth's nationally recognized student-leadership program offers students numerous opportunities to get involved. Within residence halls, students serve as residence assistants, medics, cultural-diversity advocates, and small-group coordinators. Whitworth's student leaders focus on building strong peer relationships and respect for shared values so that students become good decision-makers rather than just good rule-followers. In fact, Whitworth students meet each fall to establish their own policies for living in the community and maintaining accountability to the campus code of conduct.

A DIVERSE COMMUNITY: As a Christian institution, Whitworth takes seriously Christ's example of loving across racial, ethnic, gender, socioeconomic, and religious differences. With such a high standard, Whitworth remains focused on being an inclusive community that seeks out and welcomes people with diverse backgrounds and perspectives. Whitworth partners with the Northwest Leadership Foundation on the innovative Act Six Leadership & Scholarship Initiative, which brings a multicultural cadre of up to 10 first-generation, lower-income students from Spokane to Whitworth each year. Whitworth, the first college to join the program, provides scholarships that cover 100 percent of financial need as well as extensive training to student participants.

CAREERS WITH A PURPOSE: Whitworth has a strong track record for placing students in both successful careers and top graduate schools, including Harvard University Law School, Massachusetts Institute of Technology, Princeton Theological Seminary, and Stanford University. But aside from preparing graduates to succeed in their careers, Whitworth also encourages them to find and live out their vocations by connecting their deepest convictions to their work.

http://www.whitworth.edu/
P: (800) 533-4668

PRIVATE - CHRISTIAN

STUDENT PROFILE
2,344 undergraduate students
98% of undergrad students are full time
38% male – 62% female
95% freshman retention rate
75% graduated in 6 years

FACULTY PROFILE
156 full-time faculty
6 part-time faculty
11 to 1 student/faculty ratio

ADMISSIONS
4,545 Total Applicants
2,837 Total Admissions
584 Total Freshman Enrollment
62.42% of applicants admitted

SAT Ranges: CR 530-630, M 530-640, W 510-630

ACT Ranges: C 23-29

TUITION & COSTS
Tuition: $38,168
Fees: $928
Total: $39,096
R&B: $10,714
Room: $5,792
Board: $4,922
Total: $49,810

FINANCIAL
$24,331 avg grant/scholarship amount (total)
$4,984 avg loan amount (total)
FINANCIAL
$21,334 avg grant/scholarship amount (total)
$5,673 avg loan amount (total)

ABOUT THE AUTHORS

WES CREEL

Founder

Having helped his four daughters find their dream schools, Wes knows firsthand what parents go through during the complicated and intimidating college search process. He founded Colleges of Distinction in 2001 to help high school students and parents navigate the college admissions landscape. The first in his family to attend college, Wes was interested in helping other aspiring college grads.

Wes would later help launch the Center for Student Opportunity (CSO) in 2005, a national nonprofit organization based in Bethesda, Md., that works to empower first-generation college students throughout their college careers. The CSO develops and provides tools and resources to help first-generation college students and their supporters – parents, counselors, and mentors – on the road to and through college.

Wes grew up in Texas and New York. He attended the Virginia Military Institute on an Army ROTC scholarship and received his bachelor's degree in history from Syracuse University. While working on a Ph.D. in American Civilization at the University of Texas, he was bitten by the entrepreneurial bug. He founded his first company in 1978, and for 10 years served as President and CEO of Creel Morrell, a marketing communications firm headquartered in Houston. In the 1980s, Creel Morrell became an industry leader and was on Inc. Magazine's list of the 500 fastest-growing companies in America for three straight years.

Wes' interests include running (including the Boston Marathon – six times!) and following the sports teams of Syracuse University and Texas Christian University (his fourth daughter is a recent grad). He also contributes to the CollegesofDistinction.com resource section and is loving his newfound status as grandfather to his two granddaughters.

TYSON SCHRITTER

Chief Operating Officer

In 2009, Tyson joined the Colleges of Distinction team as editor of its website and Guidebook. Now editor and operating partner, Tyson is also in charge of marketing and media relations. In addition, he is a critical member of the Colleges of Distinction qualification team. A graduate of the University of Idaho in Moscow, Idaho, Tyson received a bachelor's degree in Political Science.

As a member of the Colleges of Distinction qualification team, Tyson has been visiting college campuses and interviewing college staff across the country for the past seven years. He brings those years of experience to helping students find a college or university that is the right fit for them and that helps them learn, grow and succeed.

MADISON DOPKISS

Editor-in-Chief

Serving as Lead Engagement Director, Madison is responsible for maintaining member relations. Starting with the interview, Madison is present at each step of development process to ensure that every school receives the unique attention it deserves.

From consultations to customer service, Madison strives to provide each CoD member with an experience they can be proud of.

When it comes time to publish the annual Colleges of Distinction guidebook, Madison assumes the role of Editor-in-Chief. Alongside Nathan Wilgeroth, she serves as a critique partner, helping each school find its distinct voice. She conducts the final proof-read and makes sure that the entire book makes it through its design and publishing phases.

Madison is a graduate of Saint Mary's College, Notre Dame. Madison credits Saint Mary's for teaching her the value of ambition—that success knows no gender, and that women are equally as talented as men.

NATHAN WILGEROTH

Staff Writer & Content Editor

Having worked as an intern throughout his senior year at Boston University, Nathan familiarized himself with the many great Colleges of Distinction schools through the editing and promotion of their online profiles. Now graduated, he works as Account Executive & Lead Copywriter to play a major role in the profiles' clarity and overall development.

As Staff Writer & Content Editor, Nathan's duties ranged from critique partnering to copywriting as he tended to the clarity of the guidebook's content. He researched each institution and collaborated with their staff to write and edit their program highlights.

Nathan's education as an English and sociology student taught him to value not only the nuance and complexity of societal issues, but also the power of art and communication to affect positive change. He has loved his growing involvement with Colleges of Distinction, getting to know hundreds of institutions that recognize the importance of a holistic, interdisciplinary perspective.

OTHER BOOKS BY COLLEGES OF DISTINCTION:

Catholic Colleges of Distinction 2017

Christian Colleges of Distinction 2017

Public Colleges of Distinction 2017

Colleges of Distinction 2016-2017

Join our mailing list at CollegesofDistinction. com to receive new posts about the college search process, admissions, financial aid and getting ready for college.

When you join, we'll send you a free set of downloadable PDFs of checklists that you can use through the college bound process.

Visit collegesofdistinction.com/checklists to sign up!

COLLEGES
OF
DISTINCTION